GCSE MATHS
the modular course

Revised Edition

David Bowles
Senior Team Leader with SEG

Paul Metcalf
Principal Examiner and Principal Moderator with SEG

Stanley Thornes (Publishers) Ltd

First published in 1997
Revised edition published in 2000 by:
Stanley Thornes (Publishers) Ltd
Ellenborough House
Wellington Street
CHELTENHAM
GL50 1YW

A catalogue record for this book is available from the British Library.

ISBN 0 7487 5510 1

00 01 02 03 04 / 10 9 8 7 6 5 4 3 2 1

Typeset by Tech Set Ltd, Gateshead, Tyne & Wear.
Printed and bound in Spain by Graficas Estella S.A.

CONTENTS

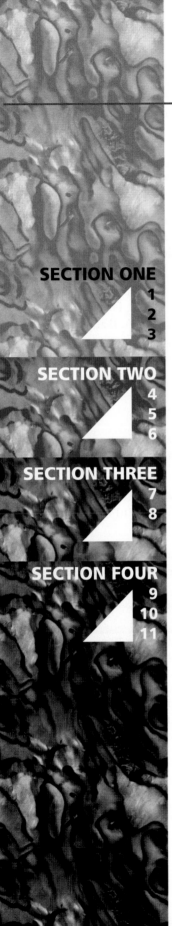

Introduction

The GCSE Modular Course is specifically designed for post-16 students and offers a modular approach to GCSE Mathematics. The modules are provided with examination papers set in Winter, Spring (except Module 3) and Summer. Certification in GCSE Mathematics is available at the end of Winter or Summer and the modules can be sat in any order, except that Module 3 must be taken last.

The GCSE Modular Mathematics course (syllabus 2520) consists of three modules covering the content of the GCSE syllabus. Each module has three tiers of entry and it is possible to enter different modules at different tiers.

Expected grades	Tier of entry	Available grades
E, F and G	Foundation Tier	D, E, F and G
C and D	Intermediate Tier	B, C, D and E
A★, A and B	Higher Tier	A★, A, B and C

Each module includes calculator and non-calculator papers and Using & Applying Mathematics is now assessed through an Applications Paper in Module 3 as shown below.

Module 1 Money Management and Number

- Assesses Number through a 40-minute calculator paper (10%) and a 40-minute non-calculator paper (10%).

Module 2 Statistics and Probability

- Assesses Handling Data through a 40-minute calculator paper (10%) and a 40-minute non-calculator paper (10%).

Module 3 Terminal Mode

- Assesses Algebra and Shape, Space and Measures through a one-hour calculator paper (20%) and a one-hour non-calculator paper (20%).
- Assesses Using and Applying Mathematics through a 2-hour Application paper (20%).

N.B. Students entered at the Higher level are allowed 1 hour 10 minutes on each of the examination papers and $2\frac{1}{2}$ hours on the Applications paper.

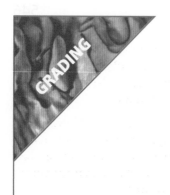

For each module, results are reported on a uniform mark scale which is related to the GCSE grades as shown. The marks for the three modules will be added to give a mark out of 600 which will then be converted to a final grade (dependent on the tier of entry of the terminal module) as shown.

Module 1 and Module 2		Module 3 (Terminal Module)		Overall	
Marks	*Grade*	*Marks*	*Grade*	*Marks*	*Grade*
0–23	U	0–71	U	0–119	U
24–35	G	72–107	G	120–179	G
36–47	F	108–143	F	180–239	F
48–59	E	144–179	E	240–299	E
60–71	D	180–215	D	300–359	D
72–83	C	216–251	C	360–419	C
84–95	B	252–287	B	420–479	B
96–107	A	288–323	A	480–539	A
108–120	A★	324–360	A★	540–600	A★

Each module includes two written papers – one calculator paper and one non-calculator paper. Both papers will assess the full range of topics except that the calculator paper will specifically include questions requiring the use of a calculator (see Ch 2.4) and the non-calculator paper will specifically include questions which prohibit the use of a calculator (see Ch 2.5 and the sample non-calculator papers at the back of the book).

The questions will be set in question-and-answer booklet form, and will normally be arranged in order of difficulty.

You are expected to have the following equipment:

- pens, sharp pencil, pencil sharpener and eraser
- ruler, protractor and compasses
- scientific calculator.

The following hints should help you when undertaking the the written papers:

- read the question carefully
- if you get stuck, miss out that question and come back to it later
- show your working and write down the calculations that you do
- make sure your answer is reasonable and sensible
- when you correct an answer, don't cross anything out until you have a better answer
- when you have finished, go back and check that you have answered all the questions.

Using and Applying Mathematics will be assessed through a separate Applications Paper which will form part of the Terminal module. Three different Applications Papers will be set covering work at the Foundation, Intermediate and Higher levels dependent upon the tier of entry in the Terminal module.

The Applications Paper will be set and marked by the board and will have a two-hour time limit ($2\frac{1}{2}$ hours on the Higher tier). The paper will consist of two tasks and you may attempt both tasks although there will be no penalty if only one task is completed. The tasks will be assessed in accordance with the assessment criteria for coursework which is common to all Examination Boards

The following advice appears on the front covers of the Applications Papers and should help you to achieve good marks:

- Do not copy out the question.
- Do not write essays. Use short sentences and be precise.
- Break the task down into stages.
- Introduce your own relevant questions which develop the task.
- Record your findings using words, tables, diagrams and symbols.
- Write down any observations you can make.
- Find general results and remember to test them.
- Extend the task further to include several features or variables and explore them thoroughly.★

★ Higher tier only.

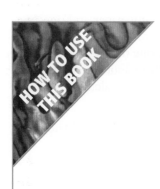

The book is divided into four sections:

Section One Money Management and Number (Module 1)
Section Two Statistics and Probability (Module 2)
Section Three Algebra }
Section Four Shape, Space and Measures } (Module 3)

Each section is divided into a number of chapters and each chapter is further divided into a series of topics. The first topic in each chapter is headed **Reinforcement** and covers material from the Foundation Tier syllabus which you need to know before you can start the chapter. Notes are included to help you revise these areas and, where appropriate, reference is provided to other parts of the book to support you in your understanding.

Each topic includes a number of **Practice** questions which you should try to complete before moving on to further work. These Practice questions are designed to consolidate the work as well as give you a flavour of examination-type questions. **Answers** to these Practice questions, along with some brief explanations where necessary, can be found at the back of the book.

Each chapter also includes a topic headed **Extension material** which covers grade A and A★ material from the Higher Tier syllabus. If you are entered for the Intermediate Tier then you *do not need* to attempt this work, which is only tested on the Higher Tier papers. If you are entered for the Higher Tier then you should work through this topic and the associated Practice questions.

Although the examination includes calculator and non-calculator papers, you are advised, wherever possible, to attempt the questions without a calculator. You may also find it helpful to check your work with a calculator. You are also recommended to work through Ch 2.4 on using a calculator and Ch 2.5 on non-calculator methods. Non-calculator papers (page 531) are also included.

Each chapter concludes with a **Summary**. This is included to summarise the work of the chapter and highlight areas that you need to know. You can use the Summary to remind yourself of the work of the chapter, or to identify areas for further consideration if you have decided that you do not need to study the whole chapter.

SECTION ONE

Money management and number

(Module 1)

CONTENTS

CHAPTER 1
Number and number problems

In this chapter you will need to:
▸ understand how numbers are classified
▸ understand squares, square roots and powers
▸ appreciate the sequence of operations

Classifying numbers

Numbers can be classified in many different ways and you need to be familiar with the following classifications:

counting numbers	1, 2, 3, 4, 5, 6, …
natural numbers	1, 2, 3, 4, 5, 6, … the same as counting numbers
odd numbers	1, 3, 5, 7, 9, 11, …
even numbers	2, 4, 6, 8, 10, 12, …
integers	…, $-5, -4, -3, -2, -1, 0, 1, 2, 3, 4, 5, …$
positive integers	$+1, +2, +3, +4, +5, …$
negative integers	$-1, -2, -3, -4, -5, …$

NOTE

The series of dots … show that the number sequences are infinite and go on for ever.

Squares

Square numbers are formed by multiplying any whole number by itself. 16 is a square number because 4 multiplied by itself is 16.

Worked Example

Write down the first six square numbers.

The first six square numbers are:
$$1 = 1 \times 1$$
$$4 = 2 \times 2$$
$$9 = 3 \times 3$$
$$16 = 4 \times 4$$
$$25 = 5 \times 5$$
$$36 = 6 \times 6$$

Square roots

Square roots are numbers which, when multiplied by themselves, give the required number.

6 is the square root of 36 because $6 \times 6 = 36$

The sign $\sqrt{}$ is used to denote the square root so that $\sqrt{36} = 6$

Worked Examples

1   6.5 is the square root of 42.25 because $6.5 \times 6.5 = 42.25$

We write $\sqrt{42.25} = 6.5$

2   8.15 is the square root of 66.4225 because $8.15 \times 8.15 = 66.4225$

We write $\sqrt{66.4225} = 8.15$

3   Use the $\sqrt{}$ button on a calculator to find the following:

$\sqrt{25}$ $\sqrt{56.25}$ $\sqrt{80}$ $\sqrt{289}$ $\sqrt{2890}$

Using your calculator:

$\sqrt{25} = 5$ exactly
$\sqrt{56.25} = 7.5$ exactly
$\sqrt{80} = 8.9442719\ldots$ approximately
$\sqrt{289} = 17$ exactly
$\sqrt{2890} = 53.75872\ldots$ approximately

PRACTICE 1.1.1

1   What are the next six square numbers after 36?

2   Which of the following are square numbers?

    125   169   1690   1000   10 000   100 000

3   **a**   Use the $\sqrt{}$ button on a calculator to find the following:

$\sqrt{49}$ $\sqrt{77.44}$ $\sqrt{90}$ $\sqrt{900}$ $\sqrt{1233.4144}$

b   Which of the answers above are exact?

Simple powers

We have already seen that when we multiply a number by itself we say that we are squaring the number.

The square of 4 is $4 \times 4 (= 16)$ and the square of 7 is $7 \times 7 (= 49)$.

Similarly when we multiply a number by itself and then by itself again we say that we are cubing the number.

The cube of 4 is $4 \times 4 \times 4 (= 64)$ and the cube of 7 is $7 \times 7 \times 7 (= 343)$.

Repeatedly writing out numbers like this can be rather cumbersome. Instead we can use a shorthand where

$$4 \times 4 = 4^2 \qquad 7 \times 7 = 7^2$$
$$4 \times 4 \times 4 = 4^3 \qquad 7 \times 7 \times 7 = 7^3$$

This method of writing can be extended to other numbers of the form:

3^5 ⟵ power or index
⟵ base

The **power** or **index** simply tells you how many times the base number is to be multiplied by itself so that 3^5 means that 3 (the base number) is to be multiplied by itself 5 times (the power or index).

$$3^5 = \underbrace{3 \times 3 \times 3 \times 3 \times 3}_{5 \text{ times}}$$

Similarly 5^8 means that 5 (the base number) is to be multiplied by itself 8 times (the power or index).

$$5^8 = \underbrace{5 \times 5 \times 5 \times 5 \times 5 \times 5 \times 5 \times 5}_{8 \text{ times}}$$

NOTE

When we see 3^5 we say '3 to the power 5' and when we see 5^8 we say '5 to the power 8'.

A number to the power 2 is also called *squared* so that 6^2 can be called '6 to the power 2' or '6 squared'.

Likewise a number to the power 3 is also called *cubed* so that 6^3 can be called '6 to the power 3' or '6 cubed'.

PRACTICE 1.1.2   Try these questions without a calculator

1   Write down different ways to say the following:
   a 5^2 **c** 15^2 **e** 11^3 **g** 3^7
   b 9^2 **d** 4^3 **f** 6^4 **h** 2^{10}

2   Evaluate each of the powers in question 1.

3   Write down the following in index form.
   a $5 \times 5 \times 5 \times 5$
   b $4 \times 4 \times 4 \times 4 \times 4 \times 4 \times 4$
   c $8 \times 8 \times 8$
   d $16 \times 16 \times 16 \times 16 \times 16 \times 16 \times 16 \times 16 \times 16 \times 16$
   e $3 \times 3 \times 3 \times 3 \times 3 \times 3$

4   Find the value of A when $A = 5^4$.

5   Find the value of C when $C = 7^3$.

6   Evaluate:
   a $3^2 + 5^3$
   b $5^2 + 4^3$

7   Which is the greater
   a 3^2 or 2^3
   b 5^2 or 2^5?

Sequence of operations

The word **BODMAS** is used to help us remember the order in which operations are undertaken:

Brackets
Of
Division
Multiplication
Addition
Subtraction

This tells us the order in which mathematical expressions should be worked out. Brackets have the highest priority and should always be worked out first. Divisions and multiplications are worked out before additions and subtractions.

If an expression contains only multiplication/division or addition/subtraction then the answer should be worked out from left to right.

Worked Examples

Evaluate the following:

a $25 - 5 + 1$	**c** $12 - 3 \times 2$	**e** $6 \times (3 + 1)$	**g** $12 - 6 \div 3$
b $6 \times 2 \div 3$	**d** $(12 - 3) \times 2$	**f** $6 \times 3 + 1$	**h** $8 - 6 \div 2 + 5$

a $25 - 5 + 1$ working from left to right
   $= 21$

b $6 \times 2 \div 3$ working from left to right
   $= 4$

c $12 - 3 \times 2$ multiplication before subtraction
   $= 12 - 6$
   $= 6$

d $(12 - 3) \times 2$ brackets $(12 - 3)$ first, then multiplication
   $= 9 \times 2$
   $= 18$

e $6 \times (3 + 1)$ brackets $(3 + 1)$ first, then multiplication
   $= 6 \times 4$
   $= 24$

f $6 \times 3 + 1$ multiplication before addition
   $= 18 + 1$
   $= 19$

g $12 - 6 \div 3$ division before subtraction
   $= 12 - 2$
   $= 10$

h $8 - 6 \div 2 + 5$ division first
   $= 8 - 3 + 5$
   $= 10$

NOTE

The word *evaluate* means *find the value of* or *work out*.

This word is often used on examination papers so it is important that you are familiar with what it means.

PRACTICE 1.1.3   Try these questions without a calculator

1 Evaluate the following:
  a $23 - 2 + 5$ and $23 - (2 + 5)$
  b $17 - 2 \times 3$ and $(17 - 2) \times 3$
  c $8 \times 5 - 1$ and $8 \times (5 - 1)$
  d $12 - 6 \div 3$ and $(12 - 6) \div 3$

2 Evaluate the following:
  a $4 \times 3 \div 2$ c $6 + 3 \times 1$ e $21 - 9 \div 3$
  b $20 - 8 \times 3$ d $6 + 6 \div 2$ f $15 - 9 \div 3 + 1$

3 Place brackets in the following equations to make them correct.
  a $4 \times 3 - 1 = 8$ c $9 + 6 \div 3 = 5$
  b $4 + 5 \times 2 = 18$ d $10 \div 5 \times 2 = 1$

Factors

The **factors** of any number are the whole numbers which divide exactly into the given number.

2 is a factor of 8 because 2 divides exactly into 8.
4 is also a factor of 8 because 4 divides exactly into 8.

Every number is divisible by 1.
Every number is divisible by itself.
So 1 and itself are always factors of the given number.

The other factors of 8 are 1 and 8.

Worked Examples

1 What are the factors of 12?

  The factors of 12 are: 1, 2, 3, 4, 6 and 12

2 What are the factors of 18?

  The factors of 18 are: 1, 2, 3, 6, 9 and 18

3 What are the common factors of 12 and 18?

  The factors of 12 are: 1, 2, 3, 4, 6 and 12
  The factors of 18 are: 1, 2, 3, 6, 9 and 18
  The common factors of 12 and 18 are: 1, 2, 3 and 6

  The **highest common factor (HCF)** of two or more numbers is the highest factor which is common to those numbers.
  The highest common factor of 12 and 18 is 6

PRACTICE 1.2.1   Try these questions without a calculator

1   Write down all the factors of the following numbers:

    a   15   **b**   24   **c**   37   **d**   49   **e**   60

2   Find the common factors of the following numbers:

    a   8 and 22   **c**   12 and 16   **e**   6, 12 and 15

    b   6 and 30   **d**   15 and 60

3   Find the highest common factor of the following numbers:

    a   8 and 12   **d**   8 and 16   **g**   12, 16 and 24

    b   15 and 20   **e**   48 and 72   **h**   30, 45 and 60

    c   12 and 18   **f**   14 and 49

Multiples

The **multiples** of any number are obtained by multiplying the number by any whole number. The multiples occur as the results of the multiplication table for the given number.

The multiples of 6 are 6, 12, 18, 24, 30, 36,…, etc., etc.
The multiples of 8 are 8, 16, 24, 32, 40, 48,…, etc., etc.

Worked Example

What are the common multiples of 6 and 8?

> The multiples of 6 are: 6, 12, 18, 24, 30, 36, 42, 48, 54,…, etc., etc.
> The multiples of 8 are: 8, 16, 24, 32, 40, 48, 56,…, etc., etc.
> The common multiples of 6 and 8 are: 24, 48, 72, 96,…, etc., etc.

> The **lowest common multiple (LCM)** of two or more numbers is the lowest multiple which is common to those numbers.
> The lowest common multiple of 6 and 8 is 24.

PRACTICE 1.2.2   Try these questions without a calculator

1   Write down the first six multiples of the following numbers:

    a   3   **b**   5   **c**   8   **d**   12   **e**   13

2   Write down the multiples of 9 which are less than 60.

3   Write down the multiples of 12 which are greater than 50 but less than 100.

4   Write down five multiples of 7 which are also even numbers.

5   Write down three multiples of 3 which are also multiples of 5.

6   Write down three multiples of 4 which are also multiples of 7.

7   Find the lowest common multiples of the following numbers:

    a   2 and 5   **c**   4 and 10   **e**   7 and 28

    b   6 and 9   **d**   12 and 18   **f**   3, 4 and 5

Prime numbers

A **prime number** is a whole number which has exactly two factors (one and itself). The following list gives the first 8 prime numbers:

Prime number	Factors	
2	1 and 2	(the only even prime number)
3	1 and 3	
5	1 and 5	
7	1 and 7	
11	1 and 11	
13	1 and 13	
17	1 and 17	
19	1 and 19	

NOTE
The number 1 is not usually considered to be a prime number as it has only one factor.

PRACTICE 1.2.3   Try these questions without a calculator

1 What are the next five prime numbers after 19?

2 Write down all the prime numbers between 50 and 60.

3 Write down all the prime numbers between 70 and 90.

Prime factors

A **prime factor** is a factor which is also a prime number.
All whole numbers can be written as a product of their prime factors.

Worked Example

What are the prime factors of 21?

The prime factors of 21 are 3 and 7.
The number 21 can be written as a product of its prime factors: 3×7.

Similarly, the number 12 can be written as $2 \times 2 \times 3$ or $2^2 \times 3$ and the number 120 can be written as $2 \times 2 \times 2 \times 3 \times 5$ or $2^3 \times 3 \times 5$.

The prime factors of a number can be found by successively dividing that number by prime numbers in increasing order
(i.e. 2, 3, 5, 7, 11, 13,…, etc.)

Worked Examples

1 Express 1260 as a product of its prime factors.

The prime factors can be found by successively dividing the number by prime numbers in increasing order i.e. dividing by 2… then 3… then 5… etc. as follows:

$$1260 \div 2 = 630$$
$$630 \div 2 = 315$$
$$315 \div 3 = 105 \qquad \text{cannot divide by 2 so try next prime i.e. 3}$$
$$105 \div 3 = 35$$
$$35 \div 5 = 7 \qquad \text{cannot divide by 3 so try next prime i.e. 5}$$
$$7 \div 7 = 1 \qquad \text{cannot divide any further}$$

$$1260 = 2 \times 2 \times 3 \times 3 \times 5 \times 7$$
$$\text{or } 1260 = 2^2 \times 3^2 \times 5 \times 7$$

2 Express 16 335 as a product of its prime factors.

The prime factors can be found by successively dividing by 2... then 3... then 5... etc. as follows:

$$16\,335 \div 3 = 5445 \quad \text{16 335 is not divisible by 2 so try next prime, i.e. 3}$$
$$5445 \div 3 = 1815$$
$$1815 \div 3 = 605$$
$$605 \div 5 = 121 \qquad \text{cannot divide by 3 so try next prime i.e. 5}$$
$$121 \div 11 = 11 \qquad \text{cannot divide by 5, or 7 so try next prime i.e. 11}$$
$$11 \div 11 = 1 \qquad \text{cannot divide any further}$$

$$16\,335 = 3 \times 3 \times 3 \times 5 \times 11 \times 11$$
$$\text{or } 16\,335 = 3^3 \times 5 \times 11^2$$

PRACTICE 1.2.4   Try these questions without a calculator

1 Write down the prime factors of the following numbers:
   a 15   **b** 24   **c** 105   **d** 39   **e** 41

2 Express the following numbers as products of prime factors:
   a 63   **b** 240   **c** 1200   **d** 1690   **e** 38 115

1.3 FRACTIONS

Fractions consist of two parts; the top line which is called the **numerator** and the bottom line which is called the **denominator.**

$$\frac{4}{7} \quad \begin{array}{l} \longleftarrow \text{numerator} \\ \longleftarrow \text{denominator} \end{array}$$

Equivalent fractions

Equivalent fractions are fractions which are equal.
The following fractions are all equivalent to $\frac{3}{4}$:

$$\frac{3}{4} = \frac{6}{8} = \frac{9}{12} = \frac{12}{16} = \frac{15}{20}$$

The following fractions are all equivalent to $\frac{2}{3}$:

$$\frac{2}{3} = \frac{4}{6} = \frac{6}{9} = \frac{8}{12} = \frac{10}{15}$$

Equivalent fractions can be created by multiplying or dividing the top and bottom lines of a fraction by the same number as follows:

$$\overset{\times 2}{\frac{2}{5}} = \frac{4}{10} \qquad \overset{\times 7}{\frac{2}{5}} = \frac{14}{35} \qquad \overset{\div 4}{\frac{4}{12}} = \frac{1}{3} \qquad \overset{\div 9}{\frac{27}{63}} = \frac{3}{7}$$

Cancelling fractions

To find a fraction in its **lowest terms** we find an equivalent fraction where the top and bottom lines are as small as possible – this process is also called **simplifying** or **cancelling down**.

Worked Examples

Write the following fractions in their lowest terms:

a $\dfrac{6}{12}$

$$\overset{\div 6}{\frac{6}{12}} = \frac{1}{2} \qquad \text{(we divide by 6 on the top and bottom lines)}$$

b $\dfrac{50}{75}$

$$\overset{\div 25}{\frac{50}{75}} = \frac{2}{3} \qquad \text{(we divide by 25 on the top and bottom lines)}$$

PRACTICE 1.3.1   Try these questions without a calculator

1 Write down three fractions that are equivalent to:

    a $\frac{1}{2}$ **b** $\frac{4}{10}$ **c** $\frac{3}{9}$ **d** $\frac{13}{100}$

2 Which two fractions are equivalent?

    a $\frac{4}{7}$ $\frac{5}{8}$ $\frac{12}{21}$

    b $\frac{3}{10}$ $\frac{4}{9}$ $\frac{24}{54}$

    c $\frac{6}{7}$ $\frac{12}{13}$ $\frac{12}{14}$

    d $\frac{10}{200}$ $\frac{4}{100}$ $\frac{12}{300}$

3 Write the following fractions in their lowest terms:

    a $\frac{3}{6}$ **c** $\frac{12}{15}$ **e** $\frac{100}{125}$ **g** $\frac{4}{7}$

    b $\frac{6}{8}$ **d** $\frac{4}{10}$ **f** $\frac{21}{84}$ **h** $\frac{44}{99}$

One number as a fraction of another

To calculate one number as a fraction of another, we write the first number over the second number as a fraction.

Worked Examples

1 Write down 20 p as a fraction of 50 p.

To calculate one number as a fraction of another, we write the first number over the second number as a fraction.

20 p as a fraction of 50 p is $\frac{20}{50} = \frac{2}{5}$ cancelling down to the lowest terms

We would say that 20 p is $\frac{2}{5}$ of 50 p.

2 Write down 20 p as a fraction of £1.00

To calculate one number as a fraction of another, we write the first number over the second number as a fraction. However, you must be careful to make sure that the units are the same.

Writing £1.00 as 100p the question becomes:

Write down 20 p as a fraction of 100 p.

20 p as a fraction of 100 p is $\frac{20}{100} = \frac{1}{5}$ cancelling down to the lowest terms

Alternatively, writing 20 p as £0.20 the question becomes:

Write down £0.20 as a fraction of £1.00

£0.20 as a fraction of £1.00 is $\frac{0.20}{1.00} = \frac{1}{5}$ multiplying top and bottom by 5 to make an equivalent fraction

---

PRACTICE 1.3.2   Try these questions without a calculator

1 Write down 30 miles as a fraction of 50 miles.

2 Write down 25 kilometres as a fraction of 60 kilometres.

3 Write down 12 ounces as a fraction of 15 ounces.

4 Write down 40 p as a fraction of £2.00.

5 Write down 3 pints as a fraction of 1 gallon.

6 Express 60 centimetres as a fraction of 1 metre. Give your answer in its lowest terms.

7 Express 300 metres as a fraction of 1 kilometre. Give your answer in its lowest terms.

8 Express 35 millilitres as a fraction of 7 litres. Give your answer in its lowest terms.

9 Express 500 milligrams as a fraction of 2.5 kilograms. Give your answer in its lowest terms.

Addition and subtraction of fractions

In order to add or subtract fractions it is important that the denominators (the numbers on the bottom of the fractions) are the same. The resulting fraction will also have this same denominator.

Worked Examples

1 Work out $\frac{3}{5} + \frac{1}{5}$.

Since the denominators are the same we can add them up as follows:

three fifths add one fifth equals four fifths

so $\frac{3}{5} + \frac{1}{5} = \frac{4}{5}$

2 Work out $\frac{7}{11} - \frac{2}{11}$.

Since the denominators are the same we can subtract them as follows:

seven elevenths subtract two elevenths equals five elevenths

so $\frac{7}{11} - \frac{2}{11} = \frac{5}{11}$

3 Work out $\frac{2}{5} + \frac{3}{10}$.

Since the denominators are not the same we need to change the fractions to equivalent fractions with the same denominator. The lowest common multiple of 5 and 10 is 10 – so a common denominator would be 10:

$$\overset{\times 2}{\frac{2}{5}} = \underset{\times 2}{\frac{4}{10}}$$

and the question becomes:

Work out $\frac{4}{10} + \frac{3}{10} = \frac{7}{10}$.

> **NOTE**
> **To find the common denominator you can use the lowest common multiple of the two denominators (see Topic 1.2).**

Worked Example

Work out $\frac{3}{5} - \frac{1}{4}$.

Since the denominators are not the same we need to change the fractions to equivalent fractions with the same denominator. The lowest common multiple of 5 and 4 is 20 – so a common denominator would be 20:

$$\overset{\times 4}{\frac{3}{5}} = \underset{\times 4}{\frac{12}{20}} \qquad \overset{\times 5}{\frac{1}{4}} = \underset{\times 5}{\frac{5}{20}}$$

and the question becomes:

Work out $\frac{12}{20} - \frac{5}{20} = \frac{7}{20}$.

PRACTICE 1.3.3   Try these questions without a calculator

1   Work out the following fractions giving your answers in their lowest
form:

a $\frac{1}{3} + \frac{1}{3}$ g $\frac{1}{4} + \frac{5}{11}$ m $\frac{3}{5} - \frac{4}{5}$

b $\frac{2}{7} + \frac{3}{7}$ h $\frac{2}{5} - \frac{1}{5}$ n $\frac{2}{9} - \frac{5}{9}$

c $\frac{4}{11} + \frac{3}{11}$ i $\frac{4}{7} - \frac{3}{7}$ o $\frac{2}{5} - \frac{5}{10}$

d $\frac{4}{9} + \frac{2}{9}$ j $\frac{5}{8} - \frac{2}{5}$ p $\frac{2}{3} - \frac{5}{7}$

e $\frac{1}{3} + \frac{1}{6}$ k $\frac{11}{12} - \frac{2}{3}$

f $\frac{2}{5} + \frac{2}{7}$ l $\frac{4}{7} - \frac{3}{8}$

Mixed numbers

A number such as $3\frac{1}{8}$ is called a mixed number as it consists of a whole number
and a fraction. When dealing with mixed numbers, it can be helpful to convert
them to **top heavy fractions** or **improper fractions** and deal with them as
before.

Worked Examples

1   Work out $1\frac{3}{7} + 4\frac{2}{7}$.

First we need to convert the fractions to improper fractions

$$1\frac{3}{7} = 1 + \frac{3}{7} = \frac{7}{7} + \frac{3}{7} = \frac{10}{7} \qquad \text{(as } 1 = \frac{7}{7}\text{)}$$
$$4\frac{2}{7} = 4 + \frac{2}{7} = \frac{28}{7} + \frac{2}{7} = \frac{30}{7} \qquad \text{(as } 4 = \frac{28}{7}\text{)}$$

Since the denominators are the same then the question becomes:

Work out $\frac{10}{7} + \frac{30}{7} = \frac{40}{7}$.

We should now convert this improper fraction to a mixed number for the
final answer:

$$1\frac{3}{7} + 4\frac{2}{7} = 5\frac{5}{7} \qquad \text{(as } \frac{40}{7} = 5\frac{5}{7}\text{)}$$

2   Work out $3\frac{1}{8} - 1\frac{3}{4}$.

First we need to convert the fractions to improper fractions:

$$3\frac{1}{8} = 3 + \frac{1}{8} = \frac{24}{8} + \frac{1}{8} = \frac{25}{8} \qquad \text{(as } 3 = \frac{24}{8}\text{)}$$
$$1\frac{3}{4} = 1 + \frac{3}{4} = \frac{4}{4} + \frac{3}{4} = \frac{7}{4} \qquad \text{(as } 1 = \frac{4}{4}\text{)}$$

Since the denominators are not the same we need to change the fractions
to equivalent fractions with the same denominator. The lowest common
multiple of the denominators 8 and 4 is 8 – so a common denominator
would be 8:

$$\overset{\times 2}{\frac{7}{4}} = \underset{\times 2}{\frac{14}{8}}$$

and the question becomes

Work out $\frac{25}{8} - \frac{14}{8} = \frac{11}{8}$.

We should now convert this improper fraction to a mixed number for the final answer:

$$3\frac{1}{8} - 1\frac{3}{4} = 1\frac{3}{8} \qquad (\text{as } \frac{11}{8} = 1\frac{3}{8})$$

<table>
<tr><td>

NOTE

Although this method always works, it is not always the most effective method for adding and subtracting mixed numbers.

</td><td>

PRACTICE 1.3.4   Try these questions without a calculator

1 Work out the following:

a $\frac{2}{7} + 1\frac{3}{7}$	**e** $4\frac{2}{3} + 3\frac{1}{4}$	**i** $1\frac{1}{4} - \frac{1}{8}$
b $10\frac{1}{3} + 2\frac{1}{4}$	**f** $3\frac{1}{4} + 1\frac{1}{5} + 2\frac{1}{10}$	**j** $3\frac{1}{5} - 1\frac{4}{5}$
c $1\frac{1}{2} + \frac{3}{4}$	**g** $1\frac{7}{8} - \frac{3}{8}$	**k** $12\frac{1}{3} - 6\frac{4}{5}$
d $2\frac{3}{5} + \frac{9}{10}$	**h** $3\frac{3}{4} - 2\frac{3}{8}$	**l** $3\frac{1}{9} - 3\frac{1}{12}$

</td></tr>
</table>

An alternative method for adding and subtracting mixed numbers is shown in the following worked examples.

Worked Examples

1 Work out $1\frac{3}{7} + 4\frac{2}{7}$.

$$1\frac{3}{7} = (1 + \frac{3}{7})$$

$$\text{and } 4\frac{2}{7} = (4 + \frac{2}{7})$$

$$\text{so } 1\frac{3}{7} + 4\frac{2}{7} = (1 + \frac{3}{7}) + (4 + \frac{2}{7})$$

$$= 1 + \frac{3}{7} + 4 + \frac{2}{7} \quad \text{removing the brackets}$$

$$= 5 + \frac{3}{7} + \frac{2}{7} \qquad \text{adding the whole numbers}$$

$$= 5 + \frac{5}{7} \qquad\qquad \text{adding the fractions}$$

$$= 5\frac{5}{7} \qquad\qquad\quad \text{as before}$$

2 Work out $3\frac{1}{8} - 1\frac{3}{4}$.

$$\text{Similarly } 3\frac{1}{8} = (3 + \frac{1}{8})$$

$$\text{and } 1\frac{3}{4} = (1 + \frac{3}{4})$$

$$\text{so } 3\frac{1}{8} - 1\frac{3}{4} = (3 + \frac{1}{8}) - (1 + \frac{3}{4})$$

$$= 3 + \frac{1}{8} - 1 - \frac{3}{4} \quad \text{removing the brackets and remembering the}$$
$$\qquad\qquad\qquad\qquad \text{negative sign outside the second set of brackets}$$

$$= 2 + \frac{1}{8} - \frac{3}{4} \qquad \text{subtracting the whole numbers}$$

$$= 2 + \frac{1}{8} - \frac{6}{8} \qquad \text{writing the fractions with the same denominator}$$

$$= 2 - \frac{5}{8} \qquad\qquad \text{subtracting the fractions}$$

$$= 1\frac{3}{8} \qquad\qquad\quad \text{as before}$$

PRACTICE 1.3.5   Try these questions without a calculator

1 Work out the following:

   a $4\frac{2}{7} + 3\frac{1}{7}$ d $6\frac{3}{7} + 3\frac{6}{7}$ g $3\frac{4}{5} - 2\frac{2}{5}$ j $8\frac{1}{4} - 4\frac{5}{8}$

   b $8\frac{1}{5} + 2\frac{1}{4}$ e $9\frac{4}{5} + 6\frac{3}{8}$ h $7\frac{5}{8} - 3\frac{1}{4}$ k $9\frac{2}{5} - 3\frac{7}{8}$

   c $2\frac{4}{5} + 1\frac{1}{8}$ f $6\frac{5}{6} + 12\frac{4}{7}$ i $16\frac{2}{5} - 14\frac{4}{5}$ l $11\frac{2}{7} - 6\frac{4}{5}$

Multiplication of fractions

To multiply two fractions you multiply the numerators together to obtain the numerator of the answer and multiply the denominators together to obtain the denominator of the answer.

Worked Examples

1 Work out $\frac{3}{5} \times \frac{7}{12}$.

   Multiplying the numerators and denominators together we get:

$$\frac{3}{5} \times \frac{7}{12} = \frac{21}{60} = \frac{7}{20} \qquad \text{cancelling down}$$

2 Work out $\frac{2}{7} \times \frac{3}{10}$.

   Multiplying the numerators and denominators together we get:

$$\frac{2}{7} \times \frac{3}{10} = \frac{6}{70} = \frac{3}{35} \qquad \text{cancelling down}$$

3 Work out $1\frac{3}{4} \times 2\frac{2}{5}$.

   In order to multiply these mixed fractions we must first convert them to improper fractions:

$$1\frac{3}{4} = \frac{7}{4} \qquad\qquad 2\frac{2}{5} = \frac{12}{5}$$

   Multiplying the numerators and denominators together we get:

$$\frac{7}{4} \times \frac{12}{5} = \frac{84}{20} = \frac{21}{5} = 4\frac{1}{5} \qquad \begin{array}{l}\text{cancelling down and converting}\\\text{to a mixed number}\end{array}$$

NOTE

In this example it would be better if the cancelling down took place before multiplying

$$\frac{7}{\overset{}{\underset{1}{4}}} \times \overset{3}{\underset{}{12}} \cdot \frac{1}{5} = \frac{7}{1} \times \frac{3}{5} = \frac{21}{5} = 4\frac{1}{5}$$

as before.

PRACTICE 1.3.6   Try these questions without a calculator

1 Work out the following:

   a $\frac{2}{5} \times \frac{1}{3}$ e $\frac{3}{7} \times \frac{14}{15}$ i $\frac{6}{13} \times 3\frac{1}{4}$ m $\frac{1}{2} \times 1\frac{1}{5} \times 1\frac{1}{3}$

   b $\frac{3}{7} \times \frac{2}{5}$ f $\frac{3}{4} \times \frac{4}{9}$ j $1\frac{1}{7} \times \frac{7}{8}$ n $(\frac{4}{5})^2$

   c $\frac{4}{9} \times \frac{2}{3}$ g $1\frac{3}{4} \times \frac{4}{5}$ k $4\frac{1}{4} \times 2\frac{2}{5}$ o $(1\frac{1}{4})^2$

   d $\frac{4}{5} \times \frac{3}{4}$ h $2\frac{1}{5} \times \frac{7}{11}$ l $7\frac{1}{3} \times 2\frac{5}{11}$ p $(3\frac{1}{3})^3$

Fractions of a quantity

Sometimes the word *of* is used instead of the multiplication sign so that $\frac{3}{4}$ of 20 should be taken as $\frac{3}{4} \times 20$.

Worked Example

What is $\frac{3}{4}$ of 20?

$\frac{3}{4}$ of 20 is the same as $\frac{3}{4} \times 20$

Multiplying the numerators and denominators together we get:

$$\frac{3}{4} \times \frac{20}{1} = \frac{60}{4} = \frac{15}{1} = 15$$

> **NOTE**
>
> 20 can be written as $\frac{20}{1}$. Also $\frac{15}{1}$ can be written as 15.

PRACTICE 1.3.7   Try these questions without a calculator

1 Work out the following:

    a $\frac{3}{4}$ of 40   **b** $\frac{2}{5}$ of 15   **c** $\frac{4}{7}$ of 14   **d** $\frac{2}{7}$ of 16

2 Work out $\frac{3}{5}$ of 15 metres.

3 Work out $\frac{2}{7}$ of 105 millilitres.

4 In a class of 24 students, $\frac{1}{3}$ cycle to college and $\frac{5}{8}$ walk to college. How many students
    a cycle to college   **b** walk to college?

5 A college has 1200 students and $\frac{3}{8}$ are following GCSE courses. How many students are following GCSE courses?

Division of fractions

To divide two fractions you multiply the first fraction by the **reciprocal** of the second fraction.

> **NOTE**
>
> The *reciprocal* of a fraction is found by turning the fraction upside down. The reciprocal of $\frac{2}{3}$ is $\frac{3}{2}$ and the reciprocal of $\frac{4}{5}$ is $\frac{5}{4}$, etc., etc.

Worked Examples

1 Work out $\frac{3}{8} \div \frac{1}{4}$.

Following the rule for dividing fractions this is the same as multiplying $\frac{3}{8}$ by the reciprocal of $\frac{1}{4}$ which is $\frac{4}{1}$:

$$\frac{3}{8} \div \frac{1}{4}$$
$$= \frac{3}{8} \times \frac{4}{1}$$

Multiplying the numerators and denominators together we get

$$\frac{3}{8} \times \frac{4}{1} = \frac{12}{8} = \frac{3}{2} = 1\frac{1}{2} \qquad \text{cancelling down and converting to a mixed number}$$

2 Work out $2 \div 1\frac{1}{4}$.

$2 = \frac{2}{1}$ as an improper fraction and $1\frac{1}{4} = \frac{5}{4}$ as an improper fraction.

So the question becomes:
Work out $\frac{2}{1} \div \frac{5}{4}$.

$$\frac{2}{1} \div \frac{5}{4}$$

$$= \frac{2}{1} \times \frac{4}{5} \qquad\qquad \frac{4}{5} \text{ is the reciprocal of } \frac{5}{4}$$

Multiplying the numerators and denominators together we get

$$\frac{2}{1} \times \frac{4}{5} = \frac{8}{5} = 1\frac{3}{5} \qquad \text{cancelling down and converting}$$
to a mixed number

3 Work out $1\frac{1}{5} \div 3\frac{3}{5}$.

$1\frac{1}{5} = \frac{6}{5}$ as an improper fraction and $3\frac{3}{5} = \frac{18}{5}$ as an improper fraction.

So the question becomes:
Work out $\frac{6}{5} \div \frac{18}{5}$.

$$\frac{6}{5} \div \frac{18}{5}$$

$$= \frac{6}{5} \times \frac{5}{18} \qquad\qquad \frac{5}{18} \text{ is the reciprocal of } \frac{18}{5}$$

Multiplying the numerators and denominators together we get

$$\frac{\overset{1}{\cancel{6}}}{\underset{1}{\cancel{5}}} \times \frac{\overset{1}{\cancel{5}}}{\underset{3}{\cancel{18}}} = \frac{1}{3} \qquad \text{cancelling down}$$

PRACTICE 1.3.8   Try these questions without a calculator

1 Work out the following:

   a $\frac{1}{3} \div \frac{2}{5}$ **d** $\frac{4}{7} \div 2$ **g** $4 \div 2\frac{2}{5}$ **j** $4\frac{1}{4} \div 1\frac{5}{12}$

   b $\frac{4}{7} \div \frac{4}{11}$ **e** $\frac{2}{9} \div \frac{2}{3}$ **h** $1\frac{4}{5} \div 2\frac{7}{10}$ **k** $3\frac{2}{7} \div 1\frac{9}{14}$

   c $\frac{3}{11} \div \frac{6}{11}$ **f** $3 \div 1\frac{1}{2}$ **i** $3\frac{1}{3} \div 2$ **l** $5\frac{1}{4} \div 10\frac{1}{2}$

2 How many $\frac{3}{4}$ litre bottles can Peter fill from a container holding 5 litres?

3 In a class of students, $\frac{1}{3}$ of the students come by car, $\frac{2}{5}$ come by train and the rest walk. What fraction of the students walk?

4 Peter travels 2 kilometres to work each day. He runs $\frac{4}{5}$ of the distance. How far does he run?

5 How many seconds are there in $1\frac{3}{4}$ minutes?

6 How many minutes are there in $\frac{2}{3}$ of an hour?

7 Gary has 50 football cards and gives $\frac{1}{5}$ of these to his friend. How many football cards does he have left?

8 In a sale, a coat is reduced by one third. If the original price of the coat is £42, what is the sale price?

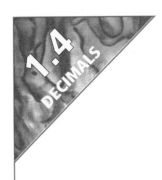

The number system which we use is called the decimal system because it is based on powers of 10. All numbers consist of a series of figures and a figure's position in the number tells us the value of that figure. For example, the figure 7 in the number 678 stands for 7×10 or 70 whereas the figure 7 in the number 7634 stands for 7×1000 or 7000.

Decimals are a form of fraction based on the idea of place value where each position to the right of the decimal point represents a power of 10 as follows:

$$. \quad \frac{1}{10} \quad \frac{1}{100} \quad \frac{1}{1000} \quad \frac{1}{10\,000}$$

just as the positions to the left of the decimal point represent powers of 10:

$$10\,000 \quad 1000 \quad 100 \quad 10 \quad 1 \;.$$

For example, the number 26.738 represents

2 tens and 6 units and 7 tenths and 3 hundredths and 8 thousandths

Similarly the number 0.6315 represents

0 units and 6 tenths and 3 hundredths and 1 thousandth and 5 ten thousandths

---

PRACTICE 1.4.1

1 What is the value of the 6 in the following numbers:
   a 216   **b** 2635   **c** 206 005   **d** 21.64   **e** 0.000 06?

2 Write down the value of the figure underlined:
   a 43**7**.2   **b** **2**96.5   **c** 235.**7**9   **d** 406.2**8**

Converting decimals to fractions

To convert a decimal to a fraction we use place value to convert the figures to the right of the decimal point.

Worked Examples

1 Convert 0.71 to a fraction.

    0.71 represents 0 units, 7 tenths and 1 hundredth

    i.e. $\frac{7}{10} + \frac{1}{100}$

    $= \frac{70}{100} + \frac{1}{100}$ writing the fractions with the same denominator

    $= \frac{71}{100}$

2 Convert 0.473 to a fraction.

    0.473 represents 0 units, 4 tenths, 7 hundredths and 3 thousandths

    i.e. $\frac{4}{10} + \frac{7}{100} + \frac{3}{1000}$

    $= \frac{400}{1000} + \frac{70}{1000} + \frac{3}{1000}$ writing the fractions with the same denominator

    $= \frac{473}{1000}$

NOTE

From the examples we can see that

$0.71 = \frac{71}{100}$ and

$0.473 = \frac{473}{1000}$

Following this pattern we can see that

$0.3011 = \frac{3011}{10\,000}$

$0.554\,33 = \frac{55\,433}{100\,000}$, etc.

3 Convert 0.65 to a fraction in its lowest terms.

From the above work we can see immediately that

$$0.65 = \tfrac{65}{100} = \tfrac{13}{20} \text{ in its lowest terms.}$$

4 Convert 3.65 to a mixed number in its lowest terms.

We have already seen that $0.65 = \tfrac{13}{20}$

so $3.65 = 3\tfrac{13}{20}$ as $3.65 = 3 + 0.65$

PRACTICE 1.4.2   Try these questions without a calculator

1 Convert the following decimals to fractions in their lowest terms.
   a 0.4   **c** 0.56   **e** 0.275   **g** 0.222
   b 0.55   **d** 0.46   **f** 0.425   **h** 0.2345

2 Convert the following decimal numbers to mixed numbers in their lowest terms.
   a 4.5   **c** 10.12   **e** 70.72   **g** 2.125
   b 7.35   **d** 20.95   **f** 12.12   **h** 17.155

Converting fractions to decimals

To convert a fraction to a decimal we simply divide the numerator (top number) by the denominator (bottom number).

Worked Examples

1 Convert $\tfrac{4}{5}$ to a decimal.

To convert a fraction to a decimal we divide the numerator by the denominator, so we work out the value of $4 \div 5 = 0.8$.

2 Convert $7\tfrac{4}{5}$ to a decimal.

Here again, we need only concentrate on the fractional part and we have already converted $\tfrac{4}{5} = 0.8$ so $7\tfrac{4}{5} = 7.8$.

3 Convert $\tfrac{4}{9}$ to a decimal.

To convert a fraction to a decimal we divide the numerator by the
denominator, so we work out the value of $4 \div 9 = 9\overline{)4.4^40^40^40^40^40^40^40^40}$ $\overset{0.4\,4\,4\,4\,4\,4\,4\,4\ldots}{}$

If a decimal goes on and on forever it is called a *recurring decimal*. The number is usually written as $0.\dot{4}$ and the dot above the 4 indicates that this number is repeated infinitely.

In recurring decimals where a group of numbers is repeated then two dots are used to indicate the group of repeating numbers as shown in these examples:

$0.\dot{2}\dot{3} = 0.232\,323\,232\,3\ldots$ $8.6\dot{7}13\dot{2} = 8.671\,327\,132\,713\,2\ldots$
$0.5\dot{3}7\dot{8} = 0.537\,878\,787\,8\ldots$ $5.33\dot{0}6\dot{4} = 5.330\,640\,640\,64\ldots$

PRACTICE 1.4.3

1 Convert the following fractions to decimals without using a calculator:

   a $\frac{3}{5}$ **d** $\frac{7}{20}$ **g** $15\frac{1}{5}$ **j** $6\frac{3}{50}$ **m** $\frac{6}{11}$

   b $\frac{7}{10}$ **e** $\frac{13}{40}$ **h** $22\frac{3}{25}$ **k** $\frac{1}{3}$

   c $\frac{1}{25}$ **f** $1\frac{3}{10}$ **i** $1\frac{9}{20}$ **l** $\frac{5}{9}$

Addition and subtraction of decimals

To add or subtract decimals it is important that the numbers are lined up properly.

To do the addition $3.62 + 25.1$ we must be careful to line up the decimal points as follows:

$$
\begin{array}{r}
3.62 \\
+\ 25.1 \\
\hline
28.72
\end{array}
$$

Similarly to do the subtraction $9.65 - 2.4$:

$$
\begin{array}{r}
9.65 \\
-\ 2.4 \\
\hline
7.25
\end{array}
$$

Worked Examples

1 Work out $9.6 + 4.78$.

To work out this addition we must be careful to line up the decimal points:

$$
\begin{array}{r}
9.6 \\
+\ 4.78 \\
\hline
14.38
\end{array}
$$

$$
\begin{array}{r}
9.60 \\
+\ 4.78 \\
\hline
14.38
\end{array}
$$

2 Work out $8.2 - 3.65$.

To work out this subtraction we must be careful to line up the decimal points. Again, it is helpful to pad out the numbers with zeros:

$$
\begin{array}{r}
8.20 \\
-\ 3.65 \\
\hline
4.55
\end{array}
$$

> **NOTE**
>
> It is sometimes helpful to pad out the numbers with zeros as shown:

PRACTICE 1.4.4

1 Work out the following without using a calculator:
     a $0.25 + 0.25$ **d** $0.421 + 0.567$ **g** $3.2 + 0.5$ **j** $0.35 + 0.04 + 0.1$
     b $0.33 + 0.68$ **e** $1.3 + 0.65$ **h** $7.3 + 2$ **k** $3.7 + 0.5 + 26$
     c $0.65 + 0.99$ **f** $0.6 + 0.003$ **i** $105 + 0.01$

2 Work out the following without using a calculator:
     a $0.75 - 0.25$ **d** $0.84 - 0.003$ **g** $12.6 - 5$
     b $0.93 - 0.68$ **e** $4.6 - 0.61$ **h** $6.8 - 2$
     c $0.55 - 0.19$ **f** $0.1 - 0.01$ **i** $15 - 0.001$

Multiplication of decimals

It is probably easier to multiply two decimals using a calculator but where this is not allowed then the following method should be used:

> **i** Multiply the two numbers together ignoring the decimal points.
> **ii** Add together the number of digits after the decimal point in each of the numbers.
> **iii** Replace the decimal point so that the number of digits after the decimal point is the same as the number in **ii** above.

Worked Examples

1 Work out 0.3×0.4.

   We first multiply the two numbers together ignoring the decimal points:
   $$3 \times 4 = 12$$

   The number of digits after the decimal point in each of the numbers is $1 + 1 = 2$.

   We now replace the decimal point so that there are 2 digits after the decimal point:
   $$0.3 \times 0.4 = 0.12$$

2 Multiply 2.55×1.2.

   We first multiply the two numbers together ignoring the decimal points:
   $$255 \times 12 = 3060$$

   The number of digits after the decimal point in each of the numbers is $2 + 1 = 3$.

   We now replace the decimal point so that there are 3 digits after the decimal point:
   $$2.55 \times 1.2 = 3.060$$

3 What is the product of 0.00015 and 0.33?

   We first multiply the two numbers together ignoring the decimal points:
   $$15 \times 33 = 495$$

> **NOTE**
> Always check that the answer is approximately correct when multiplying decimals.

> **NOTE**
> A quick way to multiply by 33 is to multiply by 11 then multiply by 3.

The number of digits after the decimal point in each of the numbers is $5 + 2 = 7$.

We now replace the decimal point so that there are 7 digits after the decimal point:

$0.000\,15 \times 0.33 = 0.000\,049\,5$

PRACTICE 1.4.5

1 Work out the following without using a calculator:
   a 0.6×0.3 **c** 20×0.6 **e** 0.001×0.225 **g** 0.04×120
   b 1.2×12 **d** 0.7×0.8 **f** 30.0×1.2 **h** $0.3 \times 0.05 \times 0.001$

Division of decimals

Division by a whole number is quite straightforward but problems arise when we are required to divide a decimal by another decimal. In these cases we treat the division like a fraction and rewrite it as an equivalent fraction.

Worked Examples

1   Divide $0.000\,63$ by 0.7.

$0.000\,63 \div 0.7$ can be written as $\dfrac{0.000\,63}{0.7}$

We can make an equivalent fraction by multiplying the numerator and the denominator by 10 as this will make the denominator a whole number.

$$\dfrac{0.000\,63}{0.7} \xrightarrow{\times 10} = \dfrac{0.0063}{7} \xleftarrow{\times 10}$$

We now need to work out $0.0063 \div 7$: $7\overline{)0.0063}\ \ ^{0.0009}$

So $0.000\,63 \div 0.7 = 0.0009$

2   Divide 0.0035 by 0.005.

$0.0035 \div 0.005$ can be written as $\dfrac{0.0035}{0.005}$

We can make an equivalent fraction by multiplying the numerator and the denominator by 1000 as this will make the denominator a whole number.

$$\dfrac{0.0035}{0.005} \xrightarrow{\times 1000} = \dfrac{3.5}{5} \xleftarrow{\times 1000}$$

We now need to work out $3.5 \div 5$: $5\overline{)3.5}\ \ ^{0.7}$

So $0.0035 \div 0.005 = 0.7$

PRACTICE 1.4.6

1 Work out the following without using a calculator:
   a $2.65 \div 5$ **c** $220 \div 0.05$ **e** $169 \div 1.3$ **g** $6.25 \div 0.125$
   b $1.44 \div 12$ **d** $12 \div 0.0001$ **f** $0.001 \div 0.05$ **h** $0.888 \div 0.000\,222$

Percentages are fractions with a denominator of 100.

11% means 11 out of 100 or $\frac{11}{100}$

79% means 79 out of 100 or $\frac{79}{100}$

In some cases we can simplify the fractions so that:

50% means 50 out of 100 or $\frac{50}{100}$ or $\frac{1}{2}$

25% means 25 out of 100 or $\frac{25}{100}$ or $\frac{1}{4}$

Changing fractions to percentages

To change a fraction to a percentage we just multiply the fraction by 100.

Worked Examples

1 Convert $\frac{1}{2}$ to a percentage.

To change a fraction to a percentage we multiply the fraction by 100.
$\frac{1}{2} \times 100 = 50$ so $\frac{1}{2} = 50\%$

2 Convert $\frac{4}{5}$ to a percentage.

To change a fraction to a percentage we multiply the fraction by 100.
$\frac{4}{5} \times 100 = 80$ so $\frac{4}{5} = 80\%$

Changing percentages to fractions

To change a percentage to a fraction we just divide the percentage by 100.

Worked Examples

1 Convert 34% to a fraction.

To change a percentage to a fraction we divide the percentage by 100.

$34\% = \frac{34}{100} = \frac{17}{50}$ so $34\% = \frac{17}{50}$

2 Convert $27\frac{1}{2}\%$ to a fraction.

To change a percentage to a fraction we divide the percentage by 100.

$27\frac{1}{2}\% = \dfrac{27\frac{1}{2}}{100} = \dfrac{55}{200} = \dfrac{11}{40}$ so $27\frac{1}{2}\% = \dfrac{11}{40}$

NOTE

The fraction $\dfrac{27\frac{1}{2}}{100}$ needs to be written as an equivalent fraction (avoiding fractions in the numerator) i.e. $\dfrac{55}{200}$.

PRACTICE 1.5.1   Try these questions without a calculator

1 Convert the following fractions to percentages:

   a $\frac{1}{2}$ **c** $\frac{2}{5}$ **e** $\frac{7}{10}$ **g** $\frac{17}{100}$

   b $\frac{1}{4}$ **d** $\frac{3}{8}$ **f** $\frac{3}{20}$ **h** $\frac{1}{6}$

2 Convert the following percentages to fractions in their lowest terms:

   a 60%   **c** 65%   **e** 62.5%

   b 45%   **d** 90%   **f** 33%

Changing decimals to percentages

To change a decimal to a percentage we just multiply the decimal by 100.

Worked Examples

1 Convert 0.5 to a percentage.

   To change a decimal to a percentage we multiply the decimal by 100.

      $0.5 \times 100 = 50$ so $0.5 = 50\%$

2 Convert 0.01 to a percentage.

   To change a decimal to a percentage we multiply the decimal by 100.

      $0.01 \times 100 = 1$ so $0.01 = 1\%$

Changing percentages to decimals

To change a percentage to a decimal we just divide the percentage by 100.

Worked Example

Convert 34% to a decimal.

   To change a percentage to a decimal we divide the percentage by 100.

      $\dfrac{34\%}{100} = 0.34$ so $34\% = 0.34$

PRACTICE 1.5.2   Try these questions without a calculator

1 Convert the following decimals to percentages:

   a 0.5   **c** 0.6   **e** 0.375

   b 0.2   **d** 0.35   **f** 0.4125

2 Convert the following percentages to decimals:

   a 25%   **c** 90%   **e** 5%   **g** 0.2%

   b 45%   **d** 22.5%   **f** 2.5%   **h** 0.01%

Equivalences and ordering

In order to compare fractions, decimals and percentages it is helpful to change all numbers into percentages.

Worked Example

Place these numbers in order with the smallest first:

$\frac{23}{100}$, $\frac{1}{5}$, 0.22, 25%, 25.6%, 0.255, $\frac{6}{25}$, 0.300

Changing each of these numbers to percentages we get:

$$\frac{23}{100} \quad = \frac{23}{100} \times 100\% \quad = 23\%$$

$$\frac{1}{5} \quad = \frac{1}{5} \times 100\% \quad = 20\%$$

$$0.22 \quad = 0.22 \times 100\% \quad = 22\%$$

$$25\% \quad\quad\quad\quad\quad\quad = 25\%$$

$$25.6\% \quad\quad\quad\quad\quad = 25.6\%$$

$$0.255 \quad = 0.255 \times 100\% = 25.5\%$$

$$\frac{6}{25} \quad = \frac{6}{25} \times 100\% \quad = 24\%$$

$$0.300 \quad = 0.300 \times 100\% = 30\%$$

So the order is:

$\frac{1}{5}$, 0.22, $\frac{23}{100}$, $\frac{6}{25}$, 25%, 0.255, 25.6%, 0.300.

PRACTICE 1.5.3   Try these questions without a calculator

1 Place these numbers in order with the smallest first:
$\frac{1}{2}$, $\frac{26}{50}$, 47.9%, $\frac{48}{100}$, $\frac{505}{1000}$, 0.46, 0.488, 51.0%

2 Which of these numbers are the same?
   a $\frac{3}{4}$, 0.76, 75.5%, $\frac{19}{25}$ c $\frac{4}{7}$, 57%, $\frac{11}{20}$, 0.57

   b $\frac{3}{8}$, 38%, 0.375, $\frac{37}{100}$

NOTE

See the work of Topic 1.3 on 'One number as a fraction of another' to remind you.

One number as a percentage of another

To calculate one number as a percentage of another, we write the first number as a fraction of the second number and then change to a percentage by multiplying by 100.

Worked Examples

1 Write down 20 p as a percentage of 50 p.

   To calculate one number as a percentage of another, we write the first number as a fraction of the second number and then change to a percentage by multiplying by 100.

   20 p as a fraction of 50 p is $\frac{20}{50} = \frac{2}{5}$ cancelling down to the lowest terms

We now change the fraction to a percentage by multiplying by 100.

$$20\,\text{p as a percentage of } 50\,\text{p is } \tfrac{2}{5} \times 100 = 40\%$$

We would say that 20 p is 40% of 50 p.

2 Write down 5 grams as a percentage of 200 grams.

To calculate one number as a percentage of another, we write the first number as a fraction of the second number and then change to a percentage by multiplying by 100.

$$5\,\text{g as a fraction of } 200\,\text{g is } \tfrac{5}{200} = \tfrac{1}{40} \qquad \text{cancelling down}$$

We now change the fraction to a percentage by multiplying by 100.

$$5\,\text{g as a percentage of } 200\,\text{g is } \tfrac{1}{40} \times 100 = \tfrac{100}{40}\% = \tfrac{5}{2}\% = 2\tfrac{1}{2}\%$$

We would say that 5 g is $2\tfrac{1}{2}\%$ of 200 g.

3 Express 8 yards as a percentage of 64 feet.

First of all we must make sure that both values are given in the same units. 8 yards is the same as 24 feet so the question can be written as:

Express 24 feet as a percentage of 64 feet.

Next, to calculate one number as a percentage of another, we write the first number as a fraction of the second number and then change to a percentage by multiplying by 100.

$$24\,\text{feet as a fraction of } 64\,\text{feet is } \tfrac{24}{64} = \tfrac{3}{8} \qquad \text{cancelling down}$$

We now change the fraction to a percentage by multiplying by 100.

$$24\,\text{feet as a percentage of } 64\,\text{feet is } \tfrac{3}{8} \times 100 = 37.5\%$$

We would say that 24 feet is 37.5% of 64 feet.

PRACTICE 1.5.4   Try these questions without a calculator

1 Write down 60 p as a percentage of 120 p.

2 Write down 80 p as a percentage of 400 p.

3 Write down 6 litres as a percentage of 60 litres.

4 Write down 3 miles as a percentage of 21 miles.

5 What is 25 p as a percentage of £6.25?

6 What is 150 cm as a percentage of 3 km?

7 Express 6 feet as a percentage of 10 yards.

8 What is 5 pints as a percentage of 3 gallons?

Percentage of an amount or quantity

Three methods for finding percentages of an amount or quantity are provided as follows:

Method 1

The first method uses the idea that any percentage can be written as a fraction with a denominator of 100. This fact is then used to convert the expression into a mathematical form which can be worked out.

Worked Examples

1 Find 45% of £16.

$45\% = \frac{45}{100}$, so the expression can be written as $\frac{45}{100} \times £16$

$$= £7.20$$

2 A supermarket sells 550 apples a day and it is expected that 2% of these apples will be rotten. How many rotten apples does the supermarket sell in a day?

The question requires us to find 2% of 550.

$2\% = \frac{2}{100}$, so the expression can be written as $\frac{2}{100} \times 550$

$$= 11 \text{ apples}$$

Method 2

The second method uses the idea that any percentage can be written as a decimal. This fact is then used to convert the expression into a mathematical form which can be worked out.

Worked Examples

1 Find 45% of £16.

$45\% = 0.45$, so the expression can be written as $0.45 \times £16$

$$= £7.20$$

2 A supermarket sells 550 apples a day and it is expected that 2% of these apples will be rotten. How many rotten apples does the supermarket sell in a day?

$2\% = 0.02$, so the expression can be written as 0.02×550

$$= 11 \text{ apples}$$

Method 3

The third method involves us finding 1% of the given amount or quantity (by dividing by 100) and then multiplying to find the required percentage.

Worked Examples

1   Find 45% of £16.

   1% of £16 $= \dfrac{£16}{100}$ $= £0.16$

   45% of £16 $= 45 \times £0.16$ $= £7.20$

2   A supermarket sells 550 apples a day and it is expected that 2% of these apples will be rotten. How many rotten apples does the supermarket sell in a day?

   1% of 550 $= \dfrac{550}{100}$ $= 5.5$ apples

   2% of 550 $= 2 \times 5.5$ $= 11$ apples

PRACTICE 1.5.5a   Try these questions without a calculator

1   Work out: **a** 25% of £16   **c** 12% of 150 apples
                     b 30% of 900 m   **d** 35% of 2000 g

2   A building society pays 7% interest on each account. How much is paid out on an account containing £3000?

3   A factory makes 620 cars a month and it is expected that 3% of these cars will be returned to the garage. How many cars will be returned to the garage?

PRACTICE 1.5.5b   Try these questions with a calculator

1   Work out: **a** 36% of £260   **c** 84% of 260 litres
                     b 58% of 300 m   **d** 92% of 4 ft 2 inches

2   A shopkeeper is paid 8% of all furniture sales as a bonus at the end of the month. What bonus will the shopkeeper receive on sales of £4600?

3   A bank charges $2\frac{1}{2}$% interest on overdraft amounts. How much will be charged on an overdraft of £450?

Percentage change

To work out the **percentage change** you can work out the increase or decrease and add or subtract it from the original amount as shown in the following examples.

Worked Examples

1   A person earning £600 per month is awarded a pay increase of 4%. What are his new monthly earnings?

   The increase in earnings is equivalent to 4% of £600

   1% of £600 $= \dfrac{£600}{100}$ $= £6$

   4% of £600 $= 4 \times £6 = £24$

   So his new monthly earnings are £600 + £24 = £624

2 A shopper buys a wardrobe for £240 and receives a cash discount of 12%. How much does the shopper pay for the wardrobe?

The discount is equivalent to 12% of £240.

$$1\% \text{ of } £240 = \frac{£240}{100} = £2.40$$

$$12\% \text{ of } £240 = 12 \times £2.40 = £28.80$$

So the amount paid is £240 − £28.80 = £211.20.

The two worked examples on percentage change can be worked out more quickly by using the following information:

If an amount is increased by 4% then the new amount
  = 100% of the original amount + 4% of the original amount
  = 104% of the original amount

Similarly, if an amount is decreased by 12% then the new amount
  = 100% of the original amount − 12% of the original amount
  = 88% of the original amount

Worked Examples

1 A person earning £600 per month is awarded a pay increase of 4%. What are his new monthly earnings?

His new monthly earnings = 104% (100% + 4%) of £600.

$$1\% \text{ of } £600 = \frac{£600}{100} = £6$$

$$104\% \text{ of } £600 = 104 \times £6 = £624 \text{ (as before)}$$

2 A shopper buys a wardrobe for £240 and receives a cash discount of 12%. How much does the shopper pay for the wardrobe?

The cost of the wardrobe = 88% (100% − 12%) of £240.

$$1\% \text{ of } £240 = \frac{£240}{100} = £2.40$$

$$88\% \text{ of } £240 = 88 \times £2.40 = £211.20 \text{ (as before)}$$

3 The population of a village is 6375 and this number decreases by 16% over a period of 10 years. What is the new population of the village?

The percentage decrease = 84% (100% − 16%) of the original population
                                        = 84% of 6375

$$1\% \text{ of } 6375 = \frac{6375}{100} = 63.75$$

$$84\% \text{ of } 6375 = 84 \times 63.75 = 5355$$

4 Jane invests £2500 in her building society account and receives 4% interest per year.
  a What amount is there in her account after one year?
  b What amount is there in her account after two years assuming the interest is reinvested?

a   The percentage increase $= 104\%$ $(100\% + 4\%)$ of the original amount

$$= 104\% \text{ of } £2500$$

$$1\% \text{ of } £2500 = \frac{£2500}{100} = £25$$

$$104\% \text{ of } £2500 = 104 \times £25 = £2600$$

b   The percentage increase $= 104\%$ $(100\% + 4\%)$ of the amount after the first year

$$= 104\% \text{ of } £2600$$

$$1\% \text{ of } £2600 = \frac{£2600}{100} = £26$$

$$104\% \text{ of } £2600 = 104 \times £26 = £2704$$

5   A baker reduces the price of bread by 10% and her sales increase by 20%. What is the percentage increase in the takings from bread?

One way to solve this problem is to take an arbitrary amount for the takings such as £100.

After a reduction of 10%, the takings
$$= 90\% \ (100\% - 10\%) \text{ of the original takings (£100)}$$
$$= 90\% \text{ of } £100 \ (1\% = £1 \text{ so } 90\% = £90)$$
$$= £90$$

After an increase of 20%, the takings
$$= 120\% \ (100\% + 20\%) \text{ of } £90$$
$$= 120\% \text{ of } £90 \ (1\% = £0.90 \text{ so } 120\% = £108)$$
$$= £108$$

£108 represents an increase of 8% on £100 so the percentage increase is 8%.

NOTE

£100 is always a good choice for an arbitrary amount as this figure is easy to deal with when using percentages.

PRACTICE 1.5.6a   Try these questions without a calculator

1   An amount of £500 is increased by 25%. What is the new amount?

2   An amount of £300 is increased by 30%. What is the new amount?

3   An amount of £68 is decreased by 25%. What is the new amount?

4   £5000 is invested in an offshore account which pays 10% interest at the end of the year. What is the new amount after
a   one year,   **b**   two years?

5   A discount warehouse reduces the price of computers by 15% and the sales increase by 20%. What is the percentage increase in the takings from computers?

PRACTICE 1.5.6b   Try these questions with a calculator

1   An amount of £220 is increased by 18%. What is the new amount?

2   An amount of £30 is increased by 2.5%. What is the new amount?

3   An amount of £320 is decreased by 90%. What is the new amount?

4 £3600 is invested in a building society which pays 7% interest at the end of the year. What is the new amount after
   a one year,
   b two years?

5 The value of a car depreciates by 14% each year. How much is a car valued at £6500 worth after
   a one year,
   b two years?

6 A car depreciates by 15% per year. How long will it take before its value is half its original value?

Reverse percentages

Questions are sometimes set where the amount is given after a percentage increase or decrease has been applied. The following worked examples illustrate how this type of question might be solved.

Worked Examples

1 After an increase of 8%, a worker's take home pay is equal to £237.60. What was the original wage?

   We know that 108% (100% + 8%) of the original wage is equal to £237.60.

   108% of the original wage = £237.60

   $$1\% \text{ of the original wage} = \frac{£237.60}{108} = £2.20$$

   100% of the original wage = $100 \times £2.20 = £220$

NOTE
100% of the original amount is equal to the original amount.

2 A car is advertised at £8580 after a discount of 22%. What was the price of the car before the discount?

   We know that 78% (100% − 22%) of the price before discount is equal to £8580.

   78% of the price before discount = £8580

   $$1\% \text{ of the price before discount} = \frac{£8580}{78} = £110$$

   100% of the price before discount =
   $100 \times £110$ $= £11\,000$

PRACTICE 1.5.7a   Try these questions without a calculator

1 A piece of material stretches 2% during the manufacturing process. The length of the material is 204 metres. What was the original length?

2 A farmer owns 60 acres of land after selling off 20% for development. How much land did the farmer originally own?

3 A student receives 4% interest on her original investment. If the new amount is £624, what was her original investment?

4 A cooker is advertised at £600 after a discount of 25%. What was the price of the cooker before the discount?

PRACTICE 1.5.7b   Try these questions with a calculator

1 A piece of metal stretches 2.5% under stress. The metal is now 71.75 m. What was the original length?

2 After an 8% increase, a person's salary is now £13 824. What was the original salary?

3 The number of students enrolling at a college dropped to 252. This is 28% less than the previous year. How many students enrolled the previous year?

4 The area of a pond is increased by 12% and now measures 7 m by 8 m. What was the original area?

The following questions provide a mix of questions about percentages.

PRACTICE 1.5.8a   Try these questions without a calculator

1 A politician gets 16 200 votes in an election and this figure is increased by 12.5% at the next election. How many votes did the politician get at the next election?

2 30% of a certain number is 120. What is the original number?

3 The population of a town is 26 400 and increases by 15% each year. What is the population of the town after
  a one year,
  b two years?

4 A car is sold for £6750 after a depreciation of 25% on the price when new. Calculate the price of the car when it was new.

PRACTICE 1.5.8b   Try these questions with a calculator

1 A sales representative increases her sales by 15% to £29 900. What was the original sales figure?

2 A kitchen is offered for £4224 after a discount of 12%. What was the price before the discount?

3 The length of a square is increased by 20%. What is the percentage increase in the area of the square?

4 An investment increases by 10% then decreases by 6% to £25 850. What was the amount invested?

Percentage increase and decrease

Percentage increases and decreases are calculated on the basis of an increase or a decrease in the original amount or quantity.

$$\text{Percentage increase} = \frac{\text{increase}}{\text{original amount}} \times 100\%$$

$$\text{Percentage decrease} = \frac{\text{decrease}}{\text{original amount}} \times 100\%$$

Worked Examples

1 A woman's wages increase from £25 000 to £27 000 per annum. What is the percentage increase?

$$\text{Percentage increase} = \frac{\text{increase}}{\text{original amount}} \times 100\%$$

$$\text{Percentage increase} = \frac{£27\,000 - £25\,000}{£25\,000} \times 100\%$$

$$= \frac{£2000}{£25\,000} \times 100\%$$

$$= 8\%$$

2 A firm produces 55 000 toys in one year and 53 500 toys the following year. Calculate the percentage decrease.

$$\text{Percentage decrease} = \frac{\text{decrease}}{\text{original amount}} \times 100\%$$

$$\text{Percentage decrease} = \frac{55\,000 - 53\,500}{55\,000} \times 100\%$$

$$= \frac{1500}{55\,000} \times 100\%$$

$$= 2.727\,27\% = 2.73\% \ (3 \text{ s.f.})$$

PRACTICE 1.5.9a   Try these questions without a calculator

1 A person's wage increases from £300 to £330 per week. What is the percentage increase?

2 A secretary's hours are decreased from 40 to $37\frac{1}{2}$ hours per week. What percentage decrease is this?

3 A house increases in value from £1 250 000 to £1 500 000. What is the percentage increase?

Percentage profit and loss

Percentage profit and loss are the same as percentage increase and decrease except that the original amount or quantity is replaced by the buying price as shown in the following formulae:

$$\text{Percentage profit} = \frac{\text{profit}}{\text{buying price}} \times 100\%$$

where profit = selling price − buying price

Where the selling price is smaller than the buying price then we work out the percentage loss using the following formulae:

$$\text{Percentage loss} = \frac{\text{loss}}{\text{buying price}} \times 100\%$$

where loss = selling price − buying price

Worked Examples

1   Oranges are bought in boxes of 48 costing £10 and sold at 25p each. What is the percentage profit?

Selling price = 48 × 25 p = £12

Profit = selling price − buying price

    = £12 − £10

    = £2

$$\text{Percentage profit} = \frac{\text{profit}}{\text{buying price}} \times 100\%$$

    $= \frac{2}{10} \times 100\%$

    $= 20\%$

2   A car was bought for £650 and sold one year later for £600. What is the percentage loss over the year?

Loss = buying price − selling price

    = £650 − £600

    = £50

$$\text{Percentage loss} = \frac{\text{loss}}{\text{buying price}} \times 100\%$$
$$= \frac{50}{650} \times 100\%$$
$$= 7.6923\%$$
$$= 7.69\% \text{ (3sf)}$$

3 A caravan is bought for £450 and sold at a profit of 20%. What was the selling price?

Buying price = £450

Profit = 20% of selling price
   = 20% of £450
   = $\frac{20}{100} \times$ £450
   = £90

Selling price = buying price + profit
   = £450 + £90
   = £540

PRACTICE 1.5.10a   Try these questions without a calculator

1 A box of 144 pens is bought for £10 and individual pens are sold at 10 p each. What is the percentage profit?

2 A picture is bought at £400 and sold at a profit of 15%. What is the selling price?

3 A diamond bought for £2800 is sold at a profit of 22%. What is the selling price?

PRACTICE 1.5.10b   Try these questions with a calculator

1 A car is bought for £380 and sold for £350. What is the percentage loss?

2 100 apples are bought for £17 but 5% are found to be damaged and not saleable. The rest are sold for 20 p each. What is the percentage profit?

3 A suite originally costing £850 is valued at £475. What is the percentage loss?

Ratio is used for comparison purposes and is very similar to fractions.

Worked Example

In a class there are 20 girls and 15 boys.

What is the ratio of girls to boys?

We say that the ratio of girls to boys is 20 to 15 which can be written as 20 : 15.

Order is important and the ratio of girls to boys is different from the ratio of boys to girls.

In this example the ratio of boys to girls is 15 to 20 which can be written as 15 : 20.

Equivalent ratios

Equivalent ratios are ratios which are the same as each other. The following ratios are all equivalent to 3 : 4:

$$3:4 = 6:8 = 9:12 = 12:16 = 15:20$$

The following ratios are all equivalent to 2 : 3:

$$2:3 = 4:6 = 6:9 = 8:12 = 10:15$$

Equivalent ratios can be created by multiplying or dividing both sides of the ratio by the same number as follows:

$$\times2 \diagdown \begin{array}{c} 2:5 \\ \end{array} \diagdown \times2 \qquad\qquad \times7 \diagdown \begin{array}{c} 2:5 \\ \end{array} \diagdown \times7$$
$$\searrow 4:10 \swarrow \qquad\qquad\qquad \searrow 14:35 \swarrow$$

Cancelling ratios

To find a ratio in its **lowest terms** we find an equivalent ratio where both sides of the ratio are as small as possible – this process is also called **simplifying** or **cancelling down** (see also the work in Topic 1.3 on 'Cancelling fractions').

Worked Examples

1 Write the following ratios in their simplest form:

　a　$6:12$

　b　$24:16$

　c　$3:\frac{1}{2}$

　　a　$\div6 \diagup \begin{array}{c}6:12\end{array} \diagdown \div6$　　　**b**　$\div8 \diagup \begin{array}{c}24:16\end{array} \diagdown \div8$　　　**c**　$\times2 \diagup \begin{array}{c}3:\frac{1}{2}\end{array} \diagdown \times2$

　　　　$\searrow 1:2 \swarrow$　　　　　　　$\searrow 3:2 \swarrow$　　　　　　　$\searrow 6:1 \swarrow$

2 Jane receives 50 p pocket money and Janet receives £2.00 pocket money. Express their pocket money as a ratio in its simplest form.

It is important that the units in both of these cases are the same, so writing £2.00 as 200 p the ratio becomes:

$$50\text{p} : 200\,\text{p}$$
$$= 50 \ \ : 200$$
$$= \ 1 \ \ :4 \quad\text{in its simplest form}$$

Alternatively, writing 50 p as £0.50 the ratio becomes:

$$£0.50 : £2.00$$
$$= \ 0.50 : 2.00$$
$$= \qquad 1 : 4 \qquad\qquad\text{multiplying both sides by 2 to obtain the}$$
$$\text{ratio in its simplest form.}$$

PRACTICE 1.6.1   Try these questions without a calculator

1   Write the following ratios in their simplest form:

    a $6:8$ **d** $3:7$ **g** $1000:100$ **j** $\frac{1}{4}:2$

    b $10:50$ **e** $12:48$ **h** $4:\frac{1}{2}$ **k** $2:1\frac{1}{4}$

    c $27:81$ **f** $4:12$ **i** $1\frac{1}{2}:5$ **l** $3\frac{1}{2}:2\frac{1}{3}$

2   In a class there are 12 girls and 18 boys. Express this as a ratio in its simplest form.

3   A company has 4 coaches and 10 minibuses. What is the ratio of the number of coaches to the number of minibuses?

4   One piece of cloth is 2 m long and another piece of cloth is 75 cm long. Express the lengths as a ratio in its simplest form.

5   Two objects weigh 6 ounces and $1\frac{1}{2}$ pounds. Express the weights as a ratio in its simplest form.

6   In one week a shop sells 350 tapes and 560 CD's.
    a What is the ratio of tapes to CD's?
    b What is the ratio of CD's to tapes?

Proportional parts

To divide an amount into proportional parts we add up the individual proportions and divide the amount by this number. The following examples are used to demonstrate proportional parts.

Worked Examples

1   £60 is to be divided between two children in the ratio $7:3$. How much does each child receive?

A ratio of $7:3$ means that there are 10 ($=7+3$) parts altogether.
The value of each part is $\frac{£60}{10} = £6$.
So 7 parts $= 7 \times £6 = £42$ and 3 parts $= 3 \times £6 = £18$.

The two children receive £42 and £18.

2   A drink is made up of water, orange and lemon in the ratio $5:1:2$. Find the amount of water, orange and lemon in a bottle of 100 ml.

A ratio of $5:1:2$ means that there are 8 ($=5+1+2$) parts altogether.
The value of each part is $\frac{100\,\text{ml}}{8} = 12.5\,\text{ml}$
So   5 parts $= 5 \times 12.5\,\text{ml} = 62.5\,\text{ml}$
and 1 part $= 1 \times 12.5\,\text{ml} = 12.5\,\text{ml}$
and 2 parts $= 2 \times 12.5\,\text{ml} = \underline{25\,\text{ml}}$
                                100 ml (to check the total)

The amount of water is 62.5 ml, the amount of orange is 12.5 ml and the amount of lemon is 25 ml.

PRACTICE 1.6.2   Try these questions without a calculator

1   Divide £1800 in the ratio 4 : 5.

2   A syndicate wins £3000 and splits the money in the ratio 2 : 3 : 7. How much does each member get?

3   A sum of £600 is to be split between two people so that one person gets three times as much as the other. How much does each person get?

4   A sum of £22 000 is to be divided between three children in the ratio of their ages. If their ages are 11 years, 7 years and 4 years how much does each child get? How much would each child get if the money was shared out one year later?

5   Amy, Brian and Catrina start up a beauty business. Amy invests £3500, Brian invests £6000 and Catrina invests £2500. At the end of the year they make a profit of £18 000 which they agree to divide in the ratio of their investments. How much does each get?

1.7 DIRECTED NUMBERS

Positive and negative numbers are often referred to as **directed numbers**. We use directed numbers when we talk about the temperature and refer to temperatures above $0°$ (positive numbers) and below 0^0 (negative numbers).

Directed numbers are denoted in a number of ways although it is always helpful to distinguish between using $+$ and $-$ to mean add and subtract and $+$ and $-$ to mean positive and negative numbers.

Two ways in which such work can be written are:

i by using brackets: $(+5) + (-3) = \ldots$
$(-7) - (+2) = \ldots$

or

ii by using superscripts: $^+5 + {}^-3 = \ldots$
$^-7 - {}^+2 = \ldots$

NOTE
Whilst Topic 1.7 uses superscripts to identify positive and negative numbers, generally we use $-$ and $+$ signs when we refer to negative and positive numbers throughout the book.

Addition and subtraction of directed numbers

The following rules apply when adding or subtracting directed numbers:

adding a positive number ($+$ $^+$) is the same as addition
subtracting a negative number ($-$ $^-$) is the same as addition
adding a negative number ($+$ $^-$) is the same as subtraction
subtracting a positive number ($-$ $^+$) is the same as subtraction.

Worked Example

Work out:

a $^+5 + {}^+2$ **c** $^+6 + {}^-3$ **e** $^+6 - {}^+2$ **g** $^-4 - {}^-3$
b $^-8 + {}^+2$ **d** $^-2 + {}^-7$ **f** $^+3 - {}^+8$ **h** $^-3 - {}^-8$

a $^+5 + {}^+2 = {}^+7$ $+$ $^+$ is the same as addition
$^+5 + 2 = {}^+7$

b $^-8 + {}^+2 = {}^-6$ $+$ $^+$ is the same as addition
$^-8 + 2 = {}^-6$

c $^+6 + {}^-3 = {}^+3$ $+ {}^-$ is the same as subtraction
$^+6 - 3 = {}^+3$

d $^-2 + {}^-7 = {}^-9$ $+ {}^-$ is the same as subtraction
$^-2 - 7 = {}^-9$

e $^+6 - {}^+2 = {}^+4$ $- {}^+$ is the same as subtraction
$^+6 - 2 = {}^+4$

f $^+3 - {}^+8 = {}^-5$ $- {}^+$ is the same as subtraction
$^+3 - 8 = {}^-5$

g $^-4 - {}^-3 = {}^-1$ $- {}^-$ is the same as addition
$^-4 + 3 = {}^-1$

h $^-3 - {}^-8 = {}^+5$ $- {}^-$ is the same as addition
$^-3 + 8 = {}^+5$

PRACTICE 1.7.1   Try these questions without a calculator

1   The temperature in Russia rose from $-8°C$ to $+4°C$. By how many degrees did the temperature rise?

2   The temperature in Arhus dropped from $-3°C$ to $-8°C$. By how many degrees did the temperature drop?

3   The temperature was recorded inside a house at $18°C$ and outside at $-6°C$. How many degrees warmer was it inside the house than outside?

4   Work out:
   a $^+6 + {}^+8$ **d** $^+17 + {}^-3$ **g** $^+6 - {}^+5$ **j** $^-6 - {}^-12$
   b $^-11 + {}^+6$ **e** $^-7 + {}^+7$ **h** $^+5 - {}^+14$ **k** $^-5 - {}^-7$
   c $^+9 + {}^+12$ **f** $^-5 + {}^-5$ **i** $^+2 - {}^+20$ **l** $^-10 - {}^-5$

Multiplication and division of directed numbers

The following rules apply when multiplying or dividing directed numbers:

if the signs are the same then the answer will be positive
if the signs are different then the answer will be negative

or $^+ \times {}^+ = {}^+$ $^- \times {}^- = {}^+$ and $^+ \div {}^+ = {}^+$ $^- \div {}^- = {}^+$
      $^+ \times {}^- = {}^-$ $^- \times {}^+ = {}^-$ $^+ \div {}^- = {}^-$ $^- \div {}^+ = {}^-$

Worked Example

Work out: **a** $^-3 \times 4$ **b** $\dfrac{^-12}{^-6}$ **c** $(^-4)^2$ **d** $^-4 \times {}^-2 \times {}^-3$ **e** $\dfrac{8}{^-5}$

a $^-3 \times 4 = {}^-12$ $^- \times {}^+ = {}^-$

b $\dfrac{^-12}{^-6} = 2$ $^- \div {}^- = {}^+$ and we do not need to write the $^+$ sign

c $(^-4)^2 = 16$ $(^-4)^2$ means $^-4 \times {}^-4$ which is $^+16$ or 16

d $^-4 \times {}^-2 \times {}^-3 = {}^-24$ $^- \times {}^- \times {}^-$ is the same as $^+ \times {}^-$
which is the same as $^-$

e $\dfrac{8}{^-5} = {}^-1.6$ $^+ \div {}^- = {}^-$ and $\dfrac{8}{5} = 1.6$, so the answer is $^-1.6$

PRACTICE 1.7.2   Try these questions without a calculator

1 Work out:

   a $^-3 \times {}^+7$ **e** $3 \times {}^-5$ **i** $\dfrac{^-15}{^-6}$ **m** $^-3 \times {}^-4 \times {}^+6$

   b $^-3 \times 7$ **f** $\dfrac{18}{-3}$ **j** $({}^+5)^2$

   c $^+9 \times {}^+5$ **g** $\dfrac{-3}{-3}$ **k** $({}^-11)^2$

   d $^-8 \times {}^-7$ **h** $\dfrac{^+12}{^+2}$ **l** $({}^-3)^3$

1.8 EXTENSION MATERIAL

Rational and irrational numbers

A **rational number** is any number which can be expressed exactly as a fraction in the form $\dfrac{p}{q}$ where p and q are integers. An **irrational number** is any number which cannot be expressed exactly as a fraction in this form.

The following numbers are all rational numbers:

$\dfrac{2}{5}$

$1\frac{1}{2}$ can be written as $\frac{3}{2}$

4 can be written as $\frac{4}{1}$ (all integers are rational numbers)

$0.\dot{3}$ is the same as $\frac{1}{3}$ which is a rational number

$\sqrt{4}$ is equal to 2 which is a rational number.

Numbers such as $\sqrt{2}$, $\sqrt{3}$, $\sqrt[3]{10}$, $\sqrt[3]{20}$, etc. are examples of irrational numbers as they cannot be expressed as a fraction. The number π is also an example of an irrational number as it cannot be expressed *exactly* as a fraction although it is often approximated as $\frac{22}{7}$ (which is itself a rational number).

NOTE

You should not need a calculator for these questions.

PRACTICE 1.8.1

1 Classify the following numbers as rational or irrational numbers:

   a $\frac{3}{7}$ **e** $\sqrt{10}$ **i** 0.3571 **m** π **q** $1 + \sqrt{4}$

   b $2\frac{1}{4}$ **f** 25 **j** $0.\dot{3}$ **n** $\pi + 1$ **r** $\sqrt[3]{8}$

   c $\sqrt{8}$ **g** 25.1 **k** $2.\dot{3}$ **o** π^2 **s** $(\sqrt{3})^2$

   d $\sqrt{9}$ **h** 1.55 **l** $\sqrt{\frac{1}{9}}$ **p** $1 + \sqrt{2}$

2 Write down
   a two rational numbers between 3 and 5,
   b two irrational numbers between 3 and 5.

Surds

Irrational numbers involving square roots are also called **surds**. We can multiply two surds by square rooting their product and we can divide two surds by square rooting their quotient.

Worked Examples

1 Find the product of the following surds.

   a $\sqrt{5} \times \sqrt{5}$ **b** $\sqrt{3} \times \sqrt{12}$ **c** $\sqrt{7} \times \sqrt{3}$

      a $\sqrt{5} \times \sqrt{5} = \sqrt{5 \times 5} = \sqrt{25} = 5$

      b $\sqrt{3} \times \sqrt{12} = \sqrt{3 \times 12} = \sqrt{36} = 6$

      c $\sqrt{7} \times \sqrt{3} = \sqrt{7 \times 3} = \sqrt{21}$

2 Find the quotient of the following surds.

   a $\dfrac{\sqrt{16}}{\sqrt{4}}$ **b** $\dfrac{\sqrt{27}}{\sqrt{3}}$ **c** $\dfrac{\sqrt{30}}{\sqrt{6}}$

      a $\dfrac{\sqrt{16}}{\sqrt{4}} = \sqrt{\dfrac{16}{4}} = \sqrt{4} = 2$ **c** $\dfrac{\sqrt{30}}{\sqrt{6}} = \sqrt{\dfrac{30}{6}} = \sqrt{5}$

      b $\dfrac{\sqrt{27}}{\sqrt{3}} = \sqrt{\dfrac{27}{3}} = \sqrt{9} = 3$

3 Simplify the following surds.

   a $\sqrt{20}$ **b** $\sqrt{75}$ **c** $\sqrt{3} + \sqrt{12}$

      a $\sqrt{20} = \sqrt{4 \times 5}$ $= \sqrt{4} \times \sqrt{5} = 2\sqrt{5}$ as $\sqrt{4} = 2$

      b $\sqrt{75} = \sqrt{25 \times 3}$ $= \sqrt{25} \times \sqrt{3} = 5\sqrt{3}$ as $\sqrt{25} = 5$

      c $\sqrt{3} + \sqrt{12}$ $= \sqrt{3} + \sqrt{(4 \times 3)}$

                       $= \sqrt{3} + \sqrt{4} \times \sqrt{3}$

                       $= \sqrt{3} + 2\sqrt{3} = 3\sqrt{3}$

NOTE
These questions will usually appear on the non-calculator paper.

PRACTICE 1.8.2   Try these questions without a calculator

1 Find the product of the following surds.

   a $\sqrt{3} \times \sqrt{3}$ **c** $\sqrt{2} \times \sqrt{18}$ **e** $\sqrt{5} \times \sqrt{3}$

   b $\sqrt{7} \times \sqrt{7}$ **d** $\sqrt{5} \times \sqrt{20}$ **f** $\sqrt{8} \times \sqrt{11}$

2 Find the quotient of the following surds.

   a $\dfrac{\sqrt{100}}{\sqrt{4}}$ **c** $\dfrac{\sqrt{121}}{\sqrt{11}}$ **e** $\dfrac{\sqrt{12}}{\sqrt{6}}$

   b $\dfrac{\sqrt{125}}{\sqrt{5}}$ **d** $\dfrac{\sqrt{10}}{\sqrt{5}}$ **f** $\dfrac{\sqrt{27}}{\sqrt{9}}$

3 Simplify the following surds.

   a $\sqrt{20} \times \sqrt{5}$ **d** $\sqrt{18} + \sqrt{2}$ **g** $\sqrt{24} + \sqrt{150}$

   b $\dfrac{\sqrt{9}}{\sqrt{4}}$ **e** $3\sqrt{3} + \sqrt{27}$ **h** $\sqrt{27} - \sqrt{3}$

   c $\sqrt{2} + \sqrt{8}$ **f** $\sqrt{5} + \sqrt{45}$ **i** $\sqrt{99} - \sqrt{44}$

Converting recurring decimals to fractions

All recurring decimals are rational numbers and can be converted to fractions by the method given below.

Worked Examples

1 Convert $0.\dot{5}$ to a fraction.

We can see that

$$10 \times \text{fraction} = 5.555\,555\,55\ldots \quad \text{multiplying the fraction by 10}$$

and $\qquad 1 \times \text{fraction} = 0.555\,555\,55\ldots$

Subtracting we get

$$9 \times \text{fraction} = 5 \qquad\qquad 5.555\,555\,55\ldots - 0.555\,555\,55\ldots$$

$$\text{fraction} = \tfrac{5}{9}$$

so $0.\dot{5} \qquad = \tfrac{5}{9}$

NOTE

Multiply the fraction by 10 if 1 figure repeats itself.
Multiply the fraction by 100 if 2 figures repeat themselves.
Multiply the fraction by 1000 if 3 figures repeat themselves, etc.

2 Convert $0.\dot{3}5\dot{1}$ to a fraction.

We can see that

$$1000 \times \text{fraction} = 351.351\,351\ldots$$

and $\qquad 1 \times \text{fraction} = 0.351\,351\ldots$

Subtracting we get

$$999 \times \text{fraction} = 351$$

$$\text{fraction} = \tfrac{351}{999}$$

cancelling down we get $\tfrac{13}{37}$

so $\qquad 0.\dot{3}5\dot{1} = \tfrac{13}{37}$

3 Convert $4.\dot{3}5\dot{1}$ to a fraction.

In this example we separate the whole part and the fractional part and deal with the fractional part as shown in example 2.

$$0.\dot{3}5\dot{1} = \tfrac{13}{37} \qquad \text{see above}$$

so $4.\dot{3}5\dot{1} = 4\tfrac{13}{37}$

4 By considering $\tfrac{5}{6}$ as a decimal, write $0.258\dot{3}$ as a fraction in its lowest form.

$\tfrac{5}{6}$ as a decimal is $6\overline{)5.^80^20^20^20^20^20^20}$ $\dfrac{0.\,8\,3\,3\,3\,3\,3\ldots}{} = 0.8\dot{3}$

Comparing this with the required fraction we can see that

$$0.258\dot{3} = 0.25 + 0.008\dot{3}$$

$$0.008\,3333\ldots = 0.833\,3333\ldots \times \tfrac{1}{100}$$

$$= \tfrac{5}{6} \times \tfrac{1}{100}$$

$$= \tfrac{5}{600}$$

so $\qquad 0.258\dot{3} = 0.25 + 0.008\dot{3}$

becomes $\qquad = \tfrac{1}{4} + \tfrac{5}{600}$

$$= \tfrac{150}{600} + \tfrac{5}{600} \quad \text{writing the fractions with the same}$$

$$= \tfrac{155}{600} \qquad\qquad \text{denominator}$$

$0.258\dot{3} = \tfrac{31}{120} \qquad \text{in its lowest form}$

PRACTICE 1.8.3　Try these questions without a calculator

1　Convert the following to fractions in their lowest terms.

　　a　$0.\dot{3}$　　　　　d　$0.\dot{2}\dot{6}$　　　　　g　$0.\dot{3}0\dot{3}$　　　　　j　$12.\dot{2}0\dot{1}$

　　b　$0.\dot{5}$　　　　　e　$0.\dot{2}3\dot{4}$　　　　　h　$0.\dot{4}02\dot{4}$　　　　k　$16.\dot{3}\dot{5}$

　　c　$0.\dot{4}\dot{6}$　　　　f　$0.\dot{2}0\dot{1}$　　　　　i　$3.\dot{8}$　　　　　　l　$201.\dot{2}\dot{3}$

2　Given that $\frac{7}{90} = 0.0\dot{7}$, write $0.5\dot{7}$ as a fraction in its lowest form.

3　Show that $0.\dot{5}\dot{0}$ is a rational number.

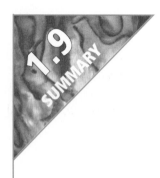

Factors

The factors of any number are the whole numbers which divide exactly into the given number.

Multiples

The multiples of any number are obtained by multiplying the number by any whole number. The multiples occur as the results of the multiplication table for the given number.

Prime numbers and prime factors

A prime number is a whole number which has exactly two factors (one and itself). A prime factor is a factor which is a prime number.

Equivalent fractions

Equivalent fractions are fractions which are equal.

Addition and subtraction of fractions

To add or subtract fractions it is important that the denominators (the numbers on the bottom of the fractions) are the same. The resulting fraction will also have the same denominator.

Multiplication of fractions

To multiply two fractions you multiply the numerators together to obtain the numerator of the answer and multiply the denominators together to obtain the denominator of the answer.

Division of fractions

To divide two fractions you multiply the first fraction by the reciprocal of the second fraction.

Converting decimals to fractions

To convert a decimal to a fraction we use place value to convert the figures to the right of the decimal point.

Converting fractions to decimals

To convert a fraction to a decimal we simply divide the numerator (top number) by the denominator (bottom number).

Multiplication of decimals

The following method should be used:
i Multiply the two numbers ignoring the decimal points.
ii Add together the number of digits after the decimal point in each of the numbers.
iii Replace the decimal point so that the number of digits after the decimal point is the same as the number in **ii** above.

Changing fractions to percentages

To change a fraction to a percentage we just multiply the fraction by 100.

Changing percentages to fractions

To change a percentage to a fraction we just divide the percentage by 100.

Changing decimals to percentages

To change a decimal to a percentage we just multiply the decimal by 100.

Changing percentages to decimals

To change a percentage to a decimal we just divide the percentage by 100.

Proportional parts

To divide an amount into proportional parts we add up the individual proportions and divide the amount by this number.

Addition and subtraction of directed numbers

The following rules apply when multiplying or dividing directed numbers:

adding a positive number $(+\,^+)$ is the same as addition
subtracting a negative number $(-\,^-)$ is the same as addition
adding a negative number $(+\,^-)$ is the same as subtraction
subtracting a positive number $(-\,^+)$ is the same as subtraction.

Multiplication and division of directed numbers

The following rules apply when multiplying or dividing directed numbers:

  if the signs are the same then the answer will be positive
  if the signs are different then the answer will be negative

or $^+\times{}^+={}^+$ $^-\times{}^-={}^+$
       $^+\times{}^-={}^-$ $^-\times{}^+={}^-$

and $^+\div{}^+={}^+$ $^-\div{}^-={}^+$
       $^+\div{}^-={}^-$ $^-\div{}^+={}^-$

Rational and irrational numbers (extension)

A rational number is any number that can be expressed in the form $\frac{p}{q}$ where p and q are integers.

Examples of rational numbers include $2, \frac{1}{3}, 0.\dot{3}, \frac{22}{7}, \sqrt{4}, \sqrt[3]{8}$, etc.

Examples of irrational numbers include $\sqrt{2}, \pi, \sqrt{10}, \sqrt[3]{20}$, etc.

Converting recurring decimals to fractions (extension)

All recurring decimals are rational numbers and can always be converted to fractions.

CHAPTER 2
Number methods

In this chapter you will need to:
▸ understand and use simple powers or indices
▸ estimate weights, lengths and capacity

Powers

We have already seen that powers can be written in the form

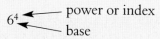

where the power or index simply tells us how many times the base number is to be multiplied by itself, so that 6^4 means that 6 (the base number) is to be multiplied by itself 4 times (the power or index).

$$6^4 = \underbrace{6 \times 6 \times 6 \times 6}_{4 \text{ times}}$$

Weights, lengths and capacity

The examination will set out to test your ability to estimate weights, lengths and capacity in metric (SI) and imperial units. To prepare for this you need to practice your ability to measure such items as:

Weight: What is the weight of this textbook?
What is the weight of an orange?
How much does a parcel weigh?
What is the weight of ...

Length: What is the length of this textbook?
What is the height of the door?
What is the width of the noticeboard?
How long is a car/bus?
How wide is this table?

Capacity: How much water will a cup hold?
What is the capacity of a suitcase?

NOTE
A useful guide to help you with capacity is that a bag of sugar weighs 1 kilogram which is approximately 2.2 pounds and a cup holds approximately 200 millilitres.

Examination questions (especially the aural paper) will expect you to be able to estimate the size of angles, so it will be helpful to appreciate how big angles of 10°, 30°, 45° and 60° are without using your protractor.

Multiplying powers

We can multiply powers as follows:

$$5^3 = 5 \times 5 \times 5 \text{ and } 5^4 = 5 \times 5 \times 5 \times 5$$
$$5^3 \times 5^4 = (5 \times 5 \times 5) \times (5 \times 5 \times 5 \times 5)$$
$$= 5 \times 5 \times 5 \times 5 \times 5 \times 5 \times 5$$
$$= 5^7$$

Similarly

$$3^2 = 3 \times 3 \text{ and } 3^7 = 3 \times 3 \times 3 \times 3 \times 3 \times 3 \times 3$$
$$3^2 \times 3^7 = (3 \times 3) \times (3 \times 3 \times 3 \times 3 \times 3 \times 3 \times 3)$$
$$= 3 \times 3 \times 3 \times 3 \times 3 \times 3 \times 3 \times 3 \times 3$$
$$= 3^9$$

Similarly

$$14^2 = 14 \times 14 \text{ and } 14^6 = 14 \times 14 \times 14 \times 14 \times 14 \times 14$$
$$14^2 \times 14^6 = (14 \times 14) \times (14 \times 14 \times 14 \times 14 \times 14 \times 14)$$
$$= 14 \times 14 \times 14 \times 14 \times 14 \times 14 \times 14 \times 14$$
$$= 14^8$$

You will notice that a quick way to multiply two powers when their bases are the same is to add their powers so that:

$$5^3 \times 5^4 = 5^{3+4} = 5^7$$
and $\quad\quad 3^2 \times 3^7 = 3^{2+7} = 3^9$
and $\quad\quad 14^2 \times 14^6 = 14^{2+6} = 14^8$

Any number to the power 1 is equal to that number so that $7^1 = 7$, $12^1 = 12$, etc. Similarly, the number 7 can be written as 7^1, 12 can be written as 12^1, etc.

PRACTICE 2.2.1   Try these questions without a calculator

1 Work out the following as shown in the previous examples (you must show all of your working).

    a $4^6 \times 4^2$ **c** $11^6 \times 11^2$ **e** $(5^3)^2$

    b $3^2 \times 3^5$ **d** $7^5 \times 7$ **f** $6^4 \times 6^2 \times 6^3$

2 Work out the following leaving your answers as single powers.

    a $3^6 \times 3^8$ **c** $9^6 \times 9^3$ **e** $6^{12} \times 6^{13}$ **g** $16^2 \times 16^3 \times 16^4$

    b $4^7 \times 4^2$ **d** $8^3 \times 8^{11}$ **f** $7^8 \times 7^2 \times 7^4$

Dividing powers

We can divide powers as follows:

$$4^8 \div 4^5 = (4 \times 4 \times 4 \times 4 \times 4 \times 4 \times 4 \times 4) \div (4 \times 4 \times 4 \times 4 \times 4)$$
$$= \frac{(4 \times 4 \times 4 \times \overset{1}{\cancel{4}} \times \overset{1}{\cancel{4}} \times \overset{1}{\cancel{4}} \times \overset{1}{\cancel{4}} \times \overset{1}{\cancel{4}})}{(\underset{1}{\cancel{4}} \times \underset{1}{\cancel{4}} \times \underset{1}{\cancel{4}} \times \underset{1}{\cancel{4}} \times \underset{1}{\cancel{4}})}$$
$$= 4 \times 4 \times 4$$
$$= 4^3$$

Similarly

$$12^5 \div 12^1 = (12 \times 12 \times 12 \times 12 \times 12) \div (12)$$

$$= \frac{(12 \times 12 \times 12 \times 12 \times \overset{1}{\cancel{12}})}{(\underset{1}{\cancel{12}})}$$

$$= 12 \times 12 \times 12 \times 12$$

$$= 12^4$$

Similarly

$$19^8 \div 19^3 = (19 \times 19 \times 19 \times 19 \times 19 \times 19 \times 19 \times 19) \div (19 \times 19 \times 19)$$

$$= \frac{(19 \times 19 \times 19 \times 19 \times 19 \times \overset{1}{\cancel{19}} \times \overset{1}{\cancel{19}} \times \overset{1}{\cancel{19}})}{(\underset{1}{\cancel{19}} \times \underset{1}{\cancel{19}} \times \underset{1}{\cancel{19}})}$$

$$= 19 \times 19 \times 19 \times 19 \times 19$$

$$= 19^5$$

You will again notice that a quick way to divide two powers when their bases are the same is to subtract their powers so that:

$$4^8 \div 4^5 = 4^{8-5} = 4^3$$

and $\qquad 12^5 \div 12^1 = 12^{5-1} = 12^4$

and $\qquad 19^8 \div 19^3 = 19^{8-3} = 19^5$

PRACTICE 2.2.2   Try these questions without a calculator

1 Work out the following as shown in the previous examples (you must show all of your working).

    a $5^7 \div 5^2$ **c** $8^8 \div 8^2$ **e** $21^4 \div 21$

    b $6^7 \div 6^3$ **d** $14^5 \div 14$ **f** $3^6 \div 3^5$

2 Work out the following leaving your answers as single powers.

    a $10^4 \div 10^2$ **c** $17^{11} \div 17^6$ **e** $9^{10} \div 9^3$

    b $8^7 \div 8^3$ **d** $16^{10} \div 16^9$ **f** $4^6 \div 4$

PRACTICE 2.2.3   Try these questions without a calculator

1 Express the following as single powers.

    a $5^2 \times 5^4$ **c** $6^3 \times 6^4$ **e** $6^8 \div 6^5$ **g** $16^9 \div 16^7$

    b $4^8 \times 4^{10}$ **d** $18^6 \times 18^4 \times 18^3$ **f** $25^7 \div 25^6$ **h** $2^{25} \div 2^{22}$

2 Which is the greater

    a 3^5 or 5^3 **b** 11^2 or 2^{11}?

3 Evaluate the following.

    a 6^2 **c** $(2^2)^3$ **e** 17^1 **g** $9^5 \div 9^4$

    b 4^3 **d** $(2^3)^2$ **f** 18^1 **h** $22^{12} \div 22^{11}$

4 Work out the following leaving your answer in index form.

a $3^2 \times 3^4$	**g** $(6^5)^2$	**m** $16^8 \div 16^4$	**q** $6^7 \div 6^7$
b $4^7 \times 4^{11}$	**h** $(3^7)^2$	**n** $\dfrac{(6^5 \times 6^3)}{6^4}$	**r** $4^5 \div 4^6$
c $6^5 \times 6^8$	**i** $(4^5)^3$		**s** $5^3 \div 5^6$
d $11^7 \times 11^4$	**j** $4^8 \div 4^5$	**o** $\dfrac{(10^8 \times 10^5)}{(10^7 \times 10^6)}$	**t** $4^2 \div 4^{11}$
e $6^5 \times 6$	**k** $9^3 \div 9^2$		
f $4^3 \times 4^4 \times 4^7$	**l** $5^{12} \div 5^7$	**p** $7^3 \div 7^3$	

The last few questions in Practice 2.2.3 introduced us to the idea of zero and negative numbers as powers, but what exactly do these mean?

The power zero

$$7^3 \div 7^3 = 7^{3-3} = 7^0$$

Another way to work this out is to write 7^3 as $7 \times 7 \times 7$ and do the division:

$$7^3 \div 7^3 = \frac{7 \times 7 \times 7}{7 \times 7 \times 7}$$

$$= 1$$

Similarly

$$6^7 \div 6^7 = 6^{7-7} = 6^0 = 1$$

So any number to the power zero is equal to 1.

Negative powers

$$4^5 \div 4^6 = 4^{5-6} = 4^{-1}$$

Another way to work this out is to write out 4^5 and 4^6 and do the division:

$$4^5 \div 4^6 = \frac{\overset{1}{\cancel{4}} \times \overset{1}{\cancel{4}} \times \overset{1}{\cancel{4}} \times \overset{1}{\cancel{4}} \times \overset{1}{\cancel{4}}}{\underset{1}{\cancel{4}} \times \underset{1}{\cancel{4}} \times \underset{1}{\cancel{4}} \times \underset{1}{\cancel{4}} \times \underset{1}{\cancel{4}} \times 4}$$

$$= \frac{1}{4}$$

which is the same as

$$= \frac{1}{4^1} \quad \text{(since 4 can be written as } 4^1\text{)}$$

Similarly

$$5^3 \div 5^6 = 5^{3-6} = 5^{-3} = \frac{1}{5^3}$$

and

$$4^2 \div 4^{11} = 4^{2-11} = 4^{-9} = \frac{1}{4^9}$$

PRACTICE 2.2.4   Try these questions without a calculator

1 Write the following as numbers with positive powers.
 a $4^3 \div 4^8$ **c** $2^3 \div 2^5$ **e** $7^2 \div 7^{21}$ **g** 4^{-5}
 b $6^7 \div 6^{12}$ **d** $12^5 \div 12^9$ **f** 6^{-3} **h** 11^{-3}

2 Evaluate the following (leaving your answers as fractions where necessary)
 a 5^{-1} **c** 23^0 **e** $12^3 \div 12^4$ **g** $18^6 \div 18^6$ **i** $(5 \times 5^4)/5^5$
 b 3^{-2} **d** 24^0 **f** $2^6 \div 2^8$ **h** $(\frac{1}{2})^0$ **j** $100^{100} \div 100^{99}$

Standard form is a mathematical shorthand for very large and very small numbers. A number in standard form is written as:

 $a \times 10^n$

where a is a number between 1 and 10 and 10^n is a power of 10 where n is an integer.

Very large numbers

These are some powers of 10 where n is a positive integer:
  $10^0 = 1$
  $10^1 = 10$
  $10^2 = 100$
  $10^3 = 1000$
  $10^4 = 10\,000$
  $10^5 = 100\,000$
  $10^6 = 1\,000\,000$

Worked Examples

1 Write 4 500 000 in standard form.

 To express a number in standard form we must identify the value of a which is a number between 1 and 10.

 In this example, $a = 4.5$ and 4 500 000 $= 4.5 \times 1\,000\,000$
                                                 $= 4.5 \times 10^6$

2 Write 3870 in standard form.

 In this example, $a = 3.87$ and 3870 $= 3.87 \times 1000$
                                              $= 3.87 \times 10^3$

3 Write 2 756 000 000 in standard form.

 In this example, $a = 2.756$ and 2 756 000 000 $= 2.756 \times 1\,000\,000\,000$
                                                    $= 2.756 \times 10^9$

4   Rewrite 3.4×10^6 as an ordinary number.

   $3.4 \times 10^6 = 3.4 \times 10 \times 10 \times 10 \times 10 \times 10 \times 10$
   $\qquad\quad = 3\,400\,000$

5   Rewrite 6.4873×10^3 as an ordinary number.

   $6.4873 \times 10^3 = 6.4873 \times 10 \times 10 \times 10$
   $\qquad\qquad\quad = 6487.3$

NOTE

Questions on standard form look difficult but none of these questions requires you to use a calculator.

PRACTICE 2.3.1   Try these questions without a calculator

1   Put the following numbers in standard form.
   a 14 000
   b 9 000 000
   c 130 000 000
   d 158 000 000 000
   e 4 500 000 000
   f 375 000 000 000
   g 200 600 000
   h 21 005 000 000 000

2   Put the following in ordinary form.
   a 1.3×10^6
   b 1.43×10^9
   c 1.75×10^8
   d 1.04×10^3
   e 8.898×10^8
   f 9.865×10^7
   g 3.9958×10^5
   h 3.99×10^2
   i 4.9631×10^2

3   The following information gives the surface area of various planets in square miles. Convert these figures to ordinary form.
   a Pluto 4.3×10^7 miles^2
   b Earth 1.97×10^8 miles^2
   c Mercury 2.888×10^7 miles^2
   d Saturn 1.7483×10^{10} miles^2
   e Mars 5.587×10^7 miles^2
   f Neptune 2.9802×10^9 miles^2

4   Arrange the figures in question 3 in order of size (smallest first).

5   The following information gives the area of various oceans and seas in square kilometres. Convert these figures to ordinary form.
   a Arctic Ocean 1.4×10^7 km^2
   b Mediterranean Sea 2.5×10^6 km^2
   c Atlantic Ocean 8.236×10^7 km^2
   d Gulf of Mexico 1.544×10^6 km^2
   e Pacific Ocean $1.652\,42 \times 10^8$ km^2

6   Arrange the figures in question 4 in order of size (largest first).

7   Arrange each of the following numbers in order of size (smallest first).
   a 1.26×10^4, 9.78×10^2, 4.2835×10^3
   b 1×10^5, 99 000, 9.89×10^4

8   Which is bigger
   a 2.21×10^4 or 7.21×10^3
   b 9.68×10^6 or 3.25×10^7
   c 1.1×10^8 or 99 999 999?

9   Find the value of n in each of the following.
   a $3.5 \times 10^n = 350\,000$
   b $6.75 \times 10^n = 67\,500$
   c $8.33 \times 10^n = 83\,300\,000$
   d $1 \times 10^n = 100$
   e $5.69 \times 10^n = 56.9$
   f $4.006 \times 10^n = 400\,600$

Very small numbers

These are some powers of 10 where n is a negative integer:

$$10^{-1} = 1/10 = 0.1$$
$$10^{-2} = 1/100 = 0.01$$
$$10^{-3} = 1/1000 = 0.001$$
$$10^{-4} = 1/10\,000 = 0.0001$$
$$10^{-5} = 1/100\,000 = 0.000\,01$$
$$10^{-6} = 1/1\,000\,000 = 0.000\,001$$

Worked Examples

1 Write 0.025 in standard form.

To express a number in standard form we must identify the value of a which is a number between 1 and 10.

In this example, $a = 2.5$ and $0.025 = 2.5 \times 0.01$
$$= 2.5 \times 10^{-2}$$

> **NOTE**
>
> Alternatively
> write   0.025
> place the dp   0 02.5
> find n 0⌢02.5
> so $n = -2$
> $0.025 = 2.5 \times 10^{-2}$

2 Write 0.000 000 562 in standard form.

In this example, $a = 5.62$ and $0.000\,000\,562 = 5.62 \times 0.000\,000\,1$
$$= 5.62 \times 10^{-7}$$

> **NOTE**
>
> Alternatively
> write
> 0.000 000 562
> place the dp
> 0 000 000 5.62
> find n
> 0⌢000 000 5.62
> so $n = -7$
> $0.000\,000\,562$
> $= 5.62 \times 10^{-7}$

3 Rewrite 1.2×10^{-4} as an ordinary number.

$$1.2 \times 10^{-4} = 1.2 \times 0.0001$$
$$= 0.000\,12$$

> **NOTE**
>
> Always check these type of questions by working them backwards:
>
> write
> 0.000 12
> place the dp
> 0 000 1.2
> find n
> 0⌢0001.2
> so $n = -4$
> $0.000\,12 = 1.2 \times 10^{-4}$
> as required.

PRACTICE 2.3.2   **Try these questions without a calculator**

1 Put the following numbers in standard form.

   a 0.003   **d** 0.1   **g** 0.000 006 55
   b 0.000 075   **e** 0.000 000 625   **h** 0.000 000 922 5
   c 0.0007   **f** 0.000 000 000 008

2 Put the following in ordinary form.

   a 1×10^{-9} **c** 6.5×10^{-4} **e** 4.005×10^{-5}
   b 8×10^{-11} **d** 4.22×10^{-6} **f** 3.9958×10^{-5}

3 Arrange the following numbers in order of size (largest first).
  a 2.46×10^{-2}, 8.79×10^{-5}, 1.34×10^{-2}
  b 4.29×10^{-3}, $0.004\,28$, 4.3×10^{-2}

4 Which is bigger
  a 1.25×10^{-6} or 1.25×10^{-7}
  b 1.46×10^{-5} or 8.67×10^{-6}
  c 9.8×10^{-4} or $0.000\,99$?

> **NOTE**
> It is useful to remember that for $a \times 10^n$, n is always positive for large numbers and n is always negative for small numbers.

Adding and subtracting standard form numbers

If the numbers to be added (or subtracted) have the same power of 10 then add (or subtract) the number and replace the power of 10.

Worked Examples

1 $(5.22 \times 10^7) + (3.16 \times 10^7)$
  $= (5.22 + 3.16) \times 10^7$
  $= 8.38 \times 10^7$

2 $(4.78 \times 10^{-4}) - (2.68 \times 10^{-4})$
  $= (4.78 - 2.68) \times 10^{-4}$
  $= 2.1 \times 10^{-4}$

> **NOTE**
> Use the fact that $14.64 = 1.464 \times 10^1$

3 $(6.44 \times 10^5) + (8.2 \times 10^5)$
  $= (6.44 + 8.2) \times 10^5$
  $= 14.64 \times 10^5$
  $= 1.464 \times 10^6$ (rewriting in standard form)

> **NOTE**
> Use the fact that $10.39 = 1.039 \times 10^1$

4 $(2.33 \times 10^{-8}) + (8.06 \times 10^{-8})$
  $= (2.33 + 8.06) \times 10^{-8}$
  $= 10.39 \times 10^{-8}$
  $= 1.039 \times 10^{-7}$ (rewriting in standard form)

If the numbers to be added (or subtracted) have different powers of 10 then the numbers will need to be converted to ordinary form first.

> **NOTE**
> Remember to convert your final answer to standard form if the questions asks for this.

Worked Examples

1 $(3.45 \times 10^5) + (2.5 \times 10^4)$.

Converting to ordinary form, $3.45 \times 10^5 + 2.5 \times 10^4 = 345\,000 + 25\,000$
  $= 370\,000$
  $= 3.7 \times 10^5$

2 $(4.231 \times 10^4) - (6.49 \times 10^2)$.

Converting to ordinary form, $(4.231 \times 10^4) - (6.49 \times 10^2) = 42\,310 - 649$
$$= 41\,661$$
$$= 4.1661 \times 10^4$$

NOTE
These questions will usually appear on the non-calculator paper. You can check your answers here using a calculator if you wish.

PRACTICE 2.3.3   Try these questions without a calculator

Work out the following as shown in the previous worked examples (you must show all of your working).

1 $(4 \times 10^3) + (3 \times 10^3)$

2 $(3.7 \times 10^5) + (4.9 \times 10^5)$

3 $(4.61 \times 10^8) + (3.99 \times 10^8)$

4 $(8.65 \times 10^3) + (2.92 \times 10^3)$

5 $(2.65 \times 10^7) + (4.611 \times 10^7)$
    $+ (3.82 \times 10^7)$

6 $(7.71 \times 10^{-3}) + (2.14 \times 10^{-3})$

7 $(6.58 \times 10^{-7}) + (7.14 \times 10^{-7})$

8 $(3.6 \times 10^2) - (2.5 \times 10^2)$

9 $(2.951 \times 10^7) - (1.351 \times 10^7)$

10 $(3.962 \times 10^{11}) - (3.811 \times 10^{11})$

11 $(8.715 \times 10^6) - (8.705 \times 10^6)$

12 $(3.218 \times 10^{-4}) - (2.15 \times 10^{-4})$

13 $(6.41 \times 10^{-14}) - (6.4005 \times 10^{-14})$

14 $(3.36 \times 10^5) + (6.532 \times 10^8)$

15 $(6.32 \times 10^7) + (4.4 \times 10^6)$

16 $(1.15 \times 10^3) + (1.6 \times 10^{-1})$

17 $(1.38 \times 10^{-2}) + (4.86 \times 10^{-3})$

18 $(3.15 \times 10^3) - (3.15 \times 10^2)$

Multiplying and dividing standard form numbers

Standard form numbers can be multiplied or divided by using the laws of indices.

NOTE
See also Topic 2.2 on 'Powers, roots and reciprocals'.

Worked Examples

1 Find the product of 8.25×10^4 and 6.4×10^7.

$$(8.25 \times 10^4) \times (6.4 \times 10^7) \quad = (8.25 \times 6.4) \times (10^4 \times 10^7)$$
$$= 52.8 \times 10^{4+7}$$
$$= 52.8 \times 10^{11}$$
$$= 5.28 \times 10^{12} \quad \text{(rewriting in standard form)}$$

2 Evaluate $(8 \times 10^6) \div (2 \times 10^3)$.

$$(8 \times 10^6) \div (2 \times 10^3) \quad = \frac{(8 \times 10^6)}{(2 \times 10^3)}$$
$$= (8 \div 2) \times (10^6 \div 10^3)$$
$$= 4 \times 10^{6-3}$$
$$= 4 \times 10^3$$

3   Evaluate $(1.476 \times 10^2) \div (1.8 \times 10^{-5})$.

$$(1.476 \times 10^2) \div (1.8 \times 10^{-5}) = \frac{(1.476 \times 10^2)}{(1.8 \times 10^{-5})}$$
$$= (1.476 \div 1.8) \times (10^2 \div 10^{-5})$$
$$= 0.82 \times 10^{2--5}$$
$$= 0.82 \times 10^7$$
$$= 8.2 \times 10^6 \qquad \text{(rewriting in standard form}$$
$$\text{where } 0.82 = 8.2 \times 10^{-1})$$

4   Evaluate $(5.74 \times 10^{-12}) \div (8.2 \times 10^{-8})$.

$$(5.74 \times 10^{-12}) \div (8.2 \times 10^{-8}) = \frac{(5.74 \times 10^{-12})}{(8.2 \times 10^{-8})}$$
$$= (5.74 \div 8.2) \times (10^{-12} \div 10^{-8})$$
$$= 0.7 \times 10^{-12--8}$$
$$= 0.7 \times 10^{-12+8}$$
$$= 0.7 \times 10^{-4}$$
$$= 7 \times 10^{-5} \qquad \text{(rewriting in standard form}$$
$$\text{where } 0.7 = 7 \times 10^{-1})$$

PRACTICE 2.3.4a   Try these questions without a calculator

1 $(3 \times 10^2) \times (2 \times 10^7)$ **6** $(4.8 \times 10^{-3}) \times (3 \times 10^{-6})$

2 $(2 \times 10^8) \times (2 \times 10^3)$ **7** $(6 \times 10^4) \div (3 \times 10^3)$

3 $(3 \times 10^8)^2$ **8** $(7 \times 10^9) \div (2 \times 10^7)$

4 $(4 \times 10^3) \times (6 \times 10^4)$ **9** $(3.6 \times 10^{10}) \div (4.8 \times 10^6)$

5 $(3.5 \times 10^4) \times (2 \times 10^{-5})$ **10** $\dfrac{(3 \times 10^7) \div (4 \times 10^{13})}{6 \times 10^1}$

NOTE

Another way to answer questions involving standard form is to use your calculator with the EXP or EE button – see Topic 2.4 on 'Using a calculator'

PRACTICE 2.3.4b   Try these questions with a calculator

Work out the following as shown in the previous worked examples (you must show all of your working).

1 $(3.15 \times 10^2) \times (2.26 \times 10^5)$ **6** $(3.52 \times 10^4) \times (2.2 \times 10^{-3})$

2 $(4.185 \times 10^5) \times (2.01 \times 10^4)$ **7** $(7.65 \times 10^4) \times (3.6 \times 10^{-3}) \times (2.8 \times 10^3)$

3 $(4.7 \times 10^3) \times (4.25 \times 10^4)$ **8** $(5.423 \times 10^3) \div (6.38 \times 10^1)$

4 $(3.62 \times 10^8) \times (4.89 \times 10^{11})$ **9** $(3.458 \times 10^7) \div (4.55 \times 10^{-3})$

5 $(5.888 \times 10^{15}) \times (3 \times 10^{16})$ **10** $(1.4365 \times 10^{-5}) \div (6.5 \times 10^{-4})$

11   The Western Electricity Company employs 4.7×10^3 people and produced 6.298×10^5 kilowatt hours of electricity. What was the electricity production per employee?

12   The mass of a hydrogen atom is 1.7×10^{-24}g. One litre of air contains 2.5×10^{22} atoms of hydrogen. What is the mass of the hydrogen atoms in one litre of air?

2.4 USING A CALCULATOR

You will be expected to use a calculator for the examination (except for the aural paper) and a scientific calculator is the most appropriate for the course. When you are asked to use your calculator in the examination, it is important that you show your working otherwise marks may be lost for incorrect solutions.

Try this sum on your calculator: $2 + 3 \times 4 =$

If the answer is 14 then you are using a scientific calculator.

If the answer is 20 then you are *not* using a scientific calculator.

If you have any other answer then you have made a mistake!

Recent advances in calculator technology have seen the introduction of programmable calculators and, more recently, calculators which have direct algebraic logic which do not require users to transpose figures and functions such as $\boxed{\sqrt{}}\ \boxed{2}\ \boxed{5}$ to $\boxed{2}\ \boxed{5}\ \boxed{\sqrt{}}$.

The following functions represent those found on a variety of different types of calculators but you should consult the user manual accompanying your calculator for further information.

Function	Explanation
$\boxed{\text{ON}}$	Turns the calculator on – this function is sometimes combined with the $\boxed{\text{C}}$ function to clear an error or else clear data.
$\boxed{\text{C}}$	Clear – used to clear an error before an operation.
$\boxed{\text{AC}}$	All clear – used to clear all data.
$\boxed{\text{MODE}}$	Sets the mode for normal calculations, statistical calculations, etc.
$\boxed{\text{DRG}}$	Sets the units for angular measurement between degrees, radians and grads – normally set to degrees.
$\boxed{\text{M in}}$ or $\boxed{\text{STO}}$	Stores displayed values in the memory (memory location may need to be specified).
$\boxed{\text{MR}}$ or $\boxed{\text{RCL}}$	Recalls values stored in the memory (memory location may need to be specified).
$\boxed{\text{M+}}$	Adds the displayed value to the value stored in the memory and stores the result.
$\boxed{\text{M−}}$	Subtracts the displayed value from the value stored in the memory and stores the result.
$\boxed{\text{+/−}}$	Used to change sign – changes positive numbers to negative numbers (and negative to positive).
$\boxed{1/x}$ or $\boxed{x^{-1}}$	Calculates the reciprocal of the value in the calculator display.
$\boxed{x^2}$	Calculates the square of the value in the calculator display.
$\boxed{\sqrt{}}$	Calculates the square root of the value in the calculator display.

Information on the following function buttons is provided in a little more detail along with further worked examples.

The fraction function

The $a^{b/c}$ button is used to work with fractions as follows:

Worked Examples

1 Calculate $\frac{3}{4} - \frac{1}{8}$.

The following keys should be pressed:

[3] [$a^{b/c}$] [4] [−] [1] [$a^{b/c}$] [8] [=]

The calculator display will show ⌐ 5˩8 ¬

The display is then interpreted as $\frac{5}{8}$

2 Calculate $12\frac{1}{4} \times \frac{1}{7}$.

The following keys should be pressed:

[1] [2] [$a^{b/c}$] [1] [$a^{b/c}$] [4] [×] [1] [$a^{b/c}$] [7] [=]

The calculator display will show ⌐ 1˩3˩4 ¬

The display is then interpreted as $1\frac{3}{4}$

3 Calculate $14\frac{2}{5} \times 1.2$

The following keys should be pressed:

[1] [4] [$a^{b/c}$] [2] [$a^{b/c}$] [5] [×] [1] [.] [2] [=]

The calculator display will show 17.28

Some calculators can also be used to convert improper fractions to mixed numbers using this function.

PRACTICE 2.4.1

Use your calculator to work out the addition and subtraction questions given in Practice 1.3.3, 1.3.4 and 1.3.5 and the multiplication and division questions given in Practice 1.3.6 and 1.3.8.

The power function

The $\boxed{x^y}$ or $\boxed{y^x}$ button is used to work with powers as follows:

Worked Examples

1 Calculate 3^4

The following keys should be pressed: $\boxed{3}\ \boxed{x^y}\ \boxed{4}\ \boxed{=}$

The calculator display will show $\boxed{\quad\quad\quad\quad 81.}$

> **NOTE**
> The -4 will need to be keyed in as $\boxed{4}\ \boxed{+/-}$ if the calculator does not use direct algebraic logic.

2 Calculate 2^{-4}

The following keys should be pressed: $\boxed{2}\ \boxed{x^y}\ \boxed{-4}\ \boxed{=}$

The calculator display will show $\boxed{\quad\quad 0.0625}$

> **NOTE**
> The power or index will need to be evaluated first or else placed inside brackets as shown.

3 Calculate $81^{1/4}$

The following keys should be pressed:

$\boxed{8}\ \boxed{1}\ \boxed{x^y}\ \boxed{(}\ \boxed{1}\ \boxed{\div}\ \boxed{4}\ \boxed{)}\ \boxed{=}$

The calculator display will show $\boxed{\quad\quad\quad\quad 3.}$

> ### PRACTICE 2.4.2
> Use your calculator to work out the following:
> | | | | | |
> |---|---|---|---|---|
> | **1** 3^4 | **4** 8^0 | **7** 10^{-2} | **10** $(2/5)^4$ | **13** $27^{\frac{1}{3}}$ |
> | **2** 4^3 | **5** 127^0 | **8** 20^{-2} | **11** $(0.0009)^{\frac{1}{2}}$ | **14** $(\frac{1}{4})^{-\frac{1}{2}}$ |
> | **3** 5^1 | **6** 4^{-1} | **9** 0.5^2 | **12** $49^{\frac{1}{2}}$ | **15** $32^{-\frac{4}{5}}$ |

The standard form function

The $\boxed{EXP}$ or $\boxed{EE}$ button is used to work with standard form as follows:

Worked Examples

1 Calculate $3 \times 10^2 + 2 \times 10^{-1}$

The following keys should be pressed:

$\boxed{3}\ \boxed{EXP}\ \boxed{2}\ \boxed{+}\ \boxed{2}\ \boxed{EXP}\ \boxed{-1}\ \boxed{=}$

The calculator display will show $\boxed{\quad\quad 300.2}$

> **NOTE**
> The -1 will need to be keyed in as $\boxed{1}\ \boxed{+/-}$ if the calculator does not use direct algebraic logic.

> **NOTE**
> Some calculators include $\times 10$. Consult the user manual for further information.

2 Work out $4.3 \times 10^6 \times 2.8 \times 10^2$

The following keys should be pressed:

$\boxed{4}\ \boxed{\cdot}\ \boxed{3}\ \boxed{EXP}\ \boxed{6}\ \boxed{\times}\ \boxed{2}\ \boxed{\cdot}\ \boxed{8}\ \boxed{EXP}\ \boxed{2}\ \boxed{=}$

The calculator display will show $\boxed{\quad 1.204\quad 09}$

The display is then interpreted as 1.204×10^9

3 Work out $4.6 \times 10^2 \div 1.25 \times 10^5$

The following keys should be pressed:

$\boxed{4}$ $\boxed{\cdot}$ $\boxed{6}$ $\boxed{\text{EXP}}$ $\boxed{2}$ $\boxed{\div}$ $\boxed{1}$ $\boxed{\cdot}$ $\boxed{2}$ $\boxed{5}$ $\boxed{\text{EXP}}$ $\boxed{5}$ $\boxed{=}$

The calculator display will show $\boxed{\quad\quad 3.68 \quad \text{-}03\,}$

The display is then interpreted as 3.68×10^{-3}

PRACTICE 2.4.3

Use your calculator to work out the addition and subtraction questions given in Practice 2.3.3 and the multiplication and division questions given in Practice 2.3.4b.

Brackets

Scientific calculators obey the rules of BODMAS.

Brackets **O**f **D**ivision **M**ultiplication **A**ddition **S**ubtraction

NOTE
See section on 'Sequence of operations' in Topic 1.1 for further information.

Brackets are extremely useful for breaking down mathematical expressions to give precedence to particular parts of the expression.

Worked Examples

1 Use your calculator to evaluate $\dfrac{3.5 \times 7.5}{4.52 \div 0.38}$

It is essential to work out the numerator and denominator before undertaking the division and the use of brackets will ease the calculation.

Rewriting as $\dfrac{(3.5 \times 7.5)}{(4.52 \div 0.38)}$ allows the brackets to take precedence

The following keys should be pressed: $\boxed{(}$ $\boxed{3}$ $\boxed{\cdot}$ $\boxed{5}$ $\boxed{\times}$ $\boxed{7}$ $\boxed{\cdot}$ $\boxed{5}$ $\boxed{)}$ $\boxed{\div}$ $\boxed{(}$ $\boxed{4}$ $\boxed{\cdot}$ $\boxed{5}$ $\boxed{2}$ $\boxed{\div}$ $\boxed{0}$ $\boxed{\cdot}$ $\boxed{3}$ $\boxed{8}$ $\boxed{)}$ $\boxed{=}$

The calculator display will show $\boxed{\quad\quad 2.2068584\,}$

2 Use your calculator to evaluate $3.15 + \dfrac{10.81}{14.6 - 2.79}$

Again, it is essential to work out the numerator and denominator before undertaking the division of the fraction although the addition of 3.15 also needs consideration.

NOTE
The addition of the second set of brackets was actually superfluous as ÷ takes precedence over +.
However the addition of extra brackets causes no harm as long as they are included in matching pairs.

Rewriting as $3.15 + \left(\dfrac{10.81}{14.6 - 2.79}\right)$

The following keys should be pressed: $\boxed{3}$ $\boxed{\cdot}$ $\boxed{1}$ $\boxed{5}$ $\boxed{+}$ $\boxed{(}$ $\boxed{1}$ $\boxed{0}$ $\boxed{\cdot}$ $\boxed{8}$ $\boxed{1}$ $\boxed{\div}$ $\boxed{(}$ $\boxed{1}$ $\boxed{4}$ $\boxed{\cdot}$ $\boxed{6}$ $\boxed{-}$ $\boxed{2}$ $\boxed{\cdot}$ $\boxed{7}$ $\boxed{9}$ $\boxed{)}$ $\boxed{)}$ $\boxed{=}$

The calculator display will show $\boxed{\quad\quad 4.065326\,}$

The following exercise provides further practice at using your calculator to work out a variety of mathematical expressions.

PRACTICE 2.4.4   Try these questions with a calculator

1 $\dfrac{4.8 \times 96}{4.2 \times 0.38}$

2 $\dfrac{9.6^2 - 4.2^2}{2 \times 9.65}$

3 $5.55 + \dfrac{1.88}{4.55 + 4.79}$

4 $25 \times 4.2 + \dfrac{5(93.1 - 32 \times 2.4)}{11.3 + 9.1}$

5 $\dfrac{4.5 + 5.6}{\sqrt{4.2 + 2.1^2}}$

6 $\dfrac{29.9 + \sqrt{0.918}}{(16.2 - 6.15)^2}$

7 $\dfrac{3.5^2 - 1.1^2}{\sqrt{23.5 + 6.7}}$

8 $9.6 + \dfrac{\sqrt{1.156}}{3.16^2 + 12.2 \times 0.9}$

2.5 NON CALCULATOR METHODS

The following methods are useful for the non-calculator paper. For practice purposes you can use a calculator to check your working and make sure that your non-calculator method is correct.

Worked Example

Evaluate 162×45.

The product 162×45 is the same as $162 \times (40 + 5)$
$= 162 \times 40 + 162 \times 5$
$= 6480 + 810$
$= 7290$

It is usual to write this product out as

$$
\begin{array}{r r l}
162 & & \\
\times 45 & & \\
\hline
6480 & & \times 40 \\
810 & & \times 5 \\
\hline
7290 & & \text{adding}
\end{array}
$$

PRACTICE 2.5.1   Try these questions without a calculator

1 86×25

2 132×37

3 167×82

4 193×65

5 284×62

6 397×95

Worked Example

Work out $486 \div 18$.

To work out this division we proceed as we would with any other division except we are dividing by a two digit number as follows:

$$
\begin{array}{r}
2\ 7 \\
18\,\overline{)4\ 8^{12}6}
\end{array}
$$

An easier way to work this out is to put the working underneath as shown in the following stages:

Stage 1

$$
\begin{array}{r}
2 \\
18\,\overline{)486} \\
-36 \\
\hline
12
\end{array}
$$

18 divides into 48, 2 times
$2 \times 18 = 36$, so place 36 below 48
subtract 36 from 48 to get 12

Stage 2

$$
\begin{array}{r}
2 \\
18\,\overline{)486} \\
-36\!\downarrow \\
\hline
126
\end{array}
$$

$\longleftarrow$ Bring next digit down, i.e. 6

Stage 3

$$
\begin{array}{r}
27 \\
18\,\overline{)486} \\
36\!\downarrow \\
\hline
126 \\
-126 \\
\hline
0
\end{array}
$$

18 divides into 126, 7 times
$7 \times 18 = 126$, so place 126 below 126
subtract 126 from 126 to get 0 so division is finished

PRACTICE 2.5.2   Try these questions without a calculator

1 $512 \div 16$	**5** $924 \div 33$	**9** $3234 \div 42$
2 $945 \div 21$	**6** $1534 \div 26$	**10** $5115 \div 55$
3 $2047 \div 23$	**7** $1632 \div 24$	
4 $1196 \div 26$	**8** $2808 \div 36$	

Sometimes we will be expected to give an estimate of the value of an expression by rounding the numbers to convenient approximations as shown in the following worked examples.

2.6 ESTIMATING AND APPROXIMATING

Worked Examples

1 Estimate the value of $\dfrac{26.3 + 46.2}{62.4 \times 2.1}$

NOTE

It is usual to round off your numbers to 1 significant figure. See next section.

Rounding the numbers to convenient approximations

$$\frac{30+50}{60\times2}=\frac{80}{120}=\frac{2}{3}$$

2 Estimate the value of $\dfrac{20.3\times\sqrt{98}}{42.1\times\pi}$

Rounding the numbers to convenient approximations

$$\frac{20\times\sqrt{100}}{40\times3}$$

$$=\frac{20\times10}{120}=\frac{200}{120}=\frac{5}{3}$$

NOTE

These questions will usually appear on the non-calculator paper.

PRACTICE 2.6.1 Try these questions without a calculator

Give an approximate value for each of the following questions (leaving your answers as fractions where necessary).

1 $\dfrac{4.8\times96}{4.2\times0.48}$

2 $\dfrac{9.6^2-4.2^2}{2\times9.65}$

3 $5.55+\dfrac{1.88}{4.55+4.79}$

4 $25\times4.2+\dfrac{5(93.1-32\times2.4)}{11.3+9.1}$

5 $\dfrac{4.5+5.6}{\sqrt{4.2}+2.1^2}$

6 $\dfrac{29.9+\sqrt{0.918}}{(16.2-6.15)^2}$

7 $\dfrac{3.5^2-1.1^2}{\sqrt{23.5}+6.7}$

8 $9.6+\dfrac{\sqrt{1.156}}{3.16^2+12.2\times0.9}$

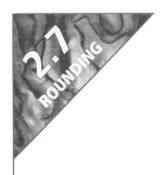

2.7 ROUNDING

Rounding off is a technique used for approximating answers when you are not using a calculator or when you are checking a calculation done on a calculator. In many real life situations approximate answers are quite acceptable (ages to the nearest year, height to the nearest inch, distance to the nearest mile, weight to the nearest kilogram, attendance figures to the nearest thousand, etc.) although you should always say to what accuracy your answer is presented.

Decimal places

Decimal places are places to the right of the decimal point. Numbers can be rounded off to a required number of decimal places (abbreviated as dp) according to the following rules:

    remove all of the decimal places not required
    look at the last digit to be removed
        – if it is less than 5 leave the remaining digits the same
        – if it is 5 or more then add 1 to the last remaining digit.

The following worked examples illustrate how different numbers can be rounded to a specified number of decimal places.

Worked Examples

1 We can round the number 14.763 581 off to any number of decimal places as follows:

14.763 581 = 14.763 58 (to 5dp)
14.763 581 = 14.7636 (to 4dp) add 1 to last remaining digit   14.7635 → 14.7636
14.763 581 = 14.764 (to 3dp) add 1 to last remaining digit   14.763 → 14.764
14.763 581 = 14.76 (to 2dp)
14.763 581 = 14.8 (to 1dp)   add 1 to last remaining digit   14.7 → 14.8

2 We can round the number 6.279 834 off to any number of decimal places as follows:

6.279 834 = 6.279 83 (to 5dp)
6.279 834 = 6.2798 (to 4dp)
6.279 834 = 6.280 (to 3dp)   add 1 to last remaining digit   6.279 → 6.280
6.279 834 = 6.28 (to 2dp)   add 1 to last remaining digit   6.27 → 6.28
6.279 834 = 6.3 (to 1dp)   add 1 to last remaining digit   6.2 → 6.3

PRACTICE 2.7.1

Correct the following to 4dp, 3dp, 2dp and 1dp.

1 4.271 63   **2** 2.160 59   **3** 11.752 37   **4** 9.229 45   **5** 13.898 03

Significant figures

The value of a figure depends upon its position in a number. The number 4832 has 4 figures altogether.

  The figure 4 is worth 4000
  The figure 8 is worth   800
  The figure 3 is worth   30
  The figure 2 is worth   2

We say that the figure 4 is the most significant figure and the figure 2 is the least significant in the number 4832.

Numbers can be rounded off to a required number of **significant figures** (abbreviated as sf) according to the following rules:

  remove all of the figures not required
  look at the last digit to be removed
    – if it is less than 5 leave the remaining digits the same
    – if it is 5 or more then add 1 to the last remaining digit
  use 0's to ensure the number is the correct size.

The following worked examples illustrate how different numbers can be rounded to a specified number of significant figures.

Worked Examples

1 We can round the number 14.763 581 off to any number of significant figures as follows:

14.763 581 = 14.763 58 (to 7sf)
14.763 581 = 14.7636 (to 6sf) add 1 to last remaining digit 14.7635 → 14.7636
14.763 581 = 14.764 (to 5sf) add 1 to last remaining digit 14.763 → 14.764
14.763 581 = 14.76 (to 4sf)
14.763 581 = 14.8 (to 3sf) add 1 to last remaining digit 14.7 → 14.8
14.763 581 = 15 (to 2sf) add 1 to last remaining digit 14 → 15
14.763 581 = 10 (to 1sf) use zeros to ensure number is correct size

2 We can round the number 1476.8952 off to any number of significant figures as follows:

1476.8952 = 1476.895 (to 7sf)
1476.8952 = 1476.90 (to 6sf) add 1 to last remaining digit 1476.89 → 1476.90
1476.8952 = 1476.9 (to 5sf) add 1 to last remaining digit 1476.8 → 1476.9
1476.8952 = 1477 (to 4sf) add 1 to last remaining digit 1476 → 1477
1476.8952 = 1480 (to 3sf) add 1 to last remaining digit 147 → 148
  use zeros to ensure correct size
1476.8952 = 1500 (to 2sf) add 1 to last remaining digit 14 → 15
  use zeros to ensure correct size
1476.8952 = 1000 (to 1sf) use zeros to ensure number is correct size

PRACTICE 2.7.2

Correct the following to 4sf, 3sf, 2sf and 1sf.

1 437.82   **2** 2194.6   **3** 0.896 57   **4** 18.692   **5** 505.05

2.8 TRIAL AND IMPROVEMENT

Trial and improvement is a mathematical technique which allows us to *home in* to the solution of a particular problem. The technique involves some initial *intelligent guess* at the solution which is then refined by further work until the answer is as accurate as required.

For example, if we had to find the square root of 2 (without using the square root button on our calculator) we would expect that the answer must lie somewhere between 1 and 2, as we know that

$$\sqrt{1} = 1 \text{ and } \sqrt{4} = 2$$

We might now try 1.5 $1.5^2 = 2.25$ so the answer lies between 1 and 1.5

We might now try 1.25 $1.25^2 = 1.5625$ so the answer lies between 1.25 and 1.5

We might now try 1.4 $1.4^2 = 1.96$ so the answer lies between 1.4 and 1.5

We might now try 1.45	$1.45^2 = 2.1025$	so the answer lies between 1.4 and 1.45
We might now try 1.42	$1.42^2 = 2.0164$	so the answer lies between 1.4 and 1.42
We might now try 1.41	$1.41^2 = 1.9881$	so the answer lies between 1.41 and 1.42
We might now try 1.415	$1.415^2 = 2.002\,225$	so the answer lies between 1.41 and 1.415
We might now try 1.413	$1.413^2 = 1.996\,569$	so the answer lies between 1.413 and 1.415
We might now try 1.414	$1.414^2 = 1.999\,396$	so the answer lies between 1.414 and 1.415

The process is very long winded and will depend on the accuracy required of the answer. We can see from our working that the answer lies between 1.414 and 1.415, so we can confidently say that the answer is 1.41 to 3 significant figures.

PRACTICE 2.8.1   Try these questions with a calculator

1 John is using his calculator to find the square root of 17 by *trial and improvement*. Complete the following and continue the method to find the square root of 17 correct to 3 decimal places.

4.1^2 = ...
4.2^2 = ...
4.15^2 = ...

2 Jane is trying to find the cube root of 19 by *trial and improvement*. She uses her calculator to calculate the following:

$2.6 \times 2.6 \times 2.6 = 17.576$
$2.7 \times 2.7 \times 2.7 = 19.683$

Continue this method to find the cube root of 19 correct to 2 decimal places.

3 Miriam is trying to find the cube root of 17 on her calculator which does not have a cube root button. She uses her calculator to calculate the following:

$2.5 \times 2.5 \times 2.5 = 15.625$
$2.6 \times 2.6 \times 2.6 = 17.576$

Continue this method to find the cube root of 17 correct to 2 decimal places.

Roots and reciprocals in index form

We have already explained the meaning of negative powers such that:

$$4^{-1} = \frac{1}{4^1} \qquad 5^{-3} = \frac{1}{5^3} \qquad 4^{-9} = \frac{1}{4^9}$$

Similarly we will now consider fractional powers as follows:

$$25^{1/2} \qquad 27^{1/3} \qquad 32^{1/5}$$

$$25^{1/2} \times 25^{1/2} = 25^{1/2+1/2} = 25 \qquad\qquad \text{so } 25^{1/2} = 5 \text{ as } 5 \times 5 = 25$$

$$27^{1/3} \times 27^{1/3} \times 27^{1/3} = 27^{1/3+1/3+1/3} = 27 \qquad \text{so } 27^{1/3} = 3 \text{ as } 3 \times 3 \times 3 = 27$$

$$32^{1/5} \times 32^{1/5} \times 32^{1/5} \times 32^{1/5} \times 32^{1/5} = 32^{1/5+1/5+1/5+1/5+1/5} = 32$$

$$\text{so } 32^{1/5} = 2 \text{ as } 2 \times 2 \times 2 \times 2 \times 2 = 32$$

so $25^{\frac{1}{2}} = 5$ and $25^{\frac{1}{2}}$ means $\sqrt[2]{25}$ or $\sqrt{25}$

$27^{\frac{1}{3}} = 3$ and $27^{\frac{1}{3}}$ means $\sqrt[3]{27}$

$32^{\frac{1}{5}} = 2$ and $32^{\frac{1}{5}}$ means $\sqrt[5]{32}$

NOTE

The square root of a number can be written as $\sqrt{}$ or $\sqrt[2]{}$. It is usual to write $\sqrt{}$.

Worked Examples

1 Evaluate $10^{\frac{1}{2}}$, $64^{\frac{1}{3}}$ and $100^{\frac{1}{5}}$

$10^{\frac{1}{2}} = \sqrt[2]{10} = \sqrt{10}$ (this number is irrational)

$64^{\frac{1}{3}} = \sqrt[3]{64} = 4$ (this number is rational)

$100^{\frac{1}{5}} = \sqrt[5]{100}$ (this number is irrational)

2 Evaluate $27^{\frac{2}{3}}$

$27^{\frac{2}{3}}$ is the same as $27^{\frac{1}{3}} \times 27^{\frac{1}{3}}$

$$= (27^{\frac{1}{3}})^2$$
$$= (3)^2$$
$$= 9$$

3 Evaluate $81^{-\frac{3}{4}}$

$$81^{-\frac{3}{4}} = \frac{1}{81^{\frac{3}{4}}}$$

$81^{\frac{3}{4}}$ is the same as $81^{\frac{1}{4}} \times 81^{\frac{1}{4}} \times 81^{\frac{1}{4}}$

$$= (81^{\frac{1}{4}})^3$$
$$= (3)^3$$
$$= 27$$

so $81^{-\frac{3}{4}} = \dfrac{1}{27}$

PRACTICE 2.9.1 Try these questions without a calculator

1 Evaluate the following:

a $9^{\frac{1}{2}}$	**c** $27^{\frac{2}{3}}$	**e** $125^{\frac{2}{3}}$	**g** $16^{-\frac{1}{2}}$	**i** $64^{-\frac{1}{6}}$
b $27^{\frac{1}{3}}$	**d** $81^{\frac{3}{4}}$	**f** $32^{\frac{4}{5}}$	**h** $144^{-\frac{1}{2}}$	**j** $64^{-\frac{5}{6}}$

2 Find the missing values in each of the following:

a $81 = 3^a$	**c** $7^c = 7$	**e** $\frac{1}{4} = 2^e$	**g** $\frac{1}{125} = 5^g$	**i** $32^i = \frac{1}{2}$
b $4^b = 1$	**d** $\frac{1}{3} = 3^d$	**f** $\frac{1}{8} = 2^f$	**h** $27^h = \frac{1}{3}$	**j** $32^j = \frac{1}{4}$

Direct and inverse proportion

Direct proportion is where there is a relationship between two quantities such that as one increases, the other increases, and as one decreases, the other one decreases. For example, if two quantities are in direct proportion, then if one doubles, the other doubles and if one is multiplied by 5, then the other is multiplied by 5.

Inverse proportion is where there is a relationship between two quantities such that as one increases, the other decreases, and as one decreases, the other one increases. For example, if two quantities are in inverse proportion, then if one doubles, the other halves and if one is multiplied by 5, then the other is divided by 5.

When dealing with direct and inverse proportion it is usual to use the sign $\propto$ which means *is proportional to*. An equation can be made by replacing $\propto$ by $=k$ where k is known as the constant of proportionality or the constant of variation.

In general if y is proportional to x, then $y \propto x$ and $y = kx$.

Similarly if y is inversely proportional to x, then $y \propto \dfrac{1}{x}$ and $y = \dfrac{k}{x}$.

The following worked examples illustrate the use of direct and inverse proportion.

> **NOTE**
> The word *varies* is also used in the context of direct and inverse proportion.

Worked Examples

Write down the following statements as equations.

a y varies directly as x squared.
b p is proportional to the square root of q.
c The wage (w) is directly proportional to the hourly rate (h).
d a is inversely proportional to the cube of b.
e u varies inversely as the square of v.
f m is inversely proportional to the cube root of n.
g The gravitational force (g) is inversely proportional to the square of the distance (d) from the earth.

a $y \propto x^2$ $y = kx^2$ **e** $u \propto \dfrac{1}{v^2}$ $u = \dfrac{k}{v^2}$

b $p \propto \sqrt{q}$ $p = k\sqrt{q}$ **f** $m \propto \dfrac{1}{\sqrt[3]{n}}$ $a = \dfrac{k}{\sqrt[3]{n}}$

c $w \propto h$ $w = kh$ **g** $g \propto \dfrac{1}{d^2}$ $g = \dfrac{k}{d^2}$

d $a \propto \dfrac{1}{b^3}$ $a = \dfrac{k}{b^3}$

Information provided relating the two variables can now be used to find the constant, k.

Worked Examples

1 T varies directly as the square of y and $T = 100$ when $y = 5$. Find the value of k and the value of T when $y = 3$.

If T varies directly as the square of y then $T \propto y^2$
and $T = ky^2$

We know that $T = 100$ when $y = 5$ so $100 = k \times 5^2$
                                                          $100 = k \times 25$
                                                          $k = 4$

The value of k is 4 and the equation is $T = 4y^2$

To find the value of T when $y = 3$ $T = 4 \times 3^2$
                                                          $T = 4 \times 9$
                                                          $T = 36$

2 If a is inversely proportional to the square root of b and $a = 6$ when $b = 4$, find the value of k and the value of a when $b = 16$.

If a is inversely proportional to the square root of b then $a \propto \dfrac{1}{\sqrt{b}}$

and $a = \dfrac{k}{\sqrt{b}}$

We know that $a = 6$ when $b = 4$ so $6 = \dfrac{k}{\sqrt{4}}$

                                                                        $6 = \dfrac{k}{2}$

                                                                        $k = 12$

The value of k is 12 and the equation is $a = \dfrac{12}{\sqrt{b}}$

To find the value of a when $b = 16$ $a = \dfrac{12}{\sqrt{b}}$

                                                                        $a = \dfrac{12}{\sqrt{16}}$

                                                                        $a = \dfrac{12}{4}$

                                                                        $a = 3$

PRACTICE 2.9.2a   Try these questions without a calculator

1 If a varies as the square of b and $a = 28$ when $b = 2$, find the value of a when
   a $b = 1$ **b** $b = 3$
2 If y varies as the cube of x and $y = 54$ when $x = 3$, find the value of y when
   a $x = 4$ **b** $x = \frac{1}{2}$

3 If y is inversely proportional to the cube root of x and $y = 3$ when $x = 8$, find the value of y when $x = 27$.

4 The extension, e, of a stretched string varies directly as the tension, T. If a tension of 8 units produces an extension of 2 cm what is the extension produced by a tension of 12 units?

PRACTICE 2.9.2b   Try these questions with a calculator

1 If p varies inversely as the cube of q and $p = 1.25$ when $q = 2$, find the value of p when
   a $q = 5$ **b** $q = \sqrt[3]{2}$

2 The mass, V, of a sphere varies directly as the cube of the radius, r. If a sphere of radius 2 cm has a mass of 33.5 g, find the mass of a sphere with radius $r = 5$ cm.

3 The value of a car, £v, is inversely proportional to its age, a years. After 5 years the car has a value of £2400. Find an equation linking v and a and hence find:
   a the value of the car after 2 years
   b the value of the car after 10 years
   c the age of the car when its value is £2000.

NOTE
We accept that the figure 7.5 cm would round up to 8 cm although 7.5 cm acts as a good approximation for 7.499 999 999 9…cm.

Upper and lower bounds

If a length is given as 7 cm to the nearest centimetre then it is possible that the length can take any value from 6.5 cm to 7.5 cm The value of 6.5 cm is called the **lower bound** for the length and the value 7.5 cm is called the **upper bound** for the length.

Worked Examples

1 A motorbike is valued at £2200 to the nearest £100. What is the maximum and minimum possible value of the motorbike?

The maximum value of the motorbike is £2250 as any value just above this would be rounded up to £2300 (to the nearest £100). Similarly the minimum value of the motorbike is £2150 as any value just below this would be rounded down to £2100 (to the nearest £100).

2 A room measures 12 metres by 9 metres to the nearest metre. Find the lower bound and the upper bound for the area of the room.

For a length of 12 m the actual values could range from 11.5 m to 12.5 m. Similarly for a length of 9 m the actual values could range from 8.5 m to 9.5 m.

   The lower bound (minimum area) $= 11.5 \times 8.5 = 97.75 \, \text{m}^2$
   The upper bound (maximum area) $= 12.5 \times 9.5 = 118.75 \, \text{m}^2$

3 The value of $a = 158$ (3sf) and the value of $b = 3$ (1sf). Calculate the minimum and maximum values of the following expressions:

a $a + b$ **b** $a - b$ **c** $a \times b$ **d** $a \div b$

Before we can evaluate the expressions we need to work out the minimum (lower bound) and maximum (upper bound) for the values of a and b.

If $a = 158$ (3sf) then minimum value $= 157.5$ maximum value $= 158.5$
If $b = 3$ (1sf) then   minimum value $= 2.5$ maximum value $= 3.5$

a $a + b$ minimum $= 157.5 + 2.5 = 160$
maximum $= 158.5 + 3.5 = 162$

b $a - b$ minimum $= 157.5 - 3.5 = 154$
maximum $= 158.5 - 2.5 = 156$

c $a \times b$ minimum $= 157.5 \times 2.5 = 393.75$
maximum $= 158.5 \times 3.5 = 554.75$

d $a \div b$ minimum $= 157.5 \div 3.5 = 45$
maximum $= 158.5 \div 2.5 = 63.4$

NOTE

To get the minimum value of $a - b$ we need to work out $a_{min} - b_{max}$ and to get the maximum value we need to work out $a_{max} - b_{min}$.

NOTE

Once again, to get the minimum value of $a \div b$ we need to work out $a_{min} \div b_{max}$ and to get the maximum value we need to work out $a_{max} \div b_{min}$.

PRACTICE 2.9.3a   Try these questions without a calculator

1 A tin of dog food weighs $800\,g$ to the nearest gram. Calculate the upper bound and the lower bound of the weight of 24 tins of dog food.

2 Two cars are priced at £8400 and £6600 to the nearest £100. What is the greatest and least possible difference in price between the two cars?

3 A student gives her age as 18 years old. What are the lower and upper bounds to her age?

PRACTICE 2.9.3b   Try these questions with a calculator

1 A room measures 13 feet by 15 feet to the nearest foot. Find the minimum and maximum possible area of the room.

2 A rectangular field measures 140 metres by 60 metres. Both measurements are given to the nearest 10 metres.
a What is the greatest possible perimeter of the field?
b Calculate the difference between the greatest and smallest possible areas of the field.

3 The area of a rectangular garden is $150\,m^2$ and the width of the garden is $10\,m$ where both figures are given to the nearest integer.
a What are the upper and lower bounds of the area?
b What are the upper and lower bounds of the length of the garden?

4 A lorry travels a distance of 120 miles in 3 hours. Both distance and time are given to the nearest integer. What are the upper and lower bounds of the average speed of the lorry?

5 A train travels a distance of 250 miles (to the nearest 10 miles) in 4 hours (to the nearest hour). What are the upper and lower bounds of the average speed of the train?

6 The power in an electical component is given by the formula

$$P = \frac{V^2}{R}$$

where P is the power in watts, V is the voltage in volts and R is the resistance in ohms. If $V = 2.4$ volts (to 1dp) and $R = 1.6$ ohms (to 1dp), what are the largest and smallest possible values of P?

Multiplying powers

A quick way to multiply two powers when their bases are the same is to add their powers so that:

$$5^3 \times 5^4 = 5^{3+4} = 5^7 \qquad \text{and} \qquad 14^2 \times 14^6 = 14^{2+6} = 14^8$$

Dividing powers

A quick way to divide two powers when their bases are the same is to subtract their powers so that:

$$4^8 \div 4^5 = 4^{8-5} = 4^3 \qquad \text{and} \qquad 19^8 \div 19^3 = 19^{8-3} = 19^5$$

The power zero

Any number to the power zero is equal to 1.

Negative powers

A number to a negative power equals the reciprocal of the number to a positive power so that:

$$4^{-1} = \frac{1}{4^1} \qquad \text{and} \qquad 5^{-9} = \frac{1}{5^9}$$

Standard form

Standard form is a mathematical shorthand for very large and very small numbers. A number in standard form is written as:

$$a \times 10^n$$

where a is a number between 1 and 10 and 10^n is a power of 10 where n is an integer (n is always positive for large numbers and n is always negative for small numbers).

Adding and subtracting standard form numbers

If the numbers to be added (or subtracted) have the same power of 10 then add (or subtract) the number and replace the power of 10.

If the numbers to be added (or subtracted) have different powers of 10 then the numbers will need to be converted to ordinary form first.

Multiplying and dividing standard form numbers

Standard form numbers can be multiplied or divided by using the laws of indices.

$$a^m \times a^n = a^{m+n} \qquad a^m \div a^n = a^{m-n}$$

Decimal places and significant figures

Numbers can be rounded off to a required number of decimal places (abbreviated to dp) or significant figures (abbreviated to sf) according to the following rules:

remove all of the decimal places/figures not required
look at the last digit to be removed
  – if it is less than 5 leave the remaining digits the same
  – if it is 5 or more then add 1 to the last remaining digit.
use 0's to ensure the number is the correct size for sf.

Trial and improvement

Trial and improvement is a mathematical technique which allows us to *home* in to the solution of a particular problem. The technique involves some initial *intelligent guess* at the solution which is then refined by further work.

Roots and reciprocals in index form (extension)

Fractional powers are such that:

$$a^{1/2} = \sqrt[2]{a}, \quad a^{1/3} = \sqrt[3]{a}, \quad a^{1/4} = \sqrt[4]{a}, \text{ etc.}$$

Similarly $a^{2/3} = \left(\sqrt[3]{a}\right)^2, \quad a^{3/4} = \left(\sqrt[4]{a}\right)^3, \text{ etc., etc.}$

Direct and inverse proportion (extension)

Direct proportion is where there is a relationship between two quantities such that as one increases, the other increases, and as one decreases, the other decreases.

Inverse proportion is where there is a relationship between two quantities such that as one increases, the other decreases, and as one decreases, the other increases.

In general if y is proportional to x, then $y \propto x$ and $y = kx$.

Similarly if y is inversely proportional to x, then $y \propto \dfrac{1}{x}$ and $y = \dfrac{k}{x}$.

Upper and lower bounds (extension)

If a length is given as 5 cm to the nearest centimetre then the length can take any value from 4.5 cm to 5.5 cm The value of 4.5 cm is called the *lower bound* for the length and the value 5.5 cm is called the *upper bound* for the length.

CHAPTER 3
Managing number

3.1 REINFORCEMENT

In this chapter you will need to:
▸ revise percentages of an amount or quantity
▸ revise percentage change
▸ revise reverse percentages

Percentage of an amount or quantity

In Topic 1.5 we looked at two different methods for finding percentages of an amount or quantity as follows:

Method 1

This method uses the fact that any percentage can be written as a fraction with a denominator of 100. We use this to convert the expression into a mathematical form which can then be worked out.

Worked Examples

1 Find 65% of £150.

$$65\% = \frac{65}{100} \text{ so the expression can be written as } \frac{65}{100} \times £150$$
$$= £97.50$$

2 Find 36.5% of £70.

$$36.5\% = \frac{36.5}{100} \text{ so the expression can be written as } \frac{36.5}{100} \times £70$$
$$= £25.55$$

Method 2

This method involves finding 1% of the given amount or quantity (by dividing by 100) and then multiplying to find the required percentage.

Worked Examples

1 Find 40% of £150.

$$1\% \text{ of } £150 \quad = \frac{£150}{100} \quad = £1.50$$
$$40\% \text{ of } £150 = 40 \times £1.50 \quad = £60.00$$

2 Find 36.5% of £70.

$$1\% \text{ of } £70 \quad = \frac{£70}{100} \quad = £0.70$$
$$36.5\% \text{ of } £70 = 36.5 \times £0.70 = £25.55$$

NOTE
$40 \times £1.50$ is the same as
$40 \times £1 + 40 \times 50p$
$= £40 + £20$
$= £60$

PRACTICE 3.1.1a   Try these questions without a calculator

1 Work out the following:
   a 25% of £280   b 35% of 500 m   c 22% of 3.5 kg

2 A shop buys 520 CDs and sells 55% of them at a profit of 50p per CD. What is the shop's total profit?

PRACTICE 3.1.1b   Try these questions with a calculator

1 Work out the following:
   a 56% of £340   b 65.2% of £166.78   c 74.5% of 130 ml

2 A salesperson is paid a $6\frac{1}{2}$% bonus on sales at the end of each month. What bonus will the salesperson receive on sales of £4600?

3 The cost of an article is increased by 26.5%. What will the increase be on an article originally costing £126.80?

Percentage change

Two different methods for calculating percentage change are shown in the following worked examples.

Worked Examples

NOTE
8×10.25 is the same as 10.25×8 which you should be able to do without a calculator.

1 A college has a population of 1025 students and intends to increase its numbers by 8% the following year. What is the expected population the following year?

The increase in population is equivalent to 8% of 1025

$$1\% \text{ of } 1025 \quad = \frac{1025}{100} \quad = 10.25$$

$$8\% \text{ of } 1025 \quad = 8 \times 10.25 \quad = 82$$

So the expected population is $1025 + 82 = 1107$

Alternatively:
The expected population is 108% (100% + 8%) of 1025

$$1\% \text{ of } 1025 \quad = \frac{1025}{100} \quad = 10.25$$

$$108\% \text{ of } 1025 \quad = 108 \times 10.25 \quad = 1107$$

2 The cost of a fitted kitchen is given as £2650 but a 7.5% discount is agreed on a cash sale. What is the final selling price of the fitted kitchen?

The discount for a cash sale is equal to 7.5% of £2650

$$1\% \text{ of } £2650 \quad = \frac{£2650}{100} \quad = £26.50$$

$$7.5\% \text{ of } £2650 \quad = 7.5 \times £26.50 \quad = £198.75$$

So the final selling price is $£2650 - £198.75 = £2451.25$

Alternatively:

The final selling price is 92.5% (100% − 7.5%) of £2650

$$1\% \text{ of } £2650 \quad = \frac{£2650}{100} \quad = £26.50$$

$$92.5\% \text{ of } £2650 = 92.5 \times £26.50 = £2451.25$$

PRACTICE 3.1.2a   Try these questions without a calculator

1   Calculate the new amount when:
   a   £500 is increased by 8%   **c**   £2000 is increased by 3.5%
   b   £800 is decreased by 10%   **d**   £400 is decreased by 12%

2   The cost of a £500 rail ticket increases by 8% each year. What is the new cost after
   a one year   **b** two years?

PRACTICE 3.1.2b   Try these questions with a calculator

1   Calculate the new amount when:
   a   £340 is increased by 16%   **c**   £2865 is decreased by 11%
   b   £265.20 is increased by 21.5%   **d**   £1628.66 is decreased by 13.7%

2   A sum of £3750 is invested in a building society account which pays 6.8% interest at the end of the year. What is the new amount after
   a one year   **b** two years?

3   The value of a motorbike depreciates by 16% each year. How much is a motorbike, initially valued at £3300, worth after two years?

Reverse percentages

The following worked examples illustrate how reverse percentage questions might be solved.

Worked Examples

1   After an increase of 5%, the cost of a Business Class ticket is advertised at £2163. What was the original cost of the ticket?

   We know that 105% (100% + 5%) of the original ticket price is equal to £2163.

   105% of the original ticket price   = £2163

$$1\% \text{ of the original ticket price} \quad = \frac{£2163}{105} \qquad = £20.60$$

   100% of the original ticket price   = 100 × £20.60   = £2060

2   The value of a director's shares in a company dropped by 3.5% to £13 461.75. What was the original value of the shares?

We know that 96.5% (100% − 3.5%) of the original share value is equal to £13 461.75.

96.5% of the original share value $= £13\,461.75$

1% of the original share value $= \dfrac{£13\,461.75}{96.5} = £139.50$

100% of the original share value $= 100 \times £139.50 = £13\,950$

PRACTICE 3.1.3a   Try these questions without a calculator

1 After an increase of 10%, the cost of a holiday is advertised at £660. What was the original cost of the holiday?

2 A car depreciates by 25% and is now worth £12 000. What was the original price?

3 A computer costs £1105 after a 15% reduction. What was the original cost of the computer?

PRACTICE 3.1.3b   Try these questions with a calculator

1 A factory reduces the prices of its conservatories by 16.5%. What was the original price of a conservatory offered for sale at £2338?

2 An investor receives 6.8% interest on her original investment. If the new amount is £2670, what was her original investment?

3 A garage sells a car for £3127 making an 18% profit on the buying price. What was the buying price?

4 A company is valued at £276 760 representing a drop of 6.5% on the value a year earlier. What was the value of the company a year earlier?

Time can be described in many different ways… six forty-five pm, eighteen forty-five hours, forty-five minutes past six, fifteen minutes to seven or a quarter to seven, etc., etc. The most common ways of describing time are to use the twelve-hour or twenty-four-hour clock.

Twelve-hour and twenty-four-hour clock

Worked Examples

1 A commuter leaves home at 0825 and arrives at her meeting at 1118. How long did the journey take?

To work out the time taken it is useful to divide the time up as follows:

	hours	minutes
0825 to 0900		35
0900 to 1100	2	
1100 to 1118		18
	2	53

The journey takes 2 hours and 53 minutes.

2 A train leaves Edinburgh at 12.26 pm and arrives in London at 6.45 pm. How long did the journey take?

Dividing the time up as follows:

	hours	minutes
12.26 pm to 1.00 pm		34
1.00 pm to 6.00 pm	5	
6.00 pm to 6.45 pm		45
	5	79

Clearly the answer 5 hours and 79 minutes is incorrect as there are 60 minutes in an hour so we need to interpret the answer as 6 hours and 19 minutes (79 minutes equals 1 hour and 19 minutes).

3 A coach arrived in London at 1632 and the journey took 4 hours and 20 minutes. What time did the journey start?

A useful method here is to subtract 4 hours and then subtract 20 minutes as follows:

$$1632 - 4 \text{ hours} \qquad = 1232$$
$$1232 - 20 \text{ minutes} \qquad = 1212$$

The coach left at 1212 (or 12.12 pm).

4 A lorry must reach its destination by a quarter past four in the afternoon and the journey takes 2 hours and 34 minutes. What is the latest time that the lorry driver should set out?

Here we must subtract 2 hours and 34 minutes from 4.15 pm (or 1615). We shall first subtract 2 hours and then subtract 34 minutes as follows:

$$4.15 \text{ pm} - 2 \text{ hours} \qquad = 2.15 \text{ pm}$$
$$2.15 \text{ pm} - 34 \text{ minutes} \quad = 1.41 \text{ pm}$$ (it may be helpful to imagine or draw a clock to solve this part)

The lorry driver should set out at 1.41 pm.

PRACTICE 3.2.1

1 Convert the following to the 24-hour clock.
  a 3.00 am   **c** 8.05 pm   **e** 5.30 am   **g** 10.15 am
  b 3.20 pm   **d** 12.45 pm   **f** 7.55 pm   **h** 11.59 pm

2 Convert the following to the 12-hour clock.
  a 1000 hrs   **c** 1250 hrs   **e** 1159 hrs   **g** 2201 hrs
  b 1130 hrs   **d** 1505 hrs   **f** 2350 hrs   **h** 0001 hrs

3 A television programme starts at a quarter past 3 and finishes at twenty to 5. How many minutes does the programme last?

4 A train leaves London at 1125 hrs and arrives at its destination at 1320 hrs. How long was the train journey?

5 A film starts at 11.20 pm and finishes at 1.10 am. How long is the film?

6 A plane leaves London Heathrow at 1930 hrs and arrives at Amsterdam 55 minutes later. What time does the plane arrive in Amsterdam?

7 At twenty past ten in the evening a student sets her alarm for five to 8 the next day. How much sleep does the student get?

8 A coach leaves London Victoria at 1540 and arrives at its destination at 1725.
  a What was the arrival time in 12-hour clock time?
  b How many minutes did the journey take?

9 A ferry journey takes $3\frac{1}{4}$ hours and leaves at 2140 hrs. If the ferry is delayed $1\frac{1}{2}$ hours, when will the ferry arrive at its destination?

3.3 IMPERIAL AND METRIC UNITS

Imperial measure

Imperial measure was the originally accepted series of weights and measures.

Length	12 inches (in)	= 1 foot (ft)
	3 feet	= 1 yard (yd)
	1760 yards	= 1 mile
	5280 feet	= 1 mile
Capacity	20 fluid ounces (fl oz)	= 1 pint (pt)
	2 pints	= 1 quart (qt)
	8 pints	= 1 gallon (gal)
Weight	16 ounces (oz)	= 1 pound (lb)
	14 pounds	= 1 stone (st)
	8 stone	= 1 hundredweight (cwt)
	20 hundredweights	= 1 ton

Metric (SI) measure

The metric system is a system of measurement based on the metre, litre and gram as a standard of measurement.

Length	10 millimetres (mm)	= 1 centimetre (cm)
	100 centimetres	= 1 metre (m)
	1000 millimetres	= 1 metre
	1000 metres	= 1 kilometre (km)

Capacity	10 millilitres (ml)	= 1 centilitre (cl)
	100 centilitres	= 1 litre (l)
	1000 millilitres	= 1 litre
	1000 litres	*= 1 kilolitre (kl)*

Weight	*10 milligrams (mg)*	*= 1 centigram (cg)*
	100 centigrams	*= 1 gram (g)*
	1000 milligrams	= 1 gram
	1000 grams	= 1 kilogram (kg)
	1000 kilograms	= 1 tonne (t)

> **NOTE**
> Units such as kilolitres and centigrams are not often used in the metric system but are included so that the patterns existing between metric units of length, capacity and weight can be seen clearly.

The following conversion information is provided as a basis for your work on this topic:

1 kilogram is approximately 2.2 pounds
1 inch is approximately 2.5 centimetres
1 foot is approximately 30 centimetres
5 miles is approximately 8 kilometres
1 gallon is approximately 4.5 litres

Worked Examples

1   How many inches in $2\frac{1}{2}$ yards?

Using the fact that	12 inches	= 1 foot
	3 feet	= 1 yard

then	$2\frac{1}{2}$ yards	$= 2\frac{1}{2} \times 3$ feet $= 7\frac{1}{2}$ feet
	$7\frac{1}{2}$ feet	$= 7\frac{1}{2} \times 12$ inches $= 90$ inches

There are 90 inches in $2\frac{1}{2}$ yards.

2   Convert 55 millilitres to litres.

Since	1000 millilitres	= 1 litre
then	1 millilitre	$= \frac{1}{1000}$ litre
and	55 millilitres	$= 55 \times \frac{1}{1000}$ litres
		$= \frac{55}{1000} = \frac{11}{200}$ litre (cancelling down)

55 millilitres $= \frac{11}{200}$ litre or 0.055 litre (giving the answer in decimal form).

3   A gallon of fuel costs £2.65. What is the price per litre?

A gallon is approximately 4.5 litres so 4.5 litres of fuel costs £2.65 and

1 litre of fuel costs $\dfrac{£2.65}{4.5}$ = £0.588 888 88…

A litre of fuel costs £0.59 (to the nearest penny).

PRACTICE 3.3.1a   Try these questions without a calculator

1   How many feet in $2\frac{1}{4}$ miles?

2   How many fluid ounces in 5 pints?

3   How many millimetres in $4\frac{3}{4}$ metres?

4   Convert 3200 centimetres to metres.

5   Convert 4570 milligrams to grams.

6   Convert 765 millimetres to kilometres.

7   How many feet in 75 cm?

8   Two feet of material cost £1.80. What is the cost per metre?

PRACTICE 3.3.1b   Try these questions with a calculator

1   How many pounds in $2\frac{1}{4}$ hundredweights?

2   Convert 4650 grams to tonnes.

3   Convert 0.5 centimetre to metres.

4   How many inches in 45 cm?

5   How many ounces in 200 g?

6   How many fluid ounces in 2.25 litres?

7   How many metres in 10 yards?

8   A gallon of oil costs £8.65. What is the price per litre?

9   500 g of butter cost £1.82. What is the cost per pound?

10 A car travels at 50 mph. What is the speed in km/h?

Examination questions will be set to test your ability to 'interpret and use mathematical information presented in written or visual form when solving problems'.

The following exercises gives examples of typical questions under this heading.

PRACTICE 3.4.1   Try these questions without a calculator

1 The following information provides details of the TV programmes one evening.

6.00	News and Weather	9.00	News and Weather
7.00	Consumer Watch	9.30	Feature Film
7.30	Soap Street	11.55	Weatherwatch
8.00	First Monday	12.05	Nightime
8.50	Your Views	1.20	Close

  a How long is the 'Feature Film'?
  b How long is the 'Nightime' programme?
  c I have 3 hours on my videotape. If I record 'Consumer Watch' and 'First Monday', how long will I have left on my video?
  d I have 1 hour and 25 minutes left on my videotape. If I record 'Soap Street' and 'Your Views', how long will I have left on my video?

2 The following information provides details of the night service buses to Trafalgar Square.

Sunbury				0055		0155		0255
Feltham Station				0104		0204		0304
Heathrow Airport	2325		0025		0125		0225	
Hounslow	2342	0012	0042	0112	0142	0212	0242	0312
Hammersmith	2359	0029	0059	0129	0159	0229	0259	0329
Earls Court Station	0008	0038	0108	0138	0208	0238	0308	0338
Hyde Park	0018	0048	0118	0148	0218	0248	0318	0348
Trafalgar Square	0025	0055	0125	0155	0225	0255	0325	0355

  a I arrive at Sunbury at 0045. How long will I have to wait for the bus to Hounslow?
  b I arrive at Hounslow at 2345. How long will I have to wait for the bus to Hyde Park?
  c How long does the journey take from Earls Court Station to Trafalgar Square?
  d How long does the journey take from Sunbury to Hammersmith?
  e I arrive at Heathrow Airport at 11.30 pm. What is the earliest time that I can get to Hammersmith by bus?
  f I arrive at Feltham Station at 1.45 am. What is the earliest time that I can get to Trafalgar Square by bus?

3 The following information details the rail service between Southampton and London.

					Also at these minutes after each hour		Until	
Southampton	0745	0801	0840	0907	15	35	1815	1842
Parkway	0754	0809	0847	0916	22	43	1822	1849
Eastleigh	0758		0851	0920		47		1853
Winchester	0809	0819	0901		32	57	1832	1903
Basingstoke	0829	0836	0918			14		1920
Woking	0902	0855	0938			33		1941
Clapham Jn		0915	0958			55		2002
London	0935	0926	1008		28	05	1929	2012

a I arrive at Southampton at 0755. What is the time of the next train to Eastleigh?

b I arrive at Winchester at 1230. How long will I have to wait for a train to Basingstoke?

c How long does the 1415 from Southampton take to reach London?

d How long does the 1457 from Winchester take to reach London?

e What is the shortest journey time from Parkway to Woking?

f I arrive at Winchester station at 0805. What is the earliest time that I can arrive in London?

g I arrive at Parkway at 1615. What is the earliest time that I can arrive at Clapham Junction?

4 The following information provides details of day trips from Newhaven to Dieppe.

24-HOUR RETURN TRIPS BY CAR				
	Jan – Mar		Apr – Dec	
	Sun – Fri	Sat	Sun – Fri	Sat
BY FERRY				
Car and 1 person	£42	£42	£64	£76
Car and 2 people	£50	£50	£70	£82
Car and up to 6 people	£59	£59	£76	£88
BY HOVERCRAFT				
Car and 1 person	£50	£52	£72	£86
Car and 2 people	£58	£60	£78	£92
Car and up to 6 people	£67	£69	£84	£98

a What is the cost for a car and 2 people on a Thursday in May on the ferry?

b How much more would it cost to travel by hovercraft?

c What is the cost for a family of 2 adults and 4 children travelling by hovercraft on a Friday in September?

d What would be the extra cost if they travelled on the ferry the following day?

5 The following information provides details of prices for a holiday in Europe.

Departure dates	1 Jan – 26 Mar			27 Mar – 27 Aug			28 Aug – 31 Dec		
Number of nights	3	4	extra nights	3	4	extra nights	3	4	extra nights
HOTEL									
Ambassador	305	335	26	355	393	35	299	329	24
Castello	329	365	31	395	445	46	335	369	33
Excelsior	335	372	34	399	455	48	335	375	34
Grande	349	389	36	409	462	49	349	385	35

Reduction of £30 for infants under 2 years old
Reduction of £25 for children aged 2–11 years old

a What is the total cost for 2 adults staying 3 nights at the Excelsior Hotel if they take the holiday in April?

b How much would they save in total if they took their holiday at the beginning of March?

c What is the total cost for 4 adults staying 5 nights at the Ambassador Hotel if they take their holiday in September?

d What is the total cost for 2 adults and their 2 children aged 8 and 14 years old if they stay 4 nights at the Grande Hotel and take their holiday in July?

e How much would they save in total if they stayed at the Ambassador Hotel?

f What is the total cost for 2 adults and their 2 children aged 2 and 6 years old if they stay 3 nights at the Hotel Castello and take their holiday in October?

g What is the cost of a holiday at the Excelsior Hotel if I fly out on the 29th August and fly back on the 2nd September?

6 The following information provides details of single (Sgl) and return (Ret) coach fares.

Boarding points	Heathrow Airport		Gatwick Airport		Manchester Airport		Birmingham Airport	
	Sgl	Ret	Sgl	Ret	Sgl	Ret	Sgl	Ret
Manchester Airport	£28	£36	£30	£38			£15	£18
Wolverhampton	£22	£29	£24	£32	£13	£17	£7	£11
Birmingham Airport	£21	£27	£23	£30	£15	£18		
Coventry	£20	£26	£22	£28	£16	£18	£5	£6
Heathrow Airport			£13	£23	£28	£36	£21	£27
London Victoria	£7	£10	£13	£23	£28	£36	£21	£27
Gatwick Airport	£13	£23			£30	£38	£23	£30
Children under 16 travel at half the adult fare								

a What is the cost of a single fare from Wolverhampton to Heathrow Airport?

b What is the cost of a single fare from Coventry to Gatwick Airport?

c What is the cost of a return fare from London Victoria to Manchester Airport?

d How much do I save by buying a return ticket instead of two single tickets on the journey from Heathrow Airport to Gatwick Airport?

e What is the total cost for 2 adults and their 2 children under 16 years of age from Coventry to Manchester Airport if they buy a single ticket?

f What is the total return cost for 2 adults and their 2 children aged 14 and 16 years of age from Wolverhampton to Gatwick Airport?

7 The table provides details of ticket prices at the Royal Theatre.

		Weekdays	Saturdays	Matinees
Stalls	Front	£21.00	£22.00	£16.00
	Rear	£18.00	£19.00	£14.00
Dress Circle	Front	£21.00	£22.00	£16.00
	Middle	£18.00	£19.00	£14.00
	Rear	£14.00	£15.00	£10.00
Upper Circle	Front	£14.50	£15.50	£10.50
	Middle	£12.00	£13.00	£9.00
	Rear	£10.00	£11.00	£8.00
Balcony	Front	£10.50	£11.50	£8.50
	Rear	£8.00	£9.00	£5.00

Concessions: Each adult buying a seat in the Stalls or Dress Circle can buy a further seat for a child under 18 at half price

a What is the total cost of 3 seats in the front of the Dress Circle on
 i a Saturday   **ii** a matinee performance?
b How much would 5 adults save altogether by sitting at the front of the Upper Circle rather than the rear of the Dress Circle?
c What is the total cost for 2 adults and their 2 children under 18 years of age to attend the Saturday evening performance at the middle of the Dress Circle?
d What is the total cost for 2 adults and their 2 children under 18 years of age to attend the Saturday evening performance at the front of the Upper Circle?
e What is the total cost for 2 adults and 3 children under 18 years of age to attend the weekday performance seated in the front of the Stalls?

8 The following information provides details of the shortest distances (in miles) between two places.

	Lon	LA	Mos	NY	Paris	Rome	Tokyo
London		5440	1550	3460	210	890	5940
Los Angeles	5440		6070	2450	5600	6330	5470
Moscow	1550	6070		4660	1540	1470	4650
New York	3460	2450	4660		6820	4270	6740
Paris	210	5600	1540	6820		680	6030
Rome	890	6300	1470	4270	680		6120
Tokyo	5940	5470	4650	6740	6030	6120	

a What is the distance between   **i** London and Moscow
 ii London and Paris   **iii** London and Tokyo?
b What is the distance between **i** Paris and Moscow **ii** Paris and Tokyo?
c How much further is it from Moscow to Los Angeles than Moscow to Rome?
d How much further is it from Rome to Los Angeles than Rome to Tokyo?
e Which place is nearest to Moscow?
f Which two places are closest together?

9 The following information provides details of the distances (in miles) between two places.

London

57	Brighton							
72	50	Portsmouth						
77	63	19	Southampton					
79	83	140	152	Dover				
120	183	148	130	202	Birmingham			
213	275	258	240	295	98	Liverpool		
402	464	448	429	484	288	219	Glasgow	
405	468	451	433	487	291	222	46	Edinburgh

a What is the distance between London and Southampton?
b What is the distance between Southampton and Liverpool?
c What is the distance between Glasgow and Portsmouth?
d Which two places are closest together?
e Which two places are furthest apart?
f How much further is it from Brighton to Glasgow than Brighton to Liverpool?
g How much further is it from Dover to Edinburgh than Dover to Portsmouth?

Payment for work

Workers are usually paid in one of the following ways:
   i a weekly wage
  ii a yearly salary
 iii an hourly rate with different rates for overtime
  iv a piecework basis
   v a commission basis.

Wages

Wages are the amounts of money earned for a week's work which is dependent upon the number of hours worked and the rate of pay.

Salaries

A salary is the amount of money a person earns in a year for a given amount of hours. The salary is usually divided into 12 equal parts and paid on a monthly basis.

Hourly pay

Hourly pay is the amount of money which is paid for each hour of work for an agreed number of hours each week.

Overtime

Overtime is money paid for working more than the agreed number of hours each week. Overtime is often paid at a different rate such as *time and a half* which means $1\frac{1}{2}$ times the normal rate or *double time* which means twice the normal rate.

Piecework

Piecework is a payment for each piece of work done and is usually combined with wages or salaries to persuade people to work harder.

Commission

Sales people who sell products are sometimes paid a low basic wage plus a percentage of the value of the goods which they sell. This percentage is called commission and the bigger the sales then the bigger the commission paid.

Gross and net wages

A person's gross wage is the amount of money earned before deductions are removed. Deductions might include:

Income Tax
National Insurance
Pension contributions, etc.

The net wage is the amount left when the deductions have been taken away. The net wage is sometimes also called the *take-home pay*.

Worked Examples

1 An employee is paid £280 for a basic 40 hour week and overtime is paid at double time. Calculate:
   a the basic hourly rate
   b the overtime rate
   c the amount of pay for 4 hours overtime.

   a The basic hourly rate $= \dfrac{£280}{40} = £7$ per hour

   b The overtime rate $= 2$ times the hourly rate
   $= 2 \times £7 = £14$ per hour

   c The amount of pay for 4 hours overtime $= 4 \times$ overtime rate
   $= 4 \times £14$ per hour $= £56$

2 A driver is paid £198 for a basic 36 hour week and overtime is paid at time and a half. Calculate:
  a the overtime rate
  b the amount of pay for 4 hours overtime
  c the total wage for a $42\frac{1}{2}$ hour week.

    a In order to find the overtime rate we first need to work out the basic hourly rate

$$\text{basic hourly rate} = \frac{£198}{36} = £5.50 \text{ per hour}$$

$$\text{the overtime rate} = 1\frac{1}{2} \text{ times the hourly rate}$$

$$= 1\frac{1}{2} \times £5.50 = £8.25 \text{ per hour}$$

    b The amount of pay for 4 hours overtime

$$= 4 \times \text{overtime rate}$$

$$= 4 \times £8.25 \text{ per hour} = £33$$

    c The driver is paid £198 for a basic 36 hour week and the remaining $6\frac{1}{2}$ hours will be paid overtime

$$\text{overtime} = 6\frac{1}{2} \times \text{overtime rate}$$

$$= 6\frac{1}{2} \times £8.25 \text{ per hour}$$

$$= £53.63 \text{ (to the nearest penny)}$$

so total wage for a $42\frac{1}{2}$ hour week

$$= £198 + £53.63 = £251.63$$

3 A secretary is paid £168 for a basic 40 hour week and overtime is paid at time and a half. Calculate the number of hours worked if the total weekly wage is £196.35.

To answer this question we first need to work out the basic hourly rate and the overtime rate.

$$\text{Basic hourly rate} = \frac{£168}{40} = £4.20 \text{ per hour}$$

$$\text{The overtime rate} = 1\frac{1}{2} \text{ times the hourly rate}$$

$$= 1\frac{1}{2} \times £4.20 = £6.30 \text{ per hour}$$

The secretary is paid £168 for a basic 40 hour week so the extra money is overtime

$$\text{overtime money} = £196.35 - £168 = £28.35$$

The overtime rate is £6.30 per hour

$$\text{number of hours} = \frac{£28.35}{£6.30} = 4\frac{1}{2} \text{ hours}$$

$$\text{Number of hours worked} = 40 \text{ (basic)} + 4\frac{1}{2} \text{ (overtime)}$$

$$= 44\frac{1}{2} \text{ hours (or 44 hours and 30 mins)}$$

4 A toy maker is paid £1.60 for each toy made plus a bonus of 30p for every toy over 100 made in one week.

   a One week she makes 80 toys. How much money does she receive?

   b The following week she makes 120 toys. How much money does she receive?

      a For making 80 toys the manufacturer will receive:
$$80 \times £1.60 = £128$$

      b For making the first 100 toys the manufacturer will receive:
$$100 \times £1.60 = £160$$
The next 20 toys are paid at £1.60 + 30p (bonus) = £1.90
$$20 \times £1.90 = £38$$
$$\text{Total} = £160 + £38 = £198$$

5 The manager of a garage gets 2% commission on every car which she sells. If she sells a car for £6800 how much commission will she receive?

Commission   = 2% of £6800

$$= \frac{2}{100} \times £6800$$

$$= £136$$

6 An estate agent gets £155 per week plus 0.05% commission on all property sold in a week. One week the estate agent sells four properties at £66 000, £57 000, £69 500 and £49 500. How much money did he earn that week?

Property sales   = £66 000 + £57 000 + £69 500 + £49 500
                    = £242 000

Commission   = 0.05% of £242 000

$$= \frac{0.05}{100} \times £242\,000$$

$$= £121$$

Money earned   = £155 (basic) + £121 (commission)
                = £276

PRACTICE 3.5.1a   Try these questions without a calculator

1 Peter is paid £4.90 per hour. Sunday overtime is paid at double time. Calculate the rate of pay for the overtime.

2 Sanjay is paid £5.60 per hour. Overtime is paid at time and a half. Calculate the rate of pay for the overtime.

3 Bronwen is paid £6.00 per hour for a 40 hour week. Overtime is paid at time and a half. How much will she be paid for a full week plus 3 hours overtime?

4 Ruth is paid 22 p for each table decoration plus a bonus of 6 p for every one over 40 made in one day.

   a One day Ruth makes 32 table decorations. How much money does she receive?

   b The following day Ruth makes 47 table decorations. How much money does she receive?

5 A car dealer receives 3% commission on every car which he sells. If he sells a car for £8800 how much commission will he receive?

6 A travel agent receives a basic wage of £160 a week plus 4% commission on all holidays sold. One week the travel agent sells £4200 worth of holidays.

   a How much commission does the travel agent earn in this week?

   b How much does the travel agent earn altogether in this week?

7 An insurance salesman receives a basic wage of £145 per week plus 8% commission on all insurance sold. What will his total earnings be in one week if he sells

   a £220 of insurance

   b £386 of insurance?

8 Nicola paid £6.50 per hour for a 38 hour week. How much will she be paid altogether for a full week with 2 hours overtime at time and a half and 4 hours overtime at double time?

PRACTICE 3.5.1b Try these questions with a calculator

1 Jamel is paid £4.50 per hour for a $42\frac{1}{2}$ hour week. How much is his basic wage?

2 Jason earns 4 p for every envelope which is filled and sealed. How much is earned on each of the following days?

Monday	80
Tuesday	75
Wednesday	92
Thursday	84
Friday	65

3 A worker is employed to pack bottles in a box. If she packs more than 400 in a day she is paid a bonus of £0.15 for every one over 400. Given that her basic wage is £45 each day how much will she get paid on each of the following days?

Monday	400
Tuesday	450
Wednesday	520
Thursday	495
Friday	370

4 Mark earns £3.90 per hour selling cosmetics plus a commission of 12% on all sales made. Complete the table for the money earned one week.

Day	Hours	Sales	Earnings
Monday	5	£86.00	
Tuesday	3	£95.00	
Thursday	$6\frac{1}{2}$	£92.00	
Friday	$4\frac{1}{2}$	£48.20	

5 A worker is paid £5.20 per hour for a $42\frac{1}{2}$ hour week. Overtime is paid at time and a half. How much will the worker be paid for a full week and 3 hours 40 minutes overtime?

6 Steven is paid £3.80 per hour as his basic wage for a 38 hour week. In one week he works a full week and 3 hours 20 minutes overtime at time and a half. How much does Steven earn that week?

7 Amanda is paid £4.20 per hour as her basic wage for a 36 hour week. In one week she works a full week and 2 hours 25 minutes overtime at time and a half. How much does Amanda earn that week?

Personal allowances

Everyone is given a personal allowance which is the amount of money you can earn before you start having to pay tax. Your personal allowance depends upon such factors as your marital status and other determining factors.

Income tax and PAYE

Income tax is a tax on income earned which is paid to the government. It is deducted automatically from a person's pay packet under the **P**ay **A**s **Y**ou **E**arn (PAYE) system. The amount of income tax paid depends upon a number of factors such as the amount of money earned, the rate of tax and an individual's personal allowance.

Taxable income is the amount of income on which income tax is to be paid. The amount of taxable income is found by subtracting the personal allowance from the annual income.

Taxable income = annual income − personal allowance

The rate of tax is divided into two categories called the lower and basic rates of income tax. The **lower rate of income tax** is 10% and is paid on the first £1520 of a person's taxable income and the **basic rate of income tax** is 22% and is paid on income between £1520 and £28 400.

For the tax year from 6 April 2000 to 5 April 2001:

Taxable income	Rate of tax
Up to £1520	10% (lower rate)
£1520 − £28 400	22% (basic rate)

NOTE

The lower rate of income tax of 10% is the same as 10 p in the £ and the basic rate of income tax of 22% is the same as 22 p in the £.

NOTE

Taxable income over £28 400 is taxed at the higher rate of 40% although questions involving the higher rate of tax are only included in the work of the higher tier of entry (see Topic 3.9 'Extension Material').

Worked Examples

1 A part-time worker earns £445.60 per month. He has a tax allowance of £4385 and pays 10% on the first £1520 of his taxable income. How much tax does he pay?

Annual income	= £445.60 × 12 = £5347.20
Taxable income	= Annual income − personal allowance
	= £5347.20 − £4385
	= £962.20

The worker pays 10% tax (lower rate) on the first £1520 of his taxable income.

$$\text{Tax at lower rate} = 10\% \text{ of } £962.20$$
$$= \frac{10}{100} \times £962.20$$
$$= £96.22$$

The shopworker pays £96.22 tax altogether.

2 Brian has an income of £958 per month. He has a single person's tax allowance of £4385 and a further allowance of £65. How much tax does Brian pay each year?

Annual income	= £958 × 12 = £11 496
Taxable income	= Annual income − personal allowances
	= £11 496 − (£4385 + £65)
	= £7046

Brian pays 10% tax (lower rate) on the first £1520 of taxable income and 22% tax (basic rate) on income between £1520 and £28 400.

On £7046, Brian pays 10% tax on the first £1520 and 22% tax on the remaining £5526 (£7046 − £1520 = £5526).

$$\text{Tax at lower rate} = 10\% \text{ of } £1520$$
$$= \frac{10}{100} \times £1520$$
$$= £152$$

$$\text{Tax at basic rate} = 22\% \text{ of } £5526$$
$$= \frac{22}{100} \times £5526$$
$$= £1215.72$$

$$\text{Total tax} = £152 + £1215.72$$
$$= £1367.72$$

Brian pays £1367.72 tax altogether.

3 Emily receives a monthly income of £785.20 from her investments. Her allowances total £4910. How much tax does she pay each month?

Annual income $= £785.20 \times 12 = £9422.40$

Taxable income $= $ Annual income $-$ personal allowances
$= £9422.40 - £4910$
$= £4512.40$

Emily pays 10% tax (lower rate) on the first £1520 of taxable income and 22% tax (basic rate) on income between £1520 and £28 400.

On £4512.40, Emily pays 10% tax on the first £1520 and 22% tax on the remaining £2992.40 ($£4512.40 - £1520 = £2992.40$).

Tax at lower rate $= 10\%$ of £1520
$= \dfrac{10}{100} \times £1520$
$= £152$

Tax at basic rate $= 22\%$ of £2992.40
$= \dfrac{22}{100} \times £2992.40$
$= £658.328$
$= £658.33$ (to the nearest penny)

Total tax $= £152 + £658.328$ (using original amount before rounding)
$= £810.328$
$= £810.33$ (to the nearest penny)

The question asks how much tax does she pay each month?

Tax each month $= \dfrac{£810.328}{12}$
$= £67.527\,33\ldots$

Emily pays £67.53 tax each month (to the nearest penny).

PRACTICE 3.5.2   Try these questions with a calculator

1   Jenny earns £125 per week. She has a personal allowance of £4385. What is her taxable income?

2   Steven earns £580.56 per month. He has a personal allowance of £4385 plus a further allowance of £105. What is his taxable income?

3   A pensioner earns £512.50 per month from her investments. She has a tax allowance of £5790. What is her taxable income?

4   Phil has a part-time job and earns £58.50 per week. His personal allowance is £4385. What is his taxable income?

5   A librarian is paid £54.20 per week for part-time work. His personal allowance is £4385. How much extra can he earn each week before he is liable to pay any tax?

NOTE
Questions on tax can relate to any year but all information will be given to you.

6   Jackie earns £7300 one year. She has a tax allowance of £4195 and pays
    20p in the £ on her taxable income. Calculate how much tax Jackie pays
    per year.

7   A businesswoman earns £26 500 one year. She has a tax allowance of
    £4195 and pays 20% on the first £4300 of her taxable income and 23% on
    the rest of her taxable income. How much tax does she pay in the year?

8   Ruth earns £480.68 per week. She has a tax allowance of £4385 and pays
    10% on the first £1520 of her taxable income and 22% on the rest of her
    taxable income. How much tax does she pay in the year?

9   Parminder earns £22 600 per annum and has a personal allowance of
    £4385 plus a further allowance of £1250. How much tax does he pay
    altogether?

10 Mr Gribble earns £855.25 per month from his investments. He has a tax
    allowance of £6050 altogether. How much tax does he pay each month?

3.6 HOUSEHOLD FINANCE AND INSURANCE

Value Added Tax

Value Added Tax (VAT) is a tax on goods or services which is paid to the
government. Some goods such as basic food, children's clothes, books and
newspapers do not attract VAT and are called zero rated.

Worked Examples

1   A washing machine is priced at £840 plus VAT at $17\frac{1}{2}\%$. How much is the
    VAT and what is the total cost of the washing machine?

    We need to find $17\frac{1}{2}\%$ of £840 as follows:

1% of £840	$= \dfrac{£840}{100}$	$= £8.40$
$17\frac{1}{2}\%$ of £840	$= 17\frac{1}{2} \times £8.40$	$= £147$

    So the VAT is £147 and the total cost is £840 + £147 = £987.

    Alternatively:

10% of £840	$= \dfrac{£840}{10}$	$= £84$
5% of £840	$= \dfrac{£84}{2}$	$= £42$
$2\frac{1}{2}\%$ of £840	$= \dfrac{£42}{2}$	$= £21$

    VAT $= £84 + £42 = £21 = £147$

    So the VAT is £147 and the total cost is £840 + £147 = £987.

2   A television set is priced at £799 which includes VAT at $17\frac{1}{2}\%$. What is the
    cost of the television set without the VAT?

NOTE

For the purposes of using a calculator it is better to write $117\frac{1}{2}$ as 117.5.

NOTE

It is helpful when dealing with reverse percentages to check the answer by adding on the VAT at $17\frac{1}{2}$% to your answer.

The price of £799 includes the actual cost of the television set plus VAT at $17\frac{1}{2}$%, so £799 represents $117\frac{1}{2}$% $(100\% + 17\frac{1}{2}\%)$ of the actual cost of the television set.

117.5% of the actual cost of the television set $= £799$

1% of the actual cost of the television set $= \dfrac{£799}{117.5} = £6.80$

100% of the actual cost of the television set $= 100 \times £6.80 = £680$

PRACTICE 3.6.1a   Try these questions without a calculator

For the following questions assume that the rate of VAT is $17\frac{1}{2}$% or else complete the exercise using any other appropriate value.

1   Find the total purchase price for the following items:
 a   An audio system priced £590 + VAT.
 b   A refrigerator priced £460 + VAT.
 c   A camera priced £235 + VAT.
 d   A fitted kitchen priced £1865 + VAT.
 e   A new car priced £9885 + VAT.

2   A bill is received for £92.00 excluding VAT at 17.5%. What is the total cost of the bill with VAT?

PRACTICE 3.6.1b   Try these questions with a calculator

1   Check your answers to question 1 in Practice 3.6.1a using a calculator.

2   Check your answers to question 2 in Practice 3.6.1a using a calculator.

3   A microwave oven is priced at £376 which includes VAT at $17\frac{1}{2}$%. What is the cost of the microwave oven without VAT?

4   A fitted bedroom is priced at £3290 which includes VAT at $17\frac{1}{2}$%. What is the cost of the fitted bedroom without VAT?

5   A dishwasher is priced at £575.75 which includes VAT at $17\frac{1}{2}$%. What is the VAT?

Electricity bills

Electricity is charged according to the number of units of electricity used since the last reading. A quarterly charge is added to the bill and VAT at 8% is applied to the final amount.

Worked Examples

1   During one quarter a householder uses 1200 units of electricity. Electricity is charged at 7p per unit and the quarterly charge is £10.33. VAT at 8% is applied to the final amount. Calculate the cost of the electricity bill.

Cost of electricity	$= 1200 \times 7\,\text{p}$
	$= 8400\,\text{p}$
	$= £84$
Cost of bill	$= \text{cost of electricity} + \text{quarterly charge}$
	$= £84 + £10.33$
	$= £94.33$
VAT	$= 8\% \text{ of } £94.33$
	$= \dfrac{8}{100} \times £94.33$
	$= £7.55 \text{ (to the nearest penny)}$
Total cost	$= \text{cost of bill} + \text{VAT}$
	$= £94.33 + £7.55$
	$= £101.88$

> **NOTE**
> The total cost can be found more quickly by calculating 108% (100% + 8%) of £94.33

2 A householder uses 280 units of electricity and 520 units of economy electricity during one quarter. Electricity is charged at 8 p per unit and economy electricity is charged at 3 p per unit. The quarterly charge is £13.25 and VAT at 8% is applied to the final amount. Calculate the cost of the electricity bill.

Cost of electricity	$= 280 \times 8\,\text{p}$
	$= 2240\,\text{p}$
	$= £22.40$
Cost of economy electricity	$= 520 \times 3\,\text{p}$
	$= 1560\,\text{p}$
	$= £15.60$
Cost of bill	$= \text{cost of all electricity} + \text{quarterly charge}$
	$= £22.40 + £15.60 + £13.25$
	$= £51.25$
VAT	$= 8\% \text{ of } £51.25$
	$= \dfrac{8}{100} \times £51.25$
	$= £4.10$
Total cost	$= \text{cost of bill} + \text{VAT}$
	$= £51.25 + £4.10$
	$= £55.35$

> **NOTE**
> The total cost can be found more quickly by calculating 108% (100% + 8%) of £51.25

PRACTICE 3.6.2a   Try these questions without a calculator

1 A householder uses 500 units of electricity. Electricity is charged at 7 p per unit and the quarterly charge is £10.33. VAT at 8% is applied to the final amount. Calculate the cost of the electricity bill.

2 A householder uses 326 units of electricity and 598 units of economy electricity during one quarter. Electricity is charged at 8 p per unit and

economy electricity is charged at 3 p per unit. The quarterly charge is £13.25 and VAT at 8% is applied to the final amount. Calculate the cost of the electricity bill.

PRACTICE 3.6.2b   Try these questions with a calculator

1   Using the following information, calculate the cost of the following electricity bills for one quarter.

   Electricity is charged at 7.2 p per unit.
   Quarterly charge is £10.33.
   VAT at 8% is applied to the final amount.

   a   600 units of electricity used   **c**   1250 units of electricity used
   b   890 units of electricity used   **d**   435 units of electricity used

2   Using the following information, calculate the cost of the following electricity bills for one quarter.

   Electricity is charged at 7.2 p per unit.
   Quarterly charge is £10.33.
   VAT at 8% is applied to the final amount.

   a   Previous reading = 4326   Present reading = 4776
   b   Previous reading = 7513   Present reading = 7921
   c   Previous reading = 3642   Present reading = 3789
   d   Previous reading = 9956   Present reading = 0128

3   Using the following information, calculate the cost of the following electricity bills for one quarter.

   Electricity is charged at 7.6 p per unit.
   Economy electricity is charged at 2.5 p per unit.
   Quarterly charge is £13.25.
   VAT at 8% is applied to the final amount.

   a   300 units of electricity used   450 units of economy electricity used
   b   260 units of electricity used   590 units of economy electricity used
   c   371 units of electricity used   653 units of economy electricity used
   d   788 units of electricity used   981 units of economy electricity used

Gas bills

Gas is charged according to the number of cubic metres of gas used since the last reading. A standing charge is added to the bill and VAT at 8% is applied to the final amount.

Worked Example

During one quarter, covering 92 days, a householder uses 800 cubic metres of gas. Gas is charged at 1.4p per kilowatt hour and the standing charge is 9.5p per day. The calorific value of the gas used is 38MJ/m³ and VAT at 8% is applied to the final amount. Calculate the cost of the gas bill.

NOTE

The cost of gas is usually expressed in pence per kilowatt hour of gas used. The procedure for converting the number of cubic metres of gas used to the number of kilowatt hours is explained on the gas bill as follows:

   multiply the number of cubic metres of gas by the calorific value (in MJ/m³), divide the result by 3.6 to convert the amount to the number of kilowatt hours.

To convert the number of cubic metres of gas used to the number of kilowatt hours:

multiply the number of cubic metres of gas by the calorific value (in MJ/m^3), then divide the result by 3.6 to convert the amount to the number of kilowatt hours

Gas used	= 800 cubic metres
	= 800 × 38 / 3.6 kilowatt hours
	= 8444 kilowatt hours
Cost of gas	= 8444 × 1.4 p
	= 11822 p (to the nearest penny)
	= £118.22 (to the nearest penny)
Standing charge	= number of days × standing charge per day
	= 92 × 9.5 p
	= 874 p
	= £8.74
Cost of bill	= cost of gas + standing charge
	= £118.22 + £8.74
	= £126.96
VAT	= 8% of £126.96
	= $\dfrac{8}{100} \times £126.96$
	= £10.16 (to the nearest penny)
Total cost	= cost of bill + VAT
	= £126.96 + £10.16
	= £137.12

NOTE
The total cost can be found more quickly by calculating 108% (100% + 8%) of £126.96

PRACTICE 3.6.3   Try these questions with a calculator

1   Over a period of 90 days, a householder uses 650 cubic metres of gas. Gas is charged at 1.4p per kilowatt hour and the standing charge is 9.1p per day. The calorific value of the gas used is $38MJ/m^3$ and VAT at 8% is applied to the final amount. Calculate the cost of the gas bill.

2   Using the following information, calculate the cost of the following gas bills over a period of 90 days.

   Gas is charged at 1.43p per kilowatt hour.
   Standing charge is 9.06p per day.
   The calorific value of the gas used is $38.2MJ/m^3$
   VAT at 8% is applied to the final amount.

   a   800 cubic metres of gas used
   b   1350 cubic metres of gas used
   c   1800 cubic metres of gas used
   d   1728 cubic metres of gas used

3 Using the following information, calculate the cost of the following gas bills over the period given.

Gas is charged at 1.43 p per kilowatt hour.
Standing charge is 9.06 p per day.
The calorific value of the gas used is 38.2 MJ/m³
VAT at 8% is applied to the final amount.

a 898 cubic metres of gas used. Statement covering 92 days.
b 1238 cubic metres of gas used. Statement covering 90 days.
c Previous reading = 1760. Present reading = 2348. Statement covering 91 days.
d Previous reading = 5213. Present reading = 6821. Statement covering 90 days.
e 1052 cubic metres of gas used. Statement from 26/10/97 to 24/01/98 inclusive.

Telephone bills

Telephone bills are calculated according to the number, duration, time and distance of telephone calls made. In addition to the call charges the bill also includes a rental charge (for the line and other facilities) and VAT at $17\frac{1}{2}\%$.

Worked Example

During one quarter a householder is charged £14.15 for telephone calls along with a rental charge of £21.09. VAT at $17\frac{1}{2}\%$ is applied to the final amount. Calculate the cost of the telephone bill.

Cost of bill	= cost of calls + quarterly rental
	= £14.15 + £21.09
	= £35.24

VAT = $17\frac{1}{2}\%$ of £35.24
= £6.17 (to the nearest penny)

Total cost = cost of bill + VAT
= £35.24 + £6.17
= £41.41

NOTE
The total cost can be found more quickly by calculating $117\frac{1}{2}\%$ $(100\% + 17\frac{1}{2}$

PRACTICE 3.6.4

1 During one quarter a householder is charged £35.84 for telephone calls along with a rental charge of £21.09. VAT at $17\frac{1}{2}\%$ is applied to the final amount. Calculate the cost of the telephone bill.

2 Using the following information, calculate the cost of the following telephone bills for one quarter.

Quarterly charge is £21.09.
VAT at $17\frac{1}{2}$% is applied to the final amount.

a £26.72 for telephone calls
b £96.25 for telephone calls
c £78.43 for telephone calls
d £25.92 for telephone calls

3 Mr Stephen's quarterly telephone bill includes the following charges:

£24.98 for telephone calls under £0.42
£27.41 for itemised telephone calls
£21.09 for line rental
£6.00   for Premier Line membership

VAT at $17\frac{1}{2}$% is applied to the final amount. Calculate the cost of Mr Stephen's telephone bill.

Insurance

Insurance can be taken out on most things but the most common types of insurance discussed here include:

Life insurance
House insurance
Contents insurance
Car insurance
Travel insurance

Life insurance is an insurance on a person's life and can be used to provide for a partner or family in the event of their death. The insurance is based on the person's age, state of health and lifestyle.

House insurance insures your home against loss or damage caused by fire, lightning, vandalism, flooding, subsidence, etc. The insurance is based on the value of the house, the area in which the house is situated and the possible cost of completely rebuilding the house.

Contents insurance insures the contents of the house (household goods, clothing and personal belongings owned by you or people living in your house) against any of the causes detailed above under house insurance.

Car insurance can be purchased under three separate categories:

Third party
Third party, fire and theft
Fully comprehensive

Third party insurance covers liability to other vehicles or people, while third party, fire and theft also covers damage and loss through fire, theft and attempted theft of the insurer's vehicle. Fully comprehensive insurance covers all of the above as well as personal effects, medical expenses and personal accident benefits.

NOTE

Where no claims are made against a car insurance policy during the course of the year then the next year's insurance is reduced by a No Claims Discount.

Travel insurance is very useful for those travelling abroad on business or pleasure and might cover such eventualities as cancellation, delay, personal accidents, medical expenses, lost baggage and personal liability.

PRACTICE 3.6.5a   Try these questions without a calculator

1 A man takes out a life insurance policy for £28 000. The company quotes an annual premium of £4.75 per £1000 insurance. Calculate the monthly premium for the policy.

2 The insurance on a car is £243 but the owner has a $33\frac{1}{3}\%$ no claims discount. What is the value of the no claims discount and the amount of insurance which the owner has to pay?

3 A travel company offers the following premium for travel insurance.

Period	2–15 years	16-64 years	65+ years
0–8 days	£14	£28	£56
9–17 days	£18.50	£37	£74
18–31 days	£24	£48	£96
each additional 7 days	£7.50	£15	£30

Infants under 2 years insured free
Winter sports – double premium

Find the cost of travel insurance for the following:
a two people aged 21 years old for a fortnight
b two people aged 21 years old for three weeks
c a family of two adults aged under 64 and their two children aged 8 and 13 years old for 7 days
d a family of two adults aged under 64 and their two children aged 3 and 1 years for 7 days
e a family of one adult aged under 64 and three children aged 5, 8 and 11 years for a fortnight
f two senior citizens aged 62 and 67 years travelling to visit relatives for six weeks
g a party of six adults on a skiing holiday for 10 days
h a family of two adults aged under 64 and their two children aged 14 and 16 years on a skiing holiday for 10 days.

PRACTICE 3.6.5b   Try these questions with a calculator

1 The following table shows the cost of insuring each £1000 worth of the value of different properties in a particular town.

Property	Cost per £1000
Bungalow	£1.15
Terraced house	£1.42
Semi detached house	£1.33
Detached house	£1.38
Flat/maisonette	£1.62

Find the cost of insuring the following:
a a terraced house valued at £48 000
b a two bedroomed flat valued at £46 500
c a semi detached house valued at £68 750
d a detached house valued at £128 500.

2 The following table shows the cost of insuring each £1000 worth of the value of the contents of a semi detached house in different areas of the country

Position	Cost per £1000
Scotland	£3.24
Wales	£4.18
North England	£8.81
South East England	£6.70
South West England	£3.66

a What is the cost of £3000 of contents insurance in Wales?
b What is the cost of £4500 of contents insurance in South East England?
c How much extra will it cost me to insure £3600 of contents in North England compared with South West England?

3.7 CREDIT AND BANKING

Credit

Credit for goods and services can be obtained in a number of ways but the most common ways discussed here include:

Hire purchase
Credit cards
Overdrafts
Personal loans
Mail order catalogues

Hire Purchase

Hire purchase is a way of paying for goods or services over a period of time. Hire purchase usually involves the payment of a deposit plus regular (weekly or monthly) payments of a fixed amount.

An advantage of hire purchase is that it is convenient and it allows you to pay for goods over a period of time. A disadvantage is that it can be an expensive way of borrowing money and a personal loan may be cheaper.

NOTE
See also the work in Topic 3.9 on 'Annual Percentage Rate' about the cost of hire purchase.

Worked Examples

1   A fitted bedroom is priced at £1700 but can be bought with a 15% deposit
    and 30 monthly payments of £58.50. Find
    a   the amount of the deposit
    b   the total credit price
    c   the amount saved by paying cash.

    a   Deposit $= 15\%$ of £1700

$$= \frac{15}{100} \times 1700 = £255$$

    b   Total credit price $=$ deposit $+$ 30 monthly payments of £58.50
$$= £255 + 30 \times £58.50$$
$$= £255 + £1755$$
$$= £2010$$

    c   Amount saved $=$ credit price $-$ cash price
$$= £2010 - £1700$$
$$= £310$$

2   A microwave oven costs £270 on a hire purchase agreement with a down
    payment of £23.25 and monthly payments of £16.45. How long was the
    hire purchase agreement in operation?

The total of the monthly payments $=$ hire purchase cost $-$ down payment
$$= £270 - £23.25$$
$$= £246.75$$

Each monthly payment $= £16.45$, so the number of months
$$= \frac{£246.75}{£16.45}$$
$$= 15$$

The hire purchase agreement lasted for 15 months.

PRACTICE 3.7.1a   Try these questions without a calculator

1   A television set priced at £480 is offered for a deposit of £50 plus 24
    monthly payments of £22.15. Find
    a   the total credit price
    b   the amount saved by paying cash.

2   A camera is advertised at £465 or it can be bought on hire purchase for a
    deposit of £46 plus 12 monthly payments of £40. Find
    a   the total credit price
    b   the amount saved by paying cash.

3   A computer can be bought for a total hire purchase cost of £1780 with
    10 monthly payments of £162. What was the amount of the deposit?

PRACTICE 3.7.1b   Try these questions with a calculator

1 A fitted kitchen is priced at £2800 but can be bought with a 12% deposit and 36 monthly payments of £85.10. Find
   a the amount of the deposit
   b the total credit price
   c the amount saved by paying cash.

2 A carpet advertised at £220 can be bought on hire purchase for a 10% deposit and 8 monthly instalments of £29.40. Find
   a the amount of the deposit
   b the total credit price
   c the amount saved by paying cash.

3 A television costs £586 on a hire purchase agreement with a down payment of £58 and monthly payments of £52.80. How long was the hire purchase agreement in operation?

Credit cards

There are two types of credit cards:

▸ Bank credit cards such as Mastercard, Barclaycard or Trustcard which are operated by banks and, more increasingly, by building societies.

▸ Store credit cards operated by many large stores and supermarkets which can be used in the stores or supermarkets when purchasing goods.

With credit cards you are given a spending limit and receive a monthly statement giving you a minimum amount to be paid that month. You pay interest on the outstanding balance each month and this is added to your account.

An advantage of credit cards is that it is convenient and gives you interest free credit if you pay off the outstanding balance each month (although some credit cards do now have a yearly subscription fee). A disadvantage is that it can be an expensive way of borrowing money and a personal loan may be cheaper.

> **NOTE**
> See also the work in Topic 3.9 on 'Annual Percentage Rate' about the cost of hire purchase.

Overdrafts

You can borrow money from a bank or building society through an overdraft facility which allows you to overdraw money from your account by agreement with the bank or building society.

An advantage of an overdraft facility is that you do not incur heavy penalties for going overdrawn although a disadvantage is that you usually have to pay for such a facility.

Personal loans

An alternative to an overdraft facility or a way to raise a lump sum of money is to take out a personal loan. The loan is paid off at regular (usually monthly) intervals at a fixed rate of interest which is agreed at the beginning of the loan. Personal loans are usually obtained from your bank or building society although there are now an increasing number of financial institutions offering personal loans.

An advantage of a personal loan is that it allows you to plan your finances as you pay off the loan with a fixed amount at regular intervals (usually monthly). The disadvantage of a personal loan is that interest has to be paid out on the amount borrowed.

Mail order catalogues

Another popular way to obtain credit is by using a mail order catalogue which allows you to purchase goods from a catalogue and pay for them over a period of time (usually 20 weeks).

An advantage of using a mail order catalogue is that it is convenient and it allows you to pay for goods over a period of time. A disadvantage is that goods can be limited and may be slightly dearer than the price you would normally pay for the same goods in the shops.

Worked Examples

1 The minimum payment on a credit card statement is given as 5% of the outstanding balance or £6.00 (whichever is greater). What is the minimum payment on a credit card statement with an outstanding balance of £125?

   5% of the outstanding balance $= 5\%$ of £125

   $$= \frac{5}{100} \times 125$$

   $$= £6.25$$

   As this amount exceeds £6.00 then the minimum payment is £6.25.

2 The following table shows the monthly repayments for loans over different periods of time.

Amount of loan	Term of loan				
	12 Mnth	24 Mnth	36 Mnth	48 Mnth	60 Mnth
£500	£46.18	£25.02	£17.97	£14.44	£12.33
£1000	£92.36	£50.04	£35.94	£28.88	£24.66
£1500	£138.53	£75.06	£53.91	£43.32	£36.99
£2000	£184.71	£100.08	£71.88	£57.78	£49.32
£2500	£230.89	£125.10	£89.85	£72.22	£61.65

   a What is the total repayment on £500 over 24 months?
   b What is the total repayment on £1500 over 48 months?

a The monthly repayment on £500 over 24 months is £25.02 per month

Total repayment = 24 months × £25.02 per month
= £600.48

b The monthly repayment on £1500 over 48 months is £43.32 per month

Total repayment = 48 months × £43.32 per month
= £2079.36

3 A new suit is priced at £138 in a mail order catalogue and offered for a deposit of 20% plus 25 weekly payments of £4.79. Find
  a the amount of the deposit
  b the total credit price
  c the amount saved by paying cash.

  a Deposit = 20% of £138 = $\dfrac{20}{100}$ × £138 = £27.60

  b Total credit price = deposit + 25 weekly payments of £4.79
  = £27.60 + 25 × £4.79
  = £27.60 + £119.75 = £147.35

  c Amount saved = credit price − cash price
  = £147.35 − £138 = £9.35

PRACTICE 3.7.2   Try these questions without a calculator

1 The mininum payment on a credit card statement is given as 3% of the outstanding balance or £5.00 (whichever is greater). Find the minimum payment on credit card statements with the following outstanding balances:
  a £358   **b** £674   **c** £103   **d** £1022   **e** £152

2 The starting balance on the statement of a storecard is £221.46 and a payment for £150 is received at the beginning of the month. The statement includes two debits for £20.52 and £35.00 as well as an interest charge of £5.26. What is the new balance showing on the statement ?

3 Geraldine takes out a personal loan for £1000 which is to be paid back in 12 monthly instalments of £92.22. What is the total amount and the interest payable on the loan?

4 The following table shows the monthly repayment for loans below £3000 over a period of time with and without the loan protection plan:

	Amount of loan	Monthly with loan protection	Monthly without loan protection
12 months	£50.00	£4.93	£4.54
	£100.00	£9.84	£9.08
	£500.00	£48.95	£45.32
	£1000.00	£97.88	£90.55
	£2000.00	£195.68	£181.22
24 months	£50.00	£2.68	£2.42
	£100.00	£5.36	£4.92
	£500.00	£26.85	£24.44
	£1000.00	£54.20	£48.80
	£2000.00	£108.85	£97.68

a What is the total repayment on £500 over 12 months with the loan protection plan?

b What is the total repayment on £1000 over 24 months without the loan protection plan?

c What is the total repayment on £2000 over 12 months with the loan protection plan?

d How much extra is the loan protection plan on £100 over 24 months?

5 A microwave oven is priced at £375 in a mail order catalogue and offered for a deposit of £40 plus 20 weekly payments of £18.50. Find
   a the total credit price
   b the amount saved by paying cash.

6 A kitchen set is priced at £126 in a mail order catalogue and offered for a deposit of 20% plus 20 weekly payments of £5.86. Find
   a the amount of the deposit
   b the total credit price
   c the amount saved by paying cash.

Foreign currency and exchange rates

The following table gives the exchange rates for the British pound at the time of going to press. The exchange rates fluctuate on a day by day basis and any examination question on foreign currency and exchange rates will provide you with the information which you need.

Country	Exchange rate	Country	Exchange rate
Australia	£1 = 2.5 dollars	Holland	£1 = 3.5 guilders
Austria	£1 = 21.7 schillings	Italy	£1 = 3058 lira
Belgium	£1 = 63.7 francs	Japan	£1 = 172.6 yen
Denmark	£1 = 11.9 kroner	New Zealand	£1 = 3.2 dollars
France	£1 = 10.4 francs	Spain	£1 = 262.8 pesetas
Germany	£1 = 3.1 marks	Sweden	£1 = 13.5 kroner
Greece	£1 = 528 drachma	United States	£1 = 1.6 dollars

Worked Examples

1   How many Austrian schillings would you get for £60?

   The exchange rate is £1 = 21.7 schillings.
   So £60 = 60 × 21.7 = 1302 schillings.

2   How much is 150 Swedish kroner worth?

   The exchange rate is:

   13.5 kroner = £1

   $$1 \text{ kroner} = \frac{£1}{13.5} \qquad (\div 13.5 \text{ to find the value of 1 kroner})$$

   $$150 \text{ kroner} = 150 \times \frac{£1}{13.5} \qquad (\times 150 \text{ to find the value of 150 kroner})$$

   $$= £11.111\,111\ldots \quad \text{(by calculator)}$$
   $$= £11.11 \quad \text{(to the nearest penny)}$$

PRACTICE 3.7.3a   Try these questions without a calculator

1   How many French francs would you get for £20?

2   How much is £200 in Japanese yen?

3   How much is 3500 guilders worth?

4   How much is 200 American dollars worth?

PRACTICE 3.7.3b   Try these questions with a calculator

Use the exchange rates on the previous page to answer the following questions.

1   How much is 2000 pesetas worth? Give your answer to the nearest penny.

2   How much is 3500 Belgian francs worth? Give your answer to an appropriate degree of accuracy.

3   A tourist in Italy changes a traveller's cheque for £50 to Italian lira. How many lira should she receive?

4   Peter brings home 500 marks from his trip to Germany. He changes his money to American dollars. How many dollars should he receive?

5   Jane brings home 40 000 drachma from her trip to Greece. She changes her money to Dutch guilders. How many guilders should she receive?

Interest

Interest is the amount of money which you pay for borrowing other people's money or which is paid to you for allowing other people to borrow your money. There are two types of interest called **simple interest** and **compound interest** which will be discussed here:

Simple interest

With simple interest, the amount of interest paid is the same each year so that the interest paid is not reinvested.

Worked Examples

1 If £500 is invested at a simple interest of 5% per annum, what would the amount be at the end of 3 years?

£500 at 5% per annum would realise   5% of £500 per year
                                        i.e. £25 per year

In 3 years this would be $3 \times £25 = £75$

So the amount after 3 years would be $£500 + £75 = £575$

The formulae used for simple interest are $A = P + \dfrac{PRT}{100}$ and $I = \dfrac{PRT}{100}$

where: A = total amount
                                I = simple interest
                                P = principal or original investment
                                R = rate (% per annum)
                                T = time (in years)

In the above example P = principal = £500
                                R = rate = 5% per annum
                                T = time (in years) = 3 years

$$A = P + \frac{PRT}{100}$$

$$A = 500 + \left(\frac{500 \times 5 \times 3}{100}\right)$$

$$A = 500 + 75 = £575 \quad \text{(as above)}$$

2 If £3200 is invested for 5 years at a simple interest of 6% per annum, calculate the amount of simple interest.

Using the formula $I = \dfrac{PRT}{100}$

where: P = principal = £3200
                                R = rate = 6% per annum
                                T = time (in years) = 5 years

$$I = \frac{3200 \times 6 \times 5}{100}$$

$$I = £960$$

3 If £680 is invested for 6 months at a simple interest of 5.25% per annum, calculate
   a the amount of simple interest
   b the total amount at the end of this time.

> **NOTE**
> It is important that the time is given in years so 6 months is converted to 0.5 year.

   a Using the formula $I = \dfrac{PRT}{100}$

      where: P = principal = £680
                    R = rate = 5.25%
                    T = time (in years) = 0.5 year
                    $I = \dfrac{680 \times 5.25 \times 0.5}{100}$
                    I = £17.85

   b The total amount is the principal + the simple interest
                    $A = P + I$
                    A = £680 + £17.85
                    A = £697.85

4 £1200 is invested at 6% simple interest per annum. How long will it take for the total amount to equal £1362?

   In this particular worked example we need to work backwards to the answer and it is helpful to write down what information we already know.
                    A = total amount = £1362
                    P = principal = £1200
                    R = rate = 6% per annum
                    T = time (in years)

   From this information we can work out the simple interest and use the formula $I = \dfrac{PRT}{100}$

                    I = total amount − principal
                    I = £1362 − £1200
                    I = £162

   Now $I = \dfrac{PRT}{100}$

   so $162 = \dfrac{1200 \times 6 \times T}{100}$

                     $162 = \dfrac{7200 \times T}{100}$

                     $162 = 72 \times T$

                     $T = \dfrac{162}{72} = 2.25$

   The time is 2.25 years or 2 years and 3 months (12 months = 1 year).

PRACTICE 3.7.4a Try these questions without a calculator

1 If £350 is invested at a simple interest of 3% per annum, what would the amount be at the end of 4 years?

2 If £625 is invested for 10 years at a simple interest of 8% per annum, calculate
   a the amount of simple interest
   b the total amount at the end of this time.

3 £200 is invested at 3% per annum. How long will it take for the simple interest paid to equal £12?

PRACTICE 3.7.4b Try these questions with a calculator

1 Calculate the simple interest and the total amount for each of the following:

   a $P = £250$ $R = 7\%$ pa $T = 3$ years
   b $P = £450$ $R = 4\frac{1}{2}\%$ pa $T = 6$ years
   c $P = £1250$ $R = 5.8\%$ pa $T = 5$ years
   d $P = £475$ $R = 5\%$ pa $T = 2\frac{1}{2}$ years
   e $P = £690$ $R = 4\%$ pa $T = 8$ months
   f $P = £2500$ $R = 6.25\%$ pa $T = 3$ years 5 months

2 £420 is invested at 5% simple interest per annum. How long will it take for the total amount to equal £483?

3 £1200 is invested for 6 years. What is the rate per cent per annum if the simple interest is equal to £252?

4 £900 is invested for 8 months. What is the rate per cent per annum if the simple interest is equal to £27?

Compound interest

With compound interest, the amount of interest paid is added to the original amount and also attracts interest.

Worked Examples

1 If £500 is invested at a compound interest of 5% per annum, what would the amount be at the end of 3 years?

   End of year 1   £500 + 5% of £500
                        £500 + £25
                        £525

   End of year 2   £525 + 5% of £525
                        £525 + £26.25
                        £551.25

   End of year 3   £551.25 + 5% of £551.25
                        £551.25 + £27.56   (to the nearest penny)
                        £578.81

The formula for compound interest is

$$A = P\left(1 + \frac{R}{100}\right)^T$$

where:

A = total amount

P = principal or original investment

R = rate (% per annum)

T = time (in years)

In the above example

P = £500

R = 5% per annum

T = 3 years

$$A = P\left(1 + \frac{R}{100}\right)^T$$

$$A = 500\left(1 + \frac{5}{100}\right)^3$$

$$A = 500\,(1.05)^3$$

$$A = 500 \times 1.157\,625$$

$$A = 578.8125$$

$$A = £578.81 \qquad \text{(to the nearest penny)}$$

2 A building society pays 8% interest per annum on its saver account. A member invests £1600 in the account and the interest is not withdrawn. Find the total amount after one year if the interest is
   a paid yearly
   b paid half yearly.

   a If the interest is paid yearly:

   At the end of the year, amount = £1600 + 8% of £1600
   = £1600 + £128
   = £1728

   Total amount after one year if interest is paid yearly = £1728

   b If the interest is paid half yearly:

   Interest for the half year = $\frac{1}{2}$ of 8% = 4% (as interest is 8% per annum)

   At the end of the half year, amount = £1600 + 4% of £1600
   = £1600 + £64
   = £1664

   At the end of the year, amount = £1664 + 4% of £1664
   = £1664 + £66.56
   = £1730.56

   Total amount after one year if interest is paid half yearly = £1730.56

NOTE
Questions on compound interest will usually appear on the calculator paper.

PRACTICE 3.7.5   Try these questions with a calculator

1 If £500 is invested at a compound interest of 4% per annum, what would the amount be at the end of 3 years?

2 Dee invests £1750 at a compound interest of 6.6% per annum. What is the interest at the end of 3 years?

3 Calculate the total amount and compound interest for each of the following:

    a $P = £250$ $R = 7\%$ pa $T = 3$ years
    b $P = £450$ $R = 4\frac{1}{2}\%$ pa $T = 2$ years
    c $P = £1250$ $R = 5.8\%$ pa $T = 3$ years

4 A building society pays 8% interest per annum on its high income account. A member invests £2800 in the account and the interest is not withdrawn. Find the total amount after one year if the interest is
    a paid yearly
    b paid half yearly.

5 Daniel invests £5000 at 5% per annum compound interest which is paid every 6 months. What will be the value of the investment in one year's time if he reinvests the interest?

6 Ruth invests £3500 in an account which pays 6% per annum compounded monthly. What will be the value of the investment in three month's time if she reinvests the interest?

Mortgages

Mortgages are taken out for the purpose of buying a house and mortgage repayments are usually spread out over a period of 25 years. Most lenders will usually advance three times a person's annual income or, if there are two people borrowing, two and a half times their combined incomes.

There are two main types of mortgage:

Repayment mortgage
Endowment mortgage

Repayment mortgage

A repayment mortgage involves the gradual repayment of the loan over the mortgage period through monthly payments of the loan plus interest. The monthly payments will fluctuate depending upon the interest rates although fixed rate mortgages are becoming more popular and allow you to plan your expenditure more effectively.

Endowment mortgage

With an endowment mortgage you only pay off the interest on the loan and make payments to a life insurance endowment policy. During the mortgage period, the loan remains unchanged and at the end of the period your endowment policy should make enough money to repay the loan outstanding.

PRACTICE 3.7.6   Try these questions with a calculator

1 A building society will advance three times a person's annual income or, if there are two people borrowing, two and a half times their combined incomes.

   a How much will Jayne be allowed to borrow on the basis of an annual income of £37 500?

   b How much more could she borrow on the basis of her partner's annual income of £25 750?

2 The Porthtowan Building Society offers Sunil a 90% mortgage on a two bedroomed house priced £78 000. How much can he borrow from the Building Society?

3 Mr and Mrs Windsor borrow £87 500 from the Kingsgrove Building Society. They have to pay 7.8% pa interest on the loan. How much interest do they pay in the first year?

4 Clive and Barbara take out a £48 000 endowment mortgage for 25 years with interest charged at 6.9% per annum.

   a What is the interest paid on the mortgage per annum?

   b What is the monthly interest payment?

   c How much interest is paid altogether over 25 years?

5 Alan buys a flat for £37 500 and obtains an endowment motgage for £33 000 from his local building society. The term of the mortgage is 20 years and interest is charged at 6.72% per annum.

   a What deposit was paid on the flat?

   b What is the interest paid on the mortgage per annum?

   c What is the monthly interest payment?

   d How much interest is paid altogether over the term of the mortgage?

3.8 COMPOUND MEASURES

Speed is an example of a compound measure as it is a combination of two other measures i.e. distance and time. The units of speed will depend upon the units in which the distance and time are measured such as miles per hour, kilometres per hour, metres per second, etc.

The formula for speed is $\qquad$ $\text{speed} = \dfrac{\text{distance}}{\text{time}}$

Worked Examples

1 A cyclist travels 42 miles in 3 hours. What is the average speed?

The formula for speed is $\quad$ $\text{speed} = \dfrac{\text{distance}}{\text{time}}$

so $\qquad\qquad\qquad\qquad\qquad$ $\text{speed} = \dfrac{42}{3} = 14$ miles per hour (mph)

2 A racing car travels 6500 metres in 3 minutes. What is its speed in kilometres per hour?

The formula for speed is $\quad$ $\text{speed} = \dfrac{\text{distance}}{\text{time}}$

so $\qquad\qquad\qquad\qquad\qquad$ $\text{speed} = \dfrac{6.5}{\frac{3}{60}} = 130$ kilometres per hour (km/h)

> **NOTE**
> The word *per* in this context is the same as divide. The units of speed can help us to remember the formula, i.e. speed can be measured in miles per hour which is distance divided by time.

> **NOTE**
> If the units are to be expressed in kilometres per hour then the distance must be in kilometres and the time must be in hours.
> 6500 metres equals 6.5 kilometres and 3 minutes = $\frac{3}{60}$ hour.

The formula for speed can be rearranged so that you can calculate distance or time

$$\text{distance} = \text{speed} \times \text{time} \qquad \text{time} = \frac{\text{distance}}{\text{speed}}$$

The formula triangle

is a useful way of remembering various formulae associated with speed. To use the triangle you just cover up the measure you want to find and the formula is what remains.

Worked Examples

1 A train travels for $3\frac{1}{4}$ hours at an average speed of 75 km/h. What is the distance covered?

Using the formula $\qquad$ $\text{distance} = \text{speed} \times \text{time}$

$\qquad\qquad\qquad\qquad\qquad$ $\text{distance} = 75 \times 3\frac{1}{4}$

$\qquad\qquad\qquad\qquad\qquad$ $\text{distance} = 243.75$ kilometres

Distance = 244 kilometres (rounding to a reasonable degree of accuracy).

2 A coach travels 138 miles at an average speed of 40 miles per hour. How long does the journey take in hours and minutes?

Using the formula $\qquad$ time $= \dfrac{\text{distance}}{\text{speed}}$

$$\text{time} = \dfrac{138}{40} = 3.45 \text{ hours}$$

The journey time is 3.45 hours which we must now convert to hours and minutes.

Since there are 60 minutes in one hour

$$3.45 \text{ hours} = 3.45 \times 60 \text{ minutes} = 27 \text{ minutes}$$
$$207 \text{ minutes} = 3 \text{ hours and } 27 \text{ minutes}$$

Or, concentrating on the 0.45 hours

$$0.45 \text{ hours} = 0.45 \times 60 \text{ minutes} = 27 \text{ minutes}$$
$$3.45 \text{ hours} = 3 \text{ hours and } 27 \text{ minutes}$$

> **NOTE**
>
> It is very important that we do not write 3.45 hours as 3 hours 45 minutes but remember that there are 60 minutes in an hour and convert to hours and minutes as shown in the worked example.

Another example of a compound measure is density as it is a combination of two other measures i.e. mass and volume. The units of density will again depend upon the units in which the mass and volume are measured.

The formula for density is $\qquad$ density $= \dfrac{\text{mass}}{\text{volume}}$

Worked Example

A roll of copper has a mass of 106.8 g and a volume of 12 cm³. What is the density of the copper?

The formula for density is $\qquad$ density $= \dfrac{\text{mass}}{\text{volume}}$

$$\text{density} = \dfrac{106.8}{12} = 8.9 \text{ g/cm}^3$$

The density of copper is 8.9 g/cm³

The formula for density can be rearranged so that you can calculate mass or volume

$$\text{mass} = \text{density} \times \text{volume} \qquad \text{volume} = \dfrac{\text{mass}}{\text{density}}$$

The formula triangle

is a useful way of remembering various formulae associated with density.

Worked Example

A block of metal measures 1 m by 0.2 m by 0.5 m and has a density of $20\,\text{g/cm}^3$. What is the mass of the block of metal in kilograms?

We first need to work out the volume and be aware that the density is given in g/cm^3 so we will need to convert metres to centimetres.

$$\text{volume} = 1\,\text{m} \times 0.2\,\text{m} \times 0.5\,\text{m} = 100\,\text{cm} \times 20\,\text{cm} \times 50\,\text{cm} = 100\,000\,\text{cm}^3$$

Using the formula $\text{mass} = \text{density} \times \text{volume}$
$$\text{mass} = 20 \times 100\,000 = 2\,000\,000\,\text{g}$$

Converting the mass to kilograms, $2\,000\,000\,\text{g} = 2000\,\text{kg}$

PRACTICE 3.8.1a   Try these questions without a calculator

1 A lorry driver drives 86 miles in 2 hours. What is her speed in mph?

2 A rambler walks 22 kilometres in 3 hours. What is her speed in km/h?

3 A train travels a distance of 175 miles in $2\frac{1}{2}$ hours. What is the speed in miles per hour?

4 A child cycles 6 kilometres in 45 minutes. What is the speed in km/h?

5 A plane travels for 3 hours at 450 mph. What is the distance covered?

6 A motorcycle travels 110 miles at 40 miles per hour. How long does the journey take?

7 What is the density of an object weighing 12 g and having a volume of $18\,\text{cm}^3$?

8 A block of metal measures 60 cm by 50 cm by 10 cm and has a density of $15\,\text{g/cm}^3$. What is the mass of the block of metal?

PRACTICE 3.8.1b   Try these questions with a calculator

1 A train travels 450 miles in 3 hours 20 minutes. What is the speed in miles per hour?

2 A car travels 125 kilometres in 1 hour 40 minutes. What is its average speed?

3 A boat travels at 8 kilometres per hour for 2 hours and 20 minutes. What is the distance covered in kilometres?

4 Kevin drives 125 miles at an average speed of 50 miles per hour. How long does the journey take?

5 A coach travels 21 miles at 45 miles per hour. How long does the journey take in minutes?

6 Sheets of aluminium have a volume of $3000\,\text{cm}^3$ and a mass of 8.1 kg. What is the density of aluminium in g/cm^3?

7 What is the density of a block of wood weighing 36 kg and measuring $20\,\text{cm} \times 40\,\text{cm} \times 50\,\text{cm}$?

8 A bar of gold has a mass of 25 g and a density of $19.3\,\text{g/cm}^3$. What is the volume of the gold?

APR

APR which is short for Annual Percentage Rate is a measurement of the total cost for credit expressed as an annual rate. The APR includes the interest on the loan itself as well as any other charges which have to be paid such as arrangement, administration, settlement fees, etc.

The APR can be used to compare one type of credit with another and must be included in any consumer credit agreement. A credit offer with an APR of 30% is a better deal than another with an APR of 35%.

In general, the APR is approximately 1.8 to 2 times the annual flat rate and this information should be used in all examination questions involving APR.

The annual flat rate is the same as the rate (% per annum) used in the simple interest formula i.e.

$$I = \frac{PRT}{100}$$

where:
I = interest
P = principal (the amount borrowed)
R = rate (% per annum)
T = time (in years)

Rearranging the formula we get $R = \dfrac{100 \times I}{P \times T}$

so the annual flat rate $R = \dfrac{100 \times I}{P \times T}$

and the annual percentage rate (APR) is approximately 1.8 to 2 times the annual flat rate.

> **NOTE**
> Interest free finance will give an APR of 0% although the retail cost may be inflated for the purposes of the offer.

Worked Example

A television set priced at £480 is offered for a deposit of £60 plus 30 monthly payments of £20.55. Find:
a the total credit price
b the interest paid
c the amount borrowed
d the annual flat rate
e the annual percentage rate.

a Total credit price   = deposit + 30 monthly payments of £20.55
   = £60 + 30 × £20.55
   = £676.50

b Interest paid   = credit price − cash price
   = £676.50 − £480
   = £196.50

    c Amount borrowed   = cash price − deposit paid

$$= £480 − £60$$

$$= £420$$

    d To find the annual flat rate we use the formula

$$R = \frac{100 \times I}{P \times T}$$

    where: I = interest = £196.50

                   P = principal = £420

                   T = time (in years) = 2.5 years (30 months = 2.5 years)

$$R = \frac{100 \times 196.50}{420 \times 2.5} = 18.7\% \text{ (3 sf)}$$

    e The annual percentage rate is approximately 2 × the flat rate

$$= 2 \times 18.7\%$$

$$= 37.4\% \text{ (3 sf)}.$$

PRACTICE 3.9.1   Try these questions with a calculator

1 A camera is advertised at £465 or it can be bought on hire purchase for a deposit of £46 plus 12 monthly payments of £40. Find
  a the total credit price   **d** the annual flat rate
  b the interest paid   **e** the approximate annual percentage rate
  c the amount borrowed

2 A fitted kitchen is priced £2800 but can be bought with a 12% deposit and 36 monthly payments of £85.10. Find
  a the total credit price   **d** the annual flat rate
  b the interest paid   **e** the approximate annual percentage rate
  c the amount borrowed

3 A stereo unit advertised at £620 can be bought on hire purchase for a 10% deposit and 24 monthly instalments of £28.65. Find
  a the amount of the deposit   **c** the annual flat rate
  b the total credit price   **d** the approximate annual percentage rate

Income tax and PAYE

As discussed earlier, income tax is a tax on income earned which is deducted automatically from a person's pay packet under the **P**ay **A**s **Y**ou **E**arn (PAYE) system.

    The rate of tax is divided into three categories called the lower, basic and higher rates of income tax. The **lower rate of income tax** is 10% and is paid on the first £1520 of your taxable income. The **basic rate of income tax** is 22% and is paid on income between £1520 and £28 400; the **higher rate of income tax** is 40% and is paid on income over £28 400.

NOTE
For the higher tier of entry, questions may include higher rates of income tax.

For the tax year from 6 April 2000 to 5 April 2001:

Taxable income	Rate of tax
Up to £1520	10% (lower rate)
£1521–£28 400	22% (basic rate)
Over £28 400	40% (higher rate)

Worked Example

A company director earns £42 880 per annum and has a tax allowance of £4385 plus an additional allowance of £125 for professional subscriptions. How much tax does she pay altogether?

$$\text{Taxable income} = \text{annual income} - \text{personal allowances}$$
$$= £42\,880 - (£4385 + £125)$$
$$= £42\,880 - £4510$$
$$= £38\,370$$

The company director pays 10% tax (lower rate) on the first £1520 of taxable income, 22% tax (basic rate) on income between £1521 and £28 400 and 40% tax (higher rate) on income above £28 400.

On £38 370, she pays 10% tax on the first £1520, 22% tax on the next £26 880 (£28 400 − £1520 = £26 880) and 40% on the remaining £9970 (£38 370 − £28 400 = £9970).

$$\text{Tax at lower rate} = 10\% \text{ of } £1520$$
$$= \frac{10}{100} \times £1520$$
$$= £152$$

$$\text{Tax at basic rate} = 22\% \text{ of } £26\,880$$
$$= \frac{22}{100} \times £26\,880$$
$$= £5913.60$$

$$\text{Tax at higher rate} = 40\% \text{ of } £9970$$
$$= \frac{40}{100} \times £9970$$
$$= £3988$$

$$\text{Total tax} = £152 + £5913.60 + £3988$$
$$= £10\,053.60$$

The company director pays £10 053.60 tax altogether.

NOTE
Remember that layout is very important when attempting this type of question.

PRACTICE 3.9.2   Try these questions with a calculator

1 Jagdeep earns £38 600 per annum and has a personal allowance of £4385. How much tax does he pay altogether?

2 Darren earns £2992 per month. He has a personal allowance of £4385 plus a further allowance of £85.
   a What is his taxable income?
   b How much tax does he pay in the year?

3 Salima earns £57 600 per annum and has a personal allowance of £4385 plus a further allowance of £265 for professional fees. How much tax does she pay altogether?

4 Mr Grabble earns £2860 per month and receives an annual income of £8560 from his investments. He has a tax allowance of £6050 altogether. How much tax does he pay each month?

5 A director is paid £590.20 per week and her personal allowance is £4385. How much extra can she earn each week before she is liable to pay income tax at the higher rate?

National Insurance

All employees below the pensionable age have to pay National Insurance contributions. How much you pay depends on whether you are employed or self employed and whether you are contracted in or out of SERPS (State Earnings Related Pension Scheme).

Class 1 National Insurance contributions (for employed workers)

Contracted into SERPS   Class 1 contributions are 10% of earnings between £76 and £535 per week (or £3952 and £27 820 per year).

Contracted out of SERPS   Class 1 contributions are 8.4% of earnings between £76 and £535 per week (or £3952 and £27 820 per year).

NOTE
The figure £535 (per week) or £27 820 (per year) is sometimes referred to as the upper earnings limit and you do not pay any more National Insurance on earnings above this amount.

Class 2 and 4 National Insurance Contributions (for self-employed workers)

If you are self employed you pay two sets of National Insurance contributions. Class 2 contributions are paid at a rate of £2 per week (unless your earnings fall below £3952). Class 4 contributions are paid as 7% of your profit between £4305 and £27 820 per year.

(*Note*: Class 3 National Insurance contributions are voluntary contributions paid to top up your contributions record.)

Worked Examples

1   Annette is paid £4.25 per hour for a 40 hour week. Calculate her weekly National Insurance contributions if she is contracted in to SERPS.

Annette's weekly pay $= £4.25 \times 40 = £170$

As she is contracted in to SERPS she pays 10% on her earnings between £76 and £170.

10% on her income betweewn £76 and £170

$$= 10\% \text{ of } £94 \quad (£170 - £76 = £94)$$

$$= \frac{10}{100} \times £94 = £9.40$$

Total National Insurance $= £9.40$ per week

2   Rachel earns £2310 per month. Calculate her monthly National Insurance contributions if she is contracted out of SERPS.

Rachel's annual pay $= £2310 \times 12 = £27\,720$

(Throughout this example we will be using the annual figures instead of the weekly figures.)

As she is contracted out of SERPS she pays 8.4% on her earnings between £3952 and £27 720.

8.4% on her income between £3952 and £27 720

$$= 8.4\% \text{ of } £23\,768 \ (£27\,720 - £3952 = £23\,768)$$

$$= \frac{8.4}{100} \times £23\,768$$

$$= £1996.512$$

Total National Insurance $= £1996.512$ per annum

To find out the National Insurance paid per month we now need to divide this figure by 12.

Monthly National Insurance $= \dfrac{£1996.512}{12} = £166.38$
$$\text{(to the nearest penny)}$$

PRACTICE 3.9.3

1 Peter is paid £4.90 per hour for a 38 hour week. Calculate his weekly National Insurance contributions if
   a he is contracted in to SERPS
   b he is contracted out of SERPS.

2 Bronwen is paid £6.00 per hour for a 40 hour week and one week receives £27 overtime. Calculate her National Insurance contributions if
   a she is contracted in to SERPS
   b she is contracted out of SERPS.

3 Philip has a part-time job and is paid £38.60 per week. Calculate his National Insurance contributions.

4 Brian is paid a salary of £18 560. Calculate his annual National Insurance contributions if he is contracted in to SERPS.

5 Salima earns £57 600 per annum. Calculate her annual National Insurance contributions if she is contracted out of SERPS.

6 A self-employed worker pays National Insurance contributions of £2 per week and 7% on profits between £4385 and £27 820. Calculate her National Insurance contribution in a year in which she makes a profit of £23 500.

Council tax

Council tax is based on the *capital value* of the property on 1 April 1991. In order to calculate the charge to be made, all properties are divided into eight valuation bands. Band A is the lowest-rated property and band H is the highest-rated property.

The Valuation Bands (England)		
Band	Value of property	
A	up to	£40 000
B	£40 001	£52 000
C	£52 001	£68 000
D	£68 001	£88 000
E	£88 001	£120 000
F	£120 001	£160 000
G	£160 001	£320 000
H	more than	£320 000

Council tax is used to pay for local services such as education, social services, housing, refuse collection, planning and recreation as well as fire services and the local police authority.

Council tax bills are sent out every March/April to each household and the amount payable will depend upon the valuation band into which the property falls and may be reduced through discount (for example, where no one or only one person lives in the property), exemption (for example, persons aged under 18 or full-time students) or benefits (for example, people on low incomes).

Worked Example

The council tax for each band of properties in Porthtowan is given in the table below.

Band	£
A	473.88
B	553.98
C	633.10
D	712.22
E	870.52
F	1028.78
G	1187.05
H	1424.46

Use the table to answer the following:
a What is the council tax for a property in Band C?
b What is the monthly council tax for a property valued at £125 000 in 1991?
c A reduction of 25% is given if only one person lives in a property. How much council tax will a single person living in a flat valued in Band A pay?

a The council tax for a property in Band C is £633.10.

b A property valued at £125 000 in 1991 will be in Band F and the council tax for a property in Band F is £1028.78.

Monthly council tax equals $\dfrac{£1028.78}{12}$

= £85.73   (to the nearest penny).

c The council tax for a property in Band A is £473.88.

25% of £473.88 = £118.47

Tax = £473.88 − £118.47 = £355.41

> **NOTE**
> An alternative method would be to work out 75% of £473.88.

PRACTICE 3.9.4   Try these questions without a calculator

Use the table given in the worked example or else your own council tax bands to work out the following:

1 What is the council tax for a property in Band H?

2 What is the council tax for a property valued at £67 500 in 1991?

3 What is the council tax for a mobile home property valued at £12 200 in 1991?

4 Four people share a house valued in Band B. How much council tax should they each pay?

5 A reduction of 50% is given if the property is unoccupied. How much council tax will you pay on an unoccupied house valued in Band F?

6 A reduction of 25% is given if only one person lives in a property. How much council tax will a single person living in a flat valued in Band G pay each month?

Imperial and Metric units

Common imperial measures include:

Length	12 inches (in)	= 1 foot (ft)
	3 feet	= 1 yard (yd)
	1760 yards	= 1 mile
	5280 feet	= 1 mile
Capacity	20 fluid ounces (fl oz)	= 1 pint (pt)
	2 pints	= 1 quart (qt)
	8 pints	= 1 gallon (gal)
Weight	16 ounces (oz)	= 1 pound (lb)
	14 pounds	= 1 stone (st)
	8 stone	= 1 hundredweight (cwt)
	20 hundredweights	= 1 ton

Common metric measures include:

Length	10 millimetres (mm)	= 1 centimetre (cm)
	100 centimetres	= 1 metre (m)
	1000 millimetres	= 1 metre
	1000 metres	= 1 kilometre (km)
Capacity	10 millilitres (ml)	= 1 centilitre (cl)
	100 centilitres	= 1 litre (l)
	1000 millilitres	= 1 litre
Weight	1000 milligrams (mg)	= 1 gram (g)
	1000 grams	= 1 kilogram (kg)
	1000 kilograms	= 1 tonne (t)

Some common conversions between imperial and metric units are

2.2 pounds is approximately 1 kilogram
1 inch is approximately 2.5 centimetres
1 foot is approximately 30 centimetres
5 miles is approximately 8 kilometres
1 gallon is approximately 4.5 litres

Payment for work

Methods for paying for work undertaken include weekly wages, yearly salaries, an hourly rate with different rates for overtime, piecework and commission.

Gross and net wages

A person's gross wage is the amount of money earned before deductions such as income tax, national insurance, pension contributions, etc. The net wage (or take-home pay) is the amount left when the deductions have been taken away.

Personal allowances

A personal allowance is the amount of money which you can earn before you pay tax and depends upon such factors as your marital status and other determining factors.

Income tax and PAYE

Income tax is a tax on income earned which is paid to the government. It is deducted automatically from a person's pay packet under the Paye As You Earn (PAYE) system.

$$\text{Taxable income} = \text{annual income} - \text{personal allowance}$$

For the tax year from 6 April 2000 to 5 April 2001

Taxable income	Rate of tax
Up to £1520	10% or 10 p in the £ (lower rate)
£1521–£28 400	22% or 22 p in the £ (basic rate)

Value Added Tax

Value Added Tax (VAT) is a tax on goods or services which is paid to the government. Some goods such as basic food, children's clothes, books and newspapers do not attract VAT and are called zero rated.

Electricity bills

Electricity is charged according to the number of units of electricity used since the last reading. A quarterly charge is added to the bill and VAT at 8% is applied to the final amount.

Gas bills

Gas is charged according to the number of cubic metres of gas used since the last reading. A standing charge is added to the bill and VAT at 8% is applied to the final amount.

Telephone bills

Telephone bills are calculated according to the number, duration, time and distance of telephone calls made. In addition to the call charges the bill also includes a rental charge (for the line and other facilities) and VAT at $17\frac{1}{2}\%$.

Insurance

Insurance can be taken out on most things but the most common types of insurance include life insurance, house insurance, contents insurance, car insurance and travel insurance (see relevant section of this chapter for further information).

Credit

Credit for goods and services can be obtained in a number of ways but include hire purchase, credit cards, overdrafts, personal loans and mail order catalogues (see relevant section of this chapter for further information).

Simple interest

With simple interest, the amount of interest paid is the same each year so that the interest paid is not reinvested.

The formulae for simple interest are $\quad A = P + \dfrac{PRT}{100}$ and $I = \dfrac{PRT}{100}$

where:
A = total amount
I = simple interest
P = principal or original investment
R = rate (% per annum)
T = time (in years)

Compound interest

With compound interest, the amount of interest paid is added to the original amount and also attracts interest.

The formula for compound interest is $\quad A = P\left(1 + \dfrac{R}{100}\right)^{T}$

where:
A = total amount
P = principal or original investment
R = rate (% per annum)
T = time (in years)

Compound measures

Compound measures are measures that are combinations of other measures, for example, speed or density (see relevant section of chapter for further information).

APR (extension)

The APR (Annual Percentage Rate) is a measurement of the total cost for credit. The APR is approximately 1.8 to 2 times the annual flat rate and this information should be used in all examination questions involving APR.

Income tax and PAYE (extension)

Income tax is a tax on income earned which is paid to the government. It is deducted automatically from a person's pay packet under the Paye As You Earn (PAYE) system.

$$\text{Taxable income} = \text{annual income} - \text{personal allowance}$$

For the tax year from 6 April 2000 to 5 April 2001

Taxable income	Rate of tax
Up to £1520	10% or 10 p in the £ (lower rate)
£1521–£28 400	22% or 22 p in the £ (basic rate)
Over £28 400	40% or 40 p in the £ (higher rate)

National Insurance (extension)

All employees below pensionable age have to pay National Insurance and details of the rates for the tax year 2000/2001 are:

Class 1 National Insurance contributions (for employed workers)

Weekly pay	Employee's contribution
Less than £76	No employee's contribution
£76–£535	Contracted in: 10% of earnings over £76 Contracted out: 8.4% of earnings over £76
Over £535	No additional liability

Class 2 and 4 National Insurance contributions (for self-employed workers)

Class 2   £2 per week (unless annual earnings fall below £3952)
Class 4   7% of profit between £4305 and £27 820 per year

Council tax (extension)

Council tax is used to pay for local services such as education, social services, housing, refuse collection, planning and recreation as well as fire services and the local police authority. The council tax is based on the *capital value* of the property on 1 April 1991 and is divided into eight valuation bands where Band A is the lowest-rated property and band H is the highest-rated property.

SECTION TWO
Statistics and probability (Module 2)

CONTENTS

CHAPTER 4
Collecting and representing data

In this chapter you will need to:
▸ distinguish between quantitative and qualitative data
▸ distinguish between discrete and continuous data

Quantitative and qualitative data

Quantitative data is data that takes numerical values and measures quantities. Examples of quantitative data include length, weight, capacity,....

Qualitative data is data that does not take numerical values but measures qualities.
Examples of qualitative data include colour, brightness, taste,....

Discrete and continuous data

Discrete data is data that can only take particular values such as whole numbers.
Examples of discrete data include the number of students in the class, the number of cars passing a point during 20 minutes,....

Continuous data is data that can take all values within any specified range.
Examples of continuous data include the heights of students in the class, the length of cars passing a point during 20 minutes,....

To help you to distinguish between discrete and continuous it might be helpful to consider the fact that:

people's shoe sizes are discrete but the sizes of people's feet are continuous and the costs of sending parcels are discrete but the weights of parcels are continuous.

PRACTICE 4.1.1

1 For each of the following, state whether they are quantitative or qualitative:
   a the height of people in a class,
   b the colour of cars in a car park,
   c the sweetness of different orange juices,
   d the lengths of pencils in a pencil case,
   e the number of students in different classes,
   f the number of leaves on different types of trees,
   g the brightness of light bulbs in six rooms,
   h the age of people in a youth club,
   i the musical ability of students in a class.

NOTE

Many people think that the age of people is discrete although age is continuous. Most people will give their age as a whole number which is rounded down so that a person is 21 years old until the date of their 22nd birthday.
This rounding of people's ages can easily cause problems in statistical analysis and particular care should be taken whenever ages are being used.

2   For each of the following, state whether they are continuous or discrete:
  a   the height of people in a class,
  b   the time taken by runners to complete a race,
  c   the number of matches in a sample of matchboxes,
  d   the lengths of pencils in a pencil case,
  e   the number of students in different classes,
  f   the number of leaves on different trees,
  g   the shoe sizes of people at a party,
  h   the age of people in a youth club.

Bias

The potential for bias in undertaking statistical work is considerable and steps should always be taken to avoid bias in any work of a statistical nature. Bias can easily be introduced in a number of ways:

  if an incorrect sampling method is used
  if the sample is unrepresentative
  if the questions are unclear
  if the questions are biased.

Examples of bias in these areas are explored in the work of the following topics.

Primary and secondary data

Primary data is data that is collected in response to a hypothesis as part of a statistical investigation whereas secondary data (second-hand data) is data that is already available such as official statistics.

The advantage of primary data is that it can be collected in response to a particular investigation although a disadvantage may be the time and expense of undertaking such data collection.

The advantage of secondary data is that the information is easy and cheap to obtain although a disadvantage may be that there is usually little information on how the data was collected or the accuracy of the information.

Useful sources of secondary data include information produced by government departments, businesses and professional institutes as well as market research organisations.

Sampling and data capture

A sample is usually considered to be a small part of the whole population and is used when it would be difficult or impossible to consider the whole population. The advantages of sampling are that it is cheaper and takes less time whereas undertaking a survey of the whole population might be impracticable in the case of destructive testing (where testing might destroy the population such as seeing how long a light bulb will last or tasting an apple to measure sweetness).

In order to get the best possible results from sampling it is important that the sample is a good indicator of the population as a whole and is truly representative. Clearly the intention is, as far as possible, to avoid any bias in the sampling and to ensure that the sample size is as large as possible.

Sampling techniques considered include:

> random sampling
> systematic sampling
> stratified sampling
> quota sampling
> convenience sampling.

Random sampling

In random sampling, each member of the population has an equally likely chance of being selected. The simplest way to do this would be to give every member of the population a number and then choose the numbers randomly using random number tables or a computer.

Systematic sampling

Systematic sampling is the same as random sampling except that there is some system involved in choosing the member of the population to be sampled. Such a system might include numbering each member of the population according to some order (e.g. alphabetical) and then choosing every tenth number to form the sample.

Stratified sampling

In stratified sampling, each member of the population is divided into some particular group or category (strata). Within each strata, a random sample or systematic sample is selected so that the sample size is proportional to the size of that group or category in the population as a whole.

For example, in a college where 55% of the students are female and 45% are male, then a representative sample of the students in the college should also include 55% females and 45% males.

Quota sampling

In quota sampling, a certain number of the population are chosen with specific characteristics which are fixed beforehand. Quota sampling is very popular in market research where the interviewers are given clear instructions on the people to be interviewed. Such instructions might include the requirement that there are as many men as women or twice as many adults as children or that the sample should include 15 shoppers and 12 commuters, etc.

Convenience sampling

Convenience sampling or opportunity sampling is a sampling technique which involves choosing the first people who come along. Such a technique is far from random and this fact should be highlighted in any such work undertaken for coursework purposes.

PRACTICE 4.2.1

1   A college wishes to undertake a survey on the part-time employment of its students. Explain how you would take
    a   a random sample of 100 students
    b   a stratified sample of 100 students.

2   Explain how you would use the electoral roll to obtain a simple random sample.

3   Explain why each of the following might not produce a truly representative sample:
    a   selecting people at random outside a food store,
    b   selecting every tenth name from the electoral register starting with M,
    c   Selecting names from the telephone directory.

4   In a telephone poll conducted one morning, 25 people were asked whether they regularly used the bus to get to work. Give three reasons why this sample might not be truly representative.

5   In an opinion poll, 500 men in Cambridge were asked how they intended to vote in the General Election.
    a   Give three reasons why this is an unreliable way of predicting the outcome of the General Election.
    b   Give three ways in which the opinion poll might be improved.

6   The populations of three villages are given below:

    Little Whitton   840
    Marchwoode   240
    Newtonabbey   720

    The local councillor wishes to undertake a survey and chooses 100 people from each village.
    a   Explain why this might not be the most appropriate sampling method.
    b   How could the councillor select a more representative sample of 300 people from the three villages?

The following survey methods will be considered:

> observation
> interviewing
> questionnaires.

Observation

This method, as its name implies, involves collecting information by observation and might include participant observation where the observer participates in the activity, or systematic observation where observation is undertaken without the participants knowing.

Interviewing

Interviewing involves a conversation between two or more people where the interviewing can be formal or informal. In informal interviews, the questions asked will follow a strict format whereas in informal interviews, the questions asked follow some general format with opportunities to change the order or the way in which the questions are presented.

Questionnaires

The use of a questionnaire is by far the most common survey method and is usually undertaken as a postal questionnaire. The advantage of a postal questionnaire is that it is relatively cheap to distribute and can involve large numbers of people. The disadvantage of postal questionnaires is the poor response rate and the inability to follow up questions set.

In designing a good questionnaire, it is important that it should be:

> simple, short, clear and precise,
> attractively laid out and quick to complete.

and the questions should be:

> free from bias and not personal or offensive,
> written in appropriate language for the respondent,
> related to the work being investigated,
> accompanied by clear instructions on how to respond.

Worked Examples

The following examples illustrate poor question design:

Given that drinking is bad for you, how much do you drink in a day?

The question is biased as it expresses the questioner's own opinion and it does not define what is meant by drinking – drinking water is not bad for you?

How often do you have a wash?

The question is clearly personal and almost certainly offensive to some people. Answers received would also be suspect as people are unlikely to answer the question truthfully.

How many hours of television do you watch?

The question is difficult to answer as it does not say over what period of time and might therefore provide a variety of answers.

Do you or do you not listen to the radio?

The question is badly composed and does not really make any sense.

Pilot survey

Before carrying out any questionnaire or survey, it is important that you are completely satisfied with the way that the questionnaire or survey has been drafted. It is often useful to undertake a small scale *dummy run* to ascertain any likely problems and highlight areas needing further clarification. This dummy run is called a pilot survey and an analysis of the data received should be used to improve the questionnaire or survey before it is undertaken properly.

PRACTICE 4.3.1

1   Name two different types of questions which should be avoided when designing a questionnaire.

2   Give two advantages of undertaking a pilot survey.

3   The following three questions about television viewing habits are included on a questionnaire:
   a   How many hours have you watched the television during the past two months?
   b   How much money do you earn in a year?
   c   Do you or do you not watch the news programmes?
   Criticise each of these questions.

4   Criticise each of the following questions and suggest alternatives to find out the information.
   a   What do you think about our new improved fruit juice?
   b   How much do you earn?

    c Do you or do you not agree with a new bypass?

    d Given that smoking is bad for you, how many cigarettes do you smoke a day?

    e Would you prefer not to sit in a non-smoking area?

    f How often do you have a shower?

5 The following appears on a questionnaire for students at a college:

How much money do you earn?

Less than £10   ☐
Between £11 and £20 ☐
More than £20   ☐

Write down three criticisms of this question.

6 A group of students are considering the possibility of producing a school magazine. Design a questionnaire which might be useful in helping them to decide whether to go ahead with the project.

Raw data

Raw data is any information which has been collected by some method but has not been organised in any way.

Tally chart

A tally chart is a useful way of collecting or collating information. A tally chart consists of a series of tallies which are grouped into fives as follows:

$$
\begin{array}{ll}
|||| & = 4 \\
\cancel{||||} & = 5 \\
\cancel{||||}\ | & = 6 \\
\cancel{||||}\ \cancel{||||} & = 10,\ \text{etc.}
\end{array}
$$

> **NOTE**
> The word *frequency* is used to denote the number of times an event happens or occurs.

Frequency distribution

A frequency distribution can be constructed from a tally chart by totalling the tallies and including a further column for these totals or frequencies.

Worked Example

Construct a frequency distribution for the following raw data which shows the number of breakfasts served in a restaurant during the month of May.

15	19	18	16	16	19	20	16
17	16	15	20	19	18	15	13
20	15	16	19	21	20	19	21
12	17	13	16	18	23	17	

The frequency distribution for this information will look like this:

Breakfasts	Tallies	Frequency
12	|	1
13	||	2
14		0
15	||||	4
16	卌 |	6
17	|||	3
18	|||	3
19	卌	5
20	||||	4
21	||	2
22		0
23	|	1
		31

The total frequency serves as a useful check.

NOTE

It is not a requirement of a frequency distribution that the tallies be included, so the frequency distribution for this data could be presented without tallies.

Breakfasts	Frequency
12	1
13	2
14	0
15	4
16	6
17	3
18	3
19	5
20	4
21	2
22	0
23	1

or else

Breakfasts	12	13	14	15	16	17	18	19	20	21	22	23
Frequency	1	2	0	4	6	3	3	5	4	2	0	1

PRACTICE 4.4.1

1 The following information gives the marks obtained in a test for 30 pupils in a class. Use tally marks to draw up a frequency table of this information.

8	7	6	8	9	10	7	5	4	10
6	8	7	9	9	4	8	9	7	6
10	9	5	6	7	5	9	8	8	7

2 The following information shows how 50 people paid for their goods at a certain store. Use tally marks to draw up a frequency table of this information.

cheque	visa	mastercard	storecard	cash	cash
mastercard	cheque	visa	cash	cash	cash
cheque	storecard	storecard	cash	cheque	cash
visa	cheque	cash	cash	visa	cheque
mastercard	cash	cheque	mastercard	visa	cash
storecard	cash	cheque	cash	cash	visa
cash	cheque	mastercard	cheque	cash	visa
mastercard	cash	cheque	storecard	cash	cheque
visa	mastercard				

3 The following information shows the colours of cars in a car park one lunchtime. Use tally marks to draw up a frequency table of this information.

red	yellow	red	red	blue	blue	green	red
green	red	blue	blue	white	blue	white	yellow
green	blue	blue	red	red	white	green	blue
blue	yellow	white	white	red	blue	blue	white
green	yellow	red	red	white	blue	green	blue

4 The following information shows how 60 people travel to college each day. Use tally marks to draw up a frequency table of this information.

bus	train	walk	cycle	walk	walk
bus	train	train	car	walk	cycle
walk	bus	train	walk	cycle	train
walk	bus	train	bus	train	car
walk	cycle	walk	train	train	walk
bus	train	train	car	walk	bus
walk	walk	walk	car	cycle	bus
train	car	walk	train	bus	walk
walk	bus	cycle	walk	cycle	bus
train	walk	walk	cycle	cycle	train

Grouped frequency distribution

Sometimes it is easier to put the data into a series of groups or classes. The groups or classes into which the data are arranged are called class intervals.

Worked Example

For the previous example we might group the data in a number of ways as shown:

Breakfasts	Frequency
12 – 13	3
14 – 15	4
16 – 17	9
18 – 19	8
20 – 21	6
22 – 23	1

or else

Breakfasts	Frequency
12 – 14	3
15 – 17	13
18 – 20	12
21 – 23	3

or else

Breakfasts	Frequency
12 – 15	7
16 – 19	17
20 – 23	7

You will see from the examples above that as the number of groups or classes decrease so the information about the distribution of frequencies becomes more and more lost. Unfortunately, the more the classes, the more the work required to analyse the information, so it is important to strike a balance.

In general, it is helpful to divide the data into approximately 6 to 10 groups or classes as shown in the following worked example.

Worked Example

The following information gives the lengths of 50 leaves measured to the nearest millimetre. Using suitable class intervals, construct a frequency distribution for this information.

41	30	39	31	13	21	42	35	26	34
36	33	31	11	30	32	16	17	41	36
25	35	24	21	26	14	34	47	22	40
29	33	18	27	18	38	20	39	30	33
28	43	37	28	23	38	32	20	31	25

From the previous distribution we can see that the smallest length is 11 mm and the largest length is 47 mm giving us a range of 36 mm.

If we have 10 classes then each class interval would be $\frac{36}{10} = 3.6$ mm, with 8 classes then each class interval would be $\frac{36}{8} = 4.5$ mm and with 6 classes then each class interval would be $\frac{36}{6} = 6$ mm.

Realistic possibilities would suggest that class sizes should be whole numbers and it is helpful to choose easily identifiable class intervals such as:

$$10\text{-}14,\ 15\text{-}19,\ 20\text{-}24,\dots$$
or $11\text{-}15,\ 16\text{-}20,\ 21\text{-}25,\dots$
or $10\text{-}15,\ 16\text{-}20,\ 21\text{-}25,\dots$
or $11\text{-}16,\ 17\text{-}22,\ 23\text{-}28,\dots$
or $10\text{-}16,\ 17\text{-}23,\ 24\text{-}30,\dots$
or $11\text{-}17,\ 18\text{-}24,\ 25\text{-}31,\dots$

Any of these series of class intervals can be used although the 11–15, 16–20, 21–25, 26–30, 31–35,… class intervals would seem to be slightly easier to work with.

Constructing a frequency distribution for this information:

Length (mm)	Tally	Frequency	
11–15	|||	3	
16–20	ЖΉ |	6	
21–25	ЖΉ ||	7	
26–30	ЖΉ ||||	9	
31–35	ЖΉ ЖΉ ||	12	The total
36–40	ЖΉ |||	8	frequency,
41–45	||||	4	again, serves
46–50	|	1	as a useful
		50	check.

For the benefit of your work on frequency distributions, the following definitions are included.

Class interval

Class interval is used to refer to the groups or classes into which the data is split. The class interval is chosen by considering the range of the whole data and dividing this into convenient class intervals.

Class limits

The class limits are the values given in each class interval. In the class interval 11–15, the class limits are 11 and 15. We usually say that the lower class limit is 11 and the upper class limit is 15. For the class interval 16–20, the lower class limit is 16 and the upper class limit is 20.

Class boundaries

In the previous distribution, the first class interval (11–15) will contain leaves with lengths ranging from 10.5 to 15.5 mm since the leaves are given to the nearest millimetre. Similarly the second class interval (16–20) will contain leaves with lengths 15.5 to 20.5 mm.

The boundaries enclosing the classes are 10.5 mm, 15.5 mm, 20.5 mm, etc. and we say that the first class interval has class boundaries of 10.5 mm and 15.5 mm. We say that 10.5 mm is the lower class boundary and 15.5 mm is the upper class boundary.

For the second class interval the lower class boundary is 15.5 mm and the upper class boundary is 20.5 mm. We can see that the upper class boundary of one class interval is the same as the lower class boundary of the next class interval.

Class width

NOTE

The class width is sometimes referred to as the class length or the class size.

The class width is the difference between the upper and lower class boundaries. For the data in the previous distribution all of the class widths are the same and the class width equals $15.5 - 10.5 = 5$ mm (or $20.5 - 15.5 = 5$ mm, …etc.).

PRACTICE 4.4.2

1 Draw up a grouped frequency table for the information which shows the number of calls made. Use class intervals of 0–4, 5–9, 10–14, 15–19, etc.

10	5	3	8	9	4	12	25	12
13	18	7	14	18	22	11	5	9
20	20	26	17	15	6	3	22	19

2 Draw up a grouped frequency table for the following information which shows approximations to the value of π. Use class intervals of width 0.05 starting at 3.00.

3.08 3.12 3.16 3.18 3.15 3.14 3.13 3.22 3.01 3.06 3.21
3.17 3.13 3.10 3.09 3.12 3.07 3.14 3.12 3.09 3.15 3.16

3 Copy and complete the frequency table for the following information which shows the annual wages for 50 jobs advertised in a newspaper one weekend.

£26 850	£34 500	£33 000	£44 500	£32 750	£38 850
£38 650	£42 000	£55 000	£32 000	£33 850	£44 500
£36 500	£31 500	£26 500	£35 000	£46 500	£44 000
£35 500	£43 000	£26 000	£28 000	£54 000	£33 500
£52 600	£49 500	£47 500	£36 500	£45 000	£26 500
£38 500	£36 250	£41 600	£50 000	£37 950	£45 000
£32 200	£25 500	£49 000	£41 500	£52 000	£33 500
£38 000	£31 500	£37 950	£37 500	£38 700	£40 000
£37 200	£26 600				

Wages	Tally	Frequency
£25 000–£29 999		
£30 000–£34 999		
£35 000–£39 999		
£40 000–£44 999		
£45 000–£49 999		
£50 000–£54 999		
£55 000–£59 999		

4 Copy and complete the frequency table for the following information
which shows the length of time (measured in minutes to the nearest
minute) it takes for 40 workers to travel to work one morning .

23	14	16	33	44	25	36	38	22	24
33	41	28	24	48	16	37	32	30	42
25	20	45	36	39	26	18	22	14	23
29	25	22	38	36	20	24	26	41	29

Time (mins)	Tally	Frequency
$10 \leqslant t < 15$		
$15 \leqslant t < 20$		
$20 \leqslant t < 25$		
$25 \leqslant t < 30$		
$30 \leqslant t < 35$		
$35 \leqslant t < 40$		
$40 \leqslant t < 45$		
$45 \leqslant t < 50$		

4.5 PICTORIAL REPRESENTATIONS

Once data have been collected it is helpful to represent such data pictorially.
There are a variety of representations available for use but you should make
sure that the representation is appropriate to the type of data being
represented.

The following representations will be considered:

   pictograms
   bar charts
   line graphs
   pie charts
   frequency polygons
   scatter diagrams
   histograms (see Extension Material).

NOTE
Cumulative Frequency
Diagrams are fully
discussed in Topic 5.3
'Measures of spread'.

NOTE
The words *pictograph* or *ideograph* are sometimes used instead of pictogram

Pictograms

A pictogram is a simple way of representing data by using pictures (or some other representation) to show the data. A pictogram must have a key to tell the reader what individual pictures stand for.

The advantage of the pictogram is that it is easy to construct and has a strong visual impact although a disadvantage is that it can only be used to show a few variables.

Worked Example

The following distribution shows the number of people entering an exhibition on different days of the week. Show this information as a pictogram.

Day	Number
Thursday	22
Friday	27
Saturday	33
Sunday	21

The information can be shown as a pictogram:

NOTE
It might be easier to allow ♀ to stand for more than one person in order to make the drawing of the pictogram more simple.

	Number of people at an exhibition
Thursday	人人人人人人人人人人人人人人人人人人人人人人
Friday	人人人人人人人人人人人人人人人人人人人人人人人人人人人
Saturday	人人人人人人人人人人人人人人人人人人人人人人人人人人人人人人人人人
Sunday	人人人人人人人人人人人人人人人人人人人人人

Key 人 = 1 person

or else allowing 人 = 2 people, then:

	Number of people at an exhibition
Thursday	人人人人人人人人人人人
Friday	人人人人人人人人人人人人人
Saturday	人人人人人人人人人人人人人人人人
Sunday	人人人人人人人人人人人

In this pictogram,

) = 1 person and

人 = 2 people

or else allowing 人 = 4 people, then:

	Number of people at an exhibition
Thursday	人人人人人)
Friday	人人人人人人人
Saturday	人人人人人人人人)
Sunday	人人人人人)

In this pictogram,

) = 1 person

) = 2 people

人 = 3 people and

人 = 4 people

PRACTICE 4.5.1

1   The following distribution shows the number of people queuing at a local post office at different times during the same day. Show this information as a pictogram.

Day	Number
9.30 am	4
11.30 am	1
1.30 pm	9
3.30 pm	4
5.30 pm	2

2   The following distribution shows the number of people in the local library at midday on different days of the week . Show this information as a pictogram.

Day	Number
Monday	19
Tuesday	13
Wednesday	17
Thursday	27
Friday	33
Saturday	41

3   The following distribution shows the sales of different flavoured ice creams at a park one day. Show this information as a pictogram.

Flavour	Frequency
Strawberry	51
Vanilla	77
Chocolate	38
Other	14

4   Draw a pictogram to illustrate the frequency distribution found in question 3 of Practice 4.4.1 on page 139.

5   Draw a pictogram to illustrate the frequency distribution found in question 4 of Practice 4.4.1 on page 139.

Bar charts

Bar charts are a very common way of representing data and use bars (horizontal or vertical) to represent the number or frequency of the data. Both axes of the bar chart should be labelled to help the reader interpret the graph.

The advantage of the bar chart is that it makes visual comparison easy but a disadvantage is that only simple information can be shown.

Worked Examples

1 The following bar chart shows the average price of a house in different areas.

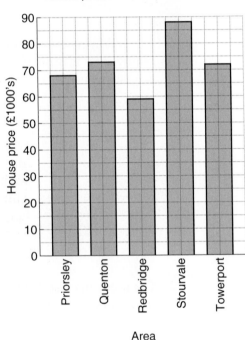

House prices in different areas

a What was the average price of a house in Quenton?
b What was the cheapest average house price?
c Where is the most expensive average house price to be found?
d Where was the average house price £68 000?
e Which two areas had average house prices which were roughly the same?

The chart can be used to answer the questions as follows:
a The average price of a house in Quenton was £73 000.
b The cheapest average house price was £59 000.
c The most expensive average house price can be found in Stourvale.
d The average house price was £68 000 in Priorsley.
e The two areas which had average house prices roughly the same were Quenton and Towerport.

2 The following grouped frequency table shows the heights of 30 rose bushes to the nearest inch.

Height (in.)	11–15	16–20	21–25	26–30	31–35
Frequency	4	7	11	6	2

Draw a bar chart to illustrate this information.

In the case of continuous data it is important to ensure that the bars are drawn at the class boundaries, hence, in this example, the bars are drawn at $10\frac{1}{2}$–$15\frac{1}{2}$, $15\frac{1}{2}$–$20\frac{1}{2}$, $20\frac{1}{2}$–$25\frac{1}{2}$,… etc., etc. as follows

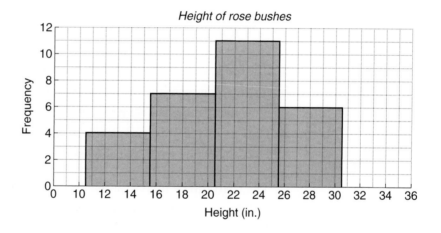

Compound bar charts

The compound bar chart is similar to the bar chart except that the bars are replaced by a series of different bars representing different aspects of the data.

The advantage of the compound bar chart is that it allows information to be compared in a variety of ways although a disadvantage is that only a few items can be included.

Worked Example

The following chart shows the sales of new and second-hand cars during the first week of March over a period of 4 years.

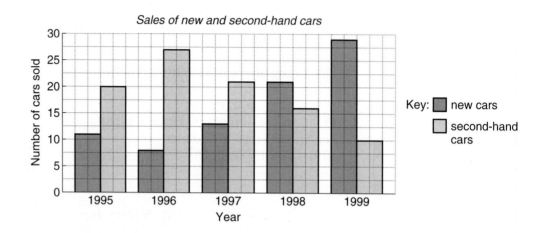

Sales of new and second-hand cars

a In what year were the most new cars sold?

b In what year were the most second-hand cars sold?

c How many new cars were sold in 1998?

d How many second-hand cars were sold in 1996?

e How many cars were sold altogether in 1997?

The chart can be used to answer the questions as follows:

a The most new cars were sold in 1999.

b The most second-hand cars were sold in 1996.

c 21 new cars were sold in 1998.

d 27 second-hand cars were sold in 1996.

e 34 cars (13 new and 21 second-hand) were sold altogether in 1997.

NOTE

Component bar charts are also sometimes called composite bar charts or sectional bar charts.

Component bar charts

The component bar chart is used to show how an individual item can be split into a series of components. The advantage of the component bar chart is that it allows you to appreciate how an item is divided into its constituent parts although a disadvantage is that only a few items can be included.

Worked Example

The component bar chart represents the number of different airline tickets sold for a flight from London to Manchester on different days of the same week.

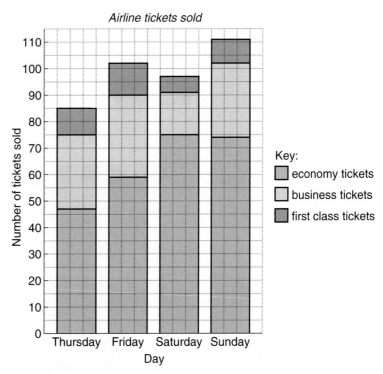

Airline tickets sold

Key:
- economy tickets
- business tickets
- first class tickets

a Calculate the total number of each type of ticket sold over the four days.

b Express this information as a percentage component bar chart.

a The number of economy tickets $= 47 + 59 + 75 + 74 = 255$
The number of business tickets $= 28 + 31 + 16 + 28 = 103$
The number of first tickets $= 10 + 12 + 6 + 9 = 37$

b Expressing this information as a percentage component bar chart we need to work out the percentage of economy, business and first class tickets for each day.

Total number of tickets for Thursday $= 47 + 28 + 10 = 85$

Percentage of economy tickets $= \frac{47}{85} \times 100 = 55.3\%$

Percentage of business tickets $= \frac{28}{85} \times 100 = 32.9\%$

Percentage of first class tickets $= \frac{10}{85} \times 100 = 11.8\%$

Total number of tickets for Friday $= 59 + 31 + 12 = 102$

Percentage of economy tickets $= \frac{59}{102} \times 100 = 57.8\%$

Percentage of business tickets $= \frac{31}{102} \times 100 = 30.4\%$

Percentage of first class tickets $= \frac{12}{102} \times 100 = 11.8\%$

Total number of tickets for Saturday $= 75 + 16 + 6 = 97$

Percentage of economy tickets $= \frac{75}{97} \times 100 = 77.3\%$

Percentage of business tickets $= \frac{16}{97} \times 100 = 16.5\%$

Percentage of first class tickets $= \frac{6}{97} \times 100 = 6.2\%$

Total number of tickets for Sunday $= 74 + 28 + 9 = 111$

Percentage of economy tickets $= \frac{74}{111} \times 100 = 66.7\%$

Percentage of business tickets $= \frac{28}{111} \times 100 = 25.2\%$

Percentage of first class tickets $= \frac{9}{111} \times 100 = 8.1\%$

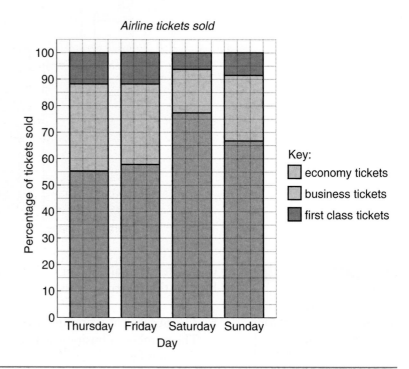

Airline tickets sold

PRACTICE 4.5.2

1 The following information shows the number of flights from a regional
airport on one day of the week made by different airlines.

Airline	No. of flights
Eagle Air Services	6
Air European	7
Falconair	3
Europa Airlines	2

Draw a bar chart to illustrate this information.

2 Five coins were tossed 100 times and the number of heads showing uppermost was recorded as shown in the table.

Number	Frequency
0	2
1	17
2	29
3	34
4	15
5	3

Draw a bar chart to illustrate this frequency distribution.

3 Draw a bar chart to illustrate the frequency distribution given in question 2 of Practice 4.5.1 on page 145.

4 Draw a bar chart to illustrate the frequency distribution given in question 3 of Practice 4.5.1 on page 145.

5 The following information shows the length of time it takes for a group of people to complete a sponsored walk. The times are given in hours to the nearest hour.

Time	Frequency
1–2	3
2–3	17
3–4	26
4–5	8
5–6	1

Draw a bar chart to illustrate this grouped frequency distribution.

6 The following frequency distribution shows the weight of 40 animals in a zoo given to the nearest stone.

Weight	1–5	6–10	11–15	16–20	21–25
Frequency	9	16	9	4	2

Draw a bar chart to illustrate this distribution.

7 Draw a bar chart to illustrate the distribution found in question 4 of Practice 4.4.2 on page 143.

8 The following information shows the number of people in a department store on different days of the week.

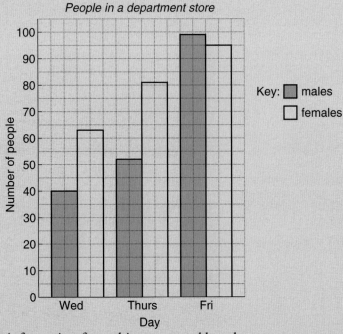

Use the information from this compound bar chart to create a component bar chart.

9 The following information shows the favourite subjects of students at a college.

Favourite subject	Girls	Boys
Mathematics	9	18
Science	11	14
Languages	20	11
Humanities	10	8
Arts	23	18

Ilustrate this information as:

a a compound bar chart

b a component bar chart.

10 The following information shows the revenue (in thousands of £) spent on advertising over three consecutive years.

Year	Papers	Radio	Television
1997	45	26	39
1998	38	46	32
1999	40	53	27

Ilustrate this information as:

a a compound bar chart

b a component bar chart.

11 The number of vehicles passing a certain point over a period of
    5 hours on two consecutive days is shown in the diagram below.

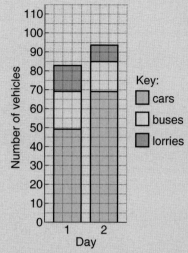

Number of vehicles passing a certain point

Use the diagram to answer the following questions.
a What was the total number of vehicles for each day?
b How many lorries were there on the first day?
c How many buses were there on the second day?

Use the information from the diagram to create a percentage
component bar chart.

Line graphs

Line graphs are drawn by plotting points and then joining the points, in order,
with a series of straight lines.

The advantage of the line graph is that it makes visual comparison easy but
a disadvantage is that only simple information can be shown and readings
between the points might not be representative.

Worked Example

The following information shows the temperatures of a patient over a period
of 6 hours.

Time	1000	1100	1200	1300	1400	1500
Temp. (°C)	38.5	39.6	40.0	39.1	38.5	37.9

a Draw a line graph to represent this data.
b What was the maximum temperature recorded?
c Use your line graph to estimate the patient's temperature at 1130.
d After 1300, the patient's temperature began to fall at a constant rate until it
   reached 37 °C. Use your line graph to estimate the time at which the
   temperature reached 37 °C.

a

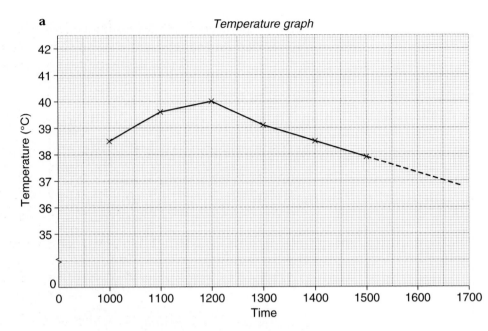

Temperature graph

b The maximum temperature recorded was 40 °C at 1200.

(Although this is the maximum recorded temperature it is not necessarily the maximum temperature as the temperature could have gone above 40 °C just before or just after 1200.)

c To find the patient's temperature at 1130 we read off the value at 1130. The patient's temperature at 1130 is 39.8 °C.

(This value is only approximate as we do not know exactly how the temperature changed between 1100 and 1200.)

d To estimate the time at which the temperature reached 37 °C we need to continue the graph as shown by the dotted line and read off the time when the temperature equals 37 °C.

The temperature reached 37 °C at 1630.

NOTE

Care must always be taken when dealing with time to interpret the information correctly. The time is half way between 1600 and 1700 which is 1630 not 1650.

PRACTICE 4.5.3

1 The number of microwave ovens sold at an electrical shop is shown in the table below.

Month	Oct	Nov	Dec	Jan	Feb
Sales	20	46	102	42	16

Draw a line graph to illustrate this information.

2   The number of hours of sunshine at a certain holiday resort is shown in the table below:

Month	May	Jun	Jul	Aug	Sep	Oct
Hrs of sunshine	15	$16\frac{1}{2}$	$16\frac{1}{2}$	14	$12\frac{1}{2}$	$10\frac{1}{2}$

Draw a line graph to illustrate this information.

3   The weight of a child is recorded at birth and at the end of each month as follows:

Age (months)	0	1	2	3	4	5	6
Weight (kg)	3.5	4.2	5.3	6.5	7.1	7.5	8.2

Draw a line graph to represent this information.

4   The temperature in a lecture theatre is taken at hourly intervals as shown:

Time	0800	0900	1000	1100	1200	1300	1400	1500	1600
Temp. (°C)	15.5	16.0	16.5	18.0	19.5	20.5	20.5	20.0	18.5

Draw a line graph to represent this information.

Use your graph to estimate:
a   the time at which the temperature rose above 20 °C
b   the temperature at 1430 hours.

Explain why these answers are only estimates.

5   The number of students in the common room was counted at hourly intervals and the results recorded on a line graph.

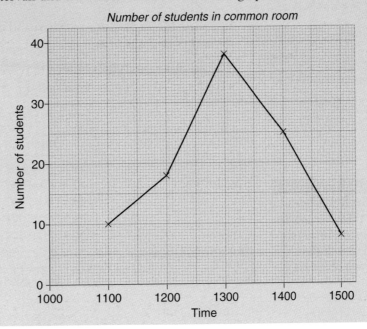

Number of students in common room

a How many students were in the common room at 1100?
b How many students were in the common room at 1300?
c How many students were in the common room at 1430?
d Why is your answer to **c** only an approximation?
e What is the maximum number of students recorded in the common room?

Pie charts

A pie chart (or circular diagram) is a circle divided into sectors (or slices) whose angles (or areas) are used to represent the data.

The advantages of a pie chart are that it can have a strong visual impact and easily shows how the whole thing is divided into its constituent parts and what size these parts are in relation to one another and to the whole.

The disadvantages of a pie chart are that it requires some difficult calculations to find the respective angles and it can only be used for a few variables. Also, the drawing of the pie chart is not easy as it involves having to use a protractor accurately.

The following worked examples are given to illustrate the construction of a pie chart.

Worked Examples

1 In a survey, 180 people were asked which TV channel they had been watching the previous evening at 9.00 pm. Their responses were as follows:

BBC1	59	C4	25
BBC2	19	Other	22
ITV	48	Not watching	7

Calculate the angles for a pie chart and construct the pie chart to show the different categories.

The pie chart needs to be drawn to represent 180 people. There are 360° in a full circle so each person will get $\frac{360°}{180} = 2°$ of the pie chart as follows:

Channel	Number	Angle
BBC1	59	$59 \times 2° = 118°$
BBC2	19	$19 \times 2° = 38°$
ITV	48	$48 \times 2° = 96°$
C4	25	$25 \times 2° = 50°$
Other	22	$22 \times 2° = 44°$
Not watching	7	$7 \times 2° = 14°$
		Total 360°

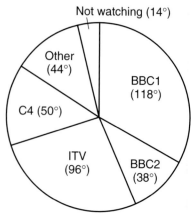

TV channel watched

Not watching (14°)
Other (44°)
BBC1 (118°)
C4 (50°)
ITV (96°)
BBC2 (38°)

2 500 students at a college are surveyed regarding the GNVQ courses which they are following. The responses were as follows:

Leisure & toursim	225	Performing arts	51
Business	126	Engineering	15
Health & social care	83		

Calculate the angles and construct the pie chart to show the different categories.

The pie chart needs to be drawn to represent 500 people so each person will get $\frac{360}{500}$ of the pie chart as follows:

Course	Number	Angle
Leisure & toursim	225	$225 \times \frac{360}{500} = 162°$
Business	126	$126 \times \frac{360}{500} = 90.7°$
Health & social care	83	$83 \times \frac{360}{500} = 59.8°$
Performing arts	51	$51 \times \frac{360}{500} = 36.7°$
Engineering	15	$15 \times \frac{360}{500} = 10.8°$
		Total 360°

NOTE

It is possible that, because of rounding errors, that the angles will not add up to exactly 360°.

NOTE

When constructing your own pie charts, the radius of the circle should be not less than 4 cm.

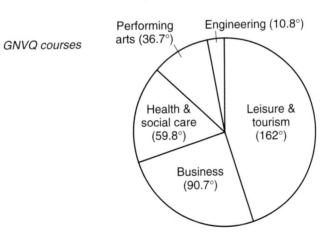

GNVQ courses

3 The following pie chart shows how a sample of students come to college in the morning.

How students travel to college

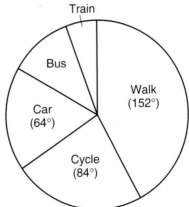

21 students cycle to college in the morning.

a How many students walk?

b How many students come by car?

Twice as many students come by bus as come by train.

c How many students come by bus?

d How many students come by train?

e How many students were there altogether in the sample?

From the diagram we can see that the number of students who cycle to the college is represented by an angle of 84°.

$$84° \text{ represents } 21 \text{ people}$$

so $1°$ represents $\frac{21}{84} = \frac{1}{4}$ person (or 1 person is represented by 4°)

a The number of students who walk is represented by 152°.
So the number who walk is $152 \times \frac{1}{4} = 38$ students.

b The number of students who come by car is represented by 64°.
So the number who walk is $64 \times \frac{1}{4} = 16$ students.

We are told that twice as many students come by bus as come by train. The angles for these two sectors add up to 60°. We can find this out by adding all of the given angles and subtracting them from 360°.

Dividing 60° in the ratio 2 : 1, so that the angle for the bus is twice as much as that for the train, we get:

Bus   40°   Train   20°

c The number of students who come by bus is represented by 40°.
So the number who come by bus is $40 \times \frac{1}{4} = 10$ students.

d The number of students who come by train is represented by 20°.
So the number who come by train is $20 \times \frac{1}{4} = 5$ students.

e To find out how many students there were in the sample we can add up all of the figures above or else appreciate that the total number of students is represented by the angle of 360°.
So the number in the sample is $360 \times \frac{1}{4} = 90$ students.

PRACTICE 4.5.4a   Try these questions without a calculator

1 A survey of favourite pets produced the following information.

Pet	cat	dog	rabbit	bird	fish
Frequency	10	13	6	3	4

Draw a pie chart to represent this information.

2 Katie keeps a note of all the first class tickets that she sells on the Eurostar service to Paris as follows. Draw a pie chart to represent this information.

Ticket	Frequency
Business	92
Leisure first	35
Child	17
Senior	24
Pass holder	12

3 Draw a pie chart to illustrate the frequency distribution given in question 3 of Practice 4.5.1 on page 145.

4 Draw a pie chart to illustrate the frequency distribution given in question 1 of Practice 4.5.2 on page 150.

5 Draw a pie chart to illustrate the frequency distribution given in question 2 of Practice 4.5.2 on page 151.

PRACTICE 4.5.4b   Try these questions with a calculator

1 The following information shows the types of properties advertised in an estate agent's window. Draw a pie chart to represent this information.

Type	Frequency
Bungalow	11
Semi detached	17
Detached	14
Terraced	18
Flat	20

2 Draw a pie chart to illustrate the frequency distribution found in question 2 of Practice 4.4.1 on page 139.

3 Draw a pie chart to illustrate the frequency distribution given in question 2 of Practice 4.5.1 on page 145.

4 The incomplete pie chart shows the outcomes of 30 different football matches where the outcome is either a win, draw or lose.

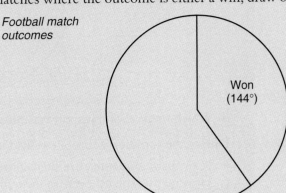

Football match outcomes

Won (144°)

a Calculate the number of matches won.

7 matches were lost altogether.

b Calculate the angle needed for this on the pie chart.

c Complete the pie chart for the information given.

5 The pie chart shows how 200 students travelled to college one day in winter.

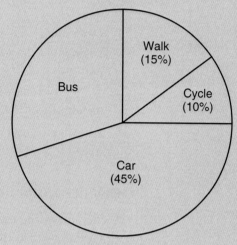

How students travel to college in winter

a Which method of transport was most popular in winter?

b What percentage of the students travelled by bus?

c Calculate the number of students who travelled by bus.

In a similar survey the following summer, the following pie chart was obtained:

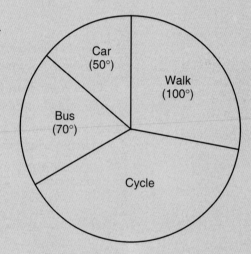

How students travel to college in summer

d Which method of transport was most popular in summer?

During the summer 50 people walked to the college.

e How many students were there altogether in the summer?

f How many students cycle to the college?

Frequency polygons

A frequency polygon can be obtained from a bar chart or histogram by joining up the mid-points of the top of each bar with straight lines to form a polygon. In the case of the first and last class intervals, the lines are extended to the base line so that the area under the frequency polygon is the same as the area under the bar chart or histogram.

Worked Example

The following frequency distribution shows the length of 50 leaves measured to the nearest millimetre.

Length	Frequency
11–15	3
16–20	6
21–25	7
26–30	9
31–35	12
36–40	8
41–45	4
46–50	1

Draw a frequency polygon to represent this information.

The length is a continuous variable and a bar chart of the information can be drawn as follows:

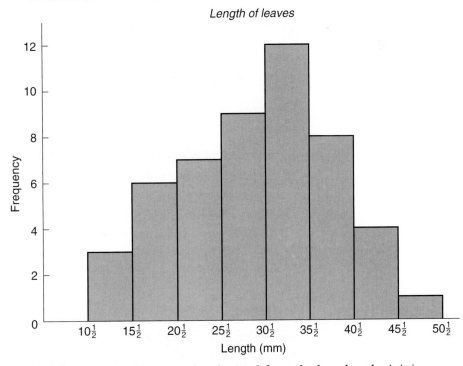

Length of leaves

> **NOTE**
>
> Remember that with continuous data the bars are drawn at the class boundaries.

The frequency polygon can be obtained from the bar chart by joining up the mid-points of the top of each bar with straight lines to form a polygon as shown by the dotted lines on the following diagram.

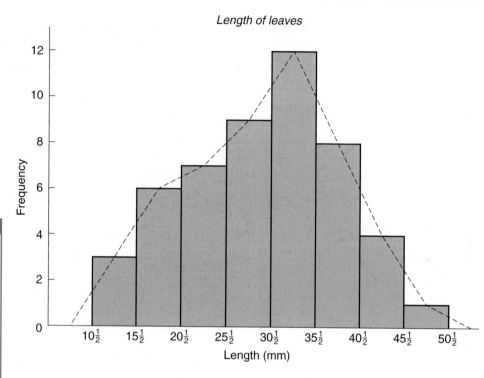

Length of leaves

> **NOTE**
>
> The class interval before the 11–15 class would be 6–10 with a mid-point of 8. The class interval after the 46–50 class would be 51–55 with a mid-point of 53. The lines of the frequency polygon are extended to the base line at the mid-points 8 and 53 so that the area under the polygon is the same as the area under the bar chart.

The frequency polygon can be more quickly drawn without the bar chart by plotting the frequencies at the mid-points of each interval. The mid-point of the interval is exactly halfway between the lower class boundary and the upper class boundary.

PRACTICE 4.5.5

1 The diameters of 100 cylinders are measured as follows.

Dia. (mm)	2.91-2.93	2.94-2.96	2.97-2.99	3.00-3.02	3.03-3.05	3.06-3.08	3.09-3.11
Frequency	1	3	17	53	20	4	2

Draw a frequency polygon to represent this information.

2 Draw a frequency polygon to illustrate the frequency distribution given in question 4 of Practice 4.4.2 on page 143.

3 Draw a frequency polygon to illustrate the frequency distribution given in question 5 of Practice 4.5.2 on page 151.

4 Draw a frequency polygon to show the frequency distribution given in question 6 of Practice 4.5.2 on page 151.

Scatter diagrams

Scatter diagrams are useful when the data collected links two or more variables and you want to find out if there is any link or correlation between the two variables. In a scatter diagram each of the two sets of data is assigned to a different axis and the information collected can be represented as different coordinates on the scatter diagram.

Where there is a link or correlation between the two variables you can draw a line of best fit as shown in the following worked example.

Worked Example

The following information shows the marks awarded to 11 different students on two science examination papers.

Paper 1	56	44	20	75	36	50	66	62	42	62	30
Paper 2	44	34	13	61	26	41	56	47	29	53	22

Plot these points on a scatter graph and draw the line of best fit.
Use your line of best fit to estimate

a the Paper 2 mark of a student who gained 65 marks on Paper 1
b the Paper 1 mark of a student who gained 38 marks on Paper 2.

In order to plot the points on a graph we need to consider each pair of marks as a different coordinate so we plot the points (56, 44), (44, 34), (20, 13), etc.

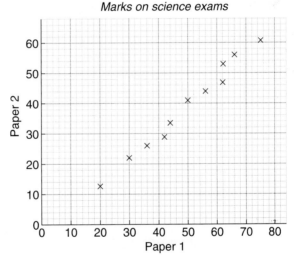

We now draw the line which best fits all of the data provided.

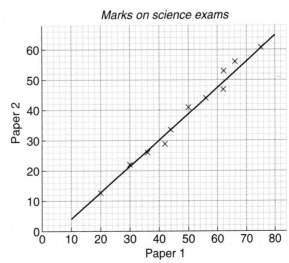

NOTE
The idea of a line of best fit is considered further in Topic 5.4 on 'Correlation'.

We can now use this line of best fit to estimate the required marks as follows:

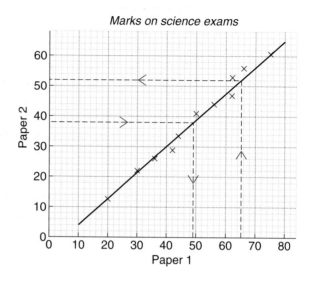

a   To find this mark we read off the Paper 2 mark corresponding to 65 marks on Paper 1.

An estimate for the Paper 2 mark would be 52.

b   To find this mark we read off the Paper 1 mark corresponding to 38 marks on Paper 2.

An estimate for the Paper 1 mark would be 49.

Further work on scatter diagrams can be found in Topic 5.4 on 'Correlation'.

PRACTICE 4.5.6

1 The following information shows the marks awarded to 10 different students on examination papers in mathematics and music.

Maths	68	28	81	85	86	50	58	38	63	99
Music	80	45	87	89	90	62	68	51	62	100

Plot these points on a graph and draw the line of best fit.

2 The following information shows the height (in cm) and the weight (in kg) of 8 students.

Height (cm)	135	105	60	101	85	74	120	130
Weight (kg)	80	45	87	89	90	62	68	51

Plot these points on a graph and draw the line of best fit.

3 The following information shows the relationship between engine size and the distance (in miles) travelled on one gallon of petrol by eight different cars.

Engine size (litres)	2.6	1.5	3.0	2.0	1.3	1.0	1.1	1.5
Distance (miles)	24.5	30.0	15.0	27.5	34.0	36.5	33.0	32.5

Plot these points on a graph and draw the line of best fit.

Use your line of best fit to estimate the distance travelled on one gallon of petrol by a car with an engine size of

a 2.4 litres
b 3.5 litres.

Explain why the second estimate is not so reliable as the first one.

Histograms

Histograms are similar to bar charts except that it is the *area* of each bar which represents the frequency. Histograms can be used for discrete data although they are mostly used for continuous and grouped data.

When drawing histograms it is important that the bars on the horizonatal axis should always be drawn at the class boundaries. The height of these bars should be such that the area is proportional to the frequency which it represents.

To make things simple it is helpful if we make the area of each bar equal to the frequency which it represents so that

$$\text{class width} \times \text{height} = \text{frequency}$$

and
$$\text{height} = \frac{\text{frequency}}{\text{class width}}$$

The height of the bars is referred to as the frequency density and the vertical axis of a histogram should be labelled frequency density rather than frequency.

$$\text{frequency density} = \frac{\text{frequency}}{\text{class width}}$$

The following worked examples consider histograms of grouped data with equal class intervals and histograms of grouped data with unequal class intervals.

Worked Examples

1 The following information shows the weight of 50 plants measured to the nearest gram.

Weight (grams)	Frequency
51–55	3
56–60	9
61–65	17
66–70	13
71–75	6
76–80	2

Draw a histogram to represent these data.

On the horizontal axis, the bars representing the frequencies should always be drawn at the class boundaries. The first class interval has a lower class boundary of 50.5 and an upper class boundary of 55.5. Similarly, the second class interval has a lower class boundary of 55.5 and an upper class boundary of 60.5, … etc., etc.

Using $\text{frequency density} = \dfrac{\text{frequency}}{\text{class width}}$, we can work out the frequency density for each bar as follows:

Weight (grams)	Frequency	Class width	Frequency density	
51–55	3	5	0.6	$\frac{3}{5} = 0.6$
56–60	9	5	1.8	$\frac{9}{5} = 1.8$
61–65	17	5	3.4	$\frac{17}{5} = 3.4$
66–70	13	5	2.6	$\frac{13}{5} = 2.6$
71–75	6	5	1.2	$\frac{6}{5} = 1.2$

Using this information to construct the histogram.

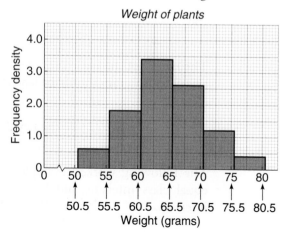

Weight of plants

NOTE

For a histogram where all the bars have the same width then the height of the bar is also proportional to the frequency.

2 The following information shows the distance travelled by 125 cyclists during a particular month.

The distance is measured in miles to the nearest mile.

Distance (miles)	Frequency
0–10	20
11–20	38
21–30	42
31–50	18
51–100	6
101–150	1

Draw a histogram to illustrate the information.

Using frequency density $= \dfrac{\text{frequency}}{\text{class width}}$, we can work out the frequency density for each bar as follows:

NOTE
For the first class interval, the lower class boundary is 0 and the upper class boundary is 10.5 so the class width is
$10.5 - 0 = 10.5$.

Distance (miles)	Frequency	Class width	Frequency density	
0–10	20	10.5	1.904 76	$\frac{20}{10.5} = 1.904\,76$
11–20	38	10	3.8	$\frac{38}{10} = 3.8$
21–30	42	10	4.2	$\frac{42}{10} = 4.2$
31–50	18	20	0.9	$\frac{18}{20} = 1.8$
51–100	6	50	0.12	$\frac{6}{50} = 0.12$
101–150	1	50	0.02	$\frac{1}{50} = 0.02$

Using this information to construct the histogram.

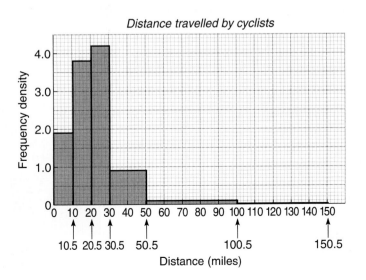

Distance travelled by cyclists

3 The following information shows the time taken for 140 workers to travel to work one morning.

The time is measured in minutes.

Time, t (mins)	Frequency
$0 \leqslant t < 10$	9
$10 \leqslant t < 15$	17
$15 \leqslant t < 20$	22
$20 \leqslant t < 25$	30
$25 \leqslant t < 30$	21
$30 \leqslant t < 40$	19
$40 \leqslant t < 60$	17
$60 \leqslant t < 90$	5

Draw a histogram to represent these data.

Using frequency density $= \dfrac{\text{frequency}}{\text{class width}}$, we can work out the frequency density for each bar as follows:

Time, t (mins)	Frequency	Class width	Frequency density	
$0 \leqslant t < 10$	9	10	0.9	$\frac{9}{10} = 0.9$
$10 \leqslant t < 15$	17	5	3.4	$\frac{17}{5} = 3.4$
$15 \leqslant t < 20$	22	5	4.4	$\frac{22}{5} = 4.4$
$20 \leqslant t < 25$	30	5	6.0	$\frac{30}{5} = 6.0$
$25 \leqslant t < 30$	21	5	4.2	$\frac{21}{5} = 4.2$
$30 \leqslant t < 40$	19	10	1.9	$\frac{19}{10} = 1.9$
$40 \leqslant t < 60$	17	20	0.85	$\frac{17}{20} = 0.85$

Using this information to construct the histogram:

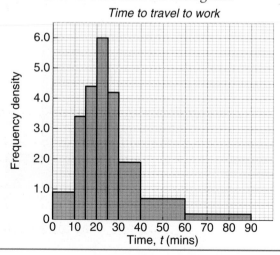

Time to travel to work

PRACTICE 4.6.1a   Try these questions without a calculator

1   The following frequency distribution shows the length of 50 leaves measured to the nearest millimetre.

Length (mm)	Frequency
11–15	3
16–20	6
21–25	7
26–30	9
31–35	12
36–40	8
41–45	4
46–50	1

Draw a histogram to represent this information.

2   Draw a histogram to illustrate the frequency distribution given in question 4 of Practice 4.4.2 on page 143.

3   The distance travelled by 200 student nurses to get to work is shown in the histogram below.

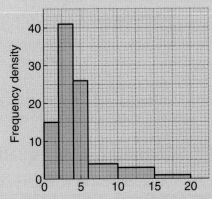

Distance travelled to work

Use the information in the histogram to complete the following table:

Distance (miles)	0–	2–	4–	6–	10–	15–20
Number of students						

PRACTICE 4.6.1b   Try these questions with a calculator

1   250 light bulbs were tested to destruction and the following times measured before the light bulbs failed.

Time (h)	0–500	500–1000	1000–1500	1500–1750	1750–2000	2000–2500	2500–3000
Frequency	0	52	68	60	39	20	11

Draw a histogram to represent this information.

2   The ages of 65 people on a coach tour were recorded as follows.

Age	Frequency
0 up to 25	6
25 up to 35	21
35 up to 45	22
45 up to 55	7
55 up to 75	7
75 up to 100	2

Draw a histogram to represent this information.

Frequency polygons

As stated earlier, a frequency polygon can be obtained from a bar chart or histogram by joining up the mid points of the top of each bar with straight lines to form a polygon. In the case of the first and last class intervals, the lines are extended to the base line so that the area under the frequency polygon is the same as the area under the bar chart or histogram.

PRACTICE 4.6.2   Try these questions with a calculator

1   Draw a frequency polygon to illustrate the frequency distribution given in question 1 of Practice 4.6.1a on page 169.

2   Draw a frequency polygon to illustrate the frequency distribution given in question 2 of Practice 4.6.1a on page 169.

Quantitative and qualitative data

Quantitative data is data that takes numerical values and measures quantities. Qualitative data is data that does not take numerical values but measures qualities.

Discrete and continuous data

Discrete data is data that can only take particular values such as whole numbers. Continuous data is data that can take all values within any specified range.

Bias

Bias is likely to occur if:
    an incorrect sampling method is used
    the sample is unrepresentative
    the questions are unclear
    the questions are biased.

Primary and secondary data

Primary data is data that is collected in response to a hypothesis as part of a statistical investigation and secondary data (second-hand data) is data that is already available.

Sampling and data capture

Sampling techniques considered include:

Random sampling

In random sampling, each member of the population has an equally likely chance of being selected.

Systematic sampling

Systematic sampling is the same as random sampling except that there is some system involved in choosing the member of the population to be sampled.

Stratified sampling

In stratified sampling, each member of the population is divided into some particular group or category (strata). Within each strata, a random sample or systematic sample is selected so that the sample size is proportional to the size of the group or category in the population as a whole.

Quota sampling

In quota sampling, a certain number of the population are chosen with specific characteristics which are decided beforehand.

Questionnaires and surveys

A good questionnaire should be:
- simple, short, clear and precise,
- attractively laid out,
- quick to complete

and the questions should be:
- free from bias and not personal or offensive,
- written in appropriate language for the respondent,
- related to the work being investigated,
- accompanied by clear instructions on how to respond.

Raw data

Raw data is any information which has been collected by some method but has not been organised in any way.

Tally chart

A tally chart consists of a series of tallies which are grouped into fives as follows:

|||| = 4
||||| = 5
||||| | = 6
||||| ||||| = 10, etc.

Frequency distribution

A frequency distribution can be constructed from a tally chart by totalling the tallies.

Grouped frequency distribution

A grouped frequency distribution is where the data are classified into a series of groups or classes.

Pictograms

A pictogram (or pictograph or ideograph) is a simple way of representing data by using pictures (or some other representation).

Bar charts

Bar charts are a very common way of representing data and use bars (horizontal or vertical) to represent the number or frequency of the data.

Compound bar charts

The compound (or multiple) bar chart is similar to the bar chart except that the bars are replaced by a series of different bars representing different aspects of the data.

Component bar charts

The component bar chart (or composite or sectional bar chart) is used to show how an individual item can be split into a series of components.

Line graphs

Line graphs are drawn by plotting points and then joining the points, in order, with a series of straight lines.

Pie charts

A pie chart (or circular diagram) is a circle divided into sectors (or slices) whose angles (or areas) are used to represent the data.

Frequency polygons

A frequency polygon can be obtained from a bar chart or histogram by joining up the mid-points of the top of each bar with straight lines to form a polygon.

Scatter diagrams

In a scatter diagram each of two sets of data is assigned to a different axis and the information collected can be represented as different coordinates on the scatter diagram.

Histograms (extension)

Histograms are similar to bar charts except that it is the *area* of each bar which represents the frequency.

The height of these bars is referred to as the frequency density and the vertical axis of a histogram should be labelled frequency density rather than frequency.

$$\text{frequency density} = \frac{\text{frequency}}{\text{class width}}$$

CHAPTER 5
Analysing and interpreting data

In this chapter you will need to:
▸ know how to construct and use a tally chart
▸ appreciate the various pictorial representations used in statistics
▸ use the statistical functions on a calculator

Tally chart

We saw in Topic 4.4 on 'Tabulating data' that a tally chart consists of a series of tallies which are grouped into fives as follows:

$$\begin{aligned}
||||\quad &= 4 \\
\cancel{||||}\quad &= 5 \\
\cancel{||||}\;|\quad &= 6 \\
\cancel{||||}\;\cancel{||||}\quad &= 10,\ \text{etc, etc.}
\end{aligned}$$

The tally chart is a useful way of organising raw data and finding frequencies.

Pictorial representations

The following representations were considered in Topic 4.5 on 'Pictorial representations':

pictograms
bar charts
line graphs
pie charts
frequency polygons
scatter diagrams
histograms (see Extension Material).

Using a calculator

We saw how to make the most of using our calculators in Topic 2.4 on 'Using a calculator'. Our calculator can also be used to help us with our statistical calculations although it is important to set the calculator to statistics mode before this can be done.

You should consult the user manual accompanying your calculator for further information on how this can be done as well as how individual data items can be input into the calculator.

Function	Explanation
MODE	Sets the mode for normal calculations, statistical calculations, etc.
n	Displays the number of data items which have been input into the calculator.
Σx	Calculates the sum of the numerical data which have been input into the calculator.
Σx^2	Calculates the sum of the squares of the numerical data which have been input into the calculator.
$\bar{x}$	Calculates the mean of the numerical data which have been input into the calculator.
σn or σx	Calculates the standard deviation of the numerical data which have been input into the calculator.

5.2 MEASURES OF CENTRAL TENDENCY

One of the most common statistical measures is the measurement of central tendency or average. There are a number of different types of average including the mode, median and arithmetic mean.

Mode

The mode is the value that occurs the most frequently.

Worked Examples

1 The following numbers were recorded when a single dice was thrown 15 times. What is the modal value?

   2, 5, 5, 6, 1, 6, 4, 2, 4, 6, 1, 1, 5, 2, 1

   The number 1 was thrown 4 times
   The number 2 was thrown 3 times
   The number 3 was thrown 0 times
   The number 4 was thrown 2 times
   The number 5 was thrown 3 times
   The number 6 was thrown 3 times

   The number 1 occurs the most frequently so we say that the mode is 1.

2 The dice was thrown one more time giving a 5. What is the modal value now?

   2, 5, 5, 6, 1, 6, 4, 2, 4, 6, 1, 1, 5, 2, 1, 5

NOTE

If there are two modes we say that the distribution is bimodal. If there are more than two modes we say that the distribution is multimodal.

The number 1 was thrown 4 times
The number 2 was thrown 3 times
The number 3 was thrown 0 times
The number 4 was thrown 2 times
The number 5 was thrown 4 times
The number 6 was thrown 3 times

The numbers 1 and 5 occur the most frequently so we say that the mode is 1 and 5.

One of the advantages of the mode is that it is easy to obtain from pictorial representations as shown in the following worked examples.

Worked Examples

Find the mode of the following pictorial representations:

a

Number of bedrooms in 20 houses

1 bed   🏠 🏠 🏠 🏠

2 bed   🏠 🏠 🏠 🏠 🏠

3 bed   🏠 🏠 🏠 🏠 🏠 🏠 🏠 🏠   Key: 🏠 1 house

4 bed   🏠 🏠

5 bed   🏠

The mode is 3 bedrooms. It is easy to distinguish the mode from a pictogram.

b

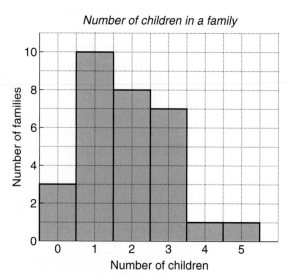

Number of children in a family

The mode is 1 child. The mode will always be represented by the tallest (or longest) bar.

c

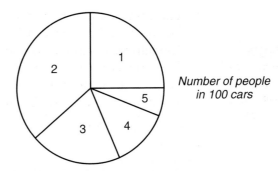

Number of people in 100 cars

The mode is 2 people. The mode will always be represented by the sector with the largest angle (or area) in the pie chart.

Mode of frequency distribution

The mode of a frequency distribution is easily found by noting which value has the highest frequency.

Worked Example

Find the mode of the following frequency distribution:

Value	Frequency
10	12
11	23
12	35
13	**42** ← the value with the highest frequency
14	21

> **NOTE**
> It is important to make sure that you write down the value and not the frequency of the value when giving the mode or modal value.

The mode or modal value of the frequency distribution is 13.

Mode of a grouped frequency distribution

The mode of a grouped frequency distribution has no meaning although it is possible to find the modal group which is the group that occurs the most frequently.

Worked Example

Find the modal group of the following grouped frequency distribution:

Weight (grams)	Frequency
25–35	14
35–45	**19** ← the group with the highest frequency
45–55	17
55–65	11

The modal group of the grouped frequency distribution is 35–45.

PRACTICE 5.2.1

1 Find the mode of the following data:
  a 4, 5, 5, 6, 6, 6, 7, 7, 8
  b 2, 3, 4, 5, 2, 3, 4, 2, 3, 2
  c 33, 36, 37, 33, 35, 35, 38, 39
  d 12.2, 13.5, 12.6, 12.3, 13.5, 12.4, 12.5, 12.3, 13.6
  e −3, −2, −2, −1, −1, −1, 0, 1, 2, 3

2 Salima is undertaking a survey of the colour of cars in the staff car park. She draws up a tally chart as follows:

Red	⊬⊬⊬ ⊬⊬⊬ |||
Blue	⊬⊬⊬ ⊬⊬⊬	
Green	⊬⊬⊬ |||
White	⊬⊬⊬ ⊬⊬⊬ ⊬⊬⊬ ||

What is the modal colour?

3 Find the mode for each of the following representations.

a

	Number of items in a shopping basket of 25 people
1 item	👜
2 items	👜 👜 👜
3 items	👜 👜 👜 👜 👜 👜
4 items	👜 👜 👜 👜 👜 👜 👜 👜 👜 👜
5 items	👜 👜 👜 👜 👜
5+ items	👜

Key: 👜 1 shopping basket

b

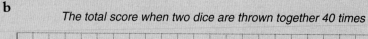
The total score when two dice are thrown together 40 times

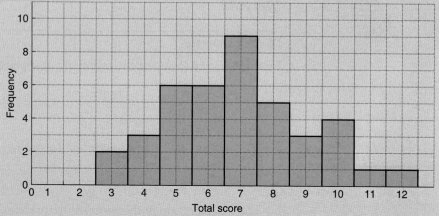

c

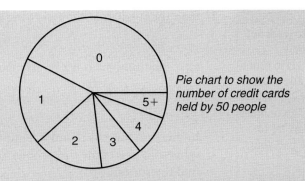

Pie chart to show the number of credit cards held by 50 people

4 Find the mode of the following frequency distribution:

Value	Frequency
20	8
21	11
22	10
23	6

5 Find the mode of the following frequency distribution:

Value	$6\frac{1}{2}$	7	$7\frac{1}{2}$	8	$8\frac{1}{2}$	9
Frequency	11	17	13	15	9	6

6 Find the modal group of the following grouped frequency distribution:

Weight (kg)	Frequency
0.5–1.5	12
1.5–2.5	15
2.5–3.5	22
3.5–4.5	17
4.5–5.5	10

Median

The median is the middle value when all of the values are arranged in numerical order.

Worked Examples

1 Find the median of the following numbers:

   12, 5, 3, 6, 10, 9, 2, 8, 9

First the numbers must be arranged in order:

   2, 3, 5, 6, (**8**,) 9, 9, 10, 12

The middle value is the 5th number so the median is 8.

NOTE

An easy way to work out where the middle number occurs is to count the numbers, add 1 and then divide by 2; i.e. $\frac{1}{2}(n+1)$. This number will tell you how far to count along to find your median value.
For example, if there are 9 numbers then the middle value will be the $\frac{1}{2}(9+1) = 5$th number. If there are 10 numbers then the middle value will be the $\frac{1}{2}(10+1) = 5\frac{1}{2}$th number (i.e. the number between the 5th and 6th number).

2 Find the median of the following numbers:

2, 12, 5, 3, 6, 10, 9, 2, 8, 9

First the numbers must be arranged in order:

2, 2, 3, 5, (6, 8,) 9, 9, 10, 12

In this case there is no middle number as there are an even number of values. To overcome this problem, we take the two middle numbers and find their mean.

The middle values are the 5th and 6th numbers so the median is $\dfrac{6+8}{2}$

$$= 7.$$

Median of a frequency distribution

The following example illustrates how to find the median of a frequency distribution.

Worked Examples

1 Find the median of the following frequency distribution which shows the number of goals scored in a series of football matches:

Number of goals	Frequency
0	2
1	3
2	5
3	2
4	1
	13

One way to find the median would be to write out the number of goals as before:

0, 0, 1, 1, 1, 2, 2, 2, 2, 2, 3, 3, 4

As there are 13 numbers then the middle value will be the $\dfrac{13+1}{2}$ = 7th number.

0, 0, 1, 1, 1, 2, (2,) 2, 2, 2, 3, 3, 4

The median number of goals is 2.

2 Find the median of the following frequency distribution which shows the number of matches in 24 different matchboxes:

Number of matches	Frequency
48	2
49	5
50	14
51	2
52	1
	24

As there are 24 numbers then the middle value will be the $\dfrac{24 + 1}{2} = 12\frac{1}{2}$th number (i.e. between the 12th and 13th number).

We can see this more clearly by looking at the cumulative frequencies (giving an accumulated total for the frequencies):

Number of matches	Frequency	Cumulative frequency
48	2	2
49	5	7
50	14	21 ← the $12\frac{1}{2}$th value will
51	2	: occur here
52	1	:

The median number of matches is 50.

Median of a grouped frequency distribution

A cumulative frequency diagram is the most appropriate way to find the median of a grouped frequency distribution. Cumulative frequency diagrams are fully discussed in Topic 5.3 in 'Measures of spread'.

PRACTICE 5.2.2

1 Find the median of the following data:
a 2, 3, 4, 6, 8, 11, 15
b 4, 4, 4, 4, 5, 5, 5, 6, 7
c 4, 5, 6, 7
d 103, 102, 101, 100
e 3, 6, 8, 2, 6, 9, 10, 2, 5
f 4, 7, 12, 4, 11, 10, 3, 5
g 4, 6, 8, −3, −5, −7, 0, −2, −4

2 Find the median of the following frequency distribution which shows the size of trainers sold at a sports shop:

Number	Frequency
5	10
$5\frac{1}{2}$	15
6	9
$6\frac{1}{2}$	3
7	2

3 Find the median of the following frequency distribution:

Number	Frequency
16	4
17	8
18	11
19	6
20	10
21	15
22	6

Arithmetic mean

The arithmetic mean or mean is the most common average and is found by adding up the values and dividing by the number of values.

NOTE

You should practice this work without a calculator.

Worked Example

The lengths of four leaves are measured as 56 mm, 48 mm, 49 mm and 61 mm. What is the mean length of the leaves?

Total length　　　$= 56 + 48 + 49 + 61$

　　　　　　　　　$= 214$ mm

Number of leaves $= 4$

Mean length　　　$= \dfrac{\text{total length}}{\text{number of leaves}}$

　　　　　　　　　$= \dfrac{214}{4}$

　　　　　　　　　$= 53.5$ mm

> **PRACTICE 5.2.3   Try these questions without a calculator**
>
> **1** Find the mean of the following data:
>   **a** 4, 6, 11
>   **b** 3, 7, 8, 4, 8
>   **c** 8, 9, 10, 11, 12
>   **d** 8, 9, 10, 11, 12, 13
>   **e** 18, 19, 20, 21, 22, 23
>   **f** 28, 29, 30, 31, 32, 33
>   **g** 2.8, 2.9, 3.0, 3.1, 3.2, 3.3
>   **h** 280, 290, 300, 310, 320, 330
>   **i** −280, −290, −300, −310, −320, −330

Sigma notation

Sigma notation (Σ) is a useful shorthand used in statistics to mean *the sum of.*

Σx means the *sum of the x values* so that in the following worked example, Σf means *the sum of the frequencies* and Σfx means *the sum of the frequency × marks.*

Mean of a frequency distribution

The following example illustrates how to find the mean of a frequency distribution.

Worked Example

Find the mean of the following frequency disribution.

Mark x	Frequency f
6	3
7	5
8	7
9	3
10	2
	$\Sigma f = 20$

One way to find the mean would be to write out the marks as before:

  6, 6, 6, 7, 7, 7, 7, 7, 8, 8, 8, 8, 8, 8, 8, 9, 9, 9, 10, 10

The mean of these 20 numbers can be found as follows:

$$\text{Mean} = \frac{6+6+6+7+7+7+7+7+8+8+8+8+8+8+8+9+9+9+10+10}{20}$$

$$= \frac{156}{20}$$

$$= 7.8$$

A quicker way to work out the mean is to appreciate that the mean of the marks can be worked out as:

$$\frac{(3 \text{ lots of } 6) + (5 \text{ lots of } 7) + (7 \text{ lots of } 8) + (3 \text{ lots of } 9) + (2 \text{ lots of } 10)}{20}$$

$$= \frac{(3 \times 6) + (5 \times 7) + (7 \times 8) + (3 \times 9) + (2 \times 10)}{20}$$

$$= \frac{156}{20}$$

$$= 7.8 \quad \text{as before}$$

Using the original table we need to work out the frequency $\times$ mark and total these as follows:

Mark x	Frequency f	Frequency $\times$ mark fx
6	3	$3 \times 6 = 18$
7	5	$5 \times 7 = 35$
8	7	$7 \times 8 = 56$
9	3	$3 \times 9 = 27$
10	2	$2 \times 10 = 20$
	$\Sigma f = 20$	$\Sigma fx = 156$

For the frequency distribution   Mean $= \dfrac{\Sigma fx}{\Sigma f}$

$$= \frac{156}{20}$$

$$= 7.8 \quad \text{as before}$$

PRACTICE 5.2.4   Try these questions without a calculator

1 Find the mean of the following data:

Mark x	Frequency f
3	7
4	9
5	4
6	3
7	1

2 A customer purchases 5 apples at 12 p each, 3 bananas at 14 p, 6 oranges at 15 p and 1 pineapple at 48 p. What is the mean cost per item of the purchases?

3   The following information shows the marks awarded to 80 students in an exam. What is the average score?

Mark	13	14	15	16	17	18	19	20
Frequency	2	0	7	11	13	19	16	12

4   Find the mean of the following data:

Age (years)	16	17	18	19	20	21
Frequency	8	4	12	4	0	2

Mean of a grouped frequency distribution

When we have data arranged in groups we use the mid point of the interval to represent the group. In this case the mean will not be exact but should be a good estimate of the mean.

Worked Examples

1   The following information shows the speed of 60 vehicles passing a motorway bridge one evening in August. Calculate an estimate of the mean speed of the vehicles.

Speed (mph)	20-30	30-40	40-50	50-60	60-70	70-80
Frequency	3	10	16	18	11	2

Speed (mph)	Mid interval value x	Frequency f	Frequency × mid-interval value fx
20–30	25	3	$3 \times 25 = 75$
30–40	35	10	$10 \times 35 = 350$
40–50	45	16	$16 \times 45 = 720$
50–60	55	18	$18 \times 55 = 990$
60–70	65	11	$11 \times 65 = 715$
70–80	75	2	$2 \times 75 = 150$
		$\Sigma f = 60$	$\Sigma fx = 3000$

For the frequency distribution   Mean $= \dfrac{\Sigma fx}{\Sigma f}$

$$= \frac{3000}{60}$$

$$= 50 \, \text{mph}$$

2 The following information shows the duration of telephone calls (to the nearest minute) monitored by the switchboard in a large office block. Calculate an estimate of the mean length of the telephone calls. Give your answer to an appropriate degree of accuracy.

Time (minutes)	Frequency
3–5	67
6–8	43
9–12	28
13–16	13
17–20	7
21–25	4
26–30	3
31–40	2

As the data is grouped, we need to use mid-interval values to calculate an estimate of the mean length of the telephone calls.

Time (minutes)	Mid-interval value x	Frequency f	Frequency × mid-interval value fx
3–5	4	67	268
6–8	7	43	301
9–12	10.5	28	294
13–16	14.5	13	188.5
17–20	18.5	7	129.5
21–25	23	4	92
26–30	28	3	84
31–40	35.5	2	71
		$\Sigma f = 167$	$\Sigma fx = 1428$

NOTE

Giving the answer to an appropriate degree of accuracy would indicate an answer of 9 minutes (to the nearest minute) bearing in mind that the time in the question was given *to the nearest minute*. Also, further inaccuracies will have resulted from the use of the mid-interval value to represent the given class interval.

For the frequency distribution $\text{Mean} = \dfrac{\Sigma fx}{\Sigma f}$

$$= \frac{1428}{167}$$

$$= 8.550\,898\,2\ldots$$

$$= 9 \text{ minutes (to the nearest minute)}$$

PRACTICE 5.2.5   Try these questions with a calculator

1 Calculate an estimate of the mean for the following distribution.

Length (mm)	0–10	10–20	20–30	30–40	40–50
Frequency	6	7	10	6	3

2 Students in a college were asked how much money they spent on entertainment each week. The following frequency distribution shows the results.

Amount (pounds)	Frequency
0 and less than 10	6
10 and less than 20	14
20 and less than 30	21
30 and less than 40	17
40 and less than 50	10
50 and less than 60	4
60 and less than 70	2
70 and less than 80	1

Use the frequency table to calculate an estimate of the mean.

3 The length of each telephone call received by a switchboard is shown in the table.

Length of call (minutes)	Frequency
0 and less than 1	65
1 and less than 2	123
2 and less than 3	72
3 and less than 4	47
4 and less than 5	23
5 and less than 6	7

Calculate an estimate of the mean length of the telephone calls.

4 The following table shows the weights of 75 teenagers. Calculate an estimate of the mean weight giving your answer to an appropriate degree of accuracy.

Weight (kg)	45–	55–	65–	75–	85–95
Frequency	14	37	18	4	2

5 The following data show the times taken to service cars at a garage with all times given to the nearest minute.

Time (mins)	5–25	26–45	46–60	61–90	91–120	121–140
Frequency	24	15	10	6	2	1

Calculate an estimate of the mean length of the time taken to service cars.

Advantages and disadvantages of the mode, median and mean

Advantages of the mode: Represents an actual value
Easy to obtain from pictorial representations

Disadvantages of the mode: Does not take account of all values
There may be no mode or many modes

Advantages of the median: Often represents an actual value
Is not affected by extreme values

Disadvantages of the median: Not widely used
Not representative for a small group

Advantages of the mean: Widely used and makes use of all the data
Mathematically produced

Disadvantages of the mean: May not correspond to an actual value
Affected by extreme values

Relationships between the mode, median and mean

A frequency distribution which produces a symmetrical, bell shaped curve is called a normal distribution. In a normal distribution the mode, median and mean are approximately equal and occur at the centre of the distribution.

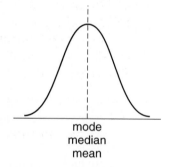

mode
median
mean

A distribution which is not symmetrical is said to be skewed. A positively skewed distribution (which has a long tail on the positive side) will occur when the mean > median > mode and a negatively skewed distribution (which has a long tail on the negative side) will occur when mode > median > mean as illustrated below.

NOTE
The mode is always at the peak of the distribution and the median divides the area under the curve into two equal halves. The bigger the diference between the mean and mode then the more skewed the distribution will be.

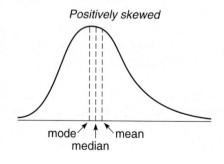

Positively skewed

mode   mean
median

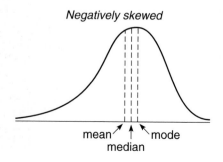

Negatively skewed

mean   mode
median

PRACTICE 5.2.6   Try these questions without a calculator

1 Find the mode, median and arithmetic mean of the following data:

   a 1, 2, 2, 3, 3, 3, 4, 4, 4, 4
   b 2, 3, 3, 4, 5, 6, 6, 6, 7, 8
   c 4, 4, 2, 2, 2, 7, 7, 7, 1, 8, 7, 3, 3, 6
   d 1, 2, 6, 5, 2, 2, 5, 9
   e 1, 2, 3, 4, 5, 6, 7, 8, 9, 10
   f 11, 12, 13, 14, 15, 16, 17, 18, 19, 20
   g 3, −3, −3, 2, −2, 1, −1, −1, 0, 0, 1, −1, 2, −1, −2, 3

2 Debbie asks some of the students in her year group how many brothers and sisters they have. She puts the information in a table.

Number of brothers						
5	1					
4	0	2				
3	2	2	1			
2	4	3	3	1		
1	5	3	2	1	1	
0	5	6	2	1		1
	0	**1**	**2**	**3**	**4**	**5**

Number of sisters

   a How many students have no sisters?
   b How many students have only one brother?
   c How many students have equal numbers of brothers and sisters?
   d How many students did Debbie survey altogether?
   e What is the modal number of sisters?
   f Calculate the mean number of brothers.

3 A teacher records the marks of 10 pupils in her record book as follows:

   28   27   32   17   23   28   28   20   27   29

   a Calculate:
      i the mean mark,   **iii** the modal mark.
      ii the median mark,

   The teacher realises that the mark recorded as 32 should have been 35.

   b What effect will this have on:
      i the mean mark,   **iii** the modal mark?
      ii the median mark,

4 The prices of eight three bedroomed houses are as follows:

   £63 000   £67 500   £59 950   £67 500
   £58 500   £66 950   £119 500   £61 000

   Which of the averages, mode, median or mean, gives the best measure for the *average* price of a three bedroom house? Give a reason to justify your answer.

It is not always appropriate to just compare data by looking at their averages since such a measure does not always give a true picture of the situation. For example, consider the mean value of the following two sets of numbers:

5, 5, 5, 5, 5, 5, 5, 5, 5, 5
1, 9, 1, 1, 9, 1, 9, 9, 9, 1

The mean of each set of data is the same although the data clearly represent different distributions.

If each of the sets represented a different student's test marks then what would you say about the performance of the two students?

We might say that the marks of the first student are more consistent than those of the second student or that the second student's marks are more spread out or dispersed.

In this topic we will look at the following measures of spread or dispersion:

range
interquartile range
mean deviation   (see Extension material)
standard deviation   (see Extension material)

Range

The range of a distribution is found by working out the difference between the highest value and the lowest value.

Worked Example

The following data give the wages of six people working in a restaurant:

£225   £245   £205   £400   £260   £225

a Calculate:
 i the mean,
 ii the range.

b Why isn't the range a good measure of spread in this instance?

a   **i** The mean $= \dfrac{£225 + £245 + £205 + £400 + £260 + £225}{6}$

$= \dfrac{£1560}{6}$

$= £260$

 ii The highest value $= £400$
    The lowest value $= £205$

    Range $=$ highest value $-$ lowest value
       $= £400 - £205$
       $= £195$

b The range is not a good measure of spread here because it is affected by extreme values. The value of £400 distorts the mean value and considerably increases the range.

> **PRACTICE 5.3.1   Try these questions without a calculator**
>
> **1** Find the range of the following sets of data:
>   **a** 2, 4, 5, 7, 11, 18
>   **b** 12, 6, 14, 15, 19, 22
>   **c** 8 cm, 11 cm, 6 cm, 15 cm, 6 cm, 4 cm, 13 cm
>   **d** 2.4 km, 6.1 km, 2.5 km, 4.7 km, 9.3 km, 5.7 km
>   **e** 5, −2, 4, 11, −3, −4, 12, 8
>   **f** −0.6, −2.4, 0.8, 6.5, 5.7, 3.4, 2.1
>   **g** $\frac{1}{4}$, $\frac{2}{3}$, $\frac{3}{5}$, $\frac{7}{8}$, $\frac{3}{20}$, $\frac{1}{10}$, $\frac{3}{7}$

Cumulative frequency diagram

Another very useful tool in statistics is provided through the use of the cumulative frequency diagram (which is also called a cumulative frequency curve or an ogive). The cumulative frequency diagram is found by plotting the *cumulative frequencies* and joining them with a smooth curve.

Worked Example

The following information gives the waiting time for patients at a dental practice. Draw the cumulative diagram for the information and use your diagram to find:

a how many patients waited less than 4 minutes
b how many patients waited more than 10 minutes.

Waiting time (mins)	Frequency
0–3	9
3–6	17
6–9	12
9–12	6
12–15	2
15–18	1

In order to draw the cumulative diagram, we need to work out the cumulative frequencies by totalling (or accumulating) the frequencies in the table.

Waiting time (mins)	Frequency	Cumulative frequencies	
0–3	9	9	
3–6	17	26	9 + 17 = 26
6–9	12	38	26 + 12 = 38
9–12	6	44	38 + 6 = 44
12–15	2	46	44 + 2 = 46
15–18	1	47	46 + 1 = 47

> **NOTE**
> You should be able to work out the cumulative frequencies without using a calculator.

> **NOTE**
> It is useful to check that the final cumulative frequency is the same as the total of the frequency column.

NOTE
It is essential that the cumulative frequencies are always plotted at the upper boundary of the class interval. See Topic 4.4 on 'Tabulating data' to remind yourself about class boundaries and class limits.

To find how many patients waited less than 4 minutes and how many patients waited more than 10 minutes we read off the corresponding cumulative frequencies on the cumulative frequency axis as follows:

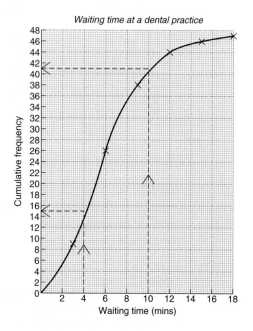

a From the diagram, we can see that 15 patients waited less than 4 minutes.
b From the diagram, we can see that 6 $(47 - 41)$ patients waited more than 10 minutes.

In part **b** the cumulative frequency curve tells us how many patients waited less than 10 minutes. All the remaining patients must have waited more than 10 minutes so we subtract the answer from 47 as there were 47 patients altogether.

Median

We have already seen that the median is the middle value when all of the values are arranged in numerical order. The cumulative frequency diagram can also be used to find the median by reading off the middle value, i.e. the $\frac{1}{2}(n + 1)$th value, on the cumulative frequency axis.

Worked Example

Find the median waiting time for the previous worked example.

The middle value is the $\frac{1}{2}(47 + 1)$th value, i.e. the 24th value on the cumulative frequency axis. The median is found by finding the corresponding time on the time axis as follows:

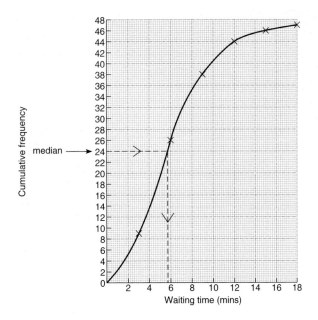

The median time is 5.8 minutes.

Quartiles

While the median divides the distribution into two equal parts, the quartiles divide the distribution into four equal parts.

The Lower Quartile or first quartile (written LQ or Q_1) is the $\frac{1}{4}(n + 1)$th value.

The Upper Quartile or third quartile (written UQ or Q_3) is the $\frac{3}{4}(n + 1)$th value.

NOTE
The middle quartile or second quartile is the same as the median.

Worked Example

Find the lower quartile and the upper quartile of the waiting time in the previous worked example.

The lower quartile is the $\frac{1}{4}(47 + 1)$th value, i.e. the 12th value on the cumulative frequency axis and the upper quartile is the $\frac{3}{4}(47 + 1)$th value, i.e. the 36th value on the cumulative frequency axis. The values for the lower quartile and the upper quartile are found from the corresponding time on the time axis as follows:

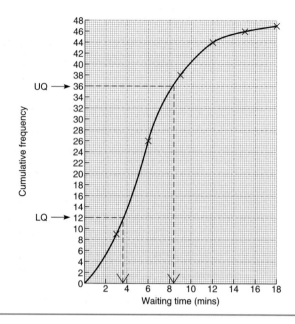

Interquartile range

The interquartile range, like the range discussed earlier, is also a measure of spread. However, unlike the range, the interquartile range only considers the middle 50% of the distribution and is therefore unaffected by extreme values.

The interquartile range is calculated as follows:

Interquartile range = upper quartile − lower quartile

Worked Example

Find the interquartile range for the waiting time in the previous worked example.

From the previous worked example we found that:

upper quartile = 8.4
lower quartile = 3.6

Interquartile range = upper quartile − lower quartile
= 8.4 − 3.6
= 4.8

> **NOTE**
>
> Another distribution with a smaller interquartile range is likely to have a smaller range and therefore be less spread out whereas a distribution with a bigger interquartile range is likely to have a larger range and therefore be more spread out.

Although cumulative frequency diagrams are usually used to find the interquartile range we can find the interquartile range from original data as shown in the following worked examples.

Worked Examples

1   The following information shows the monthly earnings of eleven people employed in a certain factory. Find the range and interquartile range and comment upon your findings.

£200, £200, £200, £200, £200, £200, £240, £240, £240, £265, £680

The range of the earnings are £680 − £200 = £480.

The value of the range is distorted by the figure of £680 which is an extreme value in view of the earnings of the other ten people.

To find the interquartile range we need to find the value of the upper and lower quartiles. The lower quartile is the $\frac{1}{4}(11 + 1)$th value, i.e. the 3rd value and the upper quartile is the $\frac{3}{4}(11 + 1)$th value, i.e. the 9th value. This information can be shown on the original data which are already presented in numerical order.

£200, £200, £200, £200, £200, £200, £240, £240, £240, £265, £680
$\qquad\qquad$↑$\qquad\qquad\qquad\qquad$↑$\qquad\qquad\qquad\qquad$↑

$\qquad$lower quartile$\qquad\qquad$median$\qquad\qquad$upper quartile

$$\begin{aligned}\text{Interquartile range} &= \text{upper quartile} - \text{lower quartile}\\ &= £240 - £200\\ &= £40\end{aligned}$$

This is a better measure of the spread of the data since it only considers the central 50% of the distribution and is unaffected by extreme values.

2   Find the range and interquartile range for the following set of data:

$\qquad$34   29   38   25   22   23   32   25   30   51   37   27   42

The range of the data is 51 − 22 = 29.

To find the interquartile range we need to find the value of the upper and lower quartiles.
The lower quartile is the $\frac{1}{4}(13 + 1)$th = $3\frac{1}{2}$th value, i.e. between the 3rd and 4th value.
The upper quartile is the $\frac{3}{4}(13 + 1)$th = $10\frac{1}{2}$th value i.e. between the 10th and 11th value.

Arranging the data into numerical order:

$\qquad$22   23   25   25   27   29   30   32   34   37   38   42   51

The lower quartile lies between the 3rd and 4th value so equals 25.
The upper quartile lies between the 10th and 11th value
i.e. between 37 and 38 = 37.5.

$$\begin{aligned}\text{Interquartile range} &= \text{upper quartile} - \text{lower quartile}\\ &= 37.5 - 25\\ &= 12.5\end{aligned}$$

Percentiles

Distributions can be split up into other equal parts such as deciles (10 equal parts) or percentiles (100 equal parts). In the case of percentiles, the 25th percentile is the same as the lower quartile, the 50th percentile is the same as the median and the 75th percentile is the same as the upper quartile.

PRACTICE 5.3.2

1 The table below shows the lifetime of 200 light bulbs given to the nearest hour.

Lifetime (hours)	Frequency
1000–1499	35
1500–1999	92
2000–2499	49
2500–2999	17
3000–3499	5
3500–3999	2

Draw a cumulative frequency curve to illustrate this information and use your graph to find:

a how many light bulbs lasted less than 2250 hours,
b how many light bulbs lasted more than 2250 hours,
c how many light bulbs lasted more than 3250 hours,
d the median,
e the interquartile range.

2 The wages of workers at a factory are shown as follows:

Income (£)	100–	150–	200–	250–	300–	350–400
Frequency	6	15	28	37	11	3

Draw a cumulative frequency curve to illustrate this information and use your graph to find:

a the median,
b the interquartile range.

3 The following table shows the number of words per sentence in a local newspaper.

Number of words per sentence	Number of sentences
1–10	15
11–20	58
21–30	92
31–40	30
41–50	5

Draw a cumulative frequency curve to illustrate this information and use your graph to estimate:

a the median,
b the percentage of sentences over 25 words in length.

4 A teacher times how long it takes her children to complete an exercise as follows:

Time (minutes)	Frequency
0 and less than 9.5	6
9.5 and less than 19.5	12
19.5 and less than 29.5	10
29.5 and less than 39.5	5
39.5 and less than 49.5	2

a Draw a cumulative frequency curve to illustrate this information and use your graph to find the median and the interquartile range of the time taken.
b The interquartile range for a different class of children is 20 minutes. What can you conclude about the times for the two groups of children?

5 The frequency distribution for the time taken to travel across the channel on the hovercraft is shown for 30 journeys.

Time, t (minutes)	Frequency
$25 \leq t < 30$	2
$30 \leq t < 35$	6
$35 \leq t < 40$	9
$40 \leq t < 45$	5
$45 \leq t < 50$	4
$50 \leq t < 55$	3
$55 \leq t < 60$	1

Draw a cumulative frequency curve to show this information and use your curve to find an estimate of the median and the interquartile range.

Scatter diagrams

The idea of a scatter diagram (or scatter graph) was first introduced in Topic 4.5 on 'Pictorial representations' and the idea will now be developed further to see how such representations can be used to find relationships between two sets of data.

The distribution of points on a scatter diagram can be used to give an indication of the relationship or **correlation** between two sets of data as illustrated in the following diagrams:

Little or no correlation   *Moderate correlation*   *Strong correlation*

In the first diagram, the points are scattered randomly over the graph indicating little or no correlation between the two sets of data.

In the second diagram, the points lie close to a straight line suggesting some moderate correlation between the two sets of data – clearly, the closer the points are to a straight line then the stronger the correlation between the two sets of data.

In the third diagram, the points are scattered along a straight line indicating a strong correlation between the two sets of data.

> **NOTE**
>
> The strength of the correlation between two sets of data can be measured by finding the correlation coefficient; this work is beyond the requirements of the GCSE syllabus.

Positive and negative correlation

Where an increase in one variable is matched with an increase in the other variable then the correlation is said to be positive (or direct).

Where an increase in one variable is matched with a decrease in the other variable then the correlation is said to be negative (or inverse).

> **NOTE**
>
> A curve, rather than a straight line, might also provide evidence of some form of correlation between two sets of data on a scatter diagram.

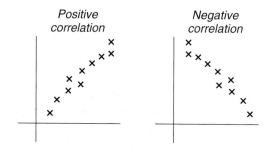

Positive correlation   *Negative correlation*

PRACTICE 5.4.1

1 For each of the following scatter diagrams, say whether there is any correlation between the two variables.

a   c   e

b   d

2 For each of the following sets of data, draw a scatter diagram and say whether there is any correlation between the two variables.

a

x	6	3	18	30	15
y	12	10	22	32	19

c

x	90	200	150	120	260	240
y	50	120	130	90	160	140

b

x	0.5	2.2	1.5	1.4	0.7
y	0.5	0.6	2.2	1.4	2.8

d

x	5	20	15	9	26	18
y	22	9	13	16	5	10

Correlation between two sets of data does not necessarily prove that there is a connection between them. For example, the following scatter diagram shows the relationship between the number of cars on the road and the sales of refrigerators over a period of time:

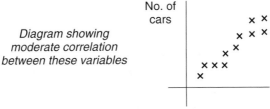

Diagram showing moderate correlation between these variables

Clearly, there is no direct relationship between the number of cars on the road and the sales of refrigerators; the relationship between them is an example of a **spurious correlation**.

Line of best fit

Where the points on a scatter diagram show moderate or strong correlation, it is possible to imagine a line about which the points lie and this line is called the line of best fit (or regression line). The line of best fit can be used to predict possible values for the data as illustrated in the following worked example.

Worked Example

The following information details the marks of 10 students on their two chemistry examination papers:

Paper 1	25	35	28	21	36	44	15	21	41	39
Paper 2	27	40	29	22	41	48	17	20	48	44

a Draw a scatter diagram and comment on the relationship between the two papers.

b By drawing in a line of best fit find the likely mark for a student who scored 32 on Paper 1 but was absent for Paper 2.

a

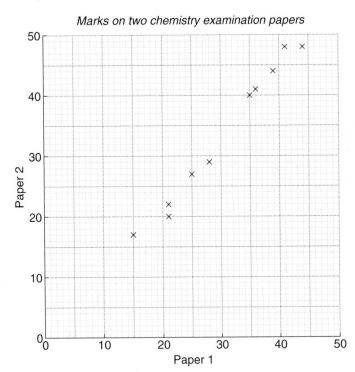

Marks on two chemistry examination papers

From the diagram we can see that there is a strong positive correlation between the two papers.

b A line of best fit can be drawn *by eye* on the scatter diagram above although it is helpful to work out the means of the individual distributions and use the point $(\bar{x}, \bar{y})$ as a fixed point on the line.

$$\text{Mean for paper } 1 = \frac{25 + 35 + 28 + 21 + 36 + 44 + 15 + 21 + 41 + 39}{10}$$

$$= \frac{305}{10} = 30.5$$

$$\text{Mean for paper } 2 = \frac{27 + 40 + 29 + 22 + 41 + 48 + 17 + 20 + 48 + 44}{10}$$

$$= \frac{336}{10} = 33.6$$

The point $(\bar{x}, \bar{y})$ is marked on the diagram as ⊙ and the line of best fit drawn 'by eye'.

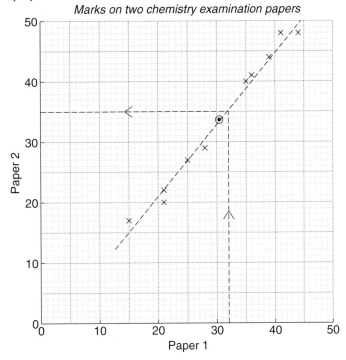

Marks on two chemistry examination papers

From the diagram we can see that the likely mark for a student who scored 32 on Paper 1 but was absent for Paper 2 is 35.

PRACTICE 5.4.2

1 The following information details the marks of 8 students in English and mathematics

Student	1	2	3	4	5	6	7	8
English	25	35	28	30	36	44	15	21
Mathematics	27	40	29	32	41	48	17	20

a Draw a scatter diagram and comment on the relationship between the two subjects.
b Draw a line of best fit and use it to estimate the following:
   i the mathematics mark of a student gaining 34 in English,
   ii the English mark of a student gaining 18 in mathematics.

2 The following information shows the petrol consumption of a car and the distance travelled.

Petrol consumption (gallons)	1	2	0.5	1.5	2	1.75
Distance travelled (miles)	25	50	18	38	60	44

a Draw a scatter diagram and comment on the relationship betwen the two measurements.
b Draw a line of best fit and use it to estimate the following:
  i the petrol consumption of a car travelling 30 miles,
  ii the distance travelled by a car whose petrol consumption was 1.25 gallons.

3 The following scatter diagram shows the relationship between the distance jumped in the long jump trials and leg length.

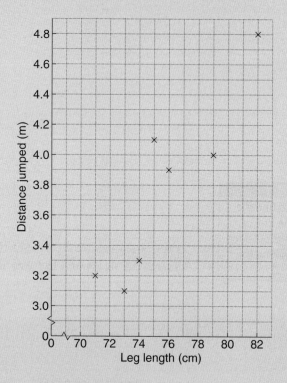

a Use the line of best fit to estimate
  i the leg length of someone who jumped a distance of 3.5 m.
  ii the distance jumped by someone with a leg length of 82 cm.
b Explain why one of these estimates is more reliable than the other.

The problem with the range and interquartile range is that they do not take account of all of the values of the distribution. Two measures of spread which take account of all the values of the distribution are the mean deviation and the standard deviation.

Mean deviation

A measure of spread which takes account of all the values of a distribution is the mean deviation. The mean deviation is found by calculating the mean of the absolute differences of each value from the mean as shown in the following worked example.

Worked Example

Find the mean deviation from the mean of the following distribution:

$$4, \ 7, \ 8, \ 10, \ 11$$

The arithmetic mean $= \dfrac{4 + 7 + 8 + 10 + 11}{5} = 8$

The differences of the distribution from the mean are:

$$-4, \ -1, \ 0, \ 2, \ 3$$

The absolute differences (ignoring the signs) of the distribution from the mean are:

$$4, \ 1, \ 0, \ 2, \ 3$$

The arithmetic mean of these differences $= \dfrac{4 + 1 + 0 + 2 + 3}{5} = 2$

So the mean deviation from the mean is 2.

PRACTICE 5.5.1 Try this question without a calculator

1 Find the mean deviation of the following data:
   a 4, 5, 9   **c** 2, 2, 2, 3, 3, 3, 6
   b 2, 4, 6, 8, 10   **d** 2, 2, 2, 4, 4, 6

Standard deviation

The problem with the mean deviation is that finding the absolute differences by just ignoring the signs does not seem to be very mathematical. One way to overcome this problem is to square all of the differences which has the effect of removing the negative values.

Fortunately, you do not need to remember the formulae for standard deviation as these are given to you on the formula sheet provided in the examination which says:

Standard deviation, s, for a set of numbers $x_1, x_2, \ldots, x_n$, having a mean of $\bar{x}$ is given by

$$s = \sqrt{\frac{\Sigma\,(x - \bar{x})^2}{n}} \quad \text{or} \quad s = \sqrt{\frac{\Sigma x^2}{n} - \left\{\frac{\Sigma x}{n}\right\}^2}$$

The following worked examples illustrate how to use these formulae to find the standard deviation of the data used earlier.

Worked Examples

1 Find the standard deviation of 4, 7, 8, 10, 11 using the formula

$$s = \sqrt{\frac{\Sigma(x - \bar{x})^2}{n}}.$$

The arithmetic mean $(\bar{x}) = \dfrac{4 + 7 + 8 + 10 + 11}{5} = 8$

The differences of the distribution from the mean, $(x - \bar{x})$ are:

$$-4, \ -1, \ 0, \ 2, \ 3$$

The squares of the differences of the distribution from the mean, $(x - \bar{x})^2$ are:

$$16, \ 1, \ 0, \ 4, \ 9$$

The mean of these squares of the differences

$$\frac{\Sigma(x - \bar{x})^2}{n} = \frac{16 + 1 + 0 + 4 + 9}{5} = 6$$

The standard deviation is the square root of this value

$$\sqrt{\frac{\Sigma(x - \bar{x})^2}{n}} \ = \ \sqrt{6} = 2.45 \text{ (3sf)}.$$

> **NOTE**
>
> The *variance* is equal to the square of the standard deviation. In this example the variance is 6 and the standard deviation $= \sqrt{\text{variance}} = \sqrt{6}$.

2 Find the standard deviation of 4, 7, 8, 10, 11 using the formula

$$s = \sqrt{\frac{\Sigma x^2}{n} - \left\{\frac{\Sigma x}{n}\right\}^2}$$

The arithmetic mean, $\dfrac{\Sigma x}{n} = \dfrac{4 + 7 + 8 + 10 + 11}{5} = 8$

The squares of the distribution are:

$$16, \ 49, \ 64, \ 100, \ 121$$

The mean of these squares, $\dfrac{\Sigma x^2}{n} = \dfrac{16 + 49 + 64 + 100 + 121}{5} = 70$

> **NOTE**
>
> For the purposes of this formula we should realise that
>
> $$\bar{x} = \frac{\Sigma x}{n}$$

The standard deviation is

$$\sqrt{\frac{\Sigma x^2}{n} - \left\{\frac{\Sigma x}{n}\right\}^2} = \sqrt{(70 - \{8\}^2)} = \sqrt{(70 - 64)} = \sqrt{6} = 2.45 \text{ (3 sf)}.$$

The following worked examples provide further insight into work on mean and standard deviation.

Worked Examples

1 The weekly pay for eight shopworkers is as follows:

£180   £180   £200   £220 £240   £260   £290   £310

Find the mean and the standard deviation of the weekly pay.

Using the given formula for the standard deviation of a set of numbers $x_1, x_2, \ldots, x_n$, having a mean of $\bar{x}$, $s = \sqrt{\dfrac{\Sigma(x - \bar{x})^2}{n}}$

The arithmetic mean $(\bar{x})$

$$= \frac{£180 + £180 + £200 + £220 + £240 + £260 + £290 + £310}{8} = \frac{£1880}{8} = £235$$

The differences of the distribution from the mean, $(x - \bar{x})$ are:

$-55, \ -55, \ -35, \ -15, \ 5, \ 25, \ 55, \ 75$

The squares of the differences of the distribution from the mean, $(x - \bar{x})^2$ are:

3025, 3025, 1225, 225, 25, 625, 3025, 5625

The mean of these squares of the differences, $\dfrac{\Sigma(x - \bar{x})^2}{n}$

$$= \frac{3025 + 3025 + 1225 + 225 + 25 + 625 + 3025 + 5625}{8} = \frac{16\,800}{8} = 2100$$

The standard deviation is $\sqrt{\dfrac{\Sigma(x - \bar{x})^2}{n}} = \sqrt{2100} = 45.825\,756\,949\,5 = 45.8$ (3sf)

Another way to find the mean and standard deviation is to present the information in tabular form as follows:

x	$(x - \bar{x})$	$(x - \bar{x})^2$
180	-55	3025
180	-55	3025
200	-35	1225
220	-15	225
240	5	25
260	25	625
290	55	3025
310	75	5625
$\Sigma x = 1880$		$\Sigma(x - \bar{x})^2 = 16\,800$

$$\text{The mean, } \bar{x} = \frac{\Sigma x}{n} = \frac{1880}{8} = 235$$

$$\text{Standard deviation, } s = \sqrt{\frac{\Sigma(x-\bar{x})^2}{n}} = \sqrt{\frac{16\,800}{8}} = \sqrt{2100}$$

$$= 45.825\,756\,949\,5 = 45.8 \text{ (3 sf).}$$

2 In the previous worked example all eight shopworkers are given a £40 bonus for Christmas. How does the bonus affect the mean and standard deviation?

After the £40 bonus the pay for the shopworkers is as follows:

£220   £220   £240   £260   £280   £300   £330   £350

Presenting the information in tabular form as follows:

x	$(x-\bar{x})$	$(x-\bar{x})^2$
220	-55	3025
220	-55	3025
240	-35	1225
260	-15	225
280	5	25
300	25	625
330	55	3025
350	75	5625
$\Sigma x = 2200$		$\Sigma(x-\bar{x})^2 = 16\,800$

$$\text{The mean, } \bar{x} = \frac{\Sigma x}{n} = \frac{2200}{8} = 275$$

$$\text{Standard deviation, } s = \sqrt{\frac{\Sigma(x-\bar{x})^2}{n}} = \sqrt{\frac{16\,800}{8}} = \sqrt{2100}$$

$$= 45.825\,756\,949\,5 = 45.8 \text{ (3 sf).}$$

NOTE

The standard deviation has not changed since a uniform increase on all of the values of a distribution will not affect the spread of the distribution.

We notice that the mean increases by £40 but that the standard deviation does not alter.

3 In the previous worked example each shopworker receives a 5% pay rise the following spring. How does the pay rise affect the mean and standard deviation.

After a 5% pay rise the pay for the shopworkers is as follows:

£189   £189   £210   £231   £252   £273   £304.50   £325.50

Presenting the information in tabular form as follows:

x	$(x - \bar{x})$	$(x - \bar{x})^2$
189	-57.75	3335.0625
189	-57.75	3335.0625
210	-36.75	1350.5625
231	-15.75	248.0625
252	5.25	27.5625
273	26.25	689.0625
304.50	57.75	3335.0625
325.50	78.75	6201.5625
$\Sigma x = 1974$		$\Sigma(x - \bar{x})^2 = 18\,522$

The mean, $\bar{x} = \dfrac{\Sigma x}{n} = \dfrac{1974}{8} = 246.75$

Standard deviation, $s = \sqrt{\dfrac{\Sigma(x - \bar{x})^2}{n}} = \sqrt{\dfrac{18\,522}{8}} = \sqrt{2315.25}$

$$= 48.117\,044\,797 = 48.1 \text{ (3 sf)}.$$

We notice here that the original mean (235) and standard deviation (45.8 to 3 sf) have both increased by 5%.

In general we can show that:
- if we increase (or decrease) all of the values of a distribution by an equal amount then the mean will increase (or decrease) by that amount and the standard deviation (spread) will not be affected,
- if we multiply (or divide) all of the values of a distribution by an equal amount then the mean and the standard deviation will also be multiplied (or divided) by that same amount.

In the last worked example we might find it helpful to use the second formula to find the standard deviation This formula is particularly helpful when we know the value of the mean and avoids having to repeatedly work out the values of $(x - \bar{x})^2$.

$$s = \sqrt{\dfrac{\Sigma x^2}{n} - \left\{\dfrac{\Sigma x}{n}\right\}^2}$$

After a 5% pay rise, we can find the mean and standard deviation as follows:

x	x^2
189	35\,721
189	35\,721
210	44\,100
231	53\,361
252	63\,504
273	74\,529
304.50	92\,720.25
325.50	105\,950.25
$\Sigma x = 1974$	$\Sigma x^2 = 505\,606.5$

$$\text{The mean, } \bar{x} = \frac{\Sigma x}{n} = \frac{1974}{8} = 246.75$$

$$\frac{\Sigma x^2}{n} = \frac{505\,606.5}{8} = 63\,200.8125$$

$$\text{Standard deviation, } s = \sqrt{\frac{\Sigma x^2}{n} - \left\{\frac{\Sigma x}{n}\right\}^2} = \sqrt{63\,200.8125 - 246.75^2}$$

$$= \sqrt{63\,200.8125 - 60\,885.5625}$$
$$= \sqrt{2315.25}$$
$$= 48.117\,044\,797$$
$$= 48.1 \text{ (3sf)} \quad \text{as before}$$

Worked Example

The following five numbers have a mean of 1.5 and a standard deviation of 2.

$-2, \ 1, \ 2, \ 2.5, \ 4$

Use this information to find the mean and standard deviation of the following numbers:

a $-1, \ 2, \ 3, \ 3.5, \ 5$
b $0, \ 3, \ 4, \ 4.5, \ 6$
c $-5, \ -2, \ -1 \ ,-0.5, \ 1$
d $-8, \ 4, \ 8, \ 10, \ 16$
e $0, \ 12, \ 16, \ 18, \ 24$
f $-0.2, \ 0.1, \ 0.2, \ 0.25, \ 0.4$
g $2, \ -1, \ -2, \ -2.5, \ -4$

$-2, \ 1, \ 2, \ 2.5, \ 4$
$\bar{x} = 1.5, s = 2$ given in the original question

a $-1, \ 2, \ 3, \ 3.5, \ 5$
$\bar{x} = 2.5, s = 2$ add 1 to the original data, add 1 to the mean, standard deviation (spread) does not alter

b $0, \ 3, \ 4, \ 4.5, \ 6$
$\bar{x} = 3.5, s = 2$ add 2 to the original data, add 2 to the mean, standard deviation (spread) does not alter

c $-5, \ -2, \ -1, \ -0.5, \ 1$
$\bar{x} = -1.5, s = 2$ subtract 3 from the original data, subtract 3 from the mean, standard deviation (spread) does not alter

d $-8, \ 4, \ 8, \ 10, \ 16$
$\bar{x} = 6, s = 8$ original data multiplied by 4, mean and standard deviation multiplied by 4

e $0, \ 12, \ 16, \ 18, \ 24$
$\bar{x} = 14, s = 8$ original data multiplied by 4 and then add 8 to the answer, mean multiplied by 4 and then add 8, standard deviation multiplied by 4 only (adding 8 does not alter the spread)

f   −0.2, 0.1, 0.2, 0.25, 0.4

$\bar{x} = 0.15, s = 0.2$ original data divided by 10, mean and standard deviation divided by 10

g   2, −1, −2, −2.5, −4

$\bar{x} = -1.5, s = 2$ original data multiplied by −1, mean and standard deviation multiplied by −1 but the negative sign can be ignored for the standard deviation (spread)

Interpretation of the standard deviation

The standard deviation shows the dispersion of values about the arithmetic mean and the greater the standard deviation then the greater the dispersion. For a normal distribution, 68% of the distribution lies within one standard deviation of the mean, 95% of the distribution lies within two standard deviations of the mean and 99% of the distribution lies within three standard deviations of the mean.

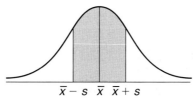

68% of the distribution lies within one standard deviation of the mean

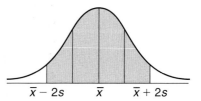

95% of the distribution lies within two standard deviations of the mean

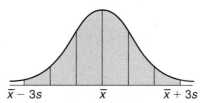

99% of the distribution lies within three standard deviations of the mean

For example, the height of 500 adults was found to have a mean of 170 cm with a standard deviation of 15 cm. Assuming that these adults conform to a normal distribution then

68% will lie within one standard deviation of the mean i.e. 68% of the adults will lie between 155 cm and 185 cm

95% will lie within two standard deviations of the mean i.e. 95% of the adults will lie between 140 cm and 200 cm

99% will lie within three standard deviations of the mean i.e. 99% of the adults will lie between 125 cm and 215 cm.

PRACTICE 5.5.2   Try these questions with a calculator

1   Find the mean and standard deviation of the following data.
    a   1, 2, 3, 4, 5, 6, 7
    b   2, 2, 4, 8
    c   −4, −1, 2, 3, 5
    d   2.5, 3.5, 4.5, 5.5, 6.5, 7.5

2   Find the mean and standard deviation of the following information
    which gives the times needed to complete a task on five successive days:

    23 mins,   42 mins,   36 mins,   29 mins,   45 mins

3   The prices of houses in an estate agent's window are:

    £84 000   £96 000   £118 000   £92 000   £94 000
    £94 000   £90 000   £98 000   £102 000   £92 000

    Calculate the means and use the formula

    $$s = \sqrt{\frac{\Sigma\,(x - \bar{x})^2}{n}}$$

    to find the standard deviation.

4   Use the formula

    $$s = \sqrt{\frac{\Sigma x^2}{n} - \left\{\frac{\Sigma x}{n}\right\}^2}$$

    to find the standard deviation of the distribution in question **4**.

PRACTICE 5.5.3   Try these questions without a calculator

1   The mean and standard deviation of the numbers −5, −2, 2, 4, 6 are 1
    and 4, respectively. Use this information to find the mean and standard
    deviation of each of the following sets of data.
    a   −4, −1, 3, 5, 7
    b   0, 3, 7, 9, 11
    c   −6, −3, 1, 3, 5
    d   −10, −4, 4, 8, 12
    e   −2.5, −1, 1, 2, 3
    f   0, 1.5, 3.5, 4.5, 5.5
    g   −0.05, −0.02, 0.02, 0.04, 0.06

Measures of central tendency

The most common statistical measure is the measurement of central tendency or average. Different averages considered include the mode, median and arithmetic mean.

Mode

The mode is the value that occurs the most frequently. If there are two modes we say that the distribution is bimodal. If there are more than two modes we say that the distribution is multimodal.

Median

The median is the middle value when all of the values are arranged in numerical order. When there are an even number of values, we take the two middle numbers and find their mean. A cumulative frequency diagram can also be used to find the median by reading off the middle value, i.e. the $\frac{1}{2}(n + 1)$th value, on the cumulative frequency axis.

Arithmetic mean

The arithmetic mean or mean is found by adding up the values and dividing by the number of values. When we have data arranged in groups we use the mid-point of the interval to represent the group.

Cumulative frequency diagram

A cumulative frequency diagram or ogive is constructed by plotting the *cumulative frequencies* (at the end of each boundary) and joining them with a smooth curve.

Range

The range of a distribution is found by working out the difference between the highest value and the lowest value – the range should always be presented as a single value.

Quartiles

Quartiles divide the distribution into four equal parts. The lower quartile is the $\frac{1}{4}(n + 1)$th value and the upper quartile is the $\frac{3}{4}(n + 1)$th value.

Interquartile range

The interquartile range only considers the middle 50% of the distribution and is unaffected by extreme values.

$$\text{Interquartile range} = \text{upper quartile} - \text{lower quartile}$$

Scatter diagrams

The distribution of points on a scatter diagram can be used to give an indication of the relationship or correlation between two sets of data:

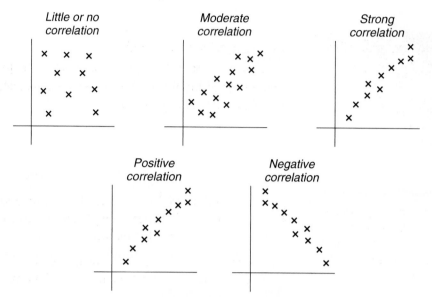

Line of best fit

Where the points on a scatter diagram show moderate or strong correlation, a line of best fit (or regression line) can be drawn and used to predict possible values for the data.

Mean deviation (extension)

The mean deviation is found by calculating the mean of the absolute differences of each value from the mean. Most measures of spread rely on the standard deviation rather than the mean deviation.

Standard deviation (extension)

The standard deviation for a set of data can be calculated using the formulae:

$$s = \sqrt{\frac{\sum (x - \bar{x})^2}{n}} \quad \text{or} \quad s = \sqrt{\frac{\sum x^2}{n} - \left\{\frac{\sum x}{n}\right\}^2}$$

Using the mean and the standard deviation (extension)

If we increase (or decrease) all of the values of a distribution by an equal amount then the mean will increase (or decrease) by that amount and the standard deviation (spread) will not be affected.

If we multiply (or divide) all of the values of a distribution by an equal amount then the mean and the standard deviation will also be multiplied (or divided) by that same amount.

CHAPTER 6
Probability

6.1 REINFORCEMENT

In this chapter you will need to:
▸ revise how to use fractions, decimals and percentages
▸ appreciate the vocabulary associated with probability
▸ understand the probability scale

NOTE

Some of these questions will appear on the non-calculator paper so you do need to revise this work.

Fractions, decimals and percentages

You will need to remind yourself how to add and multiply fractions, decimals and percentages. See Chapter 1 on 'Number and number problems' for further information.

Remember that to add fractions the denominators must be the same and the resulting fraction will also have the same denominator.

Worked Examples

1 Work out $\frac{4}{7} + \frac{2}{7}$.

Since the denominators are the same we can add them up as follows:

four sevenths add two sevenths equals six sevenths

so $\frac{4}{7} + \frac{2}{7} = \frac{6}{7}$

2 Work out $\frac{1}{6} + \frac{1}{2}$.

Since the denominators are not the same we need to change the fractions to equivalent fractions with the same denominator. A common denominator is 6, so:

$$\frac{1}{2} \overset{\times 3}{\underset{\times 3}{=}} \frac{3}{6}$$

and the question becomes:

Work out $\frac{1}{6} + \frac{3}{6}$.

one sixth add three sixths equals four sixths

so $\quad \frac{1}{6} + \frac{3}{6} = \frac{4}{6} = \frac{2}{3}$ (as an equivalent fraction in its lowest terms).

PRACTICE 6.1.1   Try these questions without a calculator

1 Work out the following fractions:

a $\frac{1}{5} + \frac{1}{5}$ c $\frac{1}{13} + \frac{3}{13}$ e $\frac{1}{4} + \frac{7}{24}$

b $\frac{3}{11} + \frac{5}{11}$ d $\frac{1}{10} + \frac{1}{5}$ f $\frac{1}{13} + \frac{9}{52}$

Similarly, to multiply two fractions you multiply the numerators together to obtain the numerator of the answer and multiply the denominators together to obtain the denominator of the answer.

NOTE

In this example it would be better to cancel before multiplying

$$\frac{3}{\cancel{4}_1} \times \frac{\cancel{8}^2}{13} = \frac{3}{1} \times \frac{2}{13} = \frac{6}{13}$$

as before.

Worked Example

Work out $\frac{3}{4} \times \frac{5}{13}$.

Multiplying the numerators and the denominators together we get:

$$\frac{3}{4} \times \frac{8}{13} = \frac{24}{52} = \frac{6}{13}$$

PRACTICE 6.1.2   Try these questions without a calculator

1 Work out the following fractions, giving the answers in their lowest terms:

a $\frac{2}{3} \times \frac{1}{12}$ c $\frac{4}{13} \times \frac{1}{6}$ e $\frac{3}{7} \times \frac{14}{15}$

b $\frac{3}{5} \times \frac{1}{6}$ d $\frac{4}{7} \times \frac{3}{12}$ f $\frac{3}{13} \times \frac{3}{52}$

Vocabulary

Probability measures the likelihood of an event happening or not happening.

Worked Example

State whether the following events are **certain, likely, unlikely** or **impossible** to occur:

a You will run a mile in under two minutes.
b You had a birthday last year.
c It will be sunny in June.
d A coin has a head on each side.
e The local supermarket will close next Friday.
f You will win the lottery next week.
g You get an odd number when throwing a dice.

Most people would agree with the following answers:

a You will run a mile in under two minutes.   impossible
b You had a birthday last year.   certain
c It will be sunny in June.   likely
d A coin has a head on each side.   impossible
e The local supermarket will close next Friday.   unlikely
f You will win the lottery next week.   unlikely
g You get an odd number when throwing a die.

This last question cannot be answered properly since the probability of getting an odd number is the same as the probability of not getting an odd number. When these probabilities are the same we call it **evens**.

Probability scale

The idea of using certain, likely, unlikely and impossible to define probability is very crude and therefore probability is usually shown on a **probability scale** which is diagrammatically represented below:

PRACTICE 6.1.3

1 Mark the probabilities of the following events on a probability scale like this one:

a The probability of scoring more than 4 on a roll of a fair six sided dice.
b The probability that you will have a drink tomorrow.
c The probability that a number chosen from the list 2, 3, 4, 5, 6 is odd.
d The probability that a card picked from a standard pack is a diamond.

To calculate the probability of an event occurring we use the following:

$$\text{probability} = \frac{\text{number of successful outcomes}}{\text{total number of possible outcomes}}.$$

Worked Examples

1 Find the probability of obtaining a three when throwing a dice.

$$\text{Probability} = \frac{\text{number of successful outcomes}}{\text{total number of possible outcomes}}$$

$$\text{probability} = \frac{1}{6} \quad \begin{array}{l}\text{(there is 1 successful outcome i.e. a 3)} \\ \text{(there are 6 possible outcomes)}\end{array}$$

2 A bag contains 20 coloured cubes. 12 cubes are green and 8 are red. A cube is selected from the bag at random. What is the probability of selecting a green cube?

$$\text{Probability} = \frac{\text{number of successful outcomes}}{\text{total number of possible outcomes}}$$

$$\text{probability} = \frac{12}{20} \quad \begin{array}{l}\text{(there are 12 successful outcomes)} \\ \text{(there are 20 possible outcomes)}\end{array}$$

$$\text{probability} = \frac{3}{5} \quad \text{(cancelling down)}$$

> **NOTE**
> Probability can be written as a fraction, as a decimal, or as a percentage.

> **NOTE**
> In probability we sometimes use the shorthand *p*(green) to mean the probability of getting a green cube and in this example *p*(green) = $\frac{3}{5}$.

PRACTICE 6.2.1

1 Write down the probability of
 a getting a head if a coin is tossed,
 b getting an odd number if a dice is rolled,
 c selecting a heart from a pack of cards,
 d selecting the ace of clubs from a pack of cards.

2 A letter is selected from the word MISSISSIPPI. What is the probability that it is the letter:
 a M **b** S **c** P **d** R?

3 A letter is picked at random from the 26 letters of the alphabet.
 a What is the probability that the letter is in the first half of the alphabet?
 b What is the probability that the letter is in the word RANDOM?
 c What is the probability that the letter is in the word PROBABILITY?

4 A machine produces 500 bolts and 35 are found to be faulty. What is the probability that a bolt chosen at random will not be faulty? Give your answer as a fraction in its lowest terms.

5   Twenty discs marked with the numbers 1 to 20 are placed in a bag. One
    disc is drawn at random. What is the probability that the number on the
    disc will be:
    a   an odd number,
    b   a multiple of 3,
    c   a prime number,
    d   a factor of 24,
    e   greater than 12,
    f   less than, or equal to, 6?

6   A box contains 40 counters of different colours. A counter is chosen at
    random from the box. The probability that the counter chosen is white
    is $\frac{1}{10}$, the probability that the counter chosen is black is 0.4 and the
    probability that the counter chosen is red is 30%. The rest of the
    counters are blue.
    a   How many counters are white?
    b   How many counters are black?
    c   How many counters are red?
    d   How many counters are blue?

7   A bag contains 20 counters and the probability of getting a red counter
    is 0.85.
    a   How many red counters are there in the bag?
    b   How many counters are not red?

8   A bag contains 7 red cubes, 8 green cubes and 10 blue cubes. What is
    the probability of drawing :
    a   a blue cube,
    b   a green cube,
    c   a cube that is not red,
    d   a yellow cube,
    e   a red, green or blue cube?

Total probability

From the last two parts of question 8 in Practice 6.2.1, you should have noted
that:

$$\text{the probability of a yellow cube} = \frac{0}{25} = 0$$

$$\text{the probability of a red or green or blue cube} = \frac{25}{25} = 1$$

We can see that

if an event is impossible then its probability $= 0$
if an event is certain to happen then its probability $= 1$

The probability that an event occurs plus the probability that the event does
not occur should always equal one.

Worked Example

The probability that Sunita passes her driving test is $\frac{7}{9}$. What is the probability that Sunita does not pass her driving test?

The probability that an event occurs plus the probability that the event does not occur should always equal one.

So the probability that Sunita passes her driving test plus the probability that Sunita does not pass her driving test should equal one.

$\frac{7}{9}$ + the probability that Sunita does not pass her driving test $= 1$

$\frac{7}{9} + \frac{2}{9} = 1$

so the probability that Sunita does not pass her driving test $= \frac{2}{9}$.

NOTE

The probability of an event occurring is equal to 1 minus the probability of the event not occurring so that the probability that Sunita does not pass her driving test is equal to 1 minus the probability that Sunita does pass her driving test.

PRACTICE 6.2.2   Try these questions without a calculator

1   The probability that it will rain tomorrow is $\frac{1}{3}$. What is the probability that it will not rain tomorrow?

2   The probability that a particular team will win the league title is 0.004. What is the probability that the team will not win the league title?

3   The probability that Jem will be late for work on Monday is 0.002. What is the probability that Jem will not be late for work on Monday?

4   A box of chocolates is such that 35% of the chocolates are plain chocolates. Calculate the probability that a chocolate chosen at random is not a plain chocolate.

5   The probability that a bus arrives early is 0.1 and the probability that the bus arrives on time is 0.5. What is the probability that the bus arrives late?

Theoretical and experimental probability

Toss a coin 10 times.
Did you get 5 heads and 5 tails?

Toss a coin another 10 times.
What happened?

When we toss a coin 10 times, we expect to get 5 heads and 5 tails. We use theoretical probability based on equally likely outcomes to tell us how many heads and how many tails we should get (in theory).

In reality, we often get slightly different results and these give us the experimental probability (from our experiment). Experimental probability is often referred to as relative frequency and if we tossed our coin 10 times and got 7 heads then we would say that the experimental probability or relative frequency of getting a head is $\frac{7}{10}$.

The more times we toss the coin, then the closer the experimental probability or relative frequency should be to the theoretical probability, although sometimes estimates of probability can only be made on the basis of experimental probability or relative frequency, for example:

the probability of a coach arriving on time,
the probability of passing a driving test,
the probability that a car will develop a fault.

Worked Examples

1 A coin is tossed 500 times. What is the expected number of heads?

The probability of getting a head when tossing a coin is $\frac{1}{2}$.

When tossing a coin 500 times,

$$\text{expected number of heads} = 500 \times \tfrac{1}{2} = 250$$

If a coin is tossed 500 times, we would expect to get 250 heads (and 250 tails).

2 A dice is thrown 100 times. How many times would you expect to throw a six?

The probability of throwing a six is $\frac{1}{6}$.

When throwing a dice 100 times,

$$\text{expected number of sixes} = 100 \times \tfrac{1}{6} = 16.6 \text{ (recurring)}.$$

If a dice is thrown 100 times, we would expect to get 17 sixes (to the nearest whole number).

3 A dice is thrown 150 times and the following frequency distribution is obtained.

Score	1	2	3	4	5	6
Frequency	21	31	26	19	33	20

a What is the relative frequency of getting a score of 6?
b What is the relative frequency of getting an odd number?

a The relative frequency of a score of 6 is $\frac{20}{150} = \frac{2}{15}$ (in its lowest terms).

b The frequency of getting an odd number is $21 + 26 + 33 = 80$.

The relative frequency of getting an odd number is $\frac{80}{150} = \frac{8}{15}$ (in its lowest terms).

NOTE

In the case where the experimental probability and the theoretical probability are not the same then it is possible that the event is biased. The words fair or honest are used to describe events that are not biased.

PRACTICE 6.2.3a   Try these questions without a calculator

1 A dice is thrown 60 times. What is the expected frequency of an odd number?

2 The probability that a person living in Brackwell will win a prize on the lottery next week is 0.000 2. If the population is 22 500, how many people living in Brackwell can be expected to win the lottery next week?

3 The probability that a new car will develop a fault in the first month is $\frac{1}{200}$. A garage sells 820 new cars one year. How many of the new cars will be expected to develop a fault in the first month?

4 A dice is thrown 200 times and the following frequency distribution is obtained.

Score	1	2	3	4	5	6
Frequency	30	35	38	29	32	36

   a What is the relative frequency of a score of 1?
   b What is the relative frequency of a score of 6?
   c What is the relative frequency of getting an even number?
   d For which score are the relative frequency and theoretical probability the closest?

5 Which of the following probabilities can be determined by considering equally likely outcomes and which can be determined through experimental probability?
   a The probability of a train arriving late.
   b The probability that an unbiased coin will land tails up.
   c The probability of a particular machine breaking down.

PRACTICE 6.2.3b   Try these questions with a calculator

1 The probability that a student will pass their statistics test is $\frac{4}{5}$. How many students should pass their statistics test in a class of 30 students?

2 The probability that a coach arrives late is $\frac{2}{7}$. How many times should the coach arrive late on 31 consecutive days?

3 The probability of passing your driving test in Kingsgrove is 68%. One month, 275 learners take their driving test. How many learners can be expected to pass their driving test?

4 1000 people were asked who they would vote for at the next election and 350 said they would vote for the SDCL party. Assuming that the sample is typical of those who vote at the next election,
   a what is the probability that a person will vote for the SDCL party?
   b If 58 000 000 votes are cast at the election, how many were for the SDCL party?

Mutually exclusive

Two or more events are called mutually exclusive if they cannot happen at the same time.

For example, when tossing a coin you can get a *head* or a *tail* but you cannot get both at the same time, and so we say that when tossing a coin, a head and a tail are mutually exclusive events. Similarly, when throwing a dice you can throw a *six* or an *odd number* but not both at the same time and so we say that when throwing a dice, a six and an odd number are mutually exclusive events.

For mutually exclusive events we can apply the addition rule (sometimes called the **or** rule) which says that:

$$p(A \textbf{ or } B) = p(A) + p(B)$$

Similarly for more than two mutually exclusive events:

$$p(A \textbf{ or } B \textbf{ or } C \textbf{ or } \ldots) = p(A) + p(B) + p(C) + \ldots \text{ etc., etc.}$$

Worked Examples

1   To finish a game a child had to throw a 3 or a 6. What is the probability of the child finishing on the next throw of the dice?

As the events are mutually exclusive we can use the addition rule to find the probability.

$$p(3) = \tfrac{1}{6} \qquad p(6) = \tfrac{1}{6}$$

$$p(3 \text{ or } 6) = p(3) + p(6)$$

$$= \tfrac{1}{6} + \tfrac{1}{6}$$

$$= \tfrac{2}{6} \ (= \tfrac{1}{3} \text{ in its lowest terms})$$

2   What is the probability of getting an even number or a number greater than 4 on the throw of a dice?

$$p(\text{even}) = \tfrac{3}{6} \qquad p(\text{greater than } 4) = \tfrac{2}{6}$$

However, since the probability of getting an even number and the probability of getting a number greater than 4 are not mutually exclusive we *cannot* use the addition rule to find the probability.

$$\text{Probability} = \frac{\text{number of successful outcomes}}{\text{total number of possible outcomes}}$$

$$\text{probability} = \frac{4}{6} \quad \begin{array}{l}\text{(there are 4 successful outcomes i.e. 2, 4, 5 and 6)}\\ \text{(there are 6 possible outcomes)}\end{array}$$

$$\text{probability} = \frac{2}{3} \quad \text{(cancelling down)}$$

3 L, M and N are three mutually exclusive events where $p(\text{event L}) = 20\%$, $p(\text{event M}) = \frac{1}{8}$ and $p(\text{event N}) = 0.1$. Calculate the probability of
   a either L or M occurring,
   b either L or M or N occurring.

   As the events are mutually exclusive,

   a $p(\text{L or M})$ $= p(\text{L}) + p(\text{M})$
                                     $= 20\% + \frac{1}{8}$
                                     $= 0.2 + 0.125$ (converting to decimals)
                                     $= 0.325$

   b $p(\text{L or M or N})$ $= p(\text{L}) + p(\text{M}) + p(\text{N})$
                                     $= 20\% + \frac{1}{8} + 0.1$
                                     $= 0.2 + 0.125 + 0.1$ (converting to decimals)
                                     $= 0.425$

PRACTICE 6.3.1 Try these questions without a calculator

1 Which of the following are mutually exclusive events?
   a Throwing a *one* and an *even number* on a throw of a dice.
   b Throwing a *five* and an *odd number* on a throw of a dice.
   c Picking a *heart* and a *diamond* from a pack of cards.
   d Picking a *heart* and the *4 of clubs* from a pack of cards.
   e Picking an *ace* and a *club* from a pack of cards.
   f Picking a *king* and a *diamond* from a pack of cards.
   g Picking the *king of hearts* and a *spade* from a pack of cards.

2 A card is drawn from a pack of 52 cards. What is the probability that it will be the ace of hearts or a king?

3 The probability that a train arrives early is 0.12 and the probability that the train arrives late is 0.26. What is the probability that the train arives early or on time?

4 A spinner with 12 sides numbered 0 to 11 is spun once. What is the probability of getting
   a a six,
   b an odd number,
   c a number greater than six,
   d a multiple of 4?

5 L, M and N are three mutually exclusive events where $p(\text{event L}) = \frac{1}{3}$, $p(\text{event M}) = \frac{2}{5}$ and $p(\text{event N}) = \frac{1}{10}$. Calculate the probability of
   a either L or M occurring,
   b either M or N occurring,
   c either L or M or N occurring.

6 The probability that a person selected at random from a population is left handed is 0.2. The probability that a person selected at random from the same population wears glasses is 0.4. Explain why the probability of a person being left handed or wearing glasses is *not* 0.6.

Diagrammatic representations can be useful in probability to ensure that all probabilities are considered especially in the case of compound (or combined) events.

Worked Examples

1 A coin is tossed and a counter randomly chosen from four counters coloured red, yellow, green and blue. What is the probability of a head and a blue counter?

It is useful to draw a diagram to illustrate the possible outcomes as follows:

		Counter			
		Red (R)	Yellow (Y)	Green (G)	Blue (B)
Coin	Head (H)	HR	HY	HG	HB
	Tail (T)	TR	TY	TG	TB

There are 8 possible results and each of them is equally likely.

The probability of a head and a blue counter (HB) is $\frac{1}{8}$.

2 Two fair dice are thrown and the sum of the uppermost faces noted. What is the probability that the sum is 9?

Once again, it is useful to draw a diagram to illustrate the possible totals as follows:

		Second dice					
		1	2	3	4	5	6
First dice	1	2	3	4	5	6	7
	2	3	4	5	6	7	8
	3	4	5	6	7	8	⑨
	4	5	6	7	8	⑨	10
	5	6	7	8	⑨	10	11
	6	7	8	⑨	10	11	12

There are 36 possible results and each of them is equally likely.
The probability that the sum is 9 is $\frac{4}{36} = \frac{1}{9}$.

PRACTICE 6.4.1   Try these questions without a calculator

1 In an experiment, Tom tosses a coin and Jenny throws a dice. Draw a possibility space for the two events.

Use your possibility space to calculate
  a the probability of a head and a six,
  b the probability of a tail and an even number.

2 A counter is selected from a box containing 4 red and 3 green counters at the same time as a six sided dice, numbered 1 to 6, is thrown. Draw a possibility space for this information and use this information to calculate
  a the probability of a red and a six,
  b the probability of a green and a three,
  c the probability of a red and an odd number.

3 A six sided dice, numbered 1 to 6, and a tetrahedral dice, numbered 1 to 4, are thrown simultaneously. Draw a possibility space for the two dice and use this information to calculate
  a the probability of a total of 3,
  b the probability of a total of 7,
  c the probability of a total of 10.

4 Two pentagonal spinners with the numbers 1 to 5 are spun and their outcomes added together. Draw a possibility space for the two spinners and use this information to calculate
  a the probability of a total of 2,
  b the probability of a total of 6,
  c the probability of a total of 9.

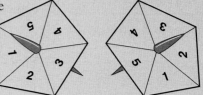

5 Two coins are tossed and a six sided dice is rolled. For two heads the score is double the number shown on the dice. For one head the score is the number shown on the dice. For no heads the score equals zero. Draw a possibility space for the scores and use this information to calculate
  a the probability of a score of 4,
  b the probability that the score is more than 4.

6 The following table shows the probabilities of selecting counters from a box. The counters are coloured red, blue and green and numbered 1, 2, 3 and 4.

		\multicolumn{4}{c}{Number}
		1	2	3	4
	Red	$\frac{1}{20}$	$\frac{1}{10}$	$\frac{1}{5}$	0
Colour	Blue	$\frac{1}{10}$	0	$\frac{1}{20}$	$\frac{1}{10}$
	Green	$\frac{1}{5}$	$\frac{1}{20}$	$\frac{1}{10}$	$\frac{1}{20}$

  a A counter is taken from the box at random. Calculate the probability that
    i it is blue and numbered 1,
    ii it is green,
    iii it is numbered 3,
    iv it is blue or numbered 4.
  b There are 14 red counters in the box.
    i How many counters are there altogether?
    ii How many blue counters are there altogether?

Tree diagrams

A tree diagram is another useful tool which can help solve problems involving probabilities. The following tree diagram shows the various possibilities that can occur when a coin is tossed twice.

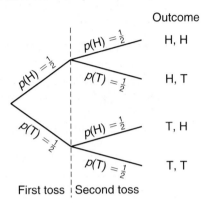

The tree diagram shows the outcomes for each toss of the coin along with the respective probabilities which are marked on each of the branches. The outcomes when two coins are tossed are clearly visible as HH, HT, TH and TT.

Worked Example

A pen is selected from a box containing 6 red, 3 green and 4 blue pens and a second pen is selected from a different box containing 3 red and 4 green pens. Draw a tree diagram to show the various possibilities that can occur.

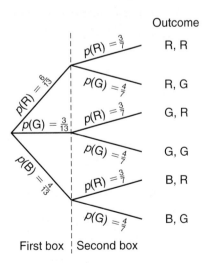

The tree diagram shows the outcomes for the two boxes along with the respective probabilities which are marked on each of the branches. The outcomes for the two boxes are clearly visible as RR, RG, GR, GG, BR and BG.

PRACTICE 6.4.2

1   Draw a tree diagram to show the various possibilities that can occur when a coin is tossed three times.

2   Draw a tree diagram to show the various possibilities that can occur when a coin is tossed four times.

3   A pen is selected from a box containing 3 red, 2 green and 5 blue pens and a second pen is selected from a different box containing 4 green and 5 blue pens. Draw a tree diagram to show the various possibilities that can occur.

4   A box contains 3 red and 4 green counters. A counter is drawn from the box, replaced and then a second counter is drawn from the box. Draw a tree diagram to show the various possibilities that can occur.

5   The probability that Heather arrives at college on time is 0.85. Draw a tree diagram to show the various possibilities that can occur on three consecutive days.

Independent events

Two or more events are said to be independent if one event happening has no effect on the other event happening.

For example, when tossing a coin twice, getting a *head* on the first throw does not affect getting a *head* on the second throw so these two events are independent. Similarly, having already thrown two heads does not affect your getting a *head* on the third throw as these events are still independent and one event happening has no effect on the other event happening.

For independent events we can apply the multiplication rule (sometimes called the **and** rule) which says that :

$$p(A \textbf{ and } B) = p(A) \times p(B)$$

Similarly for more than two independent events:

$$p(A \textbf{ and } B \textbf{ and } C \textbf{ and } \ldots) = p(A) \times p(B) \times p(C) \times \ldots \text{ etc., etc.}$$

Worked Examples

1   What is the probability of tossing a *head* on a coin and throwing a *six* on a dice?

As the events are independent we can use the multiplication rule to find the probability.

$$p(\text{head}) = \tfrac{1}{2} \qquad p(6) = \tfrac{1}{6}$$

$$p(\text{head and } 6) = p(\text{head}) \times p(6)$$

$$= \tfrac{1}{2} \times \tfrac{1}{6}$$

$$= \qquad\qquad \tfrac{1}{12}$$

2 A manufacturer makes components for washing machines. The probability that a component is faulty is 0.01. Draw and label a tree diagram to show the possible outcomes when two components are chosen at random. Calculate the probability that:

a both components are not faulty,

b exactly one component is faulty.

The following tree diagram can be used to illustrate the possibilities:

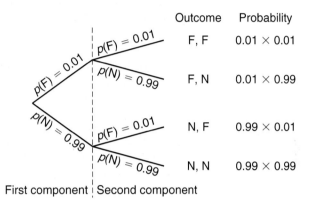

	Outcome	Probability
	F, F	0.01 × 0.01
	F, N	0.01 × 0.99
	N, F	0.99 × 0.01
	N, N	0.99 × 0.99

First component ⋮ Second component

From the diagram we can see that

a the probability that both components are not faulty

$= p$(first component is not faulty and second component is not faulty)
$= p$(first component is not faulty) $\times p$(second component is not faulty)
$= 0.99 \times 0.99$
$= 0.9801$

b To find out the probability that exactly one component is faulty we need to appreciate that this can arise in two ways, i.e. the first component is faulty and the second component is not faulty *or* the first component is not faulty and the second component is faulty

$= p$(first component is faulty and second component is not faulty *or* first component is not faulty and second component is faulty)
$= p$(first component is faulty and second component is not faulty) $+$ p(first component is not faulty and second component is faulty)
$= [p$(first component is faulty) $\times p$(second component is not faulty)$] +$ $[p$(first component is not faulty) $\times p$(second component is faulty)$]$
$= [0.01 \times 0.99] + [0.99 \times 0.01]$
$= [0.0099] + [0.0099]$
$= 0.0198$

3 The probability that Nigel passes his motorbike test is $\frac{3}{5}$ and the probability that Gary passes his motorbike test is $\frac{1}{3}$. Calculate the probability that:

a both Nigel and Gary pass their motorbike test,
b both Nigel and Gary fail their motorbike test,
c only Gary passes his motorbike test.

As the events are independent we can use the multiplication rule to find the probability.

$$p(\text{Nigel passes}) = \tfrac{3}{5} \qquad p(\text{Gary passes}) = \tfrac{1}{3}$$

a The probability that both Nigel and Gary pass their motorbike test

$$= p(\text{Nigel passes and Gary passes})$$

$$= p(\text{Nigel passes}) \times p(\text{Gary passes})$$

$$= \tfrac{3}{5} \times \tfrac{1}{3}$$

$$= \tfrac{1}{5}$$

b To find the probability that both Nigel and Gary fail their motorbike test we need to find out the probability that Nigel fails his motorbike test and that Gary fails his motorbike test.

Using the idea of total probability, the probability that Nigel fails his motorbike test is equal to 1 minus the probability that he passes his motorbike test.

The probability that Nigel fails his motorbike test $= 1 - \tfrac{3}{5} = \tfrac{2}{5}$

Similarly

the probability that Gary fails his motorbike test $= 1 - \tfrac{1}{3} = \tfrac{2}{3}$

The probability that both Nigel and Gary fail their motorbike test

$$= p(\text{Nigel fails and Gary fails})$$

$$= p(\text{Nigel fails}) \times p(\text{Gary fails})$$

$$= \tfrac{2}{5} \times \tfrac{2}{3}$$

$$= \tfrac{4}{15}$$

c The probability that only Gary passes his motorbike test is equal to the probability that Gary passes his motorbike test and Nigel fails his motorbike test

$$= p(\text{Gary passes and Nigel fails})$$

$$= p(\text{Gary passes}) \times p(\text{Nigel fails})$$

$$= \tfrac{1}{3} \times \tfrac{2}{5}$$

$$= \tfrac{2}{15}$$

PRACTICE 6.5.1a   Try these questions without a calculator.

1 A coin is tossed and a card is drawn from a pack of 52 cards. Calculate the probability that the result will be
  a a head and a diamond,   **c** a tail and the ace of hearts,
  b a head and a king,   **d** a tail and the three of spades.

2 A box contains 3 red and 4 green counters. A counter is drawn from the box and replaced and then a second counter is drawn from the box. Draw a tree diagram and use it to calculate the probability that
  a both counters will be red,
  b both counters will be green,
  c the first counter will be red and the second counter green,
  d one counter will be red and one counter will be green.

3 A company produces microchips for dishwashers. The probability that a microchip is faulty is 0.02. Draw and label a tree diagram to show the possible outcomes when two microchips are chosen at random. Calculate the probability that
  a both microchips are faulty,   **b** exactly one microchip is faulty.

4 A biased coin is such that the probability of getting a head is 0.6. Calculate the probability of getting
  a a tail,
  b two heads if the coin is tossed twice,
  c exactly one head if the coin is tossed twice.

5 What is the probability of getting five tails in five tosses of a fair coin?

PRACTICE 6.5.1b   Try these questions with a calculator

1 The probability that a person passes their music examination is 0.925. Jayne has already failed her music examination twice. What is the probability that Jayne will pass on her third attempt?

2 The probability that a person travelled abroad in the past 12 months is $\frac{5}{8}$. Calculate the proability that
  a two people chosen at random will both have been abroad in the past 12 months,
  b three people chosen at random will all have been abroad in the past 12 months,
  c at least one person from three people chosen at random will have been abroad in the past 12 months.

3 What is the probability of getting six heads in six tosses of a fair coin?

4 A biased dice is such that the probability of scoring a *one* is 0.2 and the probability of scoring a *six* is 0.4. Calculate the probability that
  a the score will be a *one* or a *six* when the dice is thrown once,
  b two *six's* will be scored when the dice is thrown twice,
  c exactly one *six* will be scored when the dice is thrown twice.

Dependent events

Two or more events are said to be dependent if one event happening has an effect on the other event happening. The following worked example is given to illustrate the difference between independent and dependent events.

Worked Example

Two cards are drawn at random from a pack of 52 cards. Find the probability that they are both kings.

There are two possibilities to consider:

Possibility 1: If the first card is replaced before the second card is drawn then the two events are independent and the probabilities for each event are the same.

The following tree diagram can be used to illustrate the possibilities:

	Outcome	Probability
$p(K) = \frac{4}{52}$	K, K	$\frac{4}{52} \times \frac{4}{52}$
$p(\bar{K}) = \frac{48}{52}$	K, $\bar{K}$	$\frac{4}{52} \times \frac{48}{52}$
$p(K) = \frac{4}{52}$	$\bar{K}$, K	$\frac{48}{52} \times \frac{4}{52}$
$p(\bar{K}) = \frac{48}{52}$	$\bar{K}$, $\bar{K}$	$\frac{48}{52} \times \frac{48}{52}$

$p(K) = \frac{4}{52}$ $p(\bar{K}) = \frac{48}{52}$

First card   Second card

> **NOTE**
> The other probabilities are also included for your information with K standing for a 'king' and $\bar{K}$ standing for '*not a king*'.

From the diagram we can see that the probability that both cards are kings

$$= p(\text{king on first and king on second})$$
$$= p(\text{king on first}) \times p(\text{king on second})$$
$$= \frac{4}{52} \times \frac{4}{52}$$
$$= \frac{1}{169} \text{ (cancelling down to lowest terms)}$$

Possibility 2: If the first card is *not* replaced before the second card is drawn then the two events are not independent and the probabilities on the second event will be affected by the outcomes on the first event.

In determining the probabilities for the second card we need to take account of the fact that the first card was not replaced so that:

if the first card was a king…
   there are now 3 kings and 48 other cards left (i.e. 51 cards left altogether) from which to choose the second card

if the first card was *not* a king…
   there are now 4 kings and 47 other cards left (i.e. 51 cards left altogether) from which to choose the second card.

The following tree diagram can be used to illustrate the possibilities:

The other probabilities
are again included for
your information.

Outcome   Probability

$p(K) = \frac{3}{51}$ K, K $\frac{4}{52} \times \frac{3}{51}$

$p(K) = \frac{4}{52}$ $p(\bar{K}) = \frac{48}{51}$ K, $\bar{K}$ $\frac{4}{52} \times \frac{48}{51}$

$p(\bar{K}) = \frac{48}{52}$ $p(K) = \frac{4}{51}$ $\bar{K}$, K $\frac{48}{52} \times \frac{4}{51}$

$p(\bar{K}) = \frac{47}{51}$ $\bar{K}$, $\bar{K}$ $\frac{48}{52} \times \frac{47}{51}$

First card | Second card

From the diagram we can see that the probability that both cards are kings

$= p(\text{king on first and king on second})$

$= p(\text{king on first}) \times p(\text{king on second})$

$= \frac{4}{52} \times \frac{3}{51}$

$= \frac{1}{221}$ (cancelling down to lowest terms)

You should leave your
answers as fractions in
their lowest terms where
appropriate.

PRACTICE 6.6.1a   Try these questions without a calculator.

1   A box contains 7 blue pens and 4 red pens. A pen is taken from the box
    and not replaced. A second pen is then taken from the box. Draw a tree
    diagram and use it to calculate
    a   the probability that both pens are blue,
    b   the probability that both pens are red,
    c   the probability that one pen is blue and the other pen is red.

2   A bag contains 4 yellow and 8 green cubes. One cube is chosen at
    random and its colour noted. The cube is not replaced and a second
    cube is chosen at random and its colour noted. Draw a tree diagram to
    represent this situation and use it to calculate
    a   the probability of obtaining two green cubes,
    b   the probability of obtaining one cube of each colour.

3   Simon has 6 brown and 12 black socks in his drawer. If he takes out two
    socks from the drawer, one after another, calculate
    a   the probability that both socks are brown,
    b   the probability that both socks are black,
    c   the probability that the socks are different colours.

4   The probability that Andre passes his driving test on the first attempt is
    $\frac{2}{5}$. If he fails the test then the probability that he passes on the next
    attempt is $\frac{6}{11}$. Draw a tree diagram to represent this situation and use it
    to calculate the probability that Andre passes the driving test on his
    third attempt.

PRACTICE 6.6.1b   Try these questions with a calculator

1   Steffy and Mariah play three sets of tennis.
    The probability that Steffy wins the first set is 0.6. If Steffy wins a set
    the probability of winning the next set is 0.7. If Mariah wins a set the
    probability of winning the next set is 0.8. Draw a tree diagram to
    represent this situation and use it to calculate the probability
    a   that Mariah will win all three sets,
    b   that Steffy will win at least two sets.

2   The diagram shows a series of road junctions.
    At junction A cars turn left with probability 0.4
    At junction B cars turn left with probability 0.7
    At junction C cars turn left with probability 0.2

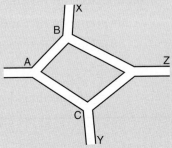

    Calculate the probability that a car passing A will arrive at:
    a   point X,   b   point Y,   c   point Z.

The following exercise provides further practice at probability questions that
are considered suitable for inclusion at the higher level.

PRACTICE 6.6.2   Try these questions with a calculator

1   A machine relies on 3 components and will work providing at least two
    of the components are working. The probability that any of the
    components is defective is 4%. Complete the following tree diagram
    giving the probabilities on each branch.

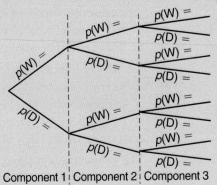

Use your tree diagram to calculate the probability
a   that exactly two components work,
b   the machine will work.

2 Nikki drives to work each morning and passes through three sets of traffic lights. The probability that she has to stop at the first set is $\frac{3}{10}$ and the probability that she has to stop at the second set is $\frac{1}{2}$. Complete the following tree diagram, for the first two sets of traffic lights, giving the probabilities on each branch.

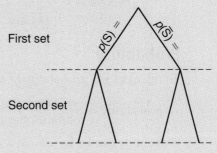

Use your tree diagram to calculate the probability

a that Nikki stops at both of the first two sets of traffic lights,
b that Nikki stops at only one of the first two sets of traffic lights.

The probability that Nikki has to stop at the third set of lights is dependent upon whether she stopped at the second set of traffic lights.

If she stops at the second set of traffic lights then the probability that she stops at the third set is $\frac{1}{5}$. If she does not stop at the second set of traffic lights then the probability that she stops at the third set is $\frac{2}{5}$. Calculate the probability

c that Nikki does not stop at any of the sets of traffic lights,
d that Nikki stops at only one of three sets of traffic lights.

3 A student takes examinations in English, history and media studies.

The probability that he passes his English examination is 0.7.
The probability that he passes his history examination is 0.6.
The probability that he passes his media studies examination is 0.9.

Given that the results are independent of one another calculate the probability that

a he passes English or media studies or both,
b he fails English or history but not both.

Probability scale

Probability is usually shown on a probability scale which is diagrammatically represented below:

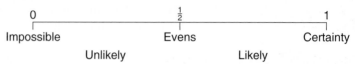

Probability

To calculate the probability of an event occurring we use the following:

$$\text{probability} = \frac{\text{number of successful outcomes}}{\text{total number of possible outcomes}}.$$

Probability can be written as a fraction, as a decimal, or as a percentage.

Total probability

If an event is impossible then its probability $= 0$. If an event is certain to happen then its probability $= 1$.

The probability of an event occuring is equal to one minus the probability of the event not occurring.

Mutually exclusive

Two or more events are called mutually exclusive if they cannot happen at the same time.

For mutually exclusive events we can apply the addition rule (sometimes called the **or** rule) which says that:

$p(A \textbf{ or } B) = p(A) + p(B)$

Similarly for more than two mutually exclusive events:

$p(A \textbf{ or } B \textbf{ or } C \textbf{ or } \ldots) = p(A) + p(B) + p(C) + \ldots$ etc., etc.

Independent events

Two or more events are said to be independent if one event happening has no effect on the other event happening.

For independent events we can apply the multiplication rule (sometimes called the **and** rule) which says that :

$p(A \textbf{ and } B) = p(A) \times p(B)$

Similarly for more than two independent events:

$p(A \textbf{ and } B \textbf{ and } C \textbf{ and } \ldots) = p(A) \times p(B) \times p(C) \times \ldots$ etc., etc.

Dependent events (extension)

Two or more events are said to be dependent if one event happening has an effect on the other event happening. Tree diagrams are very useful representations to use when dealing with dependent events.

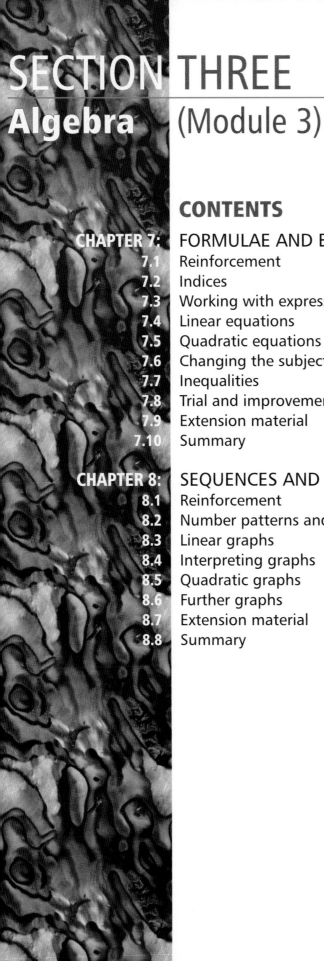

SECTION THREE
Algebra (Module 3)

CONTENTS

CHAPTER 7
Formulae and equations

In this chapter you will need to:
▸ be able to express simple formulae in words
▸ know about arithmetic index notation
▸ be familiar with the basic laws of arithmetic
▸ be familiar with algebraic notation

Simple formulae

You need to be able to express simple formulae in words:
For example, the area of a rectangle equals length times breadth.

Index notation

For further information on indices and powers see Topic 2.1 on 'Powers'.

Basic laws of arithmetic

The commutative law

When we add or multiply two numbers, it doesn't matter which comes first

i.e. $a \times b = b \times a$

For example $4 + 7 = 7 + 4$ and $4 \times 7 = 7 \times 4$
               $6 + {}^{-}8 = {}^{-}8 + 6$ and $6 \times {}^{-}8 = {}^{-}8 \times 6$
In algebra $a + b = b + a$ and $a \times b = b \times a$

> **NOTE**
> The commutative law does not work for subtraction or division. For example, $5 - 3$ is not the same as $3 - 5$ and $10 \div 5$ is not the same as $5 \div 10$.

The associative law

When we add or multiply three (or more) numbers then

$$a \times (b \times c) = (a \times b) \times c \quad \text{or} \quad a + (b + c) = (a + b) + c$$

For example $2 + 3 + 4 \ = \ (2 + 3) + 4 \ = \ 2 + (3 + 4)$
i.e. $9 \ = \ 5 \ + 4 \ = \ 2 + \ 7$
and $3 \times 5 \times 2 \ = \ (3 \times 5) \times 2 \ = \ 3 \times (5 \times 2)$
i.e. $30 \ = \ 15 \ \times 2 \ = \ 3 \times \ 10$

In algebra $a + b + c \ = \ (a + b) + c \ = \ a + (b + c)$
and $a \times b \times c \ = \ (a \times b) \times c \ = \ a \times (b \times c)$

Basic algebraic notation

Terms:

x	means	$1 \times x$	or $1x$
$-x$	means	$-1 \times x$	or $-1x$
$4x$	means	$4 \times x$	or $(x + x + x + x)$
$\dfrac{x}{4}$	means	$x \div 4$	or $\frac{1}{4}$ of x
xy	means	$x \times y$	
$3xy$	means	$3 \times x \times y$	or $(xy + xy + xy)$
$\dfrac{x}{y}$	means	$x \div y$	

7.2 INDICES

Index notation

We saw, for example, in Topic 2.1 that 6^4 means $6 \times 6 \times 6 \times 6 = 1296$.

In algebra	x^2 means	$x \times x$	(we say x *squared*)
	x^3 means	$x \times x \times x$	(we say x *cubed*)
	x^4 means	$x \times x \times x \times x$	(we say x *to the power 4*), etc.
i.e.	x^n means	$x \times x \times x \times \ldots$etc	(we say x *to the power n*)
			(multiplied n times).

Also $3x^2$ means $3 \times x^2$ or $3 \times x \times x$ or $(x^2 + x^2 + x^2)$
$(3x)^2$ means $3x \times 3x$ or $3 \times x \times 3 \times x = 9x^2$
$2a^2b^3$ means $2 \times a^2 \times b^3$ or $2 \times a \times a \times b \times b \times b$ or $(a^2b^3 + a^2b^3)$
$x + y$ means *the sum of the unknown numbers x and y*

The laws of indices

We have already seen in Topic 2.2 that, for example,

$$5^3 \times 5^4 = 5^{3+4} = 5^7 \text{ and that } 4^8 \div 4^5 = 4^{8-5} = 4^3 .$$

In algebra these basic laws can be written as:

a $x^a \times x^b = x^{a+b}$ for example, $a^3 \times a^4 = a^7$
b $x^a \div x^b = x^{a-b}$ for example, $b^7 \div b^4 = b^3$
c $(x^a)^b = x^{ab}$ for example, $(c^2)^3 = c^{2 \times 3} = c^2 \times c^2 \times c^2 = c^6$

Worked Examples

a $a^2 \times a^3 = a^{2+3} = a^5$ **d** $2d \times 5e = 10de$

b $b^5 \div b^3 = b^{5-3} = b^2$ **e** $3f \times (-4g) = -12fg$

c $(2c)^3 = 2c \times 2c \times 2c = 8c^3$ **f** $(-7h) \times (-3i) = 21hi$

g $2j \times 3k \times 4l = 24jkl$

h $3m^4n^2 \times 5m^3n^9 = 3 \times 5 \times m^{4+3} \times n^{2+9} = 15m^7n^{11}$

i $15pq^3 \div 3p^3q = (15 \div 3) \times (p \div p^3) \times (q^3 \div q) = \dfrac{5q^2}{p^2}$

j $8r^5s^3 \div 20s^2t^3 = \dfrac{2r^5s}{5t^3}$

k $\sqrt{v^6} = v^{6 \div 2} = v^3$ **l** $\sqrt[3]{w^6} = w^{6 \div 3} = w^2$ **m** $\sqrt{9x^8} = 3x^4$

PRACTICE 7.2.1   Try these questions without a calculator

1 Simplify the following:

a $2x \times 3y$	**c** $e^5 \times e^3$	**e** $(3m)^4$	**g** $(-3p)^4$
b $5c \times (-3d)$	**d** $f^8 \div f^2$	**f** $(-5n)^3$	**h** $(-5q) \times (-6r)$

i $\frac{1}{3}s \times 24t$ **q** $7j^4k^6 \times 8j^8k$

j $\frac{5}{6}u \times \frac{3}{10}v$ **r** $4mn^3 \times 5m^7n^4 \times 9m^2n^3$

k $5w \times 4x \times 6y$ **s** $24p^6 \div 8p^2$

l $5w \times 4x \times (-6y)$ **t** $4q \div 12q^2$

m $(-8x) \times 2y \times (-4z)$ **u** $5r^5s^6 \div r^3s^4$

n $(-9a) \times (-2b) \times (-5c)$ **v** $36t^8u^6v^2 \div (-3t^2u^3v)$

o $2d \times 3e \times 4f^2$ **w** $(-20w^9x^6) \div (-4w^4x)$

p $g^2h^3 \times g^7h^5 \times ghi^4$

2 **a** If $4^n = 64$, find n.   **c** If $6^{2t+1} = 216$, find t.

  b If $3^m = 81$, find m.   **d** If $(2^{2b})(2^{6b}) = 256$, find b.

Basic algebra

Algebra is simply arithmetic using letters and numbers. In algebra letters are used to represent numbers. The mathematical rules that work for arithmetic also work for algebra.

For example, when we write down that Jane is 26 years old we are making an *exact* statement, but when we say that John is P years old we are making a *general* statement. We can use any *particular* value of P that is appropriate.

Worked Examples

1 Write in algebraic notation:

  a the sum of the number p plus three times the number q,

  b four times the number m subtracted from three times the number n,

  c seven times x squared divided by six times y cubed.

  a $p + 3q$ **b** $3n - 4m$ **c** $\dfrac{7x^2}{6y^3}$

2 Jane is 26 years old and John is P years old. How old will they be
   a in five years,
   b last year?

   a In five years: Jane will be $26 + 5 = 31$ John will be $P + 5$
   b Last year: Jane was $26 - 1 = 25$ John was $P - 1$

PRACTICE 7.3.1

1 Write the following in algebraic notation.
   a The sum of five times the number x plus four times the number y.
   b Three times the number c minus 2.
   c Double the number p and divide it by the number q squared.
   d The cost of 4 pounds of apples plus 2 pounds of bananas, where a is
      the cost of 1 pound of apples and b is the cost of 1 pound of bananas.
   e The value of a number divided by four and added to the cube of the
      number, where x is the number.

2 Ally is y years old now. Write down:
   a her dad's age if he is four times as old as Ally is now,
   b Ally's age in six year's time,
   c her dad's age seven years ago,
   d her dad's age when Ally was half as old as she is now,
   e Ally's age when her dad will be five times as old as Ally is now.

Words and terms

- Any letter used to represent a number is called a *variable* or *unknown*. They
  are called variables because their values can change.
- Anything that has a fixed value is called a *constant*.
- 2 or 0.5 or π are constants because their values do not change.
- Any number in front of a variable is called a *coefficient*.
  When we write the term $7x^2$ we say that 7 *is the coefficient of* x^2.
- An algebraic statement which is a collection of terms is called an *expression*.
- An expression is a collection of constants, variables and symbols. For
  example, the expression $4x^3 + 7x^2 - 5x + 9$ is a statement of three variable
  terms and one constant. The terms in any expression must be connected by
  plus $(+)$ or minus $(-)$ signs.
- Any term may have more than one variable in it. For example, the area of a
  rectangle of length l and width w could be written as lw.
- Usually we put letters in alphabetical order in a term and the number
  always comes first. For example, we would write $5a^3bc^2$ rather than a^3c^25b.
- If any expression has more than one term of the same *type* in it then these
  terms can be combined. These are called *like* terms. Thus in the expression
  $5x^2 + 8x - 4 + 6x^2 - 3x$, the $5x^2$ and $6x^2$ are *like* terms as are the
  $8x$ and $-3x$. The expression could be simplified into $11x^2 + 5x - 4$.
- When we are deciding whether terms are *like*, do not forget that the order
  of letters within the term is *not* important. Thus $5cd$ and $4dc$ are like terms
  as are $3p^2qr^3$, $5r^3p^2q$ and $-6qp^2r^3$.

> **NOTE**
> The $11x^2$ and $5x$ terms
> are *not* like terms. They
> are in fact *unlike* terms.

Worked Examples

Simplify:

a $2f + 7f - 3f$
b $2a + 3b + 6a + 9b$
c $x - y - 2z + 5x - 4y + z$

d $4b^2 - 7b + 4 - 2b^2 - 9b - 5$
e $3pqr + 7qrp - 4rqp$
f $2cd^2 + 4c^2d + 8cd^2 - c^2d$

a $2f + 7f - 3f = 6f$

b $2a + 3b + 6a + 9b = 2a + 6a + 3b + 9b$
$$= 8a + 12b$$

c $x - y - 2z + 5x - 4y + z = x + 5x - y - 4y - 2z + z$
$$= 6x - 5y - z$$

d $4b^2 - 7b + 4 - 2b^2 - 9b - 5 = 4b^2 - 2b^2 - 7b - 9b + 4 - 5$
$$= 2b^2 - 16b - 1$$

e $3pqr + 7qrp - 4rqp = 6pqr$

f $2cd^2 + 4c^2d + 8cd^2 - c^2d = 2cd^2 + 8cd^2 + 4c^2d - c^2d$
$$= 10cd^2 + 3c^2d$$

PRACTICE 7.3.2   Try these questions without a calculator

1 Simplify:

a $4a + 7a + 9a$

b $5b - 9b + 6b$

c $4c + c - 7c$

d $4d + 7e + 8d + 8e$

e $5f - 3g - 2f + 6g$

f $2h - 7k - 9l - 5h - 5k + 4l$

g $x + 3y + 6x - 1 - 7m$

h $8p - 7q + 3 - 6q - 7p$

i $2r + \frac{3}{2}s - \frac{1}{2}r + \frac{5}{4}s$

j $7t + 9u - 6u - t^2$

k $11v^2 - 4v + 9$

l $4w + 3w^2 - w^2 - 5w - 8$

m $2x^2 + (2x)^2$

n $\dfrac{4}{y} + \dfrac{7}{y} - \dfrac{3}{y}$

o $\dfrac{2}{z} - \dfrac{5}{z^2} + \dfrac{9}{z^2} - \dfrac{3}{z}$

p $2 - 3x + 4x^2 + 9x^3 - 5 + 4x - 4x^2 + 2x^3$

q $\dfrac{b}{c} + \dfrac{4b}{c} - \dfrac{2b}{c}$

r $3de + 5ef - 7fg + 4gd$

s $4x^3y + 5x^2y^2 - 3xy^3 + 2x^2y^2 - 2xy^3 + 8x^3y$

t $(2z)^3 + 4z^2 + 5z^3$

Using brackets in algebra

We saw in Topic 1.1 that there is a definite order for doing operations. We use the word **BODMAS**. The **B** for **B**rackets is used in algebra as well. Brackets are used when we wish to group terms together. Anything written inside brackets should be done before any other operations.

For example, Mrs Lavers has three pints of milk, m, and two cartons of cream, c, delivered each day for a week.

So, for 1 day, we say $\hspace{4cm}$ $3m + 2c$

Thus, for 7 days, we say $\hspace{3.5cm}$ $7(3m + 2c)$

NOTE

$7(3m + 2c)$ means
7 times $(3m + 2c)$.

If we removed the brackets we would get $\;\; 21m + 14c$.
The two expressions $7(3m + 2c)$ and $21m + 14c$ are said to be **mathematically equivalent**.

When removing brackets, each term *inside* the bracket is multiplied by the term *outside*.

Remember to use the rules for multiplying signs when removing the brackets. A term without a sign in front of it is always taken as positive $(+)$. The rules are simple:

when multiplying or dividing:

if the signs are the same, i.e. both $(+)$ or both $(-)$, the result is $(+)$,
if the signs are different, i.e. one $(+)$ and one $(-)$, the result is $(-)$.

Worked Examples

Simplify:

a $3(x + 2y)$ $\hspace{2cm}$ **e** $-4(6g - 2h)$ $\hspace{1.5cm}$ **i** $6r - 3(5r + 4s - 3t)$

b $4(2a - 3b)$ $\hspace{2cm}$ **f** $-8(-2x - 5y)$ $\hspace{1.5cm}$ **j** $2(a + 3b) + 4(2a - 2b)$

c $2(-4c - 5d)$ $\hspace{2cm}$ **g** $3x(2x + 4y - 5z)$

d $-5(3e + 7f)$ $\hspace{2cm}$ **h** $5p + 4(p - 2q + 5)$

a $\begin{aligned} 3(x + 2y) &= 3 \times x + 3 \times 2y \\ &= 3x + 6y \end{aligned}$

b $\begin{aligned} 4(2a - 3b) &= 4 \times 2a + 4 \times -3b \\ &= 8a - 12b \end{aligned}$

c $\begin{aligned} 2(-4c - 5d) &= 2 \times -4c + 2 \times -5d \\ &= -8c - 10d \end{aligned}$

d $\begin{aligned} -5(3e + 7f) &= -5 \times 3e + -5 \times 7f \\ &= -15e - 35f \end{aligned}$

e $\begin{aligned} -4(6g - 2h) &= -4 \times 6g + -4 \times -2h \\ &= -24g + 8h \end{aligned}$

f $\begin{aligned} -8(-2x - 5y) &= -8 \times -2x + -8 \times -5y \\ &= 16x + 40y \end{aligned}$

g $\begin{aligned} 3x(2x + 4y - 5z) &= 3x \times 2x + 3x \times 4y + 3x \times -5z \\ &= 6x^2 + 12xy - 15xz \end{aligned}$

h $\begin{aligned} 5p + 4(p - 2q + 5) &= 5p + 4 \times p + 4 \times -2q + 4 \times 5 \\ &= 5p + 4p - 8q + 20 \\ &= 9p - 8q + 20 \end{aligned}$

$$\begin{aligned}\mathbf{i}\quad 6r - 3(5r + 4s - 3t) &= 6r - 3 \times 5r - 3 \times 4s - 3 \times -3t\\ &= 6r - 15r - 12s + 9t\\ &= -9r - 12s + 9t\end{aligned}$$

$$\begin{aligned}\mathbf{j}\quad 2(a + 3b) + 4(2a - 2b) &= 2 \times a + 2 \times 3b + 4 \times 2a + 4 \times -2b\\ &= 2a + 6b + 8a - 8b\\ &= 10a - 2b\end{aligned}$$

PRACTICE 7.3.3   Try these questions without a calculator

1 Remove the brackets:

a $2(a + 3)$ **f** $-4(3x + 2y)$ **k** $3w(x + 2y - 3z)$

b $2(3a - 1)$ **g** $-3(4y - 3z)$ **l** $-3w(4w - 5x + 3)$

c $3(2b - 7)$ **h** $-7(-3a + 2b)$ **m** $5(3x^2 + 2x + 7)$

d $4(2b + 3c)$ **i** $-6(-4c - 3d)$ **n** $4y(7y^2 - y + 3)$

e $5(6f - 3g)$ **j** $\frac{2}{3}(9e - 15f)$

2 Remove the brackets, collect like terms and simplify:

a $2z + 3(z + 5)$ **j** $5(2y^2 - 3y + 4) - 2(y^2 - 3y - 5)$

b $2z - 3(z + 5)$ **k** $2x(x^2 + 3x - 1) + 3(4x^2 - 6x + 2)$

c $2z - 3(z - 5)$ **l** $4xy - 3x(y + 2)$

d $4(a - 3) + 2(a + 7)$ **m** $5m(n - 3) - 2n(m + 4)$

e $5(2b - 3) - 3(2b + 1)$ **n** $4p(2p + 3q) + 3p(5p - q)$

f $-2(-2c - 3) - (4c - 7)$ **o** $4p(2p + 3q) - 3p(5p - q)$

g $-(5d + 3e - 2f) + 3(2d - e + 3f)$ **p** $7y(5z + \dfrac{3}{y})$

h $-(5d + 3e - 2f) - 3(2d - e + 3f)$ **q** $-2t(4 - \dfrac{8}{t})$

i $2(x^2 + 2x - 1) + 3(x^2 - x - 7)$ **r** $7(2z + 3y) - 3(y - 2x) + 4(2x + 3z)$

Multiplying brackets together

Sometimes we want to multiply two brackets together. For example, $(x + 2)(x + 3)$ means 'multiply the bracket $(x + 2)$ by the bracket $(x + 3)$'. Now, x^2 can be represented by the area of a square of side x units.

Therefore, $(x + 2)(x + 3)$ can be represented by the area of a rectangle $(x + 2)$ units by $(x + 3)$ units as we can see in the diagram on the following page.

$x \times x$
$= x^2$

Looking at this diagram we can see that there are four areas to add together. These are: x^2, $2x$, $3x$ and 6 square units respectively.

Thus $(x + 2)(x + 3)$ must equal $x^2 + 2x + 3x + 6 = x^2 + 5x + 6$ when we collect like terms,

i.e. $(x + 2)(x + 3) = x^2 + 5x + 6$.

It is very time consuming to draw diagrams like these every time we want to multiply two brackets together. Luckily there is an algebraic way of doing the same thing.

The rule is:

Multiply *each term* in the second bracket by *each term* in the first.

There are two easy algebraic ways to do this.

Method one

Draw up a multiplication table.

$\times$	x	$^+2$
x	x^2	^+2x
$^+3$	^+3x	$^+6$

Both the like terms can be found in the diagonal marked on the diagram. Collecting these up we have $(x + 2)(x + 3) = x^2 + 3x + 2x + 6 = x^2 + 5x + 6$.

Method two

Multiply the second bracket by each term in the first bracket.
We can see how this is done by following the example:

$$(x + 2)(x + 3) = x(x + 3) + 2(x + 3) = x^2 + 3x + 2x + 6 = x^2 + 5x + 6.$$

Another way of doing the multiplication is shown below:

$$(x + 2)(x + 3) = x^2 + 3x + 2x + 6 = x^2 + 5x + 6$$
$$\text{(collecting like terms)}$$

F O I L

In the above diagram we can see that four multiplications are performed; the **F**irst two terms, the **O**uter two terms, the **I**nner two terms, and the **L**ast two terms.

These can easily be remembered by the word **FOIL.**

Remembering this word is a very useful way of dealing with the multiplication. It doesn't matter which method we choose to remember as long as we can do the multiplication.

The examples below show some more solutions involving the use of differing signs.

Worked Examples

1 Calculate $(b + 3)(b - 5)$.

$\times$	b	$^+3$
b	b^2	^+3b
$^-5$	^-5b	$^-15$

Hence $(b + 3)(b - 5) = b^2 - 5b + 3b - 15 = b^2 - 2b - 15$.

2 Calculate $(x - 4)(x - 9)$.

$$(x - 4)(x - 9) = x^2 - 9x - 4x + 36 = x^2 - 13x + 36$$

(collecting like terms)

3 Calculate $(3h + 8)(5h - 7)$.

$\times$	$5h$	$^-7$
$3h$	$15h^2$	^-21h
$^+8$	^+40h	$^-56$

Hence $(3h + 8)(5h - 7) = 15h^2 - 21h + 40h - 56 = 15h^2 + 19h - 56$

4 $(a + 4)(a + 7) = a(a + 7) + 4(a + 7)$
$\qquad\qquad\quad = a^2 + 7a + 4a + 28$
$\qquad\qquad\quad = a^2 + 11a + 28$

5 $(x + 8)(x - 2) = x(x - 2) + 8(x - 2)$
$\qquad\qquad\quad = x^2 - 2x + 8x - 16$
$\qquad\qquad\quad = x^2 + 6x - 16$

6 $(d - 3)(d + 7) = d(d + 7) - 3(d + 7)$
$\qquad\qquad\quad = d^2 + 7d - 3d - 21$
$\qquad\qquad\quad = d^2 + 4d - 21$

7 $(y - 6)(y + 3) = y(y + 3) - 6(y + 3)$
$$= y^2 + 3y - 6y - 18$$
$$= y^2 - 3y - 18$$

8 $(2x + 4)(3x + 7) = 2x(3x + 7) + 4(3x + 7)$
$$= 6x^2 + 14x + 12x + 28$$
$$= 6x^2 + 26x + 28$$

9 $(2x - 9)(4x + 11) = 2x(4x + 11) - 9(4x + 11)$
$$= 8x^2 + 22x - 36x - 99$$
$$= 8x^2 - 14x - 99$$

10 $(7x - 3)(3x - 7) = 7x(3x - 7) - 3(3x - 7)$
$$= 21x^2 - 49x - 9x + 21$$
$$= 21x^2 - 58x + 21$$

11 $(x - 4)^2 = (x - 4)(x - 4) = x(x - 4) - 4(x - 4)$
$$= x^2 - 4x - 4x + 16$$
$$= x^2 - 8x + 16$$

PRACTICE 7.3.4   Try these questions without a calculator

1 Multiply out the brackets and simplify.

  a $(a + 3)(a + 9)$ **f** $(y - 2)(y - 1)$ **k** $(x + 5)^2$

  b $(b + 7)(b - 2)$ **g** $(2x + 3)(x + 7)$ **l** $(y - 7)^2$

  c $(c + 2)(c - 5)$ **h** $(2z + 8)(3z - 4)$ **m** $(2z + 1)^2$

  d $(x - 3)(x + 4)$ **i** $(2x + 1)(3x - 12)$ **n** $(3x - 4)^2$

  e $(x - 8)(x + 5)$ **j** $(5y - 2)(2y - 3)$

2 Find the areas of the following rectangles:

  a length $(x + 7)$ cm, width $(x + 3)$ cm

  b length $(y + 3)$ cm, width $(2y + 5)$ cm

  c length $(2z + 1)$ m, width $(4z + 3)$ m.

  Illustrate each answer with a diagram.

3 **a** Write down the areas of the
      following rectangles:
       i ACEG
       ii ACDH
       iii BCEF
       iv BCDI

  b Hence write down the area
     of the rectangle HIFG.

  c Explain this result
     geometrically.

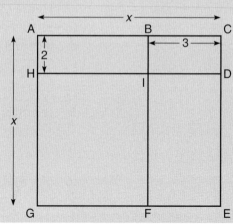

Factorisation

In arithmetic, a number can be expressed as the product of its prime factors. We call this **factorising**. Thus 6 can be written as 2×3.

We can do the same in algebra. There are several ways in which we factorise in algebra as the following sections show.

Common factor

Some series of terms have the same factor in each.
This is called a **common factor**.

For example, each term in the expression $6x + 15$ has a factor of 3.

Thus we could write	$3 \times 2x + 3 \times 5$
or	$3 \times (2x + 5)$
which we write as	$3(2x + 5)$

Worked Examples

a $3x + 12$
$= 3 \times x + 3 \times 4$
$= 3(x + 4)$

b $5x + 15y$
$= 5 \times x + 5 \times 3y$
$= 5(x + 3y)$

c $2ab - 3a$
$= a \times 2b - a \times 3$
$= a(2b - 3)$

d $16a^2b^3 - 24a^3b$
$= 8a^2b \times 2b^2 - 8a^2b \times 3a$
$= 8a^2b(2b^2 - 3a)$

PRACTICE 7.3.5   Try these questions without a calculator

1 Factorise the following expressions:

a $2a + 10$	**f** $8x^2 + 7x$	**k** $15st^2 + 3ts^2$
b $16 - 4b$	**g** $4k^2 + 6k$	**l** $10u + 15v - 20x$
c $10c - 12$	**h** $9y^2 - 3ly$	**m** $6x^2 - 3xy + 9x$
d $ef - 3e$	**i** $7yz + 21z^2$	**n** $\dfrac{yz}{5} - \dfrac{y^2z}{15} + \dfrac{3yz^2}{25}$
e $3gh + 15hk$	**j** $4xy + 12x^2y$	**o** $\dfrac{2a^2}{b^2} + \dfrac{4a^3}{b^2}$

Factorising in pairs

Sometimes, after factorising using common factors, we find that there is a common factor in the result. This means that we can find a common factor a second time and factorise again.

The second common factor is usually a bracket – these can be common factors just as well as single terms.

Worked Examples

1 Factorise $2a + 4b + a^2 + 2ab$.

Factorising each pair of terms we get $\qquad 2(a + 2b) + a(a + 2b)$

We see that the bracket $(a + 2b)$ is now a common factor.

Hence the final factors are $(a + 2b)(2 + a)$.

2 Factorise $2cd + 2ce + 3d + 3e$.

Factorising each pair of terms we get $\qquad 2c(d + e) + 3(d + e)$

We see that the bracket $(d + e)$ is now a common factor.

Hence the final factors are $(d + e)(2c + 3)$.

3 Factorise $fp + fq - gp - gq$.

Factorising each pair of terms we get $\qquad f(p + q) - g(p + q)$

We see that the bracket $(p + q)$ is now a common factor.

Hence the final factors are $(p + q)(f - g)$.

PRACTICE 7.3.6   Try these questions without a calculator

1 Factorise:

a $ab + ac + 2b + 2c$

b $cd + 2ce - d - 2e$

c $f^2g^2 - fgh + 3fg - 3h$

d $x^2 + 3x + 2x + 6$

e $y^2 - 7y - 4y + 28$

f $2z^2 - 4z + 3z - 6$

Quadratic factorisation

Look at the last three questions in Practice 7.3.6.
We can see that the middle two terms could have been combined. i.e. question **d** could have read:

Factorise $x^2 + 5x + 6$.

Hence we could have written:

$$x^2 + 5x + 6$$
$$= x^2 + 3x + 2x + 6$$
$$= x(x + 3) + 2(x + 3)$$
$$= (x + 2)(x + 3)$$

Any expression of the form $ax^2 + bx + c$, where a, b and c are constants, is called a *quadratic expression*.

A quadratic expression is one where the *highest* power is 2.

Thus a^2, $b^2 + 3$, $5c^2 - 2c$, $4d^2 - 3d + 4$, are all examples of quadratic expressions.

Some, **but not all**, can be factorised by *splitting up* the middle term to enable us to make two pairs of terms with another common factor as we did above.

Worked Examples

1 Factorise $x^2 + 9x + 20$.

$$x^2 + 9x + 20$$
$$= x^2 + 4x + 5x + 20 \qquad \text{(finding the right factors by trial)}$$
$$= x(x + 4) + 5(x + 4)$$
$$= (x + 4)(x + 5)$$

2 Factorise $y^2 - 7y + 12$.

$$y^2 - 7y + 12$$
$$= y^2 - 4y - 3y + 12 \qquad \text{(finding the right factors by trial)}$$
$$= y(y - 4) - 3(y - 4)$$
$$= (y - 4)(y - 3)$$

> **NOTE**
> The sign in the second bracket *must* be a − sign because we need −4 × −3 to make the last term +12.

3 Factorise $z^2 - z - 72$.

$$z^2 - z - 72$$
$$= z^2 + 8z - 9z - 72$$
$$= z(z + 8) - 9(z + 8)$$
$$= (z + 8)(z - 9)$$

> **NOTE**
> The sign in the second bracket *must* be a + sign because we need −9 × +8 to make the last term −72.

The last example shows us how difficult it is to work out how to *split up* the middle term to give us two sets of common factors.

Fortunately there is an easier way of working it out.

Multiplying out the brackets $(x + p)(x + q)$ we get $x^2 + px + qx + pq$

which simplifies to $x^2 + (p + q)x + pq$.

We see from this that if $x^2 + (p + q)x + pq$ is the same as $x^2 + ax + b$ then the two numbers p and q are

> *multiplied* together to make the constant term b

and

> *added* together to make the coefficient of the x term in the middle.

Hence, we can summarise from the three examples shown above.

1 Factorise $x^2 + 9x + 20$ becomes $(x + p)(x + q)$ where $p \times q = 20$ and $p + q = 9$

Thus p and q must be 4 and 5 since $4 \times 5 = 20$ and $4 + 5 = 9$
Hence $x^2 + 9x + 20 = (x + 4)(x + 5)$.

2 Factorise $y^2 - 7y + 12$ becomes $(y + p)(y + q)$ where $p \times q = 12$ and $p + q = -7$

Thus p and q must be -3 and -4 since $-3 \times -4 = 12$ and $-3 + -4 = -7$
Hence $y^2 - 7y + 12 = (y - 3)(y - 4)$.

3 Factorise $z^2 - z - 72$ becomes $(z + p)(z + q)$ where $p \times q = -72$ and $p + q = -1$

Thus p and q must be -9 and $+8$ since $-9 \times +8 = -72$ and $-9 + +8 = -1$
Hence $z^2 - z - 72 = (z - 9)(z + 8)$.

The following worked examples show the best way of setting out the factorisation of quadratic expressions.

Worked Examples

1 Factorise $x^2 + 10x + 24$.

We are looking for two numbers which *multiply* to make 24 and *add* to make 10.

The factors of 24 are given by the table

$$24 =$$

24×1
12×2
8×3
6×4

From these pairs of numbers we can get $6 \times 4 = 24$ and $6 + 4 = 10$
Hence $x^2 + 10x + 24 = (x + 6)(x + 4)$.

2 Factorise $x^2 - 15x + 36$.

We are looking for two numbers which *multiply* to make 36 and *add* to make -15.

The factors of 36 are given by the table

$$36 =$$

36×1
18×2
12×3
9×4
6×6

From these pairs of numbers we can get $-12 \times -3 = 36$ and $-12 + -3 = -15$.

Hence $x^2 - 15x + 36 = (x - 12)(x - 3)$.

3 Factorise $x^2 - x - 6$.

We are looking for two numbers which *multiply* to make -6 and *add* to make -1.

The factors of 6 are given by the table

$$6 = \overline{\begin{array}{c} 6 \times 1 \\ 3 \times 2 \end{array}}$$

From these pairs of numbers we can get $-3 \times {}^+2 = -6$ and $-3 + {}^+2 = -1$

Hence $x^2 - x - 6 = (x - 3)(x + 2)$.

4 Factorise $x^2 + 3x - 40$.

We are looking for two numbers which *multiply* to make -40 and *add* to make $+3$.

The factors of 40 are given by the table

$$40 = \overline{\begin{array}{c} 40 \times 1 \\ 20 \times 2 \\ 10 \times 4 \\ 8 \times 5 \end{array}}$$

From these pairs of numbers we can get $+8 \times {}^-5 = -40$ and $+8 + {}^-5 = +3$

Hence $x^2 + 3x - 40 = (x + 8)(x - 5)$.

PRACTICE 7.3.7   Try these questions without a calculator

1 Factorise the following quadratic expressions:

a $a^2 + 5a + 4$	**h** $h^2 - 5h - 24$	**o** $r^2 - 5r - 50$
b $b^2 + 15b + 50$	**i** $j^2 + 19j + 88$	**p** $s^2 - s - 30$
c $c^2 - 7c + 10$	**j** $k^2 + 9k + 20$	**q** $t^2 + 3t$
d $d^2 - 11d + 10$	**k** $m^2 - 10m + 21$	**r** $u^2 - 4u$
e $e^2 + 6e - 16$	**l** $n^2 - 10n + 25$	**s** $v^2 - 9$ (Hint: the v term is $0 \times v$)
f $f^2 + 10f - 75$	**m** $p^2 + 5p - 14$	
g $g^2 - 2g - 35$	**n** $q^2 + 8q - 33$	**t** $w^2 - 25$ (Hint: the w term is $0 \times w$)

Simple substitution

If we put a number in place of a letter in an expression we are said to **substitute** the value – like one footballer substituting for another in a match. This process is called **substitution**.

We can then find an exact numerical value for the algebraic expression.
So, if $x = 5$ and $y = 6$ then the value of the expression $x + 2y$ is $5 + 2 \times 6 = 17$.

For example, a firm charges a call out fee of £C and a rate per hour of £R.
The total cost of n hours work is given by the expression $C + Rn$.
Thus, if the call out fee is £20 and the hourly rate is £4, the cost of a job lasting 3 hours is £$(20 + 4 \times 3) = £32$, i.e. we *substitute* $C = 20$, $N = 3$ and $R = 4$ giving a total value of 32.
The main advantage of using letters is that we can substitute different values for C, n and R as charges vary. So, if the call out fee rises to £25 and the hourly rate to £5 the cost of the previous job is now £$(25 + 5 \times 3) = £40$.

The following examples show how to **evaluate** the algebraic expressions when the letters are substituted by numbers.

Remember the rules for multiplying and dividing signs given earlier in the chapter (Topic 7.3 under 'Using brackets').

A handy hint also is to work out the value of the expression gradually; do not try to do it *all at once*.

> **NOTE**
> When multiplying and dividing terms:
> If the signs (+ or −) are the same, the result is positive (+).
> If the signs are different, the result is negative (−).

Worked Examples

If $a = 3$, $b = 0$, $c = -2$, $x = 4$, $y = \frac{1}{2}$ and $z = -8$ evaluate:

a $x + 3y$ **c** $\dfrac{20}{x}$ **e** $ab - c$ **g** $\dfrac{ax^2}{z}$ **i** xyz

b $2ac$ **d** $ab + c$ **f** $4y + c^2$ **h** $\dfrac{6a}{(x + c)}$ **j** $\dfrac{(2x - yz)}{(a^2 + b)}$

a $\quad x + 3y = 4 + 3 \times \frac{1}{2}$
$\qquad\qquad = 5\frac{1}{2}$

b $\quad 2ac = 2 \times 3 \times -2$
$\qquad\quad = -12$

c $\quad \dfrac{20}{x} = 20 \div 4$
$\qquad\quad = 5$

d $\quad ab + c = 3 \times 0 + (-2)$
$\qquad\qquad = -2$

e $\quad ab - c = 3 \times 0 - (-2)$
$\qquad\qquad = 2$

f $\quad 4y + c^2 = 4 \times \frac{1}{2} + (-2)^2$
$\qquad\qquad = 2 + 4$
$\qquad\qquad = 6$

> **NOTE**
> Any number multiplied by 0 is 0.

NOTE
Only square the 4, i.e.
$3 \times 4^2 = 3 \times 16 = 48$.

g $\dfrac{ax^2}{z} = (3 \times 4^2 \div (-8))$

$\qquad = 48 \div (-8)$

$\qquad = -6$

h $\dfrac{6a}{(x + c)} = 6 \times 3 \div (4 + (-2))$

$\qquad = 18 \div 2$

$\qquad = 9$

i $xyz = 4 \times \frac{1}{2} \times (-8)$

$\qquad = -16$

j $\dfrac{(2x - yz)}{(a^2 + b)} = (2 \times 4 - (\frac{1}{2} \times -8)) \div (9 + 0)$

$\qquad = (8 - (-4)) \div 9$

$\qquad = (8 + 4) \div 9$

$\qquad = 12 \div 9$

$\qquad = 1\frac{1}{3}$

PRACTICE 7.3.8   Try these questions without a calculator

1 $a = 4$, $b = 3$ and $c = -6$. Evaluate:

   a $2a + 3b$ **c** $b - c$ **e** $\dfrac{ab}{c}$ **g** $4 + c$

   b $b + c$ **d** $\dfrac{c}{b}$ **f** abc **h** b^2

2 $p = -4$, $q = 0$, $r = 5$ and $s = 1$. Evaluate:

   a $3s + 4r + p$ **c** p^3 **e** $\dfrac{20}{p}$

   b $pqrs$ **d** $\dfrac{2r - p}{r + 2s}$

3 $m = 2$ and $n = -3$. Evaluate:

   a $2m^2$ **c** mn **e** $9 - n^2$ **g** $n^2 - m^2$ **i** $m - n^3$

   b $(2m)^2$ **d** $6 - mn$ **f** $m^2 + n^2$ **h** $m + n^3$ **j** $\dfrac{n^2}{m}$

4 $x = 4$, $y = 3$ and $z = 7$. Evaluate:

   a $2x^2 - 3x + 5$ **d** $\sqrt{(x^2 + y^2)}$ **g** $\dfrac{(3z + 2x - 5)}{(2y - x)^2}$

   b $(xy)^2$ **e** $\sqrt{(z^2 + 3x + y)}$ **h** $2y^3 - z^2$

   c $\dfrac{y(x^2 - 2)}{z}$ **f** $\sqrt{(z^2 - 4y - 1)}$

Substitution into formulae

A formula gives the relationship, or connection, between the variables.
A very important use for substitution is in a **formula.**

For example, $A = lb$ is a formula which tells us that the area (A) of a rectangle is equal to its length (l) multiplied by its breadth (b).

Substituting any two values in this formula allows us to find the value of the third variable.

Worked Examples

1 The formula for the sum of the interior angles of a polygon is given by $S = 180(n - 2)$. Find:

  a S when $n = 3$.

  b S when $n = 6$.

  c The sum of the interior angles of an octagon.

  d The number of sides in the polygon which has a total angle of $1440°$.

  a When $n = 3$, $S = 180(3 - 2) = 180 \times 1 = 180°$

  b When $n = 6$, $S = 180(6 - 2) = 180 \times 4 = 720°$

  c An octagon has 8 sides, thus $S = 180(8 - 2) = 180 \times 6 = 1080°$

  d When $S = 1440°$, $1440 = 180(n - 2)$
  i.e. $1440 = 180n - 360$
  Thus $1440 + 360 = 180n$
  $1800 = 180n$
  $n = 10$
  This polygon has 10 sides.

> **NOTE**
> You might like to read the section on linear equations, pages 263–265, to understand this better.

2 The kinetic (movement) energy, E joules (J), of a body is given by the formula $E = \frac{1}{2} mv^2$, where m is the mass, kg, of the body and v is the velocity, ms^{-1}.

Calculate:

  a E when $m = 2$ and $v = 3$.

  b The kinetic energy of a body of mass $5\,kg$ moving at $10\,ms^{-1}$.

  c The kinetic energy of a body of mass $500\,g$ moving at $18\,kmh^{-1}$.

  d The mass of a body of kinetic energy $147\,J$ moving at $7\,ms^{-1}$.

  e The velocity of a body of kinetic energy $162\,J$ and mass $4\,kg$.

  a When $m = 2$ and $v = 3$ $E = \frac{1}{2} \times 2 \times 3^2 = 9\,J$

  b When $m = 5$ and $v = 10$ $E = \frac{1}{2} \times 5 \times 10^2 = 250\,J$

NOTE

Cancelling, for example,

$$\frac{18 \times 1000}{60 \times 60}$$

$$= \frac{18\,000}{3600}$$

$$= \frac{180}{36}$$

$$= 5$$

c $500\,g = \frac{1}{2}\,kg$ and $18\,kmh^{-1} = \dfrac{18 \times 1000}{60 \times 60}\,ms^{-1} = 5\,ms^{-1}$

Thus $E = \frac{1}{2} \times \frac{1}{2} \times 5^2 = \frac{1}{4} \times 25 = 6.25\,J$

d   When $E = 147$ and $v = 7$,

$$147 = \tfrac{1}{2} \times m \times 7^2$$
$$147 = 24.5 \times m$$
$$147 \div 24.5 = m$$
$$6 = m$$

Thus the mass of the body is $6\,kg$.

e   When $E = 162$ and $m = 4$,

$$162 = \tfrac{1}{2} \times 4 \times v^2$$
$$162 = 2 \times v^2$$
$$81 = v^2$$
$$9 = v$$

Thus the body is moving with velocity $9\,ms^{-1}$.

PRACTICE 7.3.9a   Try these questions without a calculator

1   Use the formula $c = 3a + b$ to find:

   a c when $a = 2$ and $b = 5$

   b c when $a = 5.6$ and $b = 7.8$

   c b when $c = 14$ and $a = 4$

   d b when $c = 11$ and $a = 5$

   e a when $c = 36$ and $b = 21$.

2   A car starts with a speed u (ms^{-1}), reaches a speed v (ms^{-1}) after time t (s). The distance it has travelled, s (m), is given by the formula $s = \frac{1}{2}(u + v)t$. Find:

   a   the distance travelled when $u = 2$, $v = 7$ and $t = 10$,

   b   the distance travelled when $u = 0$, $v = 30$ and $t = 40$,

   c   how long it takes a car, accelerating from $4\,ms^{-1}$ to $24\,ms^{-1}$, to cover a distance of $560\,m$,

   d   how far the car has travelled when it accelerates from 0 to $100\,kmh^{-1}$ in $8.1\,s$.

3 The connection between the temperature in Celsius (C), and Fahrenheit (F), is given by the formula $C = \frac{5}{9}(F - 32)$.

    a Find C when $F = 68$.

    b Find C when $F = 5$.

    c Water boils at $212\,°F$. What is this temperature in $°C$?

    d Find F when $C = 15$.

    e Water freezes at $0\,°C$. What is this temperature in $°F$?

4 The area of a trapezium is given by the formula $A = \frac{1}{2}(a + b)h$, where a and b are the lengths of the parallel sides and h is the distance between them. Find:

    a A when $a = 2.7$, $b = 6.9$ and $h = 4.2$,

    b the height when the area is 72 and the lengths of the parallel sides are 8 and 10.

5 Tickets for the theatre cost £8 for adults and £5 for children. When A adults and C children go to the theatre the total cost, £P, is given by the formula $P = 8A + 5C$.
Find:

    a the cost when 4 adults and 3 children go to the theatre,

    b the number of adults in the party when the total cost is £42 and there are 2 children,

    c the number of children in the party when the total cost is £60 and there are 5 adults.

6 The fare, £F, for a family of A adults and C children to cross a lake by ferry is given by the formula $F = 7A + 4C$.

    a Find F when   **i** $A = 4$ and $C = 3$ **ii** $A = 2$ and $C = 5$.

7 The astronomer, Bode, developed a formula (called Bode's Law). This states that $d = \dfrac{(x + 4)}{10}$, where d is the distance of a planet from the Sun, measured in Astronomical Units, AU. 1 astronomical unit is equal to the distance of the Earth from the Sun; i.e. $d = 1$ for Earth.

    a For the planet Venus, $x = 3$. Find the distance of Venus from the Sun in AU.

    b For the planet Jupiter, $x = 48$. Find the distance of Jupiter from the Sun in AU.

    c The planet Saturn is 10 times as far away from the Sun as the Earth. Find the value of x for Saturn

PRACTICE 7.3.9b   Try these questions with a calculator

1   The curved surface area of a cone, A, is given by the
    formula $A = \pi r l$. If r is the radius of the base and
    l is the *slant* height, find:

    a A when $r = 5$ and $l = 7$,

    b l when $A = 150$ and $r = 8$.

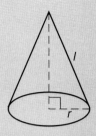

2   Mrs Thatcher goes to work each day. She walks k km to the bus stop
    and then rides d km on the bus. The length of her journey, in minutes,
    is given by the formula $L = 15k + 4d$.
    Find:

    a L when   **i** $k = 3$ and $d = 4$ **ii** $k = 2.6$ and $d = 5.9$

    b k when   **i** $L = 42$ and $d = 3$ **ii** $L = 51.2$ and $d = 5.7$

    c d when   **i** $L = 48$ and $k = 2$ **ii** $L = 52.7$ and $k = 1.8$.

3   Christopher Columbus is h m above sea level. The distance, d km, that
    he can see to the horizon is given by the formula $d = 3.6\sqrt{h}$.

    a How far is the horizon when Columbus is 100 m above sea level?

    b How far is the horizon when Columbus is 150 m above sea level?

    c How far up the cliff must Columbus go to be able to see 40 km out
        to sea?

    d Columbus climbs from a height of 81 m to 121 m above sea level.
        How much further can he now see out to sea?

    e A sailor is 85 m above sea level in the *crow's-nest* of Columbus's ship.
        A pirate ship is 33 km away. Can the lookout see the pirate ship?

    f A Concorde flight can just see Heathrow as it prepares to land. The
        plane is flying at an altitude of 772 m above the level of Heathrow.
        Use the above formula to find out Concorde's distance from
        Heathrow.

4   Modern nutritionists have a measure called Body Mass Index, BMI,
    using the formula $\text{BMI} = \dfrac{W}{h^2}$.

    W and h are a person's weight, in kg, and height, in m.

    A healthy person has a BMI of between 20 and 25.
    Someone with a BMI less than 18 is unhealthily thin.
    Someone with a BMI of 30 or more is unhealthily fat.

    a Susan is 1.75 m tall and weighs 60 kg. Calculate her BMI.

    b David is 1.65 m tall and weighs 79 kg. Calculate his BMI.

    c Jim has a BMI of 22.8, and weighs 79 kg. How tall is he?

    d Betty has a BMI of 26.2 and is 1.52 m tall. How heavy is she?

Number diagrams

Number diagrams generate sequences of numbers by substituting values into a formula stored in a diagram.

Worked Example

A rule for generating numbers is given by the following *number diagram*:

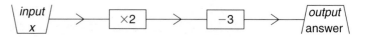

a Use the rule to find the output when the input is
   i 1   **ii** 2   **iii** 5   **iv** 6.5

b What number must be input to give an output of 0?

c What is the smallest integer input that gives an output which is a square number greater than 1?

d Write down the algebraic expression represented by this number diagram.

   a Using the diagram we get:

   $$\begin{aligned} \textbf{i}\ \ 1 &\to 1 \times 2\ (=2) \to 2 - 3 = -1 = \text{output.} \\ \textbf{ii}\ \ 2 &\to 2 \times 2\ (=4) \to 4 - 3 = \ \ \ 1 = \text{output.} \\ \textbf{iii}\ \ 5 &\to 5 \times 2\,(=10) \to 10 - 3 = \ \ \ 7 = \text{output.} \\ \textbf{iv}\ \ 6.5 &\to 6.5 \times 2\,(=13) \to 13 - 3 = \ \ 10 = \text{output.} \end{aligned}$$

NOTE

You may have to try several values before you pick the correct one.

   b From **a** we can see that an output of 0 must have come from an input between $x = 1$ and $x = 2$. Trying an input of 1.5 we get:
   $$1.5 \to 1.5 \times 2\,(=3) \to 3 - 3 = 0 = \text{output.}$$
   Hence we can see that an input of $x = 1.5$ gives an output of 0.

   c We already have an input of 2 leading to an output of 1. Trying the next few values:
   $$\begin{aligned} 3 &\to 3 \times 2\,(=6) \ \to \ 6 - 3 = 3 = \text{output} \ \ \text{(not a square number)} \\ 4 &\to 4 \times 2\,(=8) \ \to \ 8 - 3 = 5 = \text{output} \ \ \text{(not a square number)} \\ 5 &\to 5 \times 2\,(=10) \to 10 - 3 = 7 = \text{output} \ \ \text{(not a square number)} \\ 6 &\to 6 \times 2\,(=12) \to 12 - 3 = 9 = \text{output} \ \ \text{(a square number).} \end{aligned}$$

   d The algebraic formula which represents this number diagram is $2x - 3$.

PRACTICE 7.3.10a   Try these questions without a calculator

1 A rule for generating numbers is given by the following number diagram:

   a Use the rule to find the output when the input is   **i** 0   **ii** 1   **iii** 7.
   b What value of input gives an output of 0?
   c What smallest integer value of input gives an output greater than 9?
   d Write down the algebraic formula representing this number diagram.

2 A rule for generating numbers is given by the following number diagram:

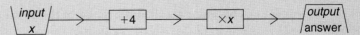

a Use the rule to find the output when the input is **i** 0 **ii** 1 **iii** 2.
b What largest integer value of input gives an output less than 50?
c Write down the algebraic formula representing this number diagram.

3 A rule for generating numbers is given by the following number diagram:

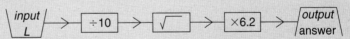

a Use the rule to find the output when the input is **i** 1 **ii** 3 **iii** 6.
b What smallest integer value of input gives an output greater than 25?
c All the outputs are multiples of one number. What is this number? Explain your answer.
d Write down the algebraic formula representing this number diagram.

PRACTICE 7.3.10b   Try this question with a calculator

1 The approximate time, in seconds, for a pendulum to swing once on its axis depends on its length, L m. The calculation is represented by the following number diagram:

\\input/ L → ÷10 → √ → ×6.2 → /output\\ answer

a Find the time of swing of a pendulum of length 90 m.
b Find the time of swing of a pendulum of length 62.5 m.
c Find the time of swing of a pendulum of length 3.844 m.
d What do you notice about the output and input in part **c**?

We have already looked at formulae. Formulae are like *equations*, i.e. they contain an equals (=) sign and have terms on each side. The difference between formulae and equations is that in a formula the variables stand for quantities which are definite.

For example, $A = LB$ stands for area of a rectangle = length times breadth. In an equation the variables stand for unknown quantities. The solution may possibly be found but not always.

For example, in the equation $3x = 6$ the only possible solution is $x = 2$. $y = 2x - 1$ has an infinite number of *solutions* i.e. possible values of x and y which *fit* the equation. $x = 1\ y = 1, x = 2\ y = 3, x = 3\ y = 5$, etc. are all possible solutions to $y = 2x - 1$.

The equation $x^2 = -4$ has *no* solutions for real values of x.

We often write equations (and formulae) with one letter on one side of the
= sign.
This letter is called the *subject* of the equation (or formula).
For instance, y is the subject in the equation $y = 2x + 1$.
However, if the letter occurs on *both* sides of the equation it is not called the
subject.
An easy example of this is the equation $x = 4 - x$.
The subject is usually on the left hand side of the equation but can be on either.

Balancing equations

Equations are like *balances*. They must have the same value on both sides of the
= sign. A visual representation in the home is the *mobile*.

The mobile will not *balance* unless the mass on each side is the same.

Worked Examples

1

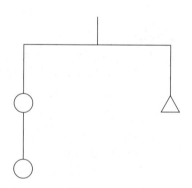

NOTE

We take the mass of the
wire as negligible.

If the mass of the △ is 6 g, find the mass of each ○ .

There are two ○'s, hence each one must be 3 g, in order to balance
the mobile.

2

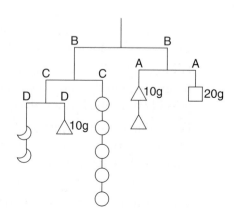

Each ☐ is of mass 20 g.

a What is the mass of the △ ?

△ = 10 g

b What mass is suspended from each A?

20 g

c What mass is suspended from each B?

40 g

d What mass is suspended from each C?

20 g

e What mass is suspended from each D?

10 g

f What is the mass of the ○ ?

○ = 4 g

g What is the mass of the ☽ ?

☽ = 5 g

PRACTICE 7.4.1

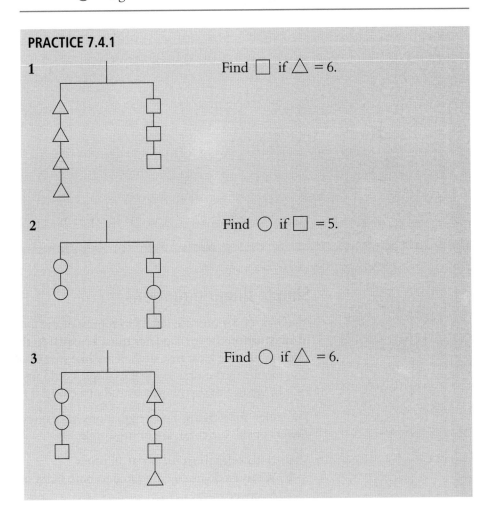

1   Find ☐ if △ = 6.

2   Find ○ if ☐ = 5.

3   Find ○ if △ = 6.

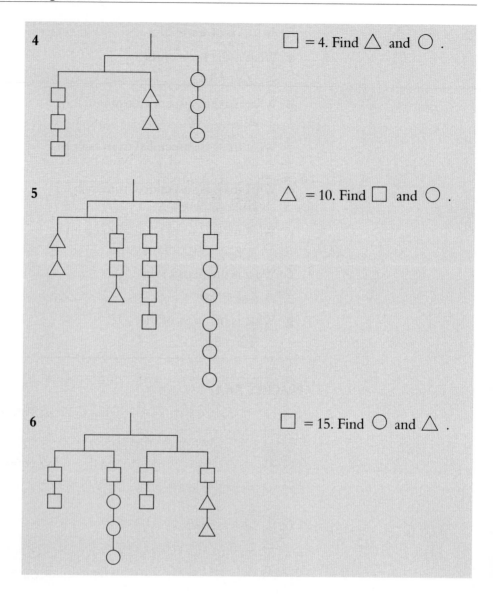

4 □ = 4. Find △ and ○ .

5 △ = 10. Find □ and ○ .

6 □ = 15. Find ○ and △ .

Simple linear equations

Algebraic equations use letters to represent the *unknown* quantity.
In an equation the *left hand side* must be equal to the *right hand side*.
The mobiles we have just studied are like simple equations (or balances).
The mobile in the first worked example could just as easily have been written
$2x = 6$. We use the symbol x instead of a circle. The value of the triangle is 6.

The rules for solving linear equations (i.e. ones with *no* squares or higher
powers of the variable), are quite simple:

  1 Both sides must *balance* at all times.
  2 We must do *exactly* the same to both sides in order to keep the equation
     balanced.

To do this we can:
- add the same amount to both sides,
- subtract the same amount from both sides,
- multiply both sides by the same amount (this means *each* term on both sides),
- divide both sides by the same amount (this means *each* term on both sides).

Equations are easiest to solve if we collect all the unknown terms on one side and all the constant terms on the other.

It is best to put the unknown terms on the side that gives the positive value.

Worked Examples

1 Solve $x + 2 = 6$.

$$x + 2 - 2 = 6 - 2 \qquad \text{(subtract 2 from both sides)}$$
$$x = 4$$

2 Solve $x - 4 = 7$.

$$x - 4 + 4 = 7 + 4 \qquad \text{(add 4 to both sides)}$$
$$x = 11$$

3 Solve $3x = 18$.

$$\frac{3x}{3} = \frac{18}{3} \qquad \text{(divide by 3 on both sides)}$$
$$x = 6$$

4 Solve $\frac{1}{4}x = 6$.

$$4 \times \tfrac{1}{4}x = 4 \times 6 \qquad \text{(multiply by 4 on both sides)}$$
$$x = 24$$

5 Solve $3x - 4 = 23$.

$$3x - 4 + 4 = 23 + 4 \qquad \text{(add 4 to both sides)}$$
$$3x = 27$$
$$\frac{3x}{3} = \frac{27}{3} \qquad \text{(divide by 3 on both sides)}$$
$$x = 9$$

PRACTICE 7.4.2

1 Solve the following equations.

a $2a = 7$	**c** $2c + 1 = 5$	**e** $9 = y - 3$	**g** $3 = 1 - y$
b $b - 9 = 7$	**d** $3d - 7 = 4$	**f** $5 = 6 - x$	**h** $7 = 3 - 2x$

NOTE

Both sides must *balance* at all times. Thus, whatever we do to one side we must do *exactly the same* to the other side.

Further Worked Examples

1 Solve $5x + 1 = 15 - 2x$.

$$5x + 1 + 2x = 15 - 2x + 2x \qquad \text{(add } 2x \text{ to both sides)}$$
$$7x + 1 = 15$$
$$7x + 1 - 1 = 15 - 1 \qquad \text{(subtract 1 from each side)}$$
$$7x = 14$$
$$\frac{7x}{7} = \frac{14}{7} \qquad \text{(divide both sides by 7)}$$
$$x = 2$$

2 Solve $4x + 8 = 6x - 5$.

$$4x + 8 + 5 = 6x - 5 + 5 \qquad \text{(add 5 to both sides)}$$
$$4x + 13 = 6x$$
$$4x - 4x + 13 = 6x - 4x \qquad \text{(subtract } 4x \text{ from each side)}$$
$$13 = 2x$$
$$\frac{13}{2} = \frac{2x}{2} \qquad \text{(divide each side by 2)}$$
$$6\tfrac{1}{2} = x$$

3 Solve $\tfrac{1}{2}x - 1 = 11 - \tfrac{1}{4}x$.

$$4 \times \tfrac{1}{2}x - 4 \times 1 = 4 \times 11 - 4 \times \tfrac{1}{4}x \qquad \text{(multiply each side by 4)}$$
$$2x - 4 = 44 - x$$
$$2x - 4 + 4 = 44 + 4 - x \qquad \text{(add 4 to each side)}$$
$$2x = 48 - x$$
$$2x + x = 48 - x + x \qquad \text{(add } x \text{ to each side)}$$
$$3x = 48$$
$$\frac{3x}{3} = \frac{48}{3} \qquad \text{(divide each side by 3)}$$
$$x = 16$$

Notice that:

1. The order of doing the different operations does not matter as long as we do exactly the same to both sides.

2. If we look at an addition or subtraction from both sides we can see an alternative rule. For example, in $3x - 4 = 5$, when we add 4 to each side we write:

$$3x - 4 + 4 = 5 + 4$$

This could be written as $3x = 5 + 4$.

It seems as if we have simply moved the 4 from the left hand side to the right hand side and changed it from $+4$ to -4.

Common sense tells us that this gives the same result and hence we have a new rule:

When adding to or subtracting from the sides of an equation, if we change the side we must change the sign.

Worked Example

Solve $4x + 7 = 37 - 2x$.

$$4x = 37 - 7 - 2x \qquad \text{(move the 7 to RHS)}$$
$$4x = 30 - 2x$$
$$4x + 2x = 30 \qquad \text{(move the } -2x \text{ to LHS)}$$
$$6x = 30$$
$$\frac{6x}{6} = \frac{30}{6} \qquad \text{(divide both sides by 6)}$$
$$x = 5$$

We should *always* check our solution by substituting our answer back into the original equation.

PRACTICE 7.4.3

1 Solve the following equations.

a $3x - 2 = 2x + 1$ **g** $4x - 7 = 3x - 11$

b $x - 3 = 3x + 5$ **h** $3 + 2x = 5 - 3x$

c $\dfrac{y}{3} = 7$ **i** $\frac{1}{3}y + 1 = 8$

d $\dfrac{y}{2} = 4\frac{1}{2}$ **j** $\frac{3}{5}y - 1 = -10$

e $\dfrac{2z}{5} = 8$ **k** $\frac{2}{3}z + 4 = 7 - \frac{1}{3}z$

f $\dfrac{3x}{4} = -12$ **l** $\frac{3}{4}x - 8 = 4 + \frac{1}{2}x$

Linear equations with brackets

If an equation has brackets in it, it is usually best to multiply out the brackets, collect like terms and then solve.

Worked Examples

1   Solve $2(3x - 1) = 28$.

$$
\begin{aligned}
6x - 2 &= 28 && \text{(multiplying out)} \\
6x - 2 + 2 &= 28 + 2 && \text{(adding 2)} \\
6x &= 30 && \text{(dividing by 6)} \\
x &= 5
\end{aligned}
$$

2   Solve $3(x - 1) = 2(x + 1)$.

$$
\begin{aligned}
3x - 3 &= 2x + 2 && \text{(multiplying out)} \\
3x - 3 + 3 &= 2x + 2 + 3 && \text{(adding 3)} \\
3x &= 2x + 5 \\
3x - 2x &= 2x - 2x + 5 && \text{(subtracting } 2x) \\
x &= 5
\end{aligned}
$$

PRACTICE 7.4.4   Try these questions without a calculator

1   Solve the following equations.

a $3(x - 2) = 12$ **f** $7(x - 4) = 4(x + 2)$

b $20 = 5(x + 2)$ **g** $3(4 - x) = 4(10 + x)$

c $5(2x + 1) = 3(4x - 5)$ **h** $5(11 - 2x) = 3(11 + 4x)$

d $3(2x - 9) = 5(3 - 3x)$ **i** $\frac{1}{5}(4x + 2) = (x - 1)$

e $5(3x - 2) = 2(6x + 1)$ **j** $6(\frac{3}{4}x - 1) = 3(\frac{1}{2}x + 10)$

Equations in context

We can use algebra to solve problems *in context*. This means solving problems that relate to everyday life.

Worked Examples

1   Hannah's dad is three times as old as Hannah. The sum of their ages is 52. How old is Hannah?

Let Hannah's age be h years. (We can use any letter we like.)
Therefore her dad is $3h$ years old.
Since the sum of their ages is 52 we can write:

$$3h + h = 52$$
i.e. $4h = 52$
i.e. $h = 13$

Therefore Hannah is 13 years old.

2 Three consecutive odd numbers add up to 93. Find these numbers.

Let the smallest of these numbers be n.
The next number is 2 more than n i.e. it is $n + 2$.
The next number is 4 more than n i.e. it is $n + 4$.

Thus we can write: $\qquad n + n + 2 + n + 4 = 93$
$\qquad$ i.e. $\qquad\qquad\qquad 3n + 6 = 93$
$\qquad$ i.e. $\qquad\qquad\qquad 3n = 87$
$\qquad$ i.e. $\qquad\qquad\qquad n = 29$

The smallest of the numbers is 29, therefore the three numbers are 29, 31 and 33.

PRACTICE 7.4.5 Try these questions without a calculator

1 The sum of two consecutive numbers is 21. Find the two numbers.

2 The length of a rectangle is 4 cm longer than the width. The perimeter is 36 cm. Find the dimensions of the rectangle.

3 Jack and Jill went up the hill to fetch a pail of water. The water weighed 15 lb more than the pail. The total weight was 18 lb. How heavy was the pail?

4 Tweedledum and Tweedledee bought a cake and cut it into 3 pieces, one for each of them and one for Alice. Tweedledum's piece was 50 g heavier than Tweedledee's and Tweedledee's piece was 30 g heavier than Alice's. The total weight was 710 g. How heavy was Alice's piece?

5 The distance from Newton Abbot to Torquay is m miles. From Torquay to Brixham is $m + 3$ miles. Brixham to Newton Abbot is $2m + 1$ miles. Valerie drives the round trip and covers 28 miles.
How far is it from Newton Abbot to Torquay?

6 Gary weighs 19 kg less than David. David weighs 14 kg less than Paul. The total weight of the three friends is 223 kg. How heavy are each of them?

7 Sian says that she is two and a half times as old as her brother Glynn. Glynn says that Sian is 12 years older than he is. They are both right. How old are they?

8 Bob bought 20 cans of beer for a party. He bought c cans (for himself) at £1.50 each and the remainder (for his guests) at £1 each. He spent £22 altogether. How many cans did he buy for himself?

9 Susan wrote down the fraction $\frac{3}{5}$. She added the same number to both the numerator and the denominator. The result, in its lowest terms, was $\frac{5}{6}$. What number did she add?

10 Scrooge left £x in his will to his nephew, Bob Cratchit and Tiny Tim. He left half to his nephew. $\frac{3}{4}$ of what he left to his nephew he left to Bob Cratchit. He left £1000 less than this to Tiny Tim. How much did Scrooge leave in his will?

11 Damon drives to London, a distance of 100 miles. He drives x miles on the motorway at an average speed of 80 mph and the remainder of the journey at an average speed of 20 mph. His journey takes him 2 hours. How far did Damon travel on the motorway?

12 Dee, Mary and Nicola go on holiday together. Dee takes £x spending money. Mary takes three times as much as Dee. Nicola takes £50 more than Dee. They take £600 altogether. Calculate how much each person takes on holiday.

13

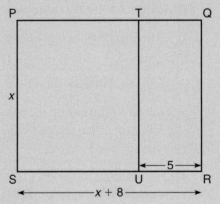

From the diagram:

a Write down the length of SU in its simplest form.
b Write down the perimeter of the rectangle PTUS in its simplest form.

This perimeter is 30 cm.

c Hence write down an equation in x.
d Solve this equation to find the value of x.
e Hence find:
   i the length of PS,
   ii the length of SU,
   iii the perimeter of the rectangle PQRS.

Simultaneous linear equations

The equation $2x + 1 = 9$ can be solved. The answer is $x = 4$.
Other equations containing one variable can usually be solved.

When we consider the equation $x + y = 9$ we find that there is more than one possible solution. $x = 1, y = 8; x = 2, y = 7; x = 4.5, y = 4.5; x = 10, y = -1$, etc. are all solutions which fit the equation.

It soon becomes clear that *there are an infinite number of solutions* to the equation $x + y = 9$.

In the same way other equations which contain two variables have an infinite number of solutions. $x = 1$, $y = 3$; $x = 2$, $y = 7$; $x = 3$, $y = 11$; $x = 2.5$, $y = 9$; $x = -2$, $y = -9$, etc. are just five of the infinite number of solutions of the equation $4x - y = 1$.

However, if we combine the two equations above, we find that there is *only one solution*, $x = 2$, $y = 7$, that fits both of the equations simultaneously i.e. at the same time.

Equations like these are called **simultaneous linear equations**.

We always need two equations with the two variables to produce one solution that fits both.

There are five main rules for solving simultaneous equations like these:

1 Find a variable with the same coefficient in both equations.

2 If the signs of these two terms are the same – *subtract* one equation from the other. If the signs of these two terms are different – *add* the equations together.

3 Solve the resulting equation in one variable.

4 Substitute this value for the first variable back in one of the original equations and solve the resulting equation in the other variable.

5 Check the solution by substituting both values back into the other original equation.

The following worked examples show you how to solve these equations.

Worked Examples

1 Solve the equations $x + y = 9$, $4x - y = 1$.

The y terms have the same coefficient in both equations, but the signs are different.

Thus, if we add the two equations together we can eliminate (get rid of) the terms in y.

$$x + y = 9$$
$$4x - y = 1$$

(adding) $\qquad x + 4x + y - y = 9 + 1$
i.e. $\qquad\qquad\qquad 5x = 10$
i.e. $\qquad\qquad\qquad\quad x = 2$

Substituting $x = 2$ back in the first original equation gives: $2 + y = 9$, i.e. $y = 7$.

Checking in the second original equation gives: $4(2) - 7 = 1$. This is correct.

Thus $x = 2$, $y = 7$ is the only solution to the simultaneous equations $x + y = 9$, $4x - y = 1$.

2 Solve the equations $2x + 3y = 11$, $2x - y = 7$.

The x terms have the same coefficient in both equations, and the signs are the same.

This time we can eliminate the x variable by subtracting one equation from the other.

$$2x + 3y = 11$$
$$2x - y = 7$$

(subtracting) $2x - 2x + 3y - (-y) = 11 - 7$ (note that $-(-y) = +y$)

i.e. $4y = 4$

i.e. $y = 1$

Substituting $y = 1$ back in the first original equation gives
   $2x + 3(1) = 11$ i.e. $x = 4$.

Checking in the second original equation gives $2(4) - 1 = 7$. This is correct.

Thus $x = 4$, $y = 1$ is the only solution to the simultaneous equations $2x + 3y = 11$, $2x - y = 7$.

3 Solve, simultaneously, the equations $2x + 3y = -4$, $4x - 3y = 10$.

The coefficients of y are the same but of different sign. Therefore we add the equations.

$$2x + 3y = -4$$
$$4x - 3y = 10$$

(adding) $2x + 4x + 3y - 3y = -4 + 10$

i.e. $6x = 6$

i.e. $x = 1$

Substituting $x = 1$ back in the first original equation gives $2(1) + 3y = -4$

i.e. $3y = -6$

i.e. $y = -2$

Checking in the second original equation gives: $4(1) - 3(-2) = 10$. This is correct.

Thus $x = 1$, $y = -2$ is the only solution to the simultaneous equations $2x + 3y = -4$, $4x - 3y = 10$.

4 Solve, simultaneously, the equations $4x + 7y = 17$, $4x + 5y = 11$.

The coefficients of x are the same and of the same sign. Therefore we subtract the equations.

$$4x + 7y = 17$$
$$4x + 5y = 11$$

(subtracting) $\quad 4x - 4x + 7y - 5y = 17 - 11$

i.e. $\qquad\qquad\qquad\qquad 2y = 6$

i.e. $\qquad\qquad\qquad\qquad y = 3$

Substituting $y = 3$ back in the first original equation gives $4x + 7(3) = 17$

i.e. $\qquad\qquad\qquad\qquad 4x = -4$

i.e. $\qquad\qquad\qquad\qquad x = -1$

Checking in the second original equation gives $4(-1) + 5(3) = 11$. This is correct.

Thus $x = -1$, $y = 3$ is the only solution to the simultaneous equations $4x + 7y = 17$, $4x + 5y = 11$.

5 Solve, simultaneously, the equations $4x - 3y = -5$, $2x - 3y = -1$.

The coefficients of y are the same and of the same sign. Therefore we subtract the equations.

$$4x - 3y = -5$$
$$2x - 3y = -1$$

(subtracting) $\quad 4x - 2x - 3y - (-3y) = -5 - (-1)$

i.e. $\qquad\qquad\qquad\qquad 2x = -4$

i.e. $\qquad\qquad\qquad\qquad x = -2$

Substituting $x = -2$ back in the first original equation gives $4(-2) - 3y = -5$

i.e. $\qquad\qquad\qquad\qquad -3y = 3$

i.e. $\qquad\qquad\qquad\qquad y = -1$

Checking in the second original equation gives $2(-2) - 3(-1) = -1$. This is correct.

Thus $x = -2$, $y = -1$ is the only solution to the simultaneous equations $4x - 3y = -5$, $2x - 3y = -1$.

PRACTICE 7.4.6   Try these questions without a calculator

1 Use the method of elimination to solve the following simultaneous equations.

a $a + b = 7$
$\quad 2a + b = 11$

c $4e + 2f = 2$
$\quad 5e - 2f = 7$

e $-3j + 4k = 5$
$\quad -3j - 7k = -50$

b $2c - d = 13$
$\quad c - d = 5$

d $3g - 4h = -15$
$\quad -3g - h = 0$

f $7m + 4n = 12$
$\quad -5m + 4n = 12$

Further simultaneous linear equations

In the above questions, there was always one variable with the same coefficients. So how can we solve a pair of simultaneous equations where this is not the case?

We do this by multiplying the equations by constants such that the coefficients of one of the variables is the same in both equations.

It doesn't matter which variable you use so long as it has the same coefficient in both equations.

Then we solve the equations as we did in the last practice exercise.

The following examples show how this is done.

Worked Examples

1 Solve the simultaneous equations $2x + 3y = 19$, $3x - y = 1$.

If we multiply the second equation throughout by 3 we would then have $3y$ in each equation.

$$\text{Hence: (equation 1)} \qquad 2x + 3y = 19$$
$$(3 \times \text{equation 2}) \qquad 9x - 3y = 3$$
$$\text{(adding)} \qquad 2x + 9x + 3y - 3y = 19 + 3$$
$$\text{i.e.} \qquad 11x = 22$$
$$\text{i.e.} \qquad x = 2$$

Substituting $x = 2$ back in the first equation gives $2(2) + 3y = 19$
$$\text{i.e.} \qquad 3y = 15$$
$$\text{i.e.} \qquad y = 5$$

Checking in the second original equation gives $3(2) - 5 = 1$. This is correct.

Thus $x = 2$, $y = 5$ is the only solution to the simultaneous equations $2x + 3y = 19$, $3x - y = 1$.

2 Solve the simultaneous equations $3x + 4y = 9$, $6x + y = -3$.

If we multiply the first equation throughout by 2 we would then have $6x$ in each equation.

$$\text{Hence: (2} \times \text{equation 1)} \qquad 6x + 8y = 18$$
$$\text{(equation 2)} \qquad 6x + y = -3$$
$$\text{(subtracting)} \qquad 6x - 6x + 8y - y = 18 - (-3)$$
$$\text{i.e.} \qquad 7y = 21$$
$$\text{i.e.} \qquad y = 3$$

Substituting $y = 3$ back in the first equation gives $3x + 4(3) = 9$

i.e. $\qquad\qquad\qquad\qquad\qquad 3x = -3$

i.e. $\qquad\qquad\qquad\qquad\qquad x = -1$

Checking in the second original equation gives $6(-1) + 3 = -3$. This is correct.

Thus $x = -1$, $y = 3$ is the only solution to the simultaneous equations $3x + 4y = 9$, $6x + y = -3$.

3 Solve the simultaneous equations $2x - 5y = -6$, $3x + 4y = 37$.

Here we cannot multiply one equation to get two coefficients the same. Therefore we must multiply **both** equations to get two coefficients equal.

We could get $6x$ in each by multiplying the first equation by 3 and the second by 2.
We could get $20y$ in each by multiplying the first equation by 4 and the second by 5.

It does not matter which we select, the answer will be the same in either case.

To prove this, the example is done in both ways. Hence:

a (3 × equation 1) $\qquad\qquad\qquad 6x - 15y = -18$

 (2 × equation 2) $\qquad\qquad\qquad \underline{6x + 8y = 74}$

 (subtracting) $\qquad 6x - 6x - 15y - 8y = -18 - 74$

 i.e. $\qquad\qquad\qquad\qquad\qquad -23y = -92$

 i.e. $\qquad\qquad\qquad\qquad\qquad\quad y = 4$

Substituting $y = 4$ back in the first equation gives $2x - 5(4) = -6$

 i.e. $\qquad\qquad\qquad\qquad\qquad 2x = 14$

 i.e. $\qquad\qquad\qquad\qquad\qquad\; x = 7$

Checking in the second original equation gives $3(7) + 4(4) = 37$. This is correct.

Thus $x = 7$, $y = 4$ is the only solution to the simultaneous equations $2x - 5y = -6$, $3x + 4y = 37$.

b (4 × equation 1) $\qquad\qquad\qquad 8x - 20y = -24$

 (5 × equation 2) $\qquad\qquad\qquad \underline{15x + 20y = 185}$

 (adding) $\qquad 8x + 15x - 20y + 20y = -24 + 185$

 i.e. $\qquad\qquad\qquad\qquad\qquad 23x = 161$

 i.e. $\qquad\qquad\qquad\qquad\qquad\; x = 7$

Substituting $y = 7$ back in the first equation gives $2(7) - 5y = -6$

i.e. $-5y = -20$

i.e. $y = 4$

Checking in the second original equation gives $3(7) + 4(4) = 37$. This is correct.

Thus $x = 7$, $y = 4$ is the only solution to the simultaneous equations $2x - 5y = -6$, $3x + 4y = 37$.

PRACTICE 7.4.7   Try this question without a calculator

1 Use the method of elimination to solve the following simultaneous equations.

a $2a + 3b = 15$
    $a + 2b = 8$

c $5e + f = 3$
    $e + 2f = -3$

e $5j + 3k = -15$
    $3j - 2k = -9$

b $4c - 6d = -24$
    $3c + 3d = -3$

d $3g + 4h = -29$
    $4g - 3h = 3$

f $7m - 3n = 20$
    $3m - 5n = 3$

Equations in context

Worked Examples

1 In a local election Mrs White was elected with an overall majority of 346. The total number of votes cast was 1418. How many votes did each of the two candidates receive?

Let the votes for the two candidates be m and n where m is the number cast for Mrs White.

The sum is 1418 i.e. $m + n = 1418$. The difference is 346 i.e. $m - n = 346$.

Hence: $m + n = 1418$

                                          $m - n = 346$

(adding) $2m = 1764$

i.e. $m = 882$

Substituting in the first equation $882 + n = 1418$

i.e. $n = 536$

Checking in the second equation $882 - 536 = 346$. This is correct.

Hence Mrs White polled 882 votes and her opponent 536.

2 On a package tour, two adults and one child can go for £1190. Similarly the fare for one adult and three children is £1320. How much does it cost for an adult and for a child?

Let the cost of an adult ticket be £a and for a child £c.

Therefore $2a + c = 1190$
and $a + 3c = 1320$

We can make the coefficients of a the same by multiplying the second equation by 2.

Hence (first equation) $\qquad\qquad 2a + c = 1190$

($2 \times$ second equation) $\qquad\quad \underline{2a + 6c = 2640}$

(subtracting) $\qquad\qquad\qquad\qquad -5c = -1450$

Hence $\qquad\qquad\qquad\qquad\qquad c = 290$

Substituting in the first equation $2a + 290 = 1190$

Hence $\qquad\qquad\qquad\qquad 2a = 900$

Hence $\qquad\qquad\qquad\qquad a = 450$

Checking in the second equation $450 + 3(290) = 1320$. This is correct.

Hence an adult ticket costs £450 and a child £290.

PRACTICE 7.4.8   Try these questions without a calculator

1 Batman and Robin are a and b years old respectively. The sum of their ages is 44. Batman is eight years older than Robin. How old is each of them?

2 Romeo and Juliet had dinner. Romeo's meal cost £2 more than Juliet's. Romeo paid the bill which totalled £15. How much did each meal cost?

3 A CD costs £x and a cassette £y. 4 CD's and 3 cassettes cost £70 and 2 CD's and 5 cassettes cost £63. How much does each cost?

4 On a train journey, adult tickets cost £a and child tickets £c. 2 adults and 3 children travel for £37.50. 1 adult and 4 children travel for £35. How much does each ticket cost?

5 Billy needs bait to go fishing. He can either buy 4 maggots and 3 worms for 47 p or 2 maggots and 5 worms for 41 p. How much do maggots and worms cost each?

6 Farmer Barleymow goes to market with £2000. For this money he can buy either 8 sheep and 4 pigs or 4 sheep and 7 pigs. How much do sheep and pigs cost each?

7 Henrietta the goose can lay either golden or brown eggs. 4 golden and 3 brown eggs together weigh 360 g, but 2 golden and 5 brown weigh 320 g. Find the weight of a golden egg.

8 The staff room coffee machine takes 20 p or 50 p coins. When emptied, it was found to contain 36 coins totalling £10.50 in value. How many of each sort of coin did the machine contain?

9 A club secretary bought 40 tickets for Torville and Dean's farewell tour. Some tickets cost £20 and the rest £12.50. The money received for the dearer tickets was £110 less than that received for the cheaper tickets. How many tickets at each price were bought?

10 This triangle is equilateral.
Find m and n.

11 This triangle is isosceles. It has a perimeter of 200 cm. Find p and q.

12 The line $y = mx + c$ passes through points (4, 10) and (7, 19). Find the values of m and c.

13 The ages of Florence and Zebedee are in the ratio 2 : 3. In four year's time they will be in the ratio 3 : 4. How old are Florence and Zebedee now?

14 Johnny Herbert drove x miles up the M5 averaging 70 mph. He then left the M5 and drove for y miles averaging 40 mph. He drove a total of 163 miles in 2.5 hours. How far did he drive along the M5?

7.5 QUADRATIC EQUATIONS

We learned how to factorise quadratic expressions in Topic 7.3.

Any quadratic expression written as an equation is called a **quadratic equation**.

Any quadratic equation can be written in the form $x^2 + ax + b = 0$, where a and b are constants. There are three main methods of solving quadratic equations – by factorising, by using a formula and by graphs.

The last two methods are shown later in the book.

Solving quadratic equations by factorising

Consider the equation $P \times Q = 0$. Clearly $P \times Q = 0$ is only possible if *either* $P = 0$ *or* $Q = 0$. If, however, P and Q are factors from a quadratic expression we can use this fact to solve quadratic equations of the form $x^2 + ax + b = 0$.

NOTE
You may like to revise pages 247–251 before you read this page.

Worked Examples

1 Solve the equation $a^2 - 5a + 6 = 0$.

Factorising: $(a - 2)(a - 3) = 0$
Remembering $P \times Q = 0$ above we can say that if $(a - 2)(a - 3) = 0$ then *either $a - 2 = 0$ or $a - 3 = 0$*.

If $a - 2 = 0$ then $a = 2$ and
if $a - 3 = 0$ then $a = 3$.

Hence the solutions of $a^2 - 5a + 6 = 0$ are $a = 2$ or $a = 3$.

2 Solve the equation $b^2 + 9b + 20 = 0$.

Factorising: $(b + 4)(b + 5) = 0$
Remembering $P \times Q = 0$ above we can say that if $(b + 4)(b + 5) = 0$ then *either $b + 4 = 0$ or $b + 5 = 0$*.

If $b + 4 = 0$ then $b = -4$ and
if $b + 5 = 0$ then $b = -5$.

Hence the solutions of $b^2 + 9b + 20 = 0$ are $b = -4$ or $b = -5$.

3 Solve the equation $c^2 - 5c - 14 = 0$.

Factorising: $(c + 2)(c - 7) = 0$
Remembering $P \times Q = 0$ above we can say that if $(c + 2)(c - 7) = 0$ then *either $c + 2 = 0$ or $c - 7 = 0$*.

If $c + 2 = 0$ then $c = -2$ and
if $c - 7 = 0$ then $c = 7$.

Hence the solutions of $c^2 - 5c - 14 = 0$ are $c = -2$ or $c = 7$.

4 Solve the equation $d^2 - 10d + 25 = 0$.

Factorising: $(d - 5)(d - 5) = 0$
Remembering $P \times Q = 0$ above we can say that if $(d - 5)(d - 5) = 0$ then *either $d - 5 = 0$ or $d - 5 = 0$*.

If $d - 5 = 0$ then $d = 5$.

Since both brackets are the same we get the same answer $d = 5$ from each of them.
We say that $d = 5$ *twice*.
Any quadratic equation like this is called a **perfect square**.

Hence the solutions of $d^2 - 10d + 25 = 0$ are $d = 5$ *twice*.

5 Solve the equation $x^2 - 4 = 0$ (special case where $a = 0$).

a $x^2 - 4 = 0$
therefore $x^2 = 4$
i.e. $x = 2$ or -2

b $x^2 - 4 = 0$ could also be factorised as $(x - 2)(x + 2) = 0$

Remembering $P \times Q = 0$ above we can say that if $(x - 2)(x + 2) = 0$ then *either* $x - 2 = 0$ *or* $x + 2 = 0$.

If $x - 2 = 0$ then $x = 2$ and
if $x + 2 = 0$ then $x = -2$.

Hence the solutions of $x^2 - 4 = 0$ are $x = 2$ or $x = -2$.

6 Solve the equation $y^2 - 3y = 0$ (special case where $b = 0$).

$y^2 - 3y = 0$
Factorising $y(y - 3) = 0$
Remembering $P \times Q = 0$ above we can say that if $y(y - 3) = 0$ then *either* $y = 0$ *or* $y - 3 = 0$.

If $y - 3 = 0$ then $y = 3$.

Hence the solution of $y^2 - 3y = 0$ is $y = 0$ or $y = 3$.

PRACTICE 7.5.1   Try these questions without a calculator

1 Solve the following quadratic equations.
a $x(x - 5) = 0$ **e** $(x - 2)(x - 6) = 0$ **i** $(x + 3)(x - 11) = 0$
b $x(x + 4) = 0$ **f** $(x - 3)(x - 7) = 0$ **j** $(y - 6)(y + 9) = 0$
c $(x - 3)(x + 3) = 0$ **g** $(x + 1)(x + 2) = 0$ **k** $(z + 4)(z + 4) = 0$
d $(x - 5)(x + 5) = 0$ **h** $(x - 6)(x - 6) = 0$

2 Solve the following quadratic equations.
a $a^2 - 9 = 0$ **f** $x^2 - 2\frac{1}{2}x = 0$ **k** $x^2 - 5x - 36 = 0$
b $b^2 - 144 = 0$ **g** $x^2 - 8x + 12 = 0$ **l** $x^2 - x - 30 = 0$
c $c^2 + 5c = 0$ **h** $x^2 - 9x + 20 = 0$ **m** $y^2 + 2y - 99 = 0$
d $d^2 + 1.8d = 0$ **i** $x^2 + 13x + 30 = 0$ **n** $z^2 + 3z - 70 = 0$
e $e^2 - 11e = 0$ **j** $x^2 + 20x + 99 = 0$

3 **a** Write down the factors of the quadratic equation which has solutions $x = 2$ and $x = 4$.

b Write the quadratic equation in factor form.

c Hence multiply out the brackets and find the quadratic equation which has $x = 2$ and $x = 4$ as solutions.

4 **a** Write down the factors of the quadratic equation which has solutions
$y = -5$ and $y = -3$.

b Write the quadratic equation in factor form.

c Hence multiply out the brackets and find the quadratic equation
which has $y = -5$ and $y = -3$ as solutions.

5 **a** Write down the factors of the quadratic equation which has solutions
$z = 2$ and $z = -1$.

b Write the quadratic equation in factor form.

c Hence multiply out the brackets and find the quadratic equation
which has $z = 2$ and $z = -1$ as solutions.

Equations in context

Worked Examples

1 A rectangle has sides of length $(x + 3)$ and $(x - 2)$ cm. The area is 36 cm^2.
Find the value of x and the dimensions of the rectangle.

Area = length × breadth = $(x + 3)(x - 2)$.

Since the area = 36 we can write $\qquad (x + 3)(x - 2) = 36$

(multiplying out) $\qquad\qquad\qquad x^2 + 3x - 2x - 6 = 36$

(collecting like terms) $\qquad\qquad\quad x^2 + x - 42 = 0$

(factorising) $\qquad\qquad\qquad\qquad (x - 6)(x + 7) = 0$

Remembering $P \times Q = 0$, we can say that if $(x - 6)(x + 7) = 0$ then
either $x - 6 = 0$ *or* $x + 7 = 0$.

If $x - 6 = 0$ then $x = 6$ and
if $x + 7 = 0$ then $x = -7$.

Hence $x = 6$ is the only practical solution in this case.
Therefore the sides of the rectangle are $6 + 3 = 9 \text{ cm}$ and $6 - 2 = 4 \text{ cm}$.

> **NOTE**
>
> $x = -7$ is not possible in this case since this would make the sides of the rectangle equal to $-7 + 3 = -4$ and $-7 - 2 = -9$. The rectangle would have *negative* length and breadth.

2 Jane and Gary's wedding portrait is 10 in. by 8 in. It is mounted on a card
with a border x in. wide all the way round. The area of the card is 168 in^2.
Find the width of the border and the dimensions of the card.

Length of the card = $(10 + 2x)$ in. (i.e. x in. on *each* side)

Similarly, width of the card = $(8 + 2x)$ in.

Therefore the area of the card = $(10 + 2x)(8 + 2x)$

Since the area = 168, we can write $\qquad (10 + 2x)(8 + 2x) = 168$

(multiplying out) $\qquad\qquad\qquad 80 + 20x + 16x + 4x^2 = 168$

(collecting like terms) $\qquad\qquad\quad 4x^2 + 36x - 88 = 0$

(dividing through by 4) $\qquad\qquad\quad x^2 + 9x - 22 = 0$

(factorising) $\qquad\qquad\qquad\qquad (x - 2)(x + 11) = 0$

NOTE

$x = -11$ is not possible in this case. It would make the sides of the card equal to
$-22 + 10 = -12$ and
$-22 + 8 = -14$.
The card would have *negative* length and breadth.
Hence the width of the border, $x = 2$, is the only practical solution in this case.

Remembering $P \times Q = 0$, we can say that if $(x - 2)(x + 11) = 0$ then *either* $x - 2 = 0$ **or** $x + 11 = 0$.

If $x - 2 = 0$ then $x = 2$ and
if $x + 11 = 0$ then $x = -11$.

Therefore the dimensions of the card are $4 + 10 = 14$ in. by $4 + 8 = 12$ in.

PRACTICE 7.5.2   Try these questions without a calculator

1   Twice a number subtracted from the square of the number equals 15. Find the two possible values of the number.

2   Two consecutive numbers are multiplied together. The product is 56. Find the numbers.

3   One number is 7 more than another. The sum of the squares of the two numbers is 289. Find the two numbers.

4   The sum of the numbers $1 + 2 + 3 + \dots + n$ is given by the formula $\frac{1}{2}n(n + 1)$. The sum is 55. Find the value of n.

5   A polygon with n sides has d diagonals. n and d are connected by the formula $2d = n(n-3)$. A certain polygon has 20 diagonals. How many sides does it have?

6   A rectangle has a length $(d + 4)$ cm and a breadth $(d - 2)$ cm. It has an area of 40 cm². Find the value of d.

7   Joe Cleverclogs scores x marks in 4 tests. In another x tests he scores 36 more marks. His mean (average) score remains the same. How many marks did he score in the first 4 tests?

8   Mike Atherton throws a cricket ball straight up into the air after making a catch. The height of the ball after t seconds is given by the formula $h = 4 + 30t - 5t^2$. The ball rises to a maximum height of 49 metres. How long did the ball take to get to this height?

9   One square has a side of length y cm. Another square has a side 5 cm longer than the first. The total area of the two squares is 97 cm². Find the length of side of the smaller square.

We know that $P = a + b + c$ is the formula for the perimeter, P, of a triangle whose sides are of lengths a, b and c.

We call P the **subject** of the formula because it starts with $P = \dots$ and there are no terms in P on the other side.

We could rearrange the formula into $a = P - b - c$, or $b = P - a - c$, or $c = P - a - b$, making either a or b or c the subject.

This process is called **transposing the formula** or **changing the subject**.

There are two main methods used to rearrange simple formulae or equations and to change the subject:

　　1 by using a number diagram,

　　or

　　2 by using the laws of algebra that we already know for equations, and rearranging.

1 Number diagram method.

　a Reconstruct the original equation, step by step, starting with the required subject, using the *number diagram* technique.

　b Reverse the number diagram formed, ending with a rearranged formula and our required subject.

2 Laws of algebra method.

In this method we simply use our previous knowledge of the laws of algebra in rearranging the formula.

It is like solving the equation but using letters as well as numbers and finding the value of another variable.

Whatever we do, we must remember that we do *exactly the same to both sides* and that at all times our equation is *balanced*.

It is usually, *but not always*, best to do operations in the following order:

　a eliminate roots by squaring, cubing, etc.,

　b clear fractions by multiplying through the equation,

　c multiply out brackets where necessary,

　d place all terms containing the subject required on one side of the equation and the rest on the other side,

　e do whatever is necessary to obtain the required subject as a single term – this might need multiplying, dividing, factorising, taking roots, etc.,

　f rewrite the equation with only the required subject on one side.

> **NOTE**
> In many equations it is not necessary to use all the above steps. We just use those that we require. The following worked examples illustrate both methods.

Worked Examples

1 The area of a square of side x is given by the formula $A = x^2$. Make x the subject.

Method 1

Build up the formula from x:　　$x \rightarrow \boxed{\text{square}} \rightarrow x^2 \;(=A)$

Reverse:　　　　　　　　　　　$\sqrt{A} \leftarrow \boxed{\text{square root}} \leftarrow A$

Hence $x = \sqrt{A}$

Method 2

$A = x^2$

square root both sides $\sqrt{A} = x$

2 Make a the subject of the equation $v = u + at$.

Method 1

Build up the formula from a:

$$a \; \rightarrow \; \boxed{\text{times } t} \; \rightarrow \; at \; \rightarrow \; \boxed{\text{add } u} \; \rightarrow \; u + at \; (= v)$$

Reverse: $\dfrac{v - u}{t} \; \leftarrow \; \boxed{\text{divide by } t} \; \leftarrow v - u \; \leftarrow \; \boxed{\text{subtract } u} \; \leftarrow v$

Hence $a = \dfrac{v - u}{t}$

Method 2

$v = u + at$

subtract u $v - u = at$

divide by t $\dfrac{v - u}{t} = a$

3 Make y the subject of the equation of the straight line $3x + 2y = 7$.

Method 1

Build up the formula from y:

$$y \; \rightarrow \; \boxed{\text{times } 2} \; \rightarrow \; 2y \; \rightarrow \; \boxed{\text{add } 3x} \; \rightarrow \; 2y + 3x \; (= 7)$$

Reverse: $\dfrac{7 - 3x}{2} \; \leftarrow \; \boxed{\text{divide by } 2} \; \leftarrow 7 - 3x \; \leftarrow \; \boxed{\text{subtract } 3x} \; \leftarrow 7$

Hence $y = \dfrac{7 - 3x}{2}$

Method 2

$3x + 2y = 7$

subtract $3x$ $2y = 7 - 3x$

divide by 2 $y = \dfrac{7 - 3x}{2}$

4 The change in kinetic energy of a body when it moves from a speed u to v is given by the formula $E = \frac{1}{2}m(v^2 - u^2)$. Make v the subject.

Method 1

Build up the formula from v:

$$v \rightarrow \boxed{\text{square}} \rightarrow v^2 \rightarrow \boxed{\text{subtract } u^2} \rightarrow v^2 - u^2 \rightarrow \boxed{\text{times } m} \rightarrow m(v^2 - u^2) \rightarrow$$

$$\boxed{\text{divide by } 2} \rightarrow \dfrac{m(v^2 - u^2)}{2} \; (= E)$$

Reverse:

$$\leftarrow \dfrac{2E}{m} \; \leftarrow \; \boxed{\text{divide by } m} \; \leftarrow 2E \; \leftarrow \; \boxed{\text{times } 2} \; \leftarrow E$$

$$\sqrt{\left(\dfrac{2E}{m} + u^2 \right)} \leftarrow \boxed{\text{square root}} \leftarrow \dfrac{2E}{m} + u^2 \leftarrow \boxed{\text{add } u^2}$$

Hence $v = \sqrt{\left(\dfrac{2E}{m} + u^2\right)}$

Method 2

$E = \frac{1}{2}m(v^2 - u^2)$

multiply by 2 $2E = m(v^2 - u^2)$

divide by m $\dfrac{2E}{m} = v^2 - u^2$

add u^2 $\dfrac{2E}{m} + u^2 = v^2$

square root both sides $\sqrt{\left(\dfrac{2E}{m} + u^2\right)} = v$

If a formula is rearranged using operations in a different order, the resulting formula might not look the same as before. However, careful checking should show that the two are mathematically equivalent.

In example 2 above, Method 2 might have been:

$v = u + at$

divide by t: $\dfrac{v}{t} = \dfrac{u}{t} + a$

subtract $\dfrac{u}{t}$ $\dfrac{v}{t} - \dfrac{u}{t} = a$

The solutions $\dfrac{v}{t} - \dfrac{u}{t}$ and $\dfrac{(v-u)}{t}$ are mathematically equivalent.

PRACTICE 7.6.1

1 Make **a** R and **b** I the subject of the formula $v = IR$.

2 Make **a** R and **b** I the subject of the formula $E = I^2R$.

3 Make **a** u and **b** t the subject of the formula $v = u + at$.

4 Make **a** u and **b** s the subject of the formula $v^2 = u^2 + 2as$.

5 Make **a** v and **b** t the subject of the formula $s = \frac{1}{2}(u + v)t$.

6 Make **a** a and **b** u the subject of the formula $s = ut + \frac{1}{2}at^2$.

7 Make **a** x and **b** a the subject of the formula $T = \dfrac{kx}{a}$.

8 Make **a** x and **b** a the subject of the formula $E = \dfrac{kx^2}{2a}$.

9 Make **a** R and **b** T the subject of the formula $I = \dfrac{PRT}{100}$.

10 Make **a** P and **b** Q the subject of the formula $R = P(Q + 3)$.

11 Make **a** v and **b** u the subject of the formula $M = m(v - u)$.

12 Make **a** a and **b** b the subject of the formula $c = 5\sqrt{\dfrac{a}{b}}$.

Changing the subject in context

Sometimes there are good reasons for changing the subject of a formula. Usually it is because the numerical value of a term inside the original formula is required.

Now that we have acquired these skills we can solve problems in context.

Worked Example

The volume of a cylinder is given by the formula $v = \pi r^2 h$.
r is the radius of the base and h is the height.
Find the radius of the base of a can of soup which contains $375\,cm^3$ and has a height $10\,cm$.

Make r the subject of the formula $v = \pi r^2 h$

(divide by πh) $\dfrac{v}{\pi h} = r^2$

(square root) $\sqrt{\left(\dfrac{v}{\pi h}\right)} = r$

(substitute $v = 375$, $h = 10$) $r = \sqrt{\dfrac{375}{3.142 \times 10}}$

Hence $r = \sqrt{\dfrac{375}{31.42}} = \sqrt{11.935} = 3.45\,cm$.

PRACTICE 7.6.2   Try these questions with a calculator (take $\pi = 3.14$ or use the π button on your calculator)

1   The circumference of a circle is given by the formula $C = 2\pi r$, where r is the radius.
    a   Make r the subject of the formula.
    b   Find the radius of a circle with a circumference of $50\,cm$.

2   The area of a circle is given by the formula $A = \pi r^2$, where r is the radius.
    a   Make r the subject of the formula.
    b   Find the radius of a circle with an area of $50\,cm^2$.

3   The volume of a cone, of height h and base radius r, is given by the formula $v = \frac{1}{3}\pi r^2 h$.
    a   Make h the subject of the formula.
    b   Find the height of a cone with a base of radius $4.5\,cm$ containing a volume of $233\,cm^3$.

4   The kinetic energy of a body of mass m is given by the formula $E = \frac{1}{2}mv^2$, where v is its velocity.
    a   Make v the subject of the formula.
    b   Find the velocity of an athlete of mass $40\,kg$ running with kinetic energy 1280 joules.

5 The period of swing, in seconds, of a simple pendulum is given by the formula $T = 2\pi \sqrt{\dfrac{L}{10}}$, where L is the length of the pendulum.

    a Make L the subject of the formula.
    b A pendulum has a swing of 3 seconds. Find its length.
       (take $\pi = 3.14$)

6 A floor tile is the shape of the pentagon shown in the diagram. All five sides are of length x cm. The area of the tile is given by the formula
$$A = \frac{(4 + \sqrt{3})}{10}\, x^2$$

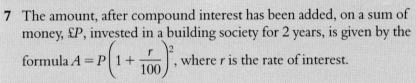

    a Make x the subject of the formula.
    b What is the length of the side of a tile whose area is 91.71 cm²?

7 The amount, after compound interest has been added, on a sum of money, £P, invested in a building society for 2 years, is given by the formula $A = P\left(1 + \dfrac{r}{100}\right)^2$, where r is the rate of interest.

    a Make r the subject of the formula.
    b £1000 invested for 2 years yields compound interest of £144.90. Find the rate of interest.

7.7 INEQUALITIES

We say that 5 *is greater than* 3, or that -1 *is less than* 2.
Such statements are called **inequalities** and we have symbols to make the writing of them easier.
The above two inequalities would be written:

$$5 > 3 \quad \text{and} \quad -1 < 2$$

If an algebraic inequality is written there may be more than one possible solution.

For example, $x > 2$ means that x can take any value above 2.

However, if we write $x \geqslant 2$, (i.e. x is greater or equal to 2), then $x = 2$ is included, in addition to the values given above.

The four basic inequality symbols are:

    $>$ which means *greater than*
    $<$ which means *less than*
    $\geqslant$ which means *greater than or equal to*
    $\leqslant$ which means *less than or equal to*.

The number line

Algebraic inequalities can be represented by a *number line*. For instance, $x > 4$ can be shown:

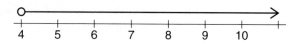

(The **o** indicates that $x = 4$ *is not* included.)
Similarly $x \geqslant 4$ can be shown:

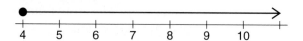

(The **●** indicates that $x = 4$ *is* included.)
Not all algebraic inequalities are represented by arrowed lines.
For instance, x is an integer and $x < 1$ is drawn on a number line as

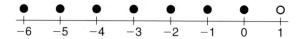

More than one inequality may be written in a single expression. For instance, the number line diagram for $-1 \leqslant x < 4$ is drawn as:

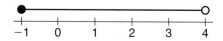

and the statement $-1 \leqslant x < 4$ and x is an integer is drawn as:

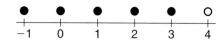

PRACTICE 7.7.1

1 Draw number line diagrams to illustrate the following inequalities:

  a $a > 5$ **d** $d \geqslant 0$ **g** $2 < g < 7$ **j** $3 \leqslant j < 6$

  b $b < 3$ **e** $e \geqslant -3$ **h** $-2 < h < 3$ **k** $-1 < k \leqslant 5$

  c $c \leqslant 2$ **f** $f \leqslant -2$ **i** $-5 < i < -1$ **l** $-7 \leqslant l \leqslant -3$

2 Repeat question 1, but where the variables are only integers.

NOTE
You may like to read pages 323–328 before reading this.

Regions of inequalities

It is possible to find areas on a graph which represent inequalities.
For example, $x > 2$ could be drawn as the shaded area opposite.

(The dotted line indicates that $x = 2$ is *not* included in the region.)

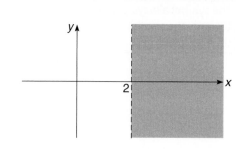

Similarly $y \leqslant 5$ could be drawn as the shaded area below.

(The solid line indicates that $y = 5$ *is* included in the region.)

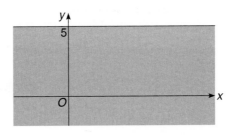

If the two expressions are combined we have the region below.

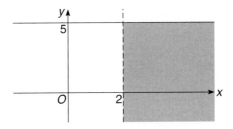

We can also find the region if we have a combined expression for x and y. The technique is best shown in the following examples.

Worked Examples

1   Shade the region indicated by the inequality $y - 2x \leqslant 6$.

  Step 1 Draw the graph of $y - 2x = 6$.

   (For a revision of how to draw straight line graphs see Chapter 8.)

  Step 2 Substitute $x = 0$ and $y = 0$ into the inequality.

  a If the resulting numerical statement is true – shade the side of the line which includes the point (0,0).

  b If the resulting numerical statement is untrue – shade the side of the line which does *not* include the point (0,0).

   In our case $0 - 0 \leqslant 6$ which *is* true. Therefore we shade the side of the line including the point (0,0). The result can be seen below.

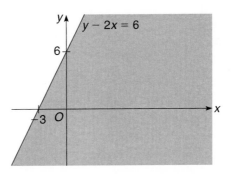

2 Shade the region indicated by the inequality $y + 3x > 8$.

Step 1 Draw the graph of $y + 3x = 8$.

Step 2 Substitute $x = 0$ and $y = 0$ into the inequality.
In this case $0 - 0 > 8$ which is untrue. Therefore we shade the side of the line opposite to the point (0,0).

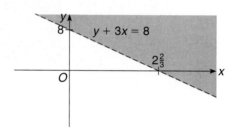

Note the solid line(for the $\leqslant$) and the dotted line (for the $>$) in the two examples.

3 Shade the region indicated by the inequalities $2y < 3x + 11$, $3y + 4x > 12$ and $x \leqslant 4$.

Step 1 Draw the graphs of $2y = 3x + 11$, $3y + 4x = 12$ and $x = 4$.

Step 2 Substitute $x = 0$ and $y = 0$ into the inequalities.
In the first case, $0 < 0 + 11$ which is true. Therefore we shade the side of the line containing point (0,0).
In the second case, $0 + 0 > 12$ which is untrue. Therefore we shade the side of the line opposite the point (0,0).
In the third case we shade the left side of the line $x = 4$.

The resulting area which is true for *all three inequalities* is shown below.

NOTE

If any line passes through (0,0) then substituting $x = 0$ and $y = 0$ will not work. In this case it is possible to use any point we like and to follow the same rules for this point as we did for (0,0).

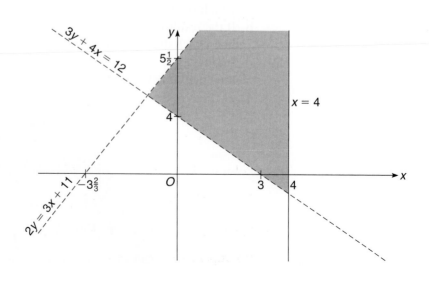

> **PRACTICE 7.7.2   Try these questions without a calculator**
>
> 1 Show, on graph paper, the regions covered by the following inequalities:
>   **a** $x > -3$ **c** $x \leqslant -1$ **e** $x + y < 5$ **g** $2y - 3x < 6$
>   **b** $y > 1$ **d** $y \geqslant 5$ **f** $y - x \geqslant 3$ **h** $3y + 4x \geqslant 12$
>
> 2 Shade the regions covered by all the inequalities in each case:
>   **a** $y - x < 5,\ x \leqslant -1,\ y \geqslant 1$
>   **b** $3y + 5x \leqslant 10,\ x \geqslant -1,\ y > 1$
>   **c** $5y + 3x > 10,\ x < 3,\ y \leqslant 5$
>   **d** $2y > 3x + 6,\ 2y + 3x < 12,\ x \geqslant -3$

Inequations

Algebraic inequalities are also known as **inequations**.
The rules for solving inequations are exactly the same as for equations – *but with one extra rule* which is as follows:
when we multiply or divide by a negative number we reverse the sign.
This is quite clear if we consider some arithmetical examples:

1 $5 > 2$
    (multiply by -1) $-5 < -2$

2 $-3 < 2$
    (multiply by -2) $6 > -4$

3 $8 > -6$
    (divide by -2) $-4 < 3$

Worked Examples

1 Solve the inequation $3a < 12$

   (divide by 3) $a < 4$

2 Solve the inequation $4b \geqslant -20$

   (divide by 4) $b \geqslant -5$

3 Solve the inequation $-2c > 8$

   (divide by -2) $c < -4$

4 Solve the inequation $-3d \geqslant -15$

   (divide by -3) $d \leqslant 5$

5 Solve the inequation $\frac{1}{2}e > -1$

   (multiply by 2) $e > -2$

6 Solve the inequation $-\frac{1}{3}f \leqslant 8$

(multiply by -3) $f \geqslant -24$

7 Solve the inequation $4g - 2 > -3$

(add 2) $4g > -1$
(divide by 4) $a > -\frac{1}{4}$

8 Solve the inequation $-2h + 3 \leqslant 1$

(subtract 3) $-2h \leqslant -2$
(divide by -2) $h \geqslant 1$

9 Solve the inequation $3x - 2 > 4x + 1$

(add 2) $3x > 4x + 3$
(subtract 4x) $-x > 3$
(divide by -1) $x < -3$

PRACTICE 7.7.3   Try this question without a calculator

1 Solve the following inequations.

a $a - 5 > 1$	**d** $3d < -2$	**g** $4 > 3 - 2g$	**j** $5j + 9 \leqslant 2j + 6$
b $2b - 5 \leqslant -1$	**e** $5 - 2e < 7$	**h** $5 \leqslant 12 + 2h$	**k** $2k + 1 < 11 - 3k$
c $4c \geqslant -6$	**f** $8 - 5f \geqslant 3$	**i** $3i + 2 > i - 4$	**l** $2 - 4l \geqslant -10 - l$

Inequations in context

Worked Examples

1 Emma buys s sweets at 3 p each and spends less than 60 p.
Form an inequation and solve it.

Emma's sweets cost her $3s$ pence. Hence we can write $3s < 60$.
Dividing by 3 we have the solution $s < 20$.

2 Emma's brother buys m marbles at 6 p each and spends less than 80 p.
Form an inequation and solve it.

Emma's brother's marbles cost him $6m$ pence.
Hence we can write $6m < 80$.

Dividing by 6 we have $m < \dfrac{80}{6}$, i.e. $m < 13$.

NOTE
The number of marbles, m, must be an integer. Hence we write $m < 13$ rather than $m < 13\frac{1}{3}$.
To be really precise we should write the answer as $m < 13$ where m is an integer.

PRACTICE 7.7.4 Try these questions without a calculator

1 Gareth's car does 35 miles per gallon on average. He has g gallons in his tank. The car will travel for 420 miles on a full tank of petrol.
Form an inequation in g and solve it.

2 Diane drives Gareth's car on a journey which takes, at most, 6 hours. The car has a maximum speed of 90 mph and Diane drives x miles.
Form an inequation in x and solve it.

3 Cecil's gas bill costs him £10 per quarter standing charge plus p pence per unit. His bill is less than £125 and Cecil uses 1150 units.
Form an inequation in p and solve it.

4 Preparations for John's 21st birthday party are under way. 110 people have been invited but at least 10% will not be able to come. Enough food has been prepared for at least 90 people. Write down inequations for the number of people, n, who do come to the party and have enough to eat. Solve them and write down all the possible solutions.

5 A sports club has r badminton racquets. Siobhan says there are more than 30. Sean says there are no more than 36. The club manager says there are an odd number. Write down the two inequations and all the possible solutions.

6 A bag contains a number of discs – some green and some red. There are r red discs and three more green than red. There are at least 5 of each colour and the total number of discs is not more than 20. Write down two inequations for r, and find all the possible solutions.

7.8 TRIAL AND IMPROVEMENT

Sometimes a quadratic equation has a solution but will not factorise. Sometimes we want to find a solution to an equation that has a power higher than x^2.

We can solve equations like these using a method called **trial and improvement** (see Topic 2.8).

NOTE
We have to use a calculator in these examples.

Worked Examples

1 Find the square root of 115 correct to 2 decimal places.

We know that $10^2 = 100$ and $11^2 = 121$.
Thus our answer lies between 10 and 11.

Taking a point between these two values: $10.5^2 = 110.25$
Thus $\sqrt{115}$ lies between 10.5 and 11.0.

Taking a point between these two values: $10.75^2 = 115.5625$
Thus $\sqrt{115}$ lies between 10.5 and 10.75.

Taking a point between these two values: $10.7^2 = 114.49$
Thus $\sqrt{115}$ lies between 10.7 and 10.75.

Taking a point between these two values: $10.73^2 = 115.1329$
Thus $\sqrt{115}$ lies between 10.7 and 10.73.

Taking a point between these two values: $10.72^2 = 114.9184$
Thus $\sqrt{115}$ lies between 10.72 and 10.73.

Taking a point between these two values: $10.725^2 = 115.025\,625$

From these results we can see that $\sqrt{115}$ is closer to 10.72 than it is to 10.73.

Hence $\sqrt{115} = 10.72$ to 2 decimal places.

2   The equation $x^3 - 2x^2 + 3x - 9 = 0$ has a solution between $x = 2$ and $x = 3$. Find this solution correct to 2 decimal places.

We know this equation has a solution between $x = 2$ and $x = 3$ since
$2^3 - 2 \times 2^2 + 3 \times 2 - 9 = -3$ and $3^3 - 2 \times 3^2 + 3 \times 3 - 9 = 9$

Taking a point between these two values:
$$2.5^3 - 2 \times 2.5^2 + 3 \times 2.5 - 9 = 1.625$$
Thus the solution lies between 2 and 2.5.

Taking a point between these two values:
$$2.3^3 - 2 \times 2.3^2 + 3 \times 2.3 - 9 = -0.513$$
Thus the solution lies between 2.3 and 2.5.

Taking a point between these two values:
$$2.4^3 - 2 \times 2.4^2 + 3 \times 2.4 - 9 = 0.504$$
Thus the solution lies between 2.3 and 2.4.

Taking a point between these two values:
$$2.35^3 - 2 \times 2.35^2 + 3 \times 2.35 - 9 = -0.017\,125$$
Thus the solution lies between 2.35 and 2.4.

Taking a point between these two values:
$$2.37^3 - 2 \times 2.37^2 + 3 \times 2.37 - 9 = 0.188\,253$$
Thus the solution lies between 2.35 and 2.37.

Taking a point between these two values:
$$2.36^3 - 2 \times 2.36^2 + 3 \times 2.36 - 9 = 0.085\,056$$
Thus the solution lies between 2.35 and 2.36.

These two values are to 2 decimal places, so to see which one gives the closest answer we take the mid point of 2.355 and get $2.355^3 - 2 \times 2.355^2 + 3 \times 2.355 - 9 = 0.033\,838\,875$

Thus the solution lies between 2.35 and 2.355
Hence the solution to the equation is 2.35 correct to 2 decimal places.

PRACTICE 7.8.1   Try these questions with a calculator

In this Practice exercise write all your answers to two decimal places.

1   Use trial and improvement to find the square roots of the following numbers:
    a 31   **b** 94   **c** 157   **d** 598   **e** 1066

2   Use trial and improvement to find:
    a the solution, between $x = 5$ and $x = 6$, of the equation $x^2 - 5x - 1 = 0$
    b the solution, between $x = 1$ and $x = 2$, of the equation
        $x^3 + x^2 + x - 5 = 0$
    c the solution, between $x = 3$ and $x = 4$, of the equation $x^3 - 3x^2 - 1 = 0$
    d the solution, between $x = 2$ and $x = 3$, of the equation
        $2x^3 - 3x^2 - 3x + 1 = 0$

3   The area of a circle is $55\,cm^2$. Use trial and improvement to find the radius.

4   The surface area of a sphere is given by the formula $A = 4\pi r^2$.
    Use trial and improvement to find the radius of a sphere with surface area $569\,cm^2$.

5   Use trial and improvement to find the length of the side of a cube of volume $240\,m^3$.

6   Use trial and improvement to find out how many miles a car, travelling at 47 mph, goes in one minute.

7.9 EXTENSION MATERIAL

NOTE
Remember indices mean the same as powers.

Indices

In Topic 7.2 we learned about algebraic indices or powers.
We now need to extend our knowledge to include zero, negative and fractional indices.

The zero index
Using the second law of indices $x^a \div x^a = x^0$ whatever the value of a.
Thus $3^2 \div 3^2 = 3^{(2-2)} = 3^0$.
However $3^2 \div 3^2 = 9 \div 9 = 1$, i.e $3^0 = 1$.

In the same way it can be shown that $2^0 = 1$, $5^0 = 1$, $7.2^0 = 1$, etc.
Thus $x^0 = 1$ whatever the value of x.

Negative indices
Using the second law of indices we know that $x^a \div x^b = x^{(a-b)}$.
Thus $4^5 \div 4^3 = 4^{(5-3)} = 4^2$, i.e. $1024 \div 64 = 16$.
In the same way $4^3 \div 4^5 = 4^{(3-5)} = 4^{-2}$. Thus $64 \div 1024 = \frac{1}{16}$.
Doing this algebraically we can see that x^{-n} means $\dfrac{1}{x^n}$.
For example, $2^{-5} = \frac{1}{32}$, $5^{-3} = \frac{1}{125}$, etc.

NOTE

With a calculator you could find the decimal equivalents of these answers.

Worked Examples

Work out the values of the following expressions.

1 5^{-3} **2** 9^{-2} **3** 4^{-5} **4** 2^{-8}

    1 $5^{-3} = \frac{1}{5^3} = \frac{1}{125}$ **3** $4^{-5} = \frac{1}{4^5} = \frac{1}{1024}$

    2 $9^{-2} = \frac{1}{9^2} = \frac{1}{81}$ **4** $2^{-8} = \frac{1}{2^8} = \frac{1}{256}$

Fractional indices

Using the first law of indices $x^{1/2} \times x^{1/2} = x^{(1/2 + 1/2)} = x^1 = x$

Thus $9^{1/2} \times 9^{1/2} = 9$. This means that $9^{1/2} = 3$

Thus $9^{1/2}$ must mean the square root of 9, or $\sqrt{9}$.

Similarly $x^{1/2}$ means $\sqrt{x}$.

In the same way $x^{1/3}$, $x^{1/4}$, etc. have similar meanings.

$x^{1/3}$ means the cube root of x, or $\sqrt[3]{x}$.

$x^{1/4}$ means the fourth root of x, or $\sqrt[4]{x}$, etc.

Thus $x^{1/n}$ means the nth root of x, or $\sqrt[n]{x}$.

NOTE

1. $4 \times 4 \times 4 \times 4 = 256$

2. $3 \times 3 \times 3 \times 3$
   $\times 3 = 243$

3. $2 \times 2 \times 2 \times 2 \times 2$
   $\times 2 \times 2 \times 2 = 256$

Worked Examples

Work out the values of the following expressions.

1 $256^{1/4}$ **2** $81^{1/2}$ **3** $243^{1/5}$ **4** $256^{1/8}$

   1 $256^{1/4} = \sqrt[4]{256} = 4$ **3** $243^{1/5} = \sqrt[5]{243} = 3$

   2 $81^{1/2} = \sqrt{81} = 9$ **4** $256^{1/8} = \sqrt[8]{256} = 2$

Let us imagine that we wish to find the value of the expression $x^{(p/r)}$.

To find the value of this expression we must remember that the p stands for the **power** and the r for the **root**. It makes no difference which you do first. For example, to find the value of $4^{(3/2)}$ you can either find the value of $\sqrt{(4^3)}$ or $(\sqrt{4})^3$,

i.e. $\sqrt{(4 \times 4 \times 4)} = \sqrt{64} = 8$ or $(\sqrt{4})^3 = 2^3 = 8$.

NOTE

These questions will normally be found on the non-calculator paper but try checking with a calculator.

Worked Examples

Work out the values of the following expressions.

1 $8^{2/3}$ **2** $32^{3/5}$ **3** $9^{3/2}$

   1 $8^{2/3} = \sqrt[3]{(8^2)} = \sqrt[3]{(64)} = 4$ or $(\sqrt[3]{8})^2 = 2^2 = 4$

   2 $32^{3/5} = \sqrt[5]{(32^3)} = \sqrt[5]{(32\,768)} = 8$ or $(\sqrt[5]{32})^3 = 2^3 = 8$

   3 $9^{3/2} = \sqrt{(9^3)} = \sqrt{(729)} = 27$ or $(\sqrt{9})^3 = 3^3 = 27$

PRACTICE 7.9.1a   Try these questions without a calculator

1 Find the values of the following expressions:

    a i 2^7 **ii** 3^5 **iii** 5^4 **iv** 6^3

    b i 2^{-9} **ii** 10^{-1} **iii** 6^{-3} **iv** 8^{-2}

    c i 3^0 **ii** 11^0 **iii** 23.654^0 **iv** $(-5)^0$

    d i $125^{1/3}$ **ii** $81^{1/4}$ **iii** $(-27)^{1/3}$ **iv** $1024^{1/10}$

    e i $16^{3/2}$ **ii** $27^{4/3}$ **iii** $81^{3/4}$ **iv** $256^{5/8}$

2 Write the following expressions in their simplest terms:

    a $p^{1/2} \times p^{-1/2}$ **c** $m^{2/3} \div m^{1/2}$ **e** $(16s^8)^{1/4}$

    b $z^{1/4} \times z^{1/5}$ **d** $n^{-1/5} \div n^{-3/10}$

3 Remove the brackets from the following expressions:

    a $(4x^3)^2$ **c** $(5pq)^3$ **e** $(y^{-3})^{-4}$ **g** $(4a)^3 \div 16a^0$ **i** $(4e^0)^5$

    b $(5w)^{-1}$ **d** $(9t^6)^{1/2}$ **f** $(4k^{1/2})^2$ **h** $[(4e)^0]^5$ **j** $[(10f)^2]^{-1}$

4 Write:

    a 625 in the form 5^x

    b 256 in the form **i** 2^a **ii** 4^b **iii** 16^c

    c $\frac{1}{36}$ in the form 6^d

    d i $\frac{1}{4}$ **ii** $\frac{1}{16}$ **iii** 8   **iv** $\frac{1}{32}$ in the forms 2^s and 4^t.

PRACTICE 7.9.1b   Try this question with a calculator

1 Use your calculator to find the values of the following:

    a $3^{1/2}$ **b** $18^{1.5}$ **c** $5^{7/2}$ **d** $\sqrt[3]{21}$ **e** $5^{-0.5}$

Difference of two squares

If we multiply the brackets $(a - b)(a + b)$ we get $a^2 + ab - ab - b^2 = a^2 - b^2$.
This leads to the formula $a^2 - b^2 = (a - b)(a + b)$
This is known as the **difference of two squares** formula and is very useful.

Worked Examples

1 Factorise   **a** $4m^2 - 9n^2$ **b** $80c^2 - 125d^2$

$$
\begin{aligned}
\textbf{a} \quad 4m^2 - 9n^2 &= (2m)^2 - (3n)^2 \\
&= (2m - 3n)(2m + 3n)
\end{aligned}
$$

$$
\begin{aligned}
\textbf{b} \quad 80c^2 - 125d^2 &= 5(16c^2 - 25d^2) \\
&= 5((4c)^2 - (5d)^2) \\
&= 5(4c - 5d)(4c + 5d)
\end{aligned}
$$

2 Use the above formula to evaluate $799^2 - 201^2$

$$
\begin{aligned}
799^2 - 201^2 &= (799 - 201)(799 + 201) \\
&= 598 \times 1000 \\
&= 598\,000
\end{aligned}
$$

PRACTICE 7.9.2

Factorise:

1 $x^2 - y^2$

2 $z^2 - 3^2$

3 $a^2 - 16$

4 $b^2 - 1$

5 $c^2 - \frac{1}{16}$

6 $9d^2 - 16e^2$

7 $49f^2 - 121g^2$

8 $h^2 - \dfrac{i^2}{25}$

9 $\dfrac{j^2}{36} - \dfrac{k^2}{81}$

10 $25p^2 - \dfrac{9}{16}q^2$

11 $r^3 - r$

12 $s^3 - st^2$

13 $98u^2 - 128v^2$

14 $256^2 - 244^2$

15 $4.91^2 - 4.9^2$

Further trial and improvement

In this method (which is also called *iteration*), we start with an initial value and keep getting more accurate solutions, closer and closer to the correct answer.

The method is best shown by some worked examples, which also show the theory. This way of obtaining the solutions to equations is only practicable if a calculator or computer is used.

Worked Examples

1 Find the square root of 45 correct to 4 decimal places.

Theory

We need to find x where $x^2 = 45$.

(Adding x^2)　　　　　　　　$2x^2 = x^2 + 45$

(dividing by x)　　　　　　　$2x = x + \dfrac{45}{x}$

(dividing by 2)　　　　　　　$x = \tfrac{1}{2}\left(x + \dfrac{45}{x}\right)$

Method

We know that $6^2 = 36$ and $7^2 = 49$ so x must be somewhere between 6 and 7.

Starting with a first estimate of, say, 6, and substituting it into the formula above we obtain:

First estimate　　　　$x_1 = \tfrac{1}{2}\left(6 + \dfrac{45}{6}\right) = 6.75$

NOTE

Calculators are needed in this section.

Second estimate $\quad x_2 = \frac{1}{2}\left(6.75 + \dfrac{45}{6.75}\right) = 6.708\,333\,333$

Third estimate $\quad x_3 = \frac{1}{2}\left(6.708\,333\,333 + \dfrac{45}{6.708\,333\,333}\right) = 6.708\,203\,9$

Fourth estimate $\quad x_4 = \frac{1}{2}\left(6.708\,203\,9 + \dfrac{45}{6.708\,203\,9}\right) = 6.708\,203\,9$

We can see from the above that the value of x is unchanged now to at least 4 decimal places. Hence the value of the square root of 45 is 6.7082 to 4 decimal places.

The formula $x_{n+1} = \frac{1}{2}\left(x_n + \dfrac{A}{x_n}\right)$ is a well known trial and improvement formula for finding the square root of a number, A. It was invented over 3000 years ago. In exam questions we are sometimes given the formula to work on but sometimes we have to develop our own.

The next two worked examples show how to develop our own *trial and improvement* formulae.

2 Find the solution, close to 5, of the equation $x^2 - 5x - 1 = 0$, correct to 4 decimal places.

Theory

Rearrange the equation $x^2 - 5x - 1 = 0$

(add $5x + 1$) $\qquad\qquad x^2 = 5x + 1$

(divide by x) $\qquad\qquad x = 5 + \dfrac{1}{x}$

Method

Starting with a first estimate of, say, 5, and substituting it into the formula above we obtain:

First estimate $\quad x_1 = 5 + \dfrac{1}{5} = 5.2$

Second estimate $\quad x_2 = 5 + \dfrac{1}{5.2} = 5.192\,307\,69$

Third estimate $\quad x_3 = 5 + \dfrac{1}{5.192\,307\,69} = 5.192\,592\,59$

Fourth estimate $\quad x_4 = 5 + \dfrac{1}{5.192\,592\,59} = 5.192\,582\,026$

We can see from the above that the value of x is unchanged now to at least 4 decimal places.

Hence the solution close to 5 of the equation $x^2 - 5x - 1 = 0$ is 5.1926 to 4 decimal places.

3 Starting with $x = 1$, find the solution, close to 3, of the equation $x^3 - 3x^2 - 1 = 0$, correct to 4 decimal places.

Theory

Rearrange the equation $x^3 - 3x^2 - 1 = 0$

(add $3x^2 + 1$) $x^3 = 3x^2 + 1$

(divide by x^2) $x = 3 + \dfrac{1}{x^2}$

Method

Starting with a first estimate of 1, and substituting it into the formula above we obtain:

First estimate $x_1 = 3 + \dfrac{1}{1^2} = 4$

Second estimate $x_2 = 3 + \dfrac{1}{4^2} = 3.0625$

Third estimate $x_3 = 3 + \dfrac{1}{3.0625^2} = 3.106\,622\,24$

Fourth estimate $x_4 = 3 + \dfrac{1}{3.106\,622\,24^2} = 3.103\,615\,11$

Fifth estimate $x_5 = 3 + \dfrac{1}{3.103\,615\,11^2} = 3.103\,816\,00$

Sixth estimate $x_6 = 3 + \dfrac{1}{3.103\,816\,00^2} = 3.103\,802\,56$

We can see from the above that the value of x is unchanged now to at least 4 decimal places.

Hence the solution of the equation $x^3 - 3x^2 - 1 = 0$ is 3.1038 to 4 decimal places.

(Compare your answers from Practice 7.8.1 with the results above.)

PRACTICE 7.9.3   Try these questions with a calculator

1 A formula for finding the fourth root of a number, A, is shown below:

$$x_{n+1} = \tfrac{1}{3}\left(2x_n + \frac{A}{(x_n)^3}\right).$$

Starting with $x = 5$ use trial and improvement to find the fourth root of 750, correct to 3 decimal places.

2 The equation $3x^2 + 19x - 15 = 0$ can be rearranged in two ways to give the trial and improvement formulae:

a $x_{n+1} = \frac{1}{3}\left(\frac{15}{x_n} - 19\right)$ and **b** $x_{n+1} = \frac{(15 - 3x_n{}^2)}{19}$.

Starting with $x = 1$, use trial and improvement to find the root, correct to 4 decimal places, for each formula.
Explain why your two solutions are so different.

3 A trial and improvement formula for solving the equation $x^3 - 3x^2 - 10 = 0$ is given below:

$$x_{n+1} = 3 + \frac{10}{x_n{}^2}$$

Starting with $x = 1$, use trial and improvement to find one solution of this equation, correct to 2 decimal places. Substitute your value for x back into the original equation. How close is your answer to 0?

4 A value for $\frac{1}{A}$ can be found using the trial and improvement formula

$x_{n+1} = x_n(2 - Ax_n)$.

Starting in each case with $x = 0.01$, find, correct to 4 decimal places, the values of

a $\frac{1}{9}$ **b** $\frac{1}{25}$ **c** $\frac{1}{\sqrt{2}}$

Solving quadratic equations by formula

Earlier in this chapter we learned how to solve quadratic equations by factorisation.
In Chapter 8 we learn how to solve them by graphical methods.

Another way of solving them is by using a formula.

The solution of the quadratic equation $ax^2 + bx + c = 0$, where a, b, and c are constants is:

NOTE
You need to memorise this formula.

$$x = \frac{-b \pm \sqrt{b^2 - (4ac)}}{2a}$$

Study the examples overleaf to see how to use the formula.

Worked Examples

Solve the equations

a $x^2 + 6x + 4 = 0$ **c** $x^2 - 7x - 10 = 0$

b $x^2 - 5x + 6 = 0$ **d** $5x^2 + 6x - 4 = 0$

a $ax^2 + bx + c = 0$

$x^2 + 6x + 4 = 0$,   i.e. $a = 1$, $b = 6$, $c = 4$

From the formula $x = \dfrac{-b \pm \sqrt{b^2 - (4ac)}}{2a}$

$x = \dfrac{-6 \pm \sqrt{6^2 - (4 \times 1 \times 4)}}{2 \times 1} = \dfrac{-6 \pm \sqrt{36 - 16}}{2} = \dfrac{-6 \pm \sqrt{20}}{2}$

$= \dfrac{-6 \pm 4.472}{2}$

i.e. $x = \dfrac{(-6 + 4.472)}{2}$ or $\dfrac{(-6 - 4.472)}{2} = \dfrac{-1.528}{2}$ or $\dfrac{-10.472}{2}$

i.e. $x = -0.764$ or -5.24 (3 sf)

b $ax^2 + bx + c = 0$

$x^2 - 5x + 3 = 0$,   i.e. $a = 1$, $b = -5$, $c = 6$

From the formula $x = \dfrac{-b \pm \sqrt{b^2 - (4ac)}}{2a}$

$x = \dfrac{-(-5) \pm \sqrt{(-5)^2 - (4 \times 1 \times 6)}}{2 \times 1} = \dfrac{5 \pm \sqrt{25 - 24}}{2} = \dfrac{5 \pm \sqrt{1}}{2}$

$= \dfrac{5 \pm 1}{2}$

i.e. $x = \dfrac{5 + 1}{2}$ or $\dfrac{5 - 1}{2} = \dfrac{6}{2}$ or $\dfrac{4}{2}$

i.e. $x = 3$ or 2

c $ax^2 + bx + c = 0$

$x^2 - 7x - 10 = 0$,   i.e. $a = 1$, $b = -7$, $c = -10$

From the formula $x = \dfrac{-b \pm \sqrt{b^2 - (4ac)}}{2a}$

$x = \dfrac{-(-7) \pm \sqrt{(-7)^2 - (4 \times 1 \times -10)}}{2 \times 1} = \dfrac{7 \pm \sqrt{49 - (-40)}}{2} = \dfrac{7 \pm \sqrt{89}}{2}$

$= \dfrac{7 \pm 9.434}{2}$

i.e. $x = \dfrac{(7 + 9.434)}{2}$ or $\dfrac{(7 - 9.434)}{2} = \dfrac{16.434}{2}$ or $\dfrac{-2.434}{2}$

i.e. $x = 8.22$ or -1.22 (2 dp)

d $ax^2 + bx + c = 0$

$5x^2 + 6x - 4 = 0$,   i.e. $a = 5$, $b = 6$, $c = -4$

From the formula $x = \dfrac{-b \pm \sqrt{b^2 - (4ac)}}{2a}$

$x = \dfrac{-6 \pm \sqrt{6^2 - (4 \times 5 \times -4)}}{2 \times 5} = \dfrac{-6 \pm \sqrt{36 - (-80)}}{10} = \dfrac{-6 \pm \sqrt{116}}{10}$

$= \dfrac{-6 \pm 10.77}{10}$

i.e. $x = \dfrac{(-6 + 10.77)}{10}$ or $\dfrac{(-6 - 10.77)}{10} = \dfrac{4.77}{10}$ or $\dfrac{-16.77}{10}$

i.e. $x = 0.477$ or -1.68 (3 sf)

PRACTICE 7.9.4   Try these questions with a calculator

Solve the following equations, using the formula. Give your answers to appropriate degrees of accuracy.

1 $x^2 + 9x + 4 = 0$ **5** $x^2 + 9x - 2 = 0$ **9** $2x^2 + 7x + 3 = 0$

2 $x^2 + 5x + 1 = 0$ **6** $x^2 + 7x - 3 = 0$ **10** $3x^2 + 5x + 1 = 0$

3 $x^2 - 4x + 2 = 0$ **7** $x^2 - 9x - 5 = 0$ **11** $5x^2 - 3x - 7 = 0$

4 $x^2 - 9x + 7 = 0$ **8** $x^2 - 2x - 7 = 0$ **12** $4x^2 + 5x - 2 = 0$

13 $5x^2 + 14x - 3 = 0$ **14** $x^2 + 5x = 0$

NOTE

Solving a quadratic equation by factorising is quicker than using the formula. Hence we only use the formula method when the equation does not factorise. The Worked Example **b** above factorises into $(x - 2)(x - 3) = 0$ and is easily solved into $x = 3$ or $x = 2$ by factorising.

Algebraic fractions

An algebraic fraction is an ordinary fraction with letters in it. Some examples are:

$$\dfrac{a}{4}, \quad \dfrac{2b}{3}, \quad \dfrac{pq}{10}, \quad \dfrac{3rs^2t^3}{4mn}, \quad \dfrac{(3x + 4)}{5}, \quad \dfrac{(2c + 3d)}{(4e + f)}, \text{ etc.}$$

We know that, in algebra, letters stand for numbers. Thus the rules for algebraic fractions are the same as for arithmetic ones. The following worked examples and practice exercises show how algebraic fractions work. You may need to revise arithmetic fractions first.

Cancelling algebraic fractions

Cancelling means simplifying a fraction to its simplest value.

Worked Examples

Simplify the following fractions:

1 $\dfrac{25a}{15b}$ **2** $\dfrac{16cd}{24de}$ **3** $\dfrac{s^2 - t^2}{3s + 3t}$

1 $\dfrac{25a}{15b} = \dfrac{\overset{5}{\cancel{25}}a}{\underset{3}{\cancel{15}}b} = \dfrac{5a}{3b}$

2 $\dfrac{16cd}{24de} = \dfrac{\overset{2}{\cancel{16}}c\cancel{d}}{\underset{3}{\cancel{24}}\cancel{d}e} = \dfrac{2c}{3e}$

3 $\dfrac{s^2 - t^2}{3s + 3t} = \dfrac{(s - t)\cancel{(s + t)}}{3\cancel{(s + t)}} = \dfrac{(s - t)}{3}$

PRACTICE 7.9.5

Simplify, where possible. If there is no simpler form, say so.

1 $\dfrac{5a^2}{10a}$ **6** $\dfrac{24h^2i^3}{15hi^2}$ **11** $\dfrac{(-6u)^2}{-3uv}$ **16** $\dfrac{3c^2 - 3cd}{6c^2 + 6cd}$

2 $\dfrac{6b}{18b^3}$ **7** $\dfrac{33j^2k^3}{21j^3k}$ **12** $\dfrac{(4uw)^2}{(-2w)^3}$ **17** $\dfrac{4e + 8f}{20ef}$

3 $\dfrac{8c}{20c}$ **8** $\dfrac{(3m)^2}{6m}$ **13** $\dfrac{20x^2y^3z^4}{32xy^4z^2}$ **18** $\dfrac{5g^2}{g^2 + gh}$

4 $\dfrac{-14de}{21e}$ **9** $\dfrac{24n^2p}{(4n)^2}$ **14** $\dfrac{4 + 8a^2}{2a}$ **19** $\dfrac{6i^2 + 12ij}{4i^2 - 2ij}$

5 $\dfrac{35f}{-50fg^2}$ **10** $\dfrac{8qr}{11st}$ **15** $\dfrac{4b + 5b^2}{3b}$ **20** $\dfrac{m^2 - 8m + 15}{m^2 - m - 6}$

21 $\dfrac{2m^2 + m - 3}{2m^2 + 17m + 21}$ **22** $\dfrac{9p^2 - 49}{12p + 28}$

Multiplying and dividing algebraic fractions

The rules for this are the same as for arithmetic fractions:
1 Multiply the numerators and denominators and cancel where possible.
2 To divide – turn the second fraction upside down and multiply.

Worked Examples

Simplify:

a $\dfrac{4a}{3b} \times \dfrac{6b}{2a^2}$ **b** $\dfrac{8c^2}{3d^2} \div \dfrac{4c}{15d}$ **c** $3e - 3f \div \dfrac{5e - 5f}{10g + 20h}$

a $\dfrac{24ab}{6a^2b} = \dfrac{4}{a}$

b $\dfrac{8c^2}{3d^2} \times \dfrac{15d}{4c} = \dfrac{120c^2d}{12cd^2} = \dfrac{10c}{d}$

c $\dfrac{3(e-f)}{1} \times \dfrac{10(g+2h)}{5(e-f)} = 6(g+2h)$

PRACTICE 7.9.6

Simplify:

1 $\dfrac{4a}{5b} \times \dfrac{7b}{21a}$ **3** $\dfrac{4e^3}{9f^3} \div \dfrac{5e^2}{18f}$ **5** $\dfrac{6i^4j^6}{5} \times \dfrac{15}{8i^2j}$ **7** $\dfrac{4kl}{3} \div \dfrac{3}{2kl}$

2 $\dfrac{2c^2}{3d^3} \times \dfrac{15d^2}{10c^3}$ **4** $\dfrac{4g^2}{9h} \div \dfrac{8g^3}{15h^4}$ **6** $\dfrac{4kl}{3} \times \dfrac{3}{2kl}$ **8** $\dfrac{(m-n)}{3} \times \dfrac{m}{(m-n)}$

9 $\dfrac{3k+3l}{5} \div \dfrac{9k+9l}{10}$ **10** $\dfrac{2m-2n}{4} \times \dfrac{3mn}{m^2-n^2}$

Adding and subtracting algebraic fractions

Again, the rules for algebra are the same as for arithmetic.
You may need to revise these from Chapter 1.

Worked Examples

Simplify:

a $\dfrac{3a}{4} + \dfrac{a}{8}$ **b** $\dfrac{5}{4b} - \dfrac{2}{3b}$ **c** $\dfrac{2d}{3e} + \dfrac{4d}{2e}$ **d** $\dfrac{4}{9f} - \dfrac{g}{3f}$ **e** $\dfrac{4}{2x} + \dfrac{7}{3y}$

a $\dfrac{3a}{4} + \dfrac{a}{8}$ **b** $\dfrac{5}{4b} - \dfrac{2}{3b}$ **c** $\dfrac{2d}{3e} + \dfrac{4d}{2e}$

$= \dfrac{6a}{8} + \dfrac{a}{8}$ $= \dfrac{15}{12b} - \dfrac{8}{12b}$ $= \dfrac{4d}{6e} + \dfrac{12d}{6e}$

$= \dfrac{7a}{8}$ $= \dfrac{7}{12b}$ $= \dfrac{16d}{6e} = \dfrac{8d}{3e}$

d $\dfrac{4}{9f} - \dfrac{g}{3f}$

$= \dfrac{4}{9f} - \dfrac{3g}{9f}$

$= \dfrac{4 - 3g}{9f}$

e $\dfrac{4}{2x} + \dfrac{7}{3y}$

$= \dfrac{12y}{6xy} + \dfrac{14x}{6xy}$

$= \dfrac{12y + 14x}{6xy}$

$= \dfrac{2(6y + 7x)}{6xy}$

$= \dfrac{(6y + 7x)}{3xy}$

PRACTICE 7.9.7

Simplify the following:

1 $\dfrac{2a}{3} + \dfrac{a}{6}$

4 $\dfrac{3d}{4e} + \dfrac{3e}{4d}$

7 $\dfrac{4}{3h} - \dfrac{3}{5i}$

10 $\dfrac{5}{t} + \dfrac{3}{t + 1}$

2 $\dfrac{4}{5b} - \dfrac{3}{2b}$

5 $\dfrac{5}{3f} - \dfrac{2}{4f}$

8 $\dfrac{(p + q)}{3} + \dfrac{(3p + 2q)}{4}$

11 $\dfrac{u}{u - 3} + \dfrac{2u}{u + 4}$

3 $\dfrac{3d}{4e} + \dfrac{4d}{3e}$

6 $\dfrac{7}{2g} + \dfrac{4}{3h}$

9 $\dfrac{5}{s - 1} - \dfrac{3}{s + 1}$

12 $\dfrac{3w}{w + 4} - \dfrac{2w}{w - 1}$

13 $4 + \dfrac{3}{z - 1}$

14 $\dfrac{5a}{a - 3} - 2$

Basic laws of arithmetic

The commutative law

When we add or multiply two numbers, it doesn't matter which comes first; $a + b = b + a$ and $a \times b = b \times a$.
The commutative law does *not* work for subtraction or division; $5 - 3$ is *not* the same as $3 - 5$, $10 \div 5$ is *not* the same as $5 \div 10$.

The associative law

When we add or multiply three (or more) numbers then:
$a + b + c = (a + b) + c = a + (b + c)$
$a \times b \times c = (a \times b) \times c = a \times (b \times c)$

Basic algebraic notation

x	means	$1 \times x$ or $1x$
$-x$	means	$-1 \times x$ or $-1x$
$4x$	means	$4 \times x$ or $(x + x + x + x)$
$\dfrac{x}{4}$	means	$x \div 4$ or $\frac{1}{4}$ of x or $\dfrac{x}{4}$
xy	means	$x \times y$
$3xy$	means	$3 \times x \times y$ or $(xy + xy + xy)$
$\dfrac{x}{y}$	means	$x \div y$

Index notation

x^n means $x \times x \times x \times \ldots$etc ($n$ times)

The laws of indices

$$x^a \times x^b = x^{a+b}$$
$$x^a \div x^b = x^{a-b}$$
$$(x^a)^b = x^{ab}$$

Basic algebra

Algebra is simply arithmetic using letters and numbers.
In algebra letters are used to represent numbers.

Words and terms

Any letter used to represent numbers is called a *variable* or *unknown*.
Anything that has a fixed value is called a *constant*.
Any number in front of a variable is called a *coefficient*.
An algebraic statement which is a collection of terms is called an *expression*.
An expression is a collection of constants, variables and symbols.
Any term may have more than one variable in it.
Usually we put letters in alphabetical order in a term and the number always comes first. If any expression has more than one term of the same *type* in it then these terms can be combined.
These are called *like* terms.

Using brackets

There is a definite order in doing operations.
We use the word **BODMAS**.
Brackets are used when we wish to group terms together.
Anything written inside brackets should be done before any other operations.

When removing brackets, each term *inside* the bracket must be multiplied by the term *outside*.
A term without a sign in front of it is always taken as positive (+).

When multiplying:
if the signs are the same the result is (+)
if the signs are different the result is (−).

Multiplying brackets together

Sometimes we want to multiply two brackets together.
Multiply *each term* in the second bracket by *each term* in the first.

Factorisation

Some series of terms have the same factor in each.
This is called a *common factor*.
Sometimes we find that there is another common factor after we have originally found one. This means that we can find a common factor a second time and factorise again. The second common factor is usually in a bracket.
Example of quadratic factorisation:

$$x^2 + 5x + 6 = (x + 2)(x + 3)$$

Any expression of the form $ax^2 + bx + c$, where a, b and c are constants, is called a *quadratic expression*.

Simple substitution

If we put a number in place of a letter in an expression we are said to *substitute* the value.

Number diagrams

Number diagrams generate sequences of numbers by substituting values into a formula stored in a diagram.

Linear equations and formulae

Formulae are like *equations* – they contain an equals (=) sign and have terms on each side.
The difference between a formula and an equation is that in a formula the variables stand for definite quantities.
In an equation the variables stand for unknown quantities.
The solution may possibly be found – but not always.
We often write equations (and formulae) with one letter on one side of the = sign.

This letter is called the *subject* of the equation (or formula).
The subject is usually on the left hand side of the equation but can be on either.

Balancing equations

Equations are like balances.
They must have the same value on both sides of the = sign.

Simple linear equations

Algebraic equations use letters to represent the *unknown* quantity.
In an equation the *left hand side* must be equal to the *right hand side*.

The rules for solving linear equations

Both sides must *balance* at all times.
We must do *exactly* the same to both sides in order to keep it balanced.
To do this we can:

- add the same amount to both sides,
- subtract the same amount from both sides,
- multiply each side by the same amount (this means *each* term on both sides),
- divide both sides by the same amount (this means *each* term on both sides).

Equations are easiest to solve if we collect all the unknown terms on one side and all the constant terms on the other.
It is best to put the unknown terms on the side that gives the positive value.
If an equation has brackets in it, it is usually best to multiply out the brackets, collect like terms and then solve.

Simultaneous linear equations

We always need two equations with the two variables to produce one solution that fits both.
There are five main rules for solving simultaneous equations:

- Find a variable with the same coefficient in both equations.
- If the signs of these two terms are the same *subtract* one equation from the other If the signs of these two terms are different *add* the equations together.
- Solve the resulting equation in one variable.
- Substitute this value for the first variable back in one of the original equations and solve the resulting equation in the other variable.
- Check the solution by substituting both values back into the other original equation.

Quadratic equations

Any quadratic expression written as an equation is called a *quadratic equation*.
Any quadratic equation can be written in the form $x^2 + ax + b = 0$, where a and b are constants.
There are three main methods of solving quadratic equations – by factorising, by using a formula and by graphs.

Solving quadratic equations by factorising

Consider the equation $P \times Q = 0$.
$P \times Q = 0$ is only possible if *either* $P = 0$ *or* $Q = 0$.
If P and Q are factors from a quadratic expression we can use this fact to solve quadratic equations of the form $x^2 + ax + b = 0$.

Changing the subject

We know that $P = a + b + c$ is the formula for the perimeter, P, of a triangle whose sides are of lengths, a, b and c.
We call P the *subject* of the formula because it starts with $P = \ldots$ and there are no terms in P on the other side.
We could rearrange the formula into $a = P - b - c$, or $b = P - a - c$, or $c = P - a - b$, making either a or b or c the subject.
This process is called *transposing the formula* or *changing the subject*.
There are two main methods used to rearrange simple formulae or equations and to change the subject:

1 By using a *number diagram* or by reconstructing the original equation, step by step, starting with the required subject, using the *number diagram* technique.
    Reverse the *number diagram* formed, ending with a rearranged formula and our required subject.

2 Laws of algebra method.
    In this method we simply use our previous knowledge of the laws of algebra in rearranging the formula.
    It is like solving the equation but using letters as well as numbers and finding the value of another variable.
    Whatever we do, we must remember that we do *exactly the same to both sides* and that at all times our equation is *balanced*.
    It is usually, *but not always*, best to do operations in the following order:

    a eliminate roots by squaring, cubing, etc.,
    b clear fractions by multiplying through the equation,
    c multiply out brackets where necessary,
    d place all terms containing the subject required on one side of the equation and the rest on the other side,

e do whatever is necessary to obtain the required subject as a single term – this might need multiplying, dividing, factorising, taking roots, etc.,

f rewrite the equation with only the required subject on one side.

Inequalities

We say that 5 *is greater than* 3, or that -1 *is less than* 2.

Such statements are called *inequalities* and we have symbols to make the writing of them easier.

The above two inequalities would be written: $5 > 3$ and $-1 < 2$.

The symbol always points towards the smaller of the two quantities.

If an algebraic inequality is written there may be more than one possible solution.

For example, $x > 2$ means that x can take any value above 2.

However, if we write $x \geqslant 2$ (i.e. x is greater or equal to 2), then $x = 2$ is included, in addition to the values given above.

The four basic inequality symbols are:

> $>$ which means *greater than*
> $<$ which means *less than*
> $\geqslant$ which means *greater than or equal to*
> $\leqslant$ which means *less than or equal to*.

The number line

Algebraic inequalities can be represented by a *number line*.

Regions of inequalities

It is possible to find areas on a graph which represent inequalities.

Inequations

Algebraic inequalities are also known as *inequations*.

The rules for solving inequations are exactly the same as for equations – but with one addition:

when we multiply or divide by a negative number we reverse the sign.

Trial and improvement

Sometimes a quadratic equation has a solution but will not factorise.

Sometimes we want to find a solution to an equation that has a power higher than x^2.

We can solve equations like these using a method called *trial and improvement*.

Indices (extension)

$x^0 = 1$ whatever the value of x

x^{-n} means $\dfrac{1}{x^n}$

$x^{1/2}$ means $\sqrt{x}$
$x^{1/3}$ means the cube root of x, or $\sqrt[3]{x}$
$x^{1/4}$ means the fourth root of x, or $\sqrt[4]{x}$, etc.
$x^{1/n}$ means the nth root of x, or $\sqrt[n]{x}$
$x^{(p/r)}$ means the $\sqrt[r]{(x^p)}$ or $(\sqrt[r]{x})^p$

Difference of two squares (extension)

$a^2 - b^2 = (a - b)(a + b)$

Solving quadratic equations by formula (extension)

The solution of the quadratic equation $ax^2 + bx + c = 0$, where a, b, and c are constants is:

$$x = \frac{-b \pm \sqrt{(b^2 - (4ac))}}{2a}$$

Solving a quadratic equation by factorising is quicker than using the formula. We only use the formula method when the equation does not factorise.

Algebraic fractions (extension)

An algebraic fraction is an ordinary fraction with letters in it.
The rules for algebraic fractions are the same as for arithmetic ones.

Cancelling algebraic fractions (extension)

Cancelling means simplifying a fraction to its simplest value.
We can only cancel when we have terms *multiplied* and *divided*.
Brackets count as terms for cancelling also.

Multiplying and dividing algebraic fractions (extension)

The rules for this are the same as for arithmetic fractions:

- multiply the numerators and denominators and cancel where possible,
- to divide – turn the second fraction upside down and multiply.

Adding and subtracting algebraic fractions (extension)

Again, the rules for algebra are the same as for arithmetic.

Linear programming (extension)

We saw how regions that satisfy certain sets of inequalities could be shown on a graph.
Linear programming is an extension of this.
Problems are generally solved in three stages:

- interpret the given information as a number of inequalities,
- show these graphically and shade out the regions that do not apply,
- investigate the unshaded area(s) left to solve particular problems.

CHAPTER 8
Sequences and graphs

In this chapter you will need to:
▸ use the four rules in algebra
▸ recognise simple patterns algebraically
▸ recognise and draw coordinates in the first quadrant
▸ use coordinates and simple graphs

Sequences

A sequence is a pattern of numbers (or any other items) that appear in a definite order.
For instance, 2, 4, 6, 8, ____, ____, is the sequence of even numbers.
It is usually possible to state the rule that generates the sequence.
Often the rule is algebraic.

Worked Examples

Find the next two terms in the following sequences and state the rule that generates them.
a Monday, Tuesday, Wednesday, _____, _____
b F, G, H, I, J, _____, _____
c 5, 10, 15, 20, _____, _____
d . .. ...
       .. ...
         ... _____, _____
e . . .
      .. ..
        ... _____, _____
f 4, 12, 36, 108, _____, _____

    a Monday, Tuesday, Wednesday, Thursday, Friday (days of the week, in order)
    b F, G, H, I, J, K, L (letters of the alphabet)
    c 5, 10, 15, 20, 25, 30 (each term is 5 more than the previous one)
    d .   ..   .
                  ..   ..
                     ...   .
         square   ....
         numbers   .....
        (1)   (4)   (9)   (16)   (25)

e   .   .   .   .   .
                . .   . .
                         . . .   .
triangle   . . . .
numbers   . . . . .
    (1)   (3)   (6)   (10)   (15)

f 4, 12, 36, 108, 324, 972 (each term is 3 times the previous term)

PRACTICE 8.1.1

1 Write down the next two terms of the following sequences.
State the rule that generates the sequence.
a 1, 3, 5, 7, …, …
b 2, 7, 12, 17, …, …
c b, e, h, k, …, …
d 2, 8, 32, 128, …, …
e March, April, May, …, …
f 8, 6, 4, 2, …, …
g 3, ⁻3, 3, ⁻3, …, …
h 2, 6, 5, 8, 8, 10, 11, 12, …, …

Coordinates

Coordinates are used to locate points on a graph.
For example, the position of point P is written as the coordinates (4, 3).
This means that the point is 4 units in the direction of the x-axis and 3 units in the direction of the y-axis.

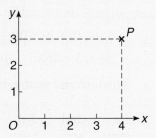

The horizontal line is usually called the **x-axis** and the vertical line is usually called the **y-axis**, although *any two variables can be used*.

The point where the two axes cross is called the **origin**.
The coordinates of the origin are therefore (0, 0).

A number pattern which is formed by some common rule is called a sequence or a **series.**

Each number in the sequence is called a **term**.
Each term in the sequence is linked by a rule.

By studying the patterns that we see between the terms we are often able to work out the rule that generates the way the sequence is made up.
It often helps if we write down the numbers in the sequence in the form of a diagram, chart or table.

Worked Examples

1   1st   2nd   3rd   4th
      term   term   term   term
      5   9   13   17

In this example each term is found by adding 4 to the previous term.

$$\overset{+4}{5 \quad 9} \quad \overset{+4}{\quad 13} \quad \overset{+4}{\quad 17}$$

Use the rule to write down the next two terms.

$$\overset{+4}{17 \quad 21} \qquad \overset{+4}{21 \quad 25}$$

The next two terms are 21 and 25.

2   1st   2nd   3rd   4th
      term   term   term   term
      2   6   18   54

In this example each term is found by multiplying the previous term by 3.

$$\overset{\times 3}{2 \quad 6} \quad \overset{\times 3}{\quad 18} \quad \overset{\times 3}{\quad 54}$$

Use the rule to write down the fifth and sixth terms.

$$54 \times 3 = 162 \qquad 162 \times 3 = 486$$

The fifth and sixth terms are 162 and 486.

3   1st   2nd   3rd   4th
      term   term   term   term
      2   3   5   9

In this example each term is found by multiplying the previous term by 2 and then subtracting 1.

$$\overset{(\times 2)-1}{2 \qquad 3} \quad \overset{(\times 2)-1}{\qquad 5} \quad \overset{(\times 2)-1}{\qquad 9}$$

Use the rule to write down the next four terms.

$$9 \times 2 - 1 = 17$$
$$17 \times 2 - 1 = 33$$
$$33 \times 2 - 1 = 65$$
$$65 \times 2 - 1 = 129$$

The next four terms are 17, 33, 65 and 129.

PRACTICE 8.2.1

Write down the rule and the next two terms of the following sequences:

1 3, 5, 7, 9, ..., ...

2 8, 10.5, 13, ..., ...

3 2, 4, 8, 16, ..., ...

4 16, 12, 8, 4, ..., ...

5 27, 9, 3, ..., ...

6 −1, −4, −7, ..., ...

7 5, −10, 20, ..., ...

8 3, 7, 15, 31, ..., ...

9 1, 3.5, 13.5, 53.5, ..., ...

10 2, -2, 2, -2, 2, ..., ...

The Fibonacci sequence

The following sequence is named after the mathematician Fibonacci.
The sequence occurs in science and natural history.

1, 1, 2, 3, 5, 8, 13, ..., ..., ...

Each term is found by adding together the two previous terms.

What are the next three terms of the Fibonacci sequence?

Invent your own sequence by using your own starting numbers.

Finding the nth term of a sequence

Worked Examples

1 Find the nth term of the sequence 3 5 7 9 ... .
How many terms are needed to reach 111?

Consider the sequence:

1st term	2nd term	3rd term	4th term	...	10th term	...	50th term	...	nth term
3	5	7	9			...		...	...

The 1st term is 3 and the rule is *add 2*.

The 2nd term is found by adding 2 to the 1st term.

The 3rd term is found by adding 2 to the 2nd term, and so on ...

1st term	$= 3$		
2nd term	$= 3 + 2$	$= 5$	
3rd term	$= 5 + 2$	$= 3 + (2 \times 2)$	$= 7$
4th term	$= 7 + 2$	$= 3 + (3 \times 2)$	$= 9$
5th term	$= 9 + 2$	$= 3 + (4 \times 2)$	$= 11$
6th term	$= 11 + 2$	$= 3 + (5 \times 2)$	$= 13$
10th term		$= 3 + (9 \times 2)$	$= 21$
50th term		$= 3 + (49 \times 2)$	$= 101$
nth term		$= 3 + ((n - 1) \times 2) = 3 + 2n - 2$	$= 2n + 1$

If the nth term is 111, we can say that $2n + 1 = 111$

i.e. $2n = 110$

$n = 55$

NOTE
You may like to revise solving linear equations on pages 262–265.

Thus, the 55th term is 111.

2 Find the nth term of the sequence 2 6 18 54 ..., ... How many terms are needed to reach 13 122?

Consider the sequence:

1st term	2nd term	3rd term	4th term	...	15th term	...	60th term	...	nth term
2	6	18	54		...		...		...

The 1st term is 2 and the rule is 'multiply by 3'.

The 2nd term is found by multiplying the 1st term by 3.

The 3rd term is found by multiplying the 2nd term by 3, and so on ...

1st term	$= 2$		
2nd term	$= 2 \times 3$	$= 6$	
3rd term	$= 6 \times 3$	$= 2 \times (3^2)$	$= 18$
4th term	$= 18 \times 3$	$= 2 \times (3^3)$	$= 54$
5th term	$= 54 \times 3$	$= 2 \times (3^4)$	$= 162$
6th term	$= 162 \times 3$	$= 2 \times (3^5)$	$= 486$
15th term		$= 2 \times (3^{14})$	$= 9\,565\,938$
60th term		$= 2 \times (3^{59})$	$= 2.826 \times 10^{28}$
nth term		$= 2 \times (3^{n-1})$	

If the nth term is 13 122 we can say that $2 \times 3^{n-1} = 13\,122$

i.e.	3^{n-1}	$= 6561$
Now	3^8	$= 6561$
thus	$n - 1 = 8$	
i.e.	n	$= 9$

Thus the 9th term is 13 122.

PRACTICE 8.2.2 Try these questions without a calculator

1 Find the 6th, 10th, 25th and nth terms of the following sequences:
   a 2, 5, 8, 11, …
   b 1, 6, 11, 16, …
   c 3, 6, 12, 24, …
   d 20, 17, 14, 11, …
   e 64, 32, 16, …

2 Find the nth term of the sequence 1 5 9 13 …. How many terms of the sequence are needed to reach 85?

3 Find the nth term of the sequence 2 10 50 250 …. How many terms of the sequence are needed to reach 6250?

4 Find the nth term of the sequence 1 −2 4 −8 …. How many terms of the sequence are needed to reach −512?

5 Find the nth term of the sequence 8 5 2 −1 …. How many terms of the sequence are needed to reach −109?

6 Find the **a** 5th, **b** 20th, **c** 50th term of the sequence 1 3 5 7 … ….

7 Find the **a** 5th, **b** 20th, **c** 50th term of the sequence 3 8 13 18 … ….

8 Find the **a** 5th, **b** 20th, **c** 50th term of the sequence 1 3 9 27 … ….

9 Find the **a** 5th, **b** 20th, **c** 50th term of the sequence 1 2 4 8 … ….

10 Find the **a** 6th, **b** 10th, **c** 15th term of the sequence 1 2 3 5 8 … ….

Further sequences

Sometimes a formula generating a sequence is more than just linear.
For example, consider the quadratic formula $x^2 + 2x + 3$.
If we substitute $x = 1, 2, 3$, etc., we obtain the following sequence of numbers:

$$1^2 + 2 \times 1 + 3 = 6 \qquad 2^2 + 2 \times 2 + 3 = 11$$
$$3^2 + 2 \times 3 + 3 = 18 \qquad 4^2 + 2 \times 4 + 3 = 27$$
$$5^2 + 2 \times 5 + 3 = 38 \qquad 6^2 + 2 \times 6 + 3 = 51$$

We can show that a sequence is quadratic by looking at the *differences* between successive terms:

```
6        11        18        27        38        51
     5        7         9        11        13
         2        2         2         2
```

(All the numbers below the top line are formed by the *differences* between the two numbers above.)

It takes two lines to reach a constant difference of 2, as shown above. This means that the sequence is *generated* by a quadratic formula, i.e. one of the form $ax^2 + bx + c$.

If the final difference is 2 then the formula is $x^2 + bx + c$.
If the final difference is 4 then the formula is $2x^2 + bx + c$.
If the final difference is 6 then the formula is $3x^2 + bx + c$, etc.
This helps us to find the formula that generates a particular sequence.

Worked Examples

1 Find the formula that generates the sequence 6 17 34 57 86 121 162 ...

First we make out a table of *differences* as shown above:

$$
\begin{array}{ccccccccccccc}
6 & & 17 & & 34 & & 57 & & 86 & & 121 & & 162 \\
& 11 & & 17 & & 23 & & 29 & & 35 & & 41 & \\
& & 6 & & 6 & & 6 & & 6 & & 6 & &
\end{array}
$$

The 6 shows us that the formula generating the sequence is $3x^2 + bx + c$.

Hence we know that
$$
\begin{aligned}
6 &= 3 \times 1^2 + 3 &&= 3 \times 1^2 + 2 \times 1 + 1 \\
17 &= 3 \times 2^2 + 5 &&= 3 \times 2^2 + 2 \times 2 + 1 \\
34 &= 3 \times 3^2 + 7 &&= 3 \times 3^2 + 2 \times 3 + 1 \\
57 &= 3 \times 4^2 + 9 &&= 3 \times 4^2 + 2 \times 4 + 1 \\
86 &= 3 \times 5^2 + 11 &&= 3 \times 5^2 + 2 \times 5 + 1 \\
121 &= 3 \times 6^2 + 13 &&= 3 \times 6^2 + 2 \times 6 + 1 \\
162 &= 3 \times 7^2 + 15 &&= 3 \times 7^2 + 2 \times 7 + 1
\end{aligned}
$$

We know that the bx term in the formula must be $2x$ because the differences go up in twos.

Hence we can write $2 \times 1, 2 \times 2, 2 \times 3$, etc. in each term and find that the constant, c, left is $+1$.

Hence we can see that the quadratic formula that generates the above sequence is

$$3x^2 + 2x + 1.$$

2 Find the formula that generates the sequence 3 6 13 24 39 58 81 ...

First we make out a table of *differences* as shown above:

$$
\begin{array}{ccccccccccccc}
3 & & 6 & & 13 & & 24 & & 39 & & 58 & & 81 \\
& 3 & & 7 & & 11 & & 15 & & 19 & & 23 & \\
& & 4 & & 4 & & 4 & & 4 & & 4 & &
\end{array}
$$

The 4 shows us that the formula generating the sequence is $2x^2 + bx + c$.

Hence we know that
$$
\begin{aligned}
3 &= 2 \times 1^2 + 1 &&= 2 \times 1^2 - 3 \times 1 + 4 \\
6 &= 2 \times 2^2 - 2 &&= 2 \times 2^2 - 3 \times 2 + 4 \\
13 &= 2 \times 3^2 - 5 &&= 2 \times 3^2 - 3 \times 3 + 4 \\
24 &= 2 \times 4^2 - 8 &&= 2 \times 4^2 - 3 \times 4 + 4 \\
39 &= 2 \times 5^2 - 11 &&= 2 \times 5^2 - 3 \times 5 + 4 \\
58 &= 2 \times 6^2 - 14 &&= 2 \times 6^2 - 3 \times 6 + 4 \\
81 &= 2 \times 7^2 - 17 &&= 2 \times 7^2 - 3 \times 7 + 4
\end{aligned}
$$

We know that the bx term in the formula must be $3x$ because the differences go up in threes.

Hence we can write $3 \times 1, 3 \times 2, 3 \times 3$, etc. in each term and find that the constant, c, left is $+4$.

Hence we can see that the quadratic formula that generates the above sequence is

$$2x^2 - 3x + 4.$$

PRACTICE 8.2.3   Try this question without a calculator

1   Use the method of differences outlined above to find the quadratic formula that generates each of the sequences below:

    a   6, 11, 18, 27, 38, 51, 66, 83
    b   2, 10, 20, 32, 46, 62, 80, 100
    c   6, 15, 28, 45, 66, 91, 120, 153
    d   2, 9, 20, 35, 54, 77, 104, 135
    e   15, 29, 49, 75, 107, 145, 189, 239
    f   4, 9, 20, 37, 60, 89, 124, 165

Two-dimensional patterns

Grids, or arrays of numbers are often used in mathematics to generate patterns. Using the knowledge gained in Chapter 7 we can formulate and then solve equations from them. The following worked examples show the methods used.

Worked Examples

1   The grid shows the numbers from 0 to 99. It shows an L shaped box on it. This box is called L_{12} because the number at the top is 12. The numbers in L_{12} total $12 + 22 + 32 + 33 = 99$.

a Use the grid to find **i** L_4 **ii** L_{36} and **iii** L_{72}.

b Fill in the other numbers in the box:

c Show that the value of L_x equals $4x + 51$.

d Use the information in **c** to write down an equation whose sum is 171.

e Solve this equation to find the value of x.

> **a**   **i** $L_4 = 4 + 14 + 24 + 25 = 67$
> **ii** $L_{36} = 36 + 46 + 56 + 57 = 195$
> **iii** $L_{72} = 72 + 82 + 92 + 93 = 339$.
>
> **b** The other numbers are $x + 10$, $x + 20$ and $x + 21$.
>
> **c** $L_x = x + x + 10 + x + 20 + x + 21 = 4x + 51$.
>
> **d** $4x + 51 = 171$
>
> **e** $4x + 51 = 171$ $4x = 171 - 51$ $4x = 120$ $x = 30$.

2 The grid shows the numbers from 0 to 99. It shows an L shaped box on it. This box is called L_{16} because the middle number is 16. The value of L_{16} is found thus: $6 \times 17 - 16 = 86$.

```
 0   1   2   3   4   5   6   7   8   9
10  11  12  13  14  15  16  17  18  19
20  21  22  23  24  25  26  27  28  29
30  31  32  33  34  35  36  37  38  39
40  41  42  43  44  45  46  47  48  49
50  51  52  53  54  55  56  57  58  59
60  61  62  63  64  65  66  67  68  69
70  71  72  73  74  75  76  77  78  79
80  81  82  83  84  85  86  87  88  89
90  91  92  93  94  95  96  97  98  99
```

a Use the grid to find   **i** L_{14} **ii** L_{31} and   **iii** L_{63}.

b Fill in the other numbers in the box:

c Show that the value of L_x equals $x^2 - 10x - 10$.

d Use the information in **c** to write down equations whose values are
 i 1   **ii** 134   **iii** 365

e Solve these equations to find the positive values of x.
 Explain the significance of the negative solutions.

a   **i** $L_{14} = 4 \times 15 - 14 = 46$
   ii $L_{31} = 21 \times 32 - 31 = 641$
   iii $L_{63} = 53 \times 64 - 63 = 3329$.

b The other numbers are $(x - 10)$ and $(x + 1)$.

c $L_x = (x - 10)(x + 1) - x = x^2 - 10x + x - 10 - x = x^2 - 10x - 10$.

d   **i** $x^2 - 10x - 10 = 1$, i.e. $x^2 - 10x - 11 = 0$
   ii $x^2 - 10x - 10 = 134$, i.e. $x^2 - 10x - 144 = 0$
   iii $x^2 - 10x - 10 = 365$, i.e. $x^2 - 10x - 375 = 0$

e   **i** $x^2 - 10x - 11 = 0$ i.e $(x - 11)(x + 1) = 0$
   either $x - 11 = 0$ or $x + 1 = 0$
   i.e. $x = 11$ or $x = -1$
   Since x must be positive the solution is $x = 11$.

   ii $x^2 - 10x - 144 = 0$ i.e $(x - 18)(x + 8) = 0$
   either $x - 18 = 0$ or $x + 8 = 0$
   i.e. $x = 18$ or $x = -8$
   Since x must be positive the solution is $x = 18$.

   iii $x^2 - 10x - 375 = 0$ i.e $(x - 25)(x + 15) = 0$
   either $x - 25 = 0$ or $x + 15 = 0$
   i.e. $x = 25$ or $x = -15$
   Since x must be positive the solution is $x = 25$.

(The negative solutions for x are those that would have been
obtained if the grid were to be extended into negative numbers.)

PRACTICE 8.2.4   Try these questions without a calculator

Use a grid like the one below to answer the following questions:

```
 0  1  2  3  4  5  6  7  8  9
10 11 12 13 14 15 16 17 18 19
20 21 22 23 24 25 26 27 28 29
30 31 32 33 34 35 36 37 38 39
40 41 42 43 44 45 46 47 48 49
50 51 52 53 54 55 56 57 58 59
60 61 62 63 64 65 66 67 68 69
70 71 72 73 74 75 76 77 78 79
80 81 82 83 84 85 86 87 88 89
90 91 92 93 94 95 96 97 98 99
```

1 The letter T is found in various places in the grid. T_5 has the numbers

$$\begin{array}{|c|c|c|} \hline 4 & 5 & 6 \\ \hline \end{array}$$
$$\boxed{15}$$

T_5 has the value $4 + 5 + 6 + 15 = 30$.

a Find the values of   **i** T_{18} **ii** T_{36} **iii** T_{73} .

b Show that the value of T_x is $4x + 10$.

c T_x has values   **i** 22   **ii** 102   **iii** 282   **iv** 374.
Write down equations for x in each case and solve them to find the value of x.

d Is T_{10} possible? Explain your answer.

2 The letter V is found in various places in the grid. V_{14} has the numbers

$$\begin{array}{c} 3 \quad \backslash \quad 5 \\ 14 \end{array}$$

V_{14} has the value $3 + 5 - 14 = -6$.

a Find the values of   **i** V_{17} **ii** V_{55} **iii** V_{82}.

b Show that the value of V_x is $x - 20$.

c V_x has values   **i** -4 **ii** 33   **iii** 77.
Write down equations for x in each case and solve them to find the value of x.

d Is V_{19} possible? Explain your answer.

NOTE

To do this question you need to be able to solve quadratic equations. Revise these on pages 277 and 278.

3 The letter V is found in various places in the grid. V_{14} has the numbers

$$\begin{array}{c} 3 \quad \backslash \quad 5 \\ 14 \end{array}$$

V_{14} has the value $3 \times 5 - 14 = 1$.

a Find the values of **i** V_{17} **ii** V_{55} **iii** V_{82} .

b Show that the value of V_x is $x^2 - 21x + 99$.

c V_x has values   **i** -9 **ii** 451   **iii** 1179.
Write down equations for x in each case and solve them to find the value of x.

4 The letter X is found in various places in the grid. X_6 has the numbers

$$\begin{array}{c} 6 \quad \backslash \quad 8 \\ 16 \quad \wedge \quad 18 \end{array}$$

X_6 has the value $8 \times 16 - 6 \times 18 = 128 - 108 = 20$.

a Find the values of   **i** X_{12} **ii** X_{55} **iii** X_{77} .

b What do you notice about all your answers?

c Show that the value of X_x is always 20.

Extending the axes

We saw, in the reinforcement at the beginning of the chapter, how to fix the positions, or coordinates, of points on a graph.

However, the axes can be extended both to the left and downwards in order to be able to *plot* the positions of points having negative coordinates.

This is shown below:

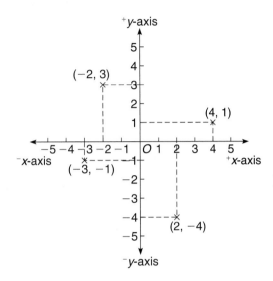

NOTE

We always put the value of the x coordinate first. The unit of measurement along each axis is called its scale.

The scales do not have to be the same on each axis but they must be the same on the positive and negative parts of the same axis.

These positions are called **cartesian**, or **rectangular**, coordinates.

The points $(-2, 3)$, $(4, 1)$, $(-3, -1)$ and $(2, -4)$ are shown on the graph above.

Functions and graphs

A **function** is another name given to an algebraic expression.

A functional graph shows us a *picture* of this expression which connects two variables.

Usually these are called x and y but any pair of letters can be used.

The horizontal, or x-axis, is called the *independent* axis.

The vertical, or y-axis, is called the *dependent*.

This is because the function is usually written in the form $y =$ (some expression in x) and the values of y *depend* on whatever values x takes.

For example, in the function $y = 3x - 1$ we can substitute any values we like for x and find the corresponding y values.

When $x = -1$, $y = 3(-1) - 1 = -4$; when $x = 1$, $y = 3(1) - 1 = 2$; when $x = 3$, $y = 3(3) - 1 = 8$.

If we *plot* these points on a graph we get the following result:

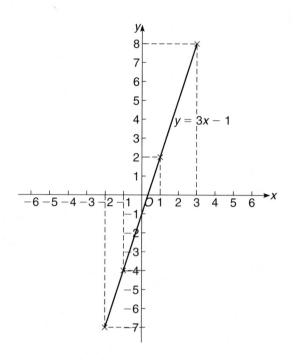

Notice that the points $(-1, -4)$, $(1, 2)$ and $(3, 8)$ all lie on a straight line. We can join these points up to get a straight lined graph, i.e. a *picture* of $y = 3x - 1$.

Looking at other points on the line, for example, $x = -2, y = -7$; $x = 0, y = -1$; $x = 2.5, y = 6.5$, we can see that these values of x and y *fit* the equation $y = 3x - 1$ also.

In fact *every point on the line*, regardless of whether x and y are integers or not, *fits* or *satisfies* the equation of the graph $y = 3x - 1$.

Worked Examples

1 Does the point $(1, 6)$ lie on the straight line $y = 8x - 2$?

2 Does the point $(2, 3)$ lie on the straight line $y = 3x + 1$?

3 The point $(-1, 2)$ lies on one of the straight lines $y = 2x - 3$ or $y = 6 + 4x$. Determine which line it lies on.

4 The x coordinates of two points on the straight line $y = 3x - 1$ are $x = -2$ and $x = 4$. Find the y coordinates of these points.

1 When $x = 1$, $y = 8(1) - 2 = 8 - 2 = 6$. Thus $(1, 6)$ does lie on the line $y = 8x - 2$.

2 When $x = 2$, $y = 3(2) + 1 = 6 + 1 = 7$. Thus $(2, 3)$ does not lie on the line $y = 3x + 1$.

3 When $x = -1$, $y = 2(-1) - 3 = -5$. Thus $(-1, 2)$ does not lie on $y = 2x - 3$.
   When $x = -1$, $y = 6 + 4(-1) = 2$. Thus $(-1, 2)$ does lie on $y = 2x - 3$.

4 When $x = -2$, $y = 3(-2) - 1 = -7$. Thus the y coordinate is -7.
   When $x = 4$, $y = 3(4) - 1 = 11$. Thus the y coordinate is 11.

PRACTICE 8.3.1   Try these questions without a calculator

1 Does the point $(-1, 1)$ lie on the straight line $y = 2 - 3x$?

2 Does the point $(2, -3)$ lie on the straight line $y = 2x - 7$?

3 The point $(1, -4)$ lies on one of the lines $y = 3 - x$, $y = 2x - 6$ and $y = 4 + 3x$. Which line does it lie on?

4 **a** The x coordinates of three points on the line $y = 3 + 2x$ are given by $x = -3$, $x = 0$ and $x = 7$. Find the y coordinates.
   b Plot these coordinates on a graph and show that all three points do indeed lie on a straight line.

Drawing linear graphs

Some examples of linear equations are:

$$y = 3 \quad x = -4 \quad y = 2x - 9 \quad y = 5 + 3x \quad 2x + 3y = 6$$

NOTE
Revise these skills on pages 280–85.

The last example does not look like the others, but using the skills learned at transposing formulae in Chapter 7 we can see that it can be made to look like the others, i.e.

$$2x + 3y = 6$$
(subtract $2x$) $3y = -2x + 6$
(divide by 3) $y = -\frac{2}{3}x + 2$

If we plotted all the points that *fitted* any of the above equations on a graph we would see that it was a straight line.

Linear graphs are just another way of saying *straight line graphs*.
We know if a graph is linear just by looking at the equation.

If the powers of x and y are both one then the graph is linear or straight.

To draw a linear graph we need to be able to find the coordinates of any two points that fit its equation and then to plot them and draw a graph.

To make sure that we haven't made a mistake we usually plot three points and make sure that they lie on one straight line.

When we have plotted the points we can draw a straight line through them and continue it from one side of the graph paper to the other.

When calculating the coordinates of points it is best to *build up* the values in a table.

The following examples show how this is done.

Worked Examples

1 Draw the graph of $y = 2x + 1$.
Take any 3 values of x; say $x = -2, x = 0, x = 3$:

x	-2	0	3
$2x$	-4	0	6
$y = 2x + 1$	-3	1	7

Plotting these points we obtain:

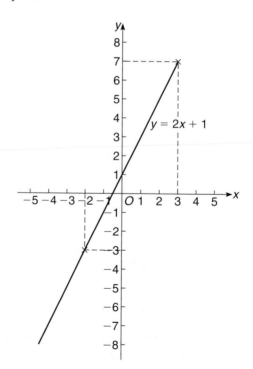

2 Plot the graph of $y = -3x + 6$.

Again, taking any three values of x; say $x = -1$, $x = 0$, and $x = 4$:

x	-1	0	4
$-3x$	3	0	-12
$y = -3x + 6$	9	6	-6

Plotting these points we obtain:

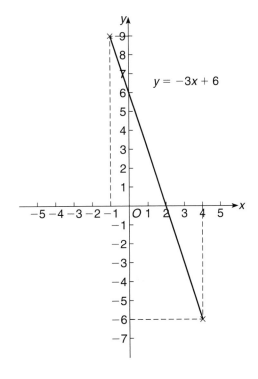

3 Plot the graph of $2y + 3x = 4$.

We cannot immediately plot this as above.

We must first transpose the equation. Hence:

$$2y + 3x = 4$$

(subtract $3x$) $\quad 2y = -3x + 4$

(divide by 2) $\quad y = -1.5x + 2$

Now taking three values of x; say $x = -4$, $x = 0$, and $x = 4$:

x	-4	0	4
$-1.5x$	6	0	-6
$y = -1.5x + 2$	8	2	-4

Plotting these points we obtain:

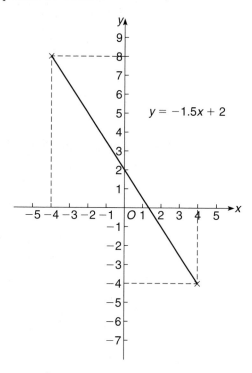

$$y = -1.5x + 2$$

PRACTICE 8.3.2a　Try these questions without a calculator

1　Using any three values for x, calculate coordinates and draw the graphs of:

  a　$y = x$ **e**　$y = x - 1$ **i**　$y = 6 - \frac{1}{2}x$ **m**　$4y + 3x = 12$

  b　$y = 3x$ **f**　$y = 2x - 3$ **j**　$y = -2x - 1$ **n**　$2y + 5x = 8$

  c　$y = -2x$ **g**　$y = 3x + 1$ **k**　$y = 4 - 3x$ **o**　$4x - 3y + 6 = 0$

  d　$y = x + 2$ **h**　$y = \frac{1}{2}x + 4$ **l**　$3y - 2x = 6$ **p**　$3x + 4y + 5 = 0$

2　Elizabeth cooks her Christmas turkey at 15 minutes per pound weight followed by a final 20 minutes.

This can be represented by the equation $y = 15x + 20$ where y is the cooking time in minutes and x the weight of the turkey in pounds.

  a　Copy and complete the following table:

x	5	15	25
$15x$			
$y = 15x + 20$			

b Using x as the horizontal axis and y as the vertical axis plot the three points calculated above and draw the graph.

c Using the graph obtained find how long Elizabeth needs to cook
   i an 8   **ii** an 18   **iii** a 23 pound turkey.

d Elizabeth puts her turkey into a pre-heated oven at 8:10 am and takes it out at 12 noon. If the turkey is perfectly cooked how heavy was it?

PRACTICE 8.3.2b   Try these questions with a calculator

1 When the gas supply industry was de-regulated in 1996 NEWGAZ offered its customers a choice of two tariffs:
   (A) An annual standing charge of £40 and gas supplied at 1.4 pence per unit, or
   (B) gas supplied at 1.6 pence per unit.

The cost of gas supplied under the two tariffs can be written as $C = 40 + 0.014n$ for tariff (A) and as $C = 0.016n$ for tariff (B), where C is the cost in £ and n the number of units.

a Copy and complete the following table:

n	10 000	25 000	55 000
$C = 40 + 0.014n$			
$C = 0.016n$			

b Using C as the vertical axis and n as the horizontal axis plot both of the graphs above *on the same grid*.

c Use the graphs obtained to find out the number of units where the cost would be the same under either tariff.

d Calculate which tariff should be used to obtain the cheapest gas if 14 000 units are used and what the saving would be.

e Calculate which tariff should be used to obtain the cheapest gas if 50 000 units are used and what the saving would be.

Solving simultaneous equations by using graphs

When we draw the graph of any straight line all the possible values of x and y which fit the equation of the graph must lie on the line.

Consider two such lines drawn on a graph.

Unless the lines are parallel *they must intersect at one point*.

Therefore, since the coordinates of x and y must satisfy the equations of the lines, the single values of x and y *at the point of intersection of the two lines,* must be the solutions of the simultaneous equations.

For example, solving the simultaneous equations $x + y = 4$ and $2x - y = 5$, we get:

$$x + y = 4$$
$$2x - y = 5$$

(adding) $\quad 3x = 9 \quad$ i.e. $x = 3$
(substituting) $3 + y = 4 \quad$ i.e. $y = 1$

If we now draw the graphs of $x + y = 4$ (i.e. $y = 4 - x$) and $2x - y = 5$ (i.e. $y = 2x - 5$), we can see that they intersect at the point $(3, 1)$.

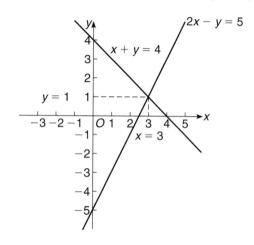

Therefore, we have an alternative method of solving a pair of simultaneous equations:

plot the graphs of the two equations and find the coordinates of the point of intersection.

PRACTICE 8.3.3

1 Solve the simultaneous equations by drawing the graphs of the equations and finding the points of intersection.

   a $2a + 3b = 15$ **c** $5e + f = 3$ **e** $5j + 3k = -15$
       $a + 2b = 8$ $e + 2f = -3$ $3j - 2k = -9$
   b $4c - 6d = -24$ **d** $3g + 4h = -29$ **f** $7m - 3n = 20$
       $3c + 3d = -3$ $4g - 3h = 3$ $3m - 5n = 3$

NOTE

$y = mx + c$ is an important equation which you need to memorise and understand.

Gradient and intercept

As we saw in the last section, any linear (or straight line) graph, can be written in the form $y = mx + c$, where m and c are *constants* for each individual line. c is usually called the **intercept** and is the place where the graph crosses the y-axis. From above we have seen that $y = 2x + 1$ crosses the y-axis at $(0, 1)$, that $y = -3x + 6$ crosses the y-axis at $(0, 6)$ and that $2y + 3x = 4$ crosses the y-axis at $(0, 2)$.

m is the coefficient of the x term and is called the **gradient** of the line. It measures how *steep* the line is compared to the x-axis.

Hence $y = 2x + 1$ has a gradient $m = 2$
$y = -3x + 6$ has a gradient $m = -3$
$2y + 3x = 4$ has a gradient $m = -1.5$

If m is positive it means that the line slopes *upwards to the right*

i.e.

If m is negative it means that the line slopes *downwards to the right*

i.e.

To find the gradient of a straight line

There are two main methods for calculating the gradient of a straight line.

1 *From the equation of the line.*
As shown in the last section the gradient is the coefficient of the x term. For example:

$y = 5x + 2$ has gradient $= 5$

$y = 3 - 4x$ has gradient $= -4$

$2y - 3x = 7$ must first be transposed:

$2y = 3x + 7$

$y = \frac{3}{2}x + \frac{7}{2}$ i.e. a gradient of $\frac{3}{2}$ or 1.5

2 *From a plotted graph.*
   a Choose *any two* convenient points on the line.
   b Calculate the vertical difference in y coordinates.
   c Calculate the horizontal difference in x coordinates.
   d The gradient $m = \dfrac{\text{the difference in } y \text{ coordinates}}{\text{the difference in } x \text{ coordinates}}$

Look along the line from left to right.
If the line slopes *upward*, both differences are positive and the line has a positive gradient.

If the line slopes *downward* from left to right, the x difference is positive and the y difference is negative (i.e. it decreases). This means that the line has a negative gradient.

For example:

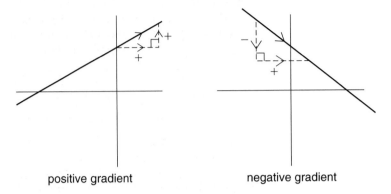

positive gradient   negative gradient

Worked Examples

1 Find the gradient of the line shown.

y difference $= 10 - 4 = 6$

x difference $= 5 - 2 = 3$

gradient $= m = \dfrac{y \text{ difference}}{x \text{ difference}} = \frac{6}{3} = 2$

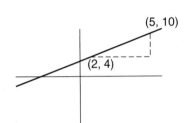

2 Find the gradient of the line shown.

y difference $= 5 - -1 = 5 + 1 = 6$

x difference $= 6 - -3 = 6 + 3 = 9$

gradient $= m = \dfrac{y \text{ difference}}{x \text{ difference}} = \frac{6}{9} = \frac{2}{3}$

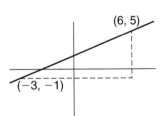

3 Find the gradient of the line shown.

y difference $= 3 - 7 = -4$ (a decrease)

x difference $= 2 - -4 = 2 + 4 = 6$

gradient $= m = \dfrac{y \text{ difference}}{x \text{ difference}} = \frac{-4}{6} = -\frac{2}{3}$

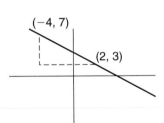

4 Find the equation of the straight line with gradient 5 which passes through the point $(2, 8)$.

The equation of a straight line is $y = mx + c$ and we know $m = 5$
Hence $y = 5x + c$.
Since the line passes through $(2, 8)$ the coordinates must fit the equation.
Hence we can substitute $x = 2$ and $y = 8$ in the equation.

Hence $\quad 8 = 5 \times 2 + c$

$\qquad\quad 8 = 10 + c$

i.e. $\quad -2 = c$

Thus, the equation of the line is $y = 5x - 2$.

PRACTICE 8.3.4   Try these questions without a calculator

1 Write down the intercept on the y axis of the following lines:
  a $y = 2x + 7$ **c** $y = 4x + 1$ **e** $y = 7 - 2x$
  b $y = 3x - 2$ **d** $2y = 3x - 9$ **f** $3y - 4x = 7$

2 Calculate the gradients of the following straight lines:
  a $y = 5x - 3$ **c** $y = 4 + x$ **e** $2y = 3x - 9$
  b $y = 7x + 2$ **d** $y = 5 - 2x$ **f** $4x - 3y = 7$

3 Calculate the gradients of the straight lines which pass through each of the following pairs of points:
  a $(1, 2), (4, 7)$ **d** $(-1, 3), (4, 2)$ **g** $(-3, -4), (-5, -6)$
  b $(0, 0), (3, 1)$ **e** $(-2, 4), (3, -2)$ **h** $(2, 4), (-2, 4)$
  c $(1, 7), (3, 2)$ **f** $(-5, -6), (4, -1)$ **i** $(1, 3), (1, 5)$

4 In each of the following diagrams use any two convenient points to calculate the gradients of the straight lines shown:

a

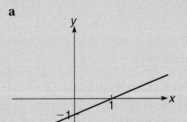

c

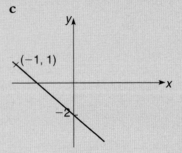

b

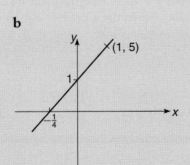

d

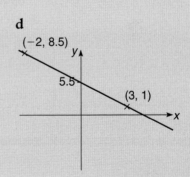

5 Each of the following equations   A: $y = 2x - 3$ B: $y = -3x + 4$
C: $2x + 3y = 4$ D: $x = 2$ E: $y = -5$ are represented by one of the graphs below.

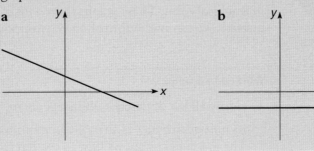

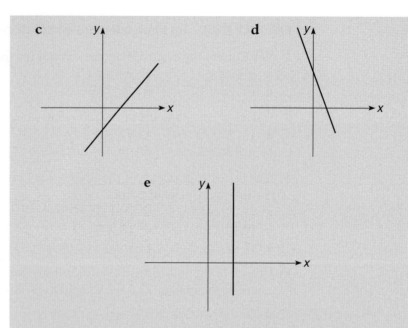

State which of the equations A to E are represented by the lines **a** to **e**.

6 A straight line has gradient 2 and passes through the point $(3, 4)$.
   a Write down the gradient, m.
   b Using your value of m above write down the equation of the line in the form $y = mx + c$.
   c We have been told that the line passes through the point $(3, 4)$. Substitute for x and y in the equation above and find the value of c.
   d Hence write down the complete equation of the straight line.

7 Find the equation of the straight line which has a gradient of -3 and which passes through the point $(1, -3)$.

8 A straight line is parallel to the line $y = 4x - 1$ and passes through $(2, 6)$. Find its equation.

9 A straight line passes through the points $(-3, -5)$ and $(2, 7)$. Find its equation.

8.4
INTERPRETING GRAPHS

We often see, in papers and magazines, a large variety of information presented in graphical form. These graphs show a lot of data very easily and, with a little practice, we can find information very quickly.

Worked Examples

1 Cornwall has declared itself independent.

   Its unit of currency is an oval shaped coin called the *Pasty*.
   The graph below shows how to convert from £ Sterling to the *Pasty*.

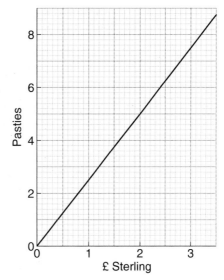

a How many *Pasties* do I get for £1?
b How much is 1 *Pasty* worth in pence?
c On holiday in Newquay I change a traveller's cheque for £25 into *Pasties*. How many do I get?
d After my holiday I find I have 76 *Pasties* left. Excluding commission, how much do I get back in £ sterling?

  a When £ = 1, *Pasties* = 2.5
  b 2.5 *Pasties* = £1, therefore 1 *Pasty* = $\frac{100}{2.5}$ = 40 pence
  c I get 25 × 2.5 = 62.5 *Pasties*
  d I get $\frac{76}{2.5}$ = £30.40.

2 The vertical height of an aeroplane after take-off is shown by the graph below.

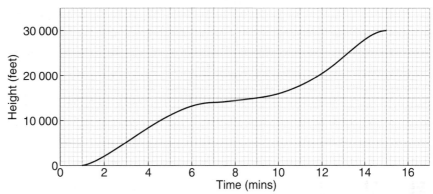

a How long does the plane taxi along the runway?
b When does the plane first reach maximum height?
c How high is the plane after **i** 2 minutes **ii** 7 minutes?
d When does the plane reach half its maximum height?

  a 1 minute
  b 15 minutes
  c **i** 2000 feet **ii** 14 000 feet
  d 8.5 minutes

PRACTICE 8.4.1

1 The graph below shows the relationship between temperature measured in degrees fahrenheit (°F) and degrees celsius (°C).

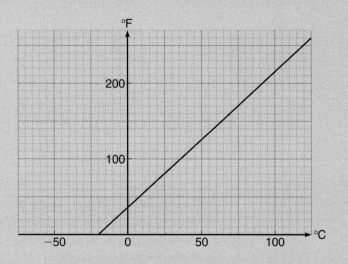

a The freezing point of water is 0 °C. What is this in °F?
b The boiling point of water is 212 °F. What is this in °C?
c Normal body temperature is 98.6 °F. What is this in °C?
d Alcohol boils at 85 °C. What is this in °F?

2 Bill walks Hugo, his dog. The distance they are from home is shown in the graph below.

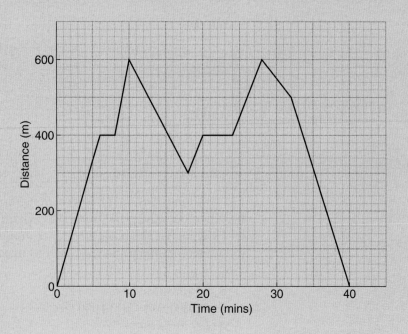

a How far are they from home after **i** 5 **ii** 12 **iii** 27 **iv** 35
   minutes?
b What is the furthest distance they get from home?
c After how long are they **i** 200 metres **ii** 550 metres from home?
d Bill stands and talks to a friend for 4 minutes. When did this
   happen?
e How long is it from the first to the second time that Bill and Hugo
   are 600 m from home?
f At one stage it began to rain. Bill and Hugo headed for home. When
   the shower stopped Bill decided to resume the walk.
   i When did this happen?
   ii How long did the shower last?
   iii How far did they walk towards home?
g How far did Bill and Hugo walk altogether?

3 The graph shows the journeys made by a van and a car starting from
   Oxford and travelling to Luton and back.

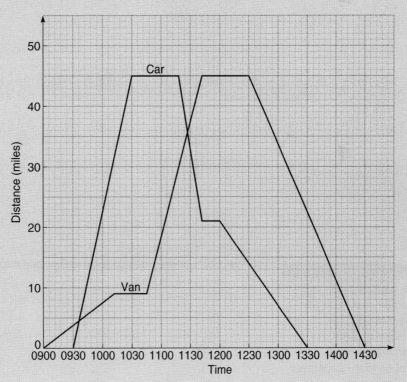

a How far had the car travelled when it met the van for the second
   time?
b Calculate, in mph, the average speed of the car between 0930 and
   1030.
c During which period of time was the van travelling at its greatest
   speed? (SEG)

4 A firm making glasses makes a profit of £y from x glasses according to the graph below.

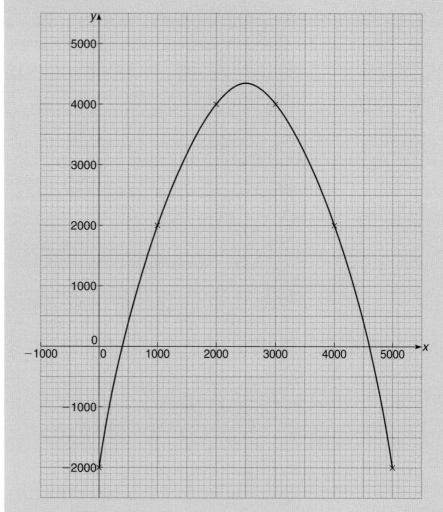

Find, from the graph:

a   the number of glasses the firm should produce in order to make the maximum profit,

b   the minimum number of glasses the firm should produce in order to make sure that it does not make a loss,

c   the range of values of x for which the profit is more than £3250.
   (SEG)

Graphs from experimental data

Graphs can be used to find relationships in experimental data.

In an experiment we sometimes suspect that the variables are connected by a linear, or straight line, relationship.

By plotting the points and then drawing the straight line that *best fits* the points we can find out the equation that connects those variables.

Worked Example

The temperatures of a cooling liquid are taken using two thermometers — one calibrated in degrees fahrenheit (°F), the other in degrees celsius (°C).

x (°C)	100	80	60	40	20	0
y (°F)	210	175	140	105	70	30

a Plot these points on graph paper.

b Draw the straight line that you think best fits the plotted points.

c Using your graph calculate
  i the intercept on the fahrenheit axis,
  ii the gradient.

d Use your values from **c** above to write down the equation $y = mx + c$ and obtain an equation which converts °C to °F.

e Use your answer to **d** above to calculate the temperature, in fahrenheit, of
  i 24 °C
  ii 66 °C.

a, b

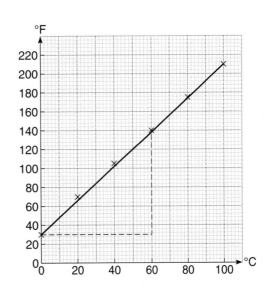

c From the graph
  i the intercept is 30,
  ii the gradient is $\frac{110}{60} = 1.83$ (3sf).

d $y = mx + c$
  i.e. $y = 1.83x + 30$
  Hence °F = 1.83 °C + 30

e Using the above equation
  i °F = 1.83 × 24 + 30 = 73.92
  ii °F = 1.83 × 66 + 30 = 150.78

PRACTICE 8.4.2

1 The table below shows the values of x and y connected by the equation $y = mx + c$.

x	2	5	8	11	14	17
y	14	24	34	44	55	65

  a Plot the points given and draw your line of best fit.
  b From your graph calculate the values for the gradient, m, and the y intercept, c.
  c Use your equation to estimate values of y when
    i $x = 4$ and **ii** $x = 10$.

2 The table below shows the values of x and y connected by the equation $y = mx + c$.

x	1	3	5	7	9	11	13	15	17
y	42	35	29	23	16	10	3	−3	−9

  a Plot the points given and draw your line of best fit.
  b From your graph calculate the values for the gradient, m, and the y intercept, c.
  c Use your equation to estimate values of y when
    i $x = 2.54$ **ii** $x = 11.7$ **iii** $x = 14$.

3 Ohm's law states that the voltage (V volts), current (I amps) and resistance (R ohms) in part of an electrical circuit are connected by the formula $V = IR$.

The following table gives some experimental values obtained by a student.

V	0	2	4	6	8	10	12	14
I	0	0.25	0.55	0.82	1.01	1.28	1.60	1.80

  a Plot these points, with I as the horizontal axis up to 2.6 and draw your line of best fit. Extend the line to $V = 20$.
  b Measure the gradient of the line. What does it represent in the equation $V = IR$?
  c Use your equation for $V = IR$ to find:
    i the current when the voltage is raised to 20 volts,
    ii the voltage that gives a current reading of 1.5 amps.

4 The recorded population of a village on 31st July over a period of time is shown below:

Year	1980	1984	1986	1989	1991	1994
Population	300	510	650	900	925	1050

a Plot the given points on a graph using the year as the horizontal axis, extended to the year 2000.

b One of the recorded figures is *clearly inaccurate*. Which year is this?

c Ignoring the inaccurate figure draw your line of best fit.

d From your graph, write down:

  i your estimate of the correct figure to replace the inaccurate one,

  ii your estimate of the population in the year 2000.

5 A second-hand car dealer estimates the resale value (£C) of a car is given by the formula $C = N - kD$, where N is the value of the car when new and D is the recorded mileage. On his forecourt there are six cars, all of the same make and model, having the same value when new. Their prices are as follows:

C	9700	9000	8750	8000	6500	5250
D	5000	16 500	25 000	42 400	68 000	93 500

a Plot these points on a graph using D as the horizontal axis and ranging from 0 to 100 000.

b Draw your line of best fit.

c Use your graph to calculate:

  i the value of the cars when new,

  ii the gradient of the line of best fit.

d Use your answer to **c** to write down the equation $C = N - kD$ inserting your values of N and k.

e Use your equation to calculate the resale value of a similar car when the mileage was   **i** 10 000 miles and   **ii** 100 000 miles.

f Mr Schumacher had £7500 to spend on a used car. What sort of mileage should it have done?

Consider the equation $y = x^2$.

We can calculate the value of y for any value of x that we choose.

x	−4	−2	0	2	4
y	16	4	0	4	16

If we worked out many values of x and y and plotted them on a graph they would show the smooth curve overleaf.

We can draw similar curves for any quadratic expression, i.e. one of the form $ax^2 + bx + c$. All are smooth curves called **parabolas**.

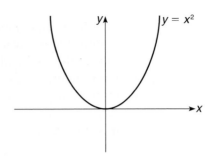

All are symmetrical (i.e. they look the same on both sides) about a line parallel to the y-axis through the lowest, or highest, point on the curve.

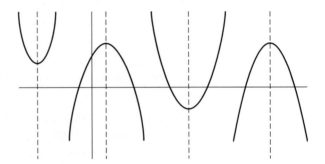

When drawing graphs of quadratic expressions it is best to follow a certain order:

1 Calculate the values of y for a number of values of x. It is simplest if these values are calculated in *stages* using a table.
2 Draw axes on a graph. Use suitable scales to fit the values from your table.
3 Plot all your calculated points.
4 Draw a *smooth* curve through your plotted points. The curve *will* be smooth – so if you have mis-calculated any values of y it will be apparent.
   If the x^2 term is positive the graph points downwards.
   If the x^2 term is negative the graph points upwards.
5 Make sure the curve is labelled with its equation. This is very important if more than one curve is to be drawn on the same graph.

Worked Example

Take values of x from -3 to 3 and draw the graph of $y = 2x^2 + x - 10$.

x	-3	-2	-1	0	1	2	3
$2x^2$	18	8	2	0	2	8	18
$+ x$	-3	-2	-1	0	1	2	3
-10	-10	-10	-10	-10	-10	-10	-10
y	5	-4	-9	-10	-7	0	11

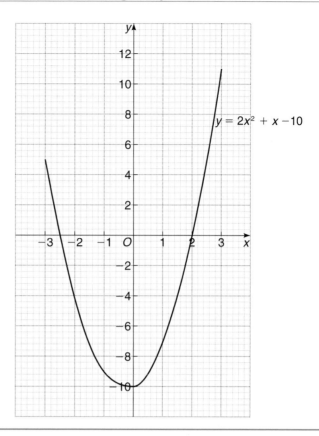

$y = 2x^2 + x - 10$

PRACTICE 8.5.1   Try this question without a calculator

1 Using appropriate scales, draw the graphs of the following quadratic expressions:
   a $y = 2x^2$ for values of x from -3 to 3.
   b $y = 6 - x^2$ for values of x from -3 to 3.
   c $y = x^2 - 3x$ for values of x from -2 to 4.
   d $y = x^2 - 5x + 4$ for values of x from 0 to 5.
   e $y = 3x^2 + 7x - 6$ for values of x from -4 to 2.
   f $y = 6 - 8x - 3x^2$ for values of x from -4 to 1.

Solving quadratic equations by using quadratic graphs

Drawing quadratic graphs enables us to solve quadratic equations.

Consider the equations $y = ax^2 + bx + c$
$$0 = ax^2 + bx + c$$

Clearly, if we want to solve the equation $ax^2 + bx + c = 0$ we need to find where, on the curve, $y = 0$.

However, on any graph, $y = 0$ anywhere along the x-axis.

Hence, the solution of $ax^2 + bx + c = 0$ lies on the graph where the curve cuts the x-axis.

A l g e b r a

Worked Example

Draw the graph of $y = 2x^2 - 2x - 7$ for values of x from -2 to 3. Find from your graph:

a the coordinates of the lowest point on the curve,
b the equation of the line of symmetry,
c the value of y when **i** $x = -1.25$ **ii** $x = 1.75$,
d the values of x when $y = 1$,
e the solution of the equation $2x^2 - 2x - 7 = 0$.

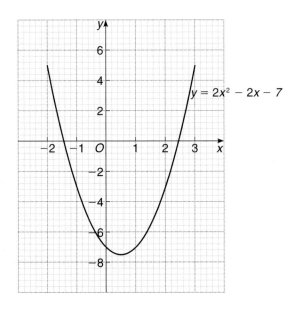

$y = 2x^2 - 2x - 7$

a (0.5, −7.5)   c i −1.375   d 2.6 or −1.6
b $x = \frac{1}{2}$ ii −4.375   e 2.4 or −1.4

PRACTICE 8.5.2

1 Use your answers to Practice 8.5.1 **1a–f** to find:

   i the coordinates of the lowest, or highest, point,
   ii the equation of the line of symmetry,
   iii the solution of each quadratic expression $= 0$.

2 The average safe braking distance, d yds, for vehicles can be modelled by the equation $d = v^2/50 + v/3$, where v is the speed of the vehicle in mph.

   a Draw up a table of values for d. Let v take values from 0 to 80 in steps of 10.
   b Draw the graph of $d = v^2/50 + v/3$ using v as the horizontal axis.

c Use your graph to find the safe braking distance when the vehicle is travelling at
i 15 mph   **ii** 45 mph   **iii** 75 mph.

d A driver suddenly sees an obstruction 50 yards ahead. He just stops in time. How fast was he travelling when he first saw it?

3 Sheena has a piece of pipe 40 cm long. She bends it into a rectangle of length x cm.

a Show that the area of the rectangle is given by the equation $A = 20x - x^2$.

b Draw up a table and draw the graph of $A = 20x - x^2$ for values of x from 0 to 20.

c Use your graph to find:
   i the area when $x = 3.6$ cm,
   ii the length and breadth of the rectangle when the area is 98 cm^2,
   iii the maximum area of the rectangle,
   iv the equation of the line of symmetry on the graph,
   v the dimensions of the rectangle which has the maximum area.

4 Chris, the *human cannonball*, is fired from a gun to land on a platform 40 m high. The equation of his path is given by $h = x - x^2/360$, where x is the horizontal distance in metres.

a Complete a table of values for h and x, for values of x from 0 to 60.

b Draw the graph of h against x.

c How far from the gun horizontally is the platform?

8.6 FURTHER GRAPHS

We now know how to draw quadratic graphs. We can extend our knowledge and draw other sorts of curved graphs. All we do is to build up the equation in the form of a table. Then we draw the graph as before.

Worked Examples

1 a Plot the graph of $y = \frac{10}{x}$ from $x = -4$ to -1 and from $x = 1$ to 4.

b Consider what happens to y as x goes from -1 to 0 and from 0 to 1. Put this in on your graph.

c Use your graph to find y when   **i** $x = -2.5$ and   **ii** $x = 1.7$.

d Draw the graph of $y = x$ on the same paper.

e Use your graph to find $\sqrt{10}$ to an appropriate degree of accuracy. Explain your answer.

NOTE
You may need a calculator to do some calculations in these examples.

a

x	-4	-3	-2	-1	1	2	3	4
$\dfrac{10}{x}$	$\dfrac{10}{-4}$	$\dfrac{10}{-3}$	$\dfrac{10}{-2}$	$\dfrac{10}{-1}$	$\dfrac{10}{1}$	$\dfrac{10}{2}$	$\dfrac{10}{3}$	$\dfrac{10}{4}$
$y = \dfrac{10}{x}$	-2.5	-3.33	-5	-10	10	5	3.33	2.5

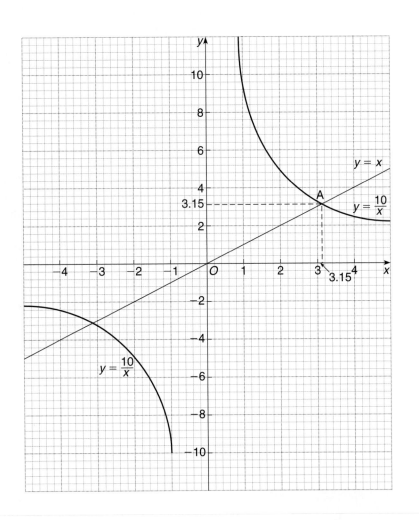

b As x goes from -1 to 0, y must go from $\dfrac{10}{-1}$ to $\dfrac{10}{0}$,
i.e. from -10 to $-\infty$.

As x goes from 0 to 1, y must go from $\dfrac{10}{0}$ to $\dfrac{10}{1}$, i.e. from ∞ to 10.

NOTE
Remember positive numbers have two square roots, one positive, one negative. Negative numbers have no square roots.

c **i** When $x = -2.5$, $y = -4$.
　　ii When $x = 1.7$, $y = 5.9$.

e Where the two graphs intersect (point A), $\dfrac{10}{x} = x$, i.e. $10 = x^2$,

i.e. $x = \sqrt{10}$. On the graph this reads as 3.15 or as -3.15.

2 a Draw the graph of $y = \dfrac{24}{x} + 2x - 10$ for values of x from 1 to 8.

b Use your graph to find:
  i the minimum value of y,
  ii the value of y when $x = 7.5$,
  iii the value of x when $y = 10$.

a

x	1	2	3	4	5	6	7	8
$\dfrac{24}{x}$	24	12	8	6	4.8	4	3.43	3
$2x$	2	4	6	8	10	12	14	16
-10	-10	-10	-10	-10	-10	-10	-10	-10
y	16	6	4	4	4.8	6	7.43	9

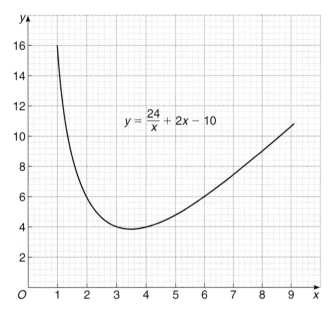

b   i Minimum value of $y = 3.46$.
  ii When $x = 7.5$, $y = 8.2$.
  iii When $y = 10$, $x = 1.4$.

3 Draw the graph of $y = x^3 - 7x - 6$ for values of x from -3 to 4. Use your graph to find   **a** a maximum value of y **b** a minimum value of y
  c the value of y when $x = 0.5$.

x	-3	-2	-1	0	1	2	3	4
x^3	-27	-8	-1	0	1	8	27	64
$-7x$	21	14	7	0	-7	-14	-21	-28
-6	-6	-6	-6	-6	-6	-6	-6	-6
y	-12	0	0	-6	-12	-12	0	30

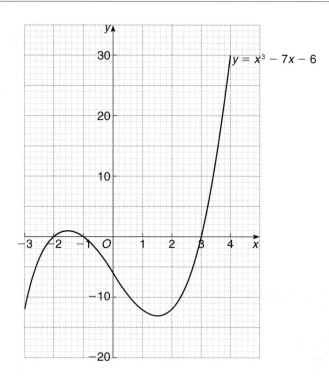

$y = x^3 - 7x - 6$

a Maximum value of $y = 1.1$
b Minimum value of $y = -13$
c When $x = 0.5$, $y = -9.4$

PRACTICE 8.6.1   Try these questions without a calculator

1 Draw the graphs of:

a $y = \dfrac{9}{x^2}$ for values of x from -4 to 4.

b $y = \dfrac{25}{(x+3)}$ for values of x from -2 to 4.

c $y = x^3 + 2x$ for values of x from -3 to 3.
d $y = x^3 - x^2 - 6x$ for values of x from -3 to 4.
e $y = 2x^3 - 7x^2 - 14x - 40$ for values of x from -5 to 3.

2 Draw the graph of $y = \dfrac{25}{x} + x - 7$ for values of x from 2 to 11.

Use your graph to find:

a the value of y when   i $x = 3.5$ ii $x = 8.7$,
b the values of x when   i $y = 3.5$ ii $y = 6$,
c the minimum value of y and the value of x which gives this value.

3 Draw the graph of $y = \dfrac{3x}{(x+1)}$ for values of x from 0 to 15.

  a Find the value of x when **i** $y = 1.75$ **ii** $y = 2.6$.

  b The graph seems to be approaching a limiting value for y. Write down what you think this value is.

4 Draw the graph of $y = x^3 - 5x^2 + 2x + 8$ for values of x from -2 to 5. Use your graph to find:

  a a maximum value of y,

  b a minimum value of y,

  c the value of y when **i** $x = -0.5$ **ii** $x = 3.2$.

Further graphical solutions

We have already seen that equations can be solved graphically by finding where the graphs cut the x-axis.

Thus $x^2 - 5x + 4 = 0$ can be solved by plotting the graph of $y = x^2 - 5x + 4$, and finding that it cuts the x-axis at $x = 1$ and $x = 4$.

We can, however, use this graph to solve other equations.

1 If the x^2 and x terms are the same the process is simple:

For example, we have drawn $y = x^2 - 5x + 4$ and want to solve the equation $x^2 - 5x + 5 = 0$.
We can see that $x^2 - 5x + 5 = 0$ is the same thing as $x^2 - 5x + 4 = -1$.
Comparing these two equations we can see that we would get the solution to $x^2 - 5x + 5 = 0$ by finding where, on the graph of $y = x^2 - 5x + 4$, the value of y is -1.

Similarly, $x^2 - 5x + 1 = 0$ could be rewritten as $x^2 - 5x + 4 = 3$ and the solution found by finding where $y = 3$ on the original graph. These solutions are shown below:

$x^2 - 5x + 4 = 0$ has solutions $x = 1$ and $x = 4$ when $y = 0$ (points A and B).

$x^2 - 5x + 5 = 0$ has solutions $x = 1.38$ and $x = 3.62$ when $y = -1$ (points C and D).

$x^2 - 5x + 1 = 0$ has solutions $x = 0.21$ and $x = 4.8$ when $y = 3$ (points E and F).

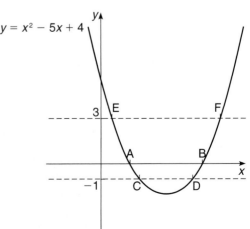

2 If the x terms are different we can still solve equations from an original graph.

For example, we have drawn the graph of $y = x^2 - 5x + 5$ and we want to solve the equation $x^2 - 7x + 5 = 0$.

Comparing these equations we get $x^2 - 7x + 5 = 0$
is equivalent to $x^2 - 5x + 5 = 2x$

We now draw $y = 2x$ on the same graph as $y = x^2 - 5x + 5$.

We see that these two graphs
intersect at two points, P and Q.

At P and Q the two equations
$x^2 - 5x + 5$ and $y = 2x$ must have
the same solution.

Thus the solution to $x^2 - 7x + 5$
$= 0$ are given by the values of x at
P and Q.

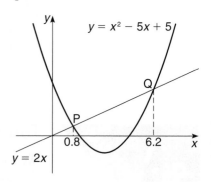

We see these are $x = 0.8$ and $x = 6.2$.

Worked Examples

1 Draw the graph of $y = x^2 - 2x - 3$ for values of x from -3 to 5.

Use your graph to solve the following equations:
a $x^2 - 2x - 3 = 0$ **c** $x^2 - 2x - 7 = 0$
b $x^2 - 2x - 1 = 0$ **d** $x^2 - x - 5 = 0$

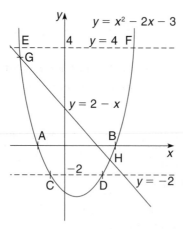

a $x^2 - 2x - 3 = 0$ is solved where $y = 0$, i.e. at A and B. These values are $x = -1$ and $x = 3$.

b $x^2 - 2x - 1 = 0$ is solved where $y = -2$ i.e. at C and D. These values are $x = -0.41$ and $x = 2.41$.

c $x^2 - 2x - 7 = 0$ is solved where $y = 4$, i.e. at E and F. These values are $x = -1.83$ and $x = 3.83$.

d $x^2 - x - 5 = 0$ can be rewritten as $x^2 - 2x - 3 = -x + 2$.
Thus we must draw $y = -x + 2$ on the same graph. The solutions are found where they intersect i.e. at G and H. These values are $x = -1.8$ and $x = 2.8$.

2 Solve the equation $x^3 - 2x^2 - 5x + 6 = 0$ by
a drawing the original graph,
b drawing the graph of $y = x^3$ and $y = 2x^2 + 5x - 6$.

a Drawing the graph of $y = x^3 - 2x^2 - 5x + 6$ and finding where it crosses the x-axis, we get:

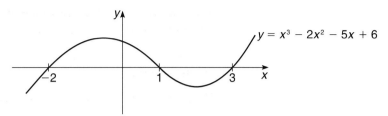

The solutions are $x = -2$, $x = 1$ and $x = 3$.

b Drawing the other two graphs on the same paper we get:

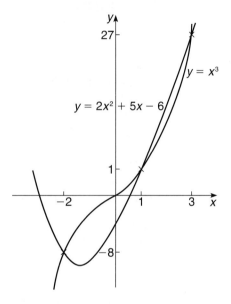

Noting where the two graphs intersect we get the answers $x = -2$, $x = 1$ and $x = 3$.

(Because it is the same equation written differently we would expect the same answers.)

PRACTICE 8.7.1a   Try these questions without a calculator

1 Draw the graph of $y = x^2 - x - 6$ and use it to solve the following equations:

a $x^2 - x - 6 = 0$	**d** $x^2 - x - 4 = 0$	**g** $x^2 - 3x - 6 = 0$
b $x^2 - x - 7 = 0$	**e** $x^2 - x - 3 = 0$	**h** $x^2 - 6 = 0$
c $x^2 - x - 9 = 0$	**f** $x^2 - 2x - 6 = 0$	**i** $x^2 - 2x - 7 = 0$

2 Draw the graph of $y = 2x^2 + x - 10$ and use it to solve the following equations:

a $2x^2 + x - 10 = 0$	**d** $2x^2 + x - 9 = 0$	**g** $2x^2 - x - 8 = 0$
b $2x^2 + x - 12 = 0$	**e** $2x^2 + x - 7 = 0$	**h** $2x^2 + 3x - 15 = 0$
c $2x^2 + x - 14 = 0$	**f** $2x^2 - x - 10 = 0$	

3 Draw, on the same paper, the graphs of $y = x^2$, $y = 2x + 5$ and $y = 6 - 3x$.
Find both the equations and the solutions at the points where each linear graph cuts the quadratic.

PRACTICE 8.7.1b   Try these questions with a calculator

1 Solve the equation $4x^3 + 20x^2 + 11x - 35 = 0$ by the two methods outlined in the worked example above.

2 Draw the graph of $y = x^2 + \dfrac{8}{x}$ for values of x from -4 to 4. (Remember what happens when $x = 0$.)
   a Use your graph to solve the following equations:

   i $x^2 + \dfrac{8}{x} = 0$ iii $x^2 + \dfrac{8}{x} - 2 = 0$ v $x^3 - x + 8 = 0$

   ii $x^3 + 8 = 0$ iv $x^2 + \dfrac{8}{x} + 3 = 0$

   b Draw, on the same graph, the graphs of $y = x$ and $y = 7 - 2x$. Find the values of x at the points of intersection of these lines with $y = x^2 + \dfrac{8}{x}$ and find also the equations to which these values are the solutions.

The gradient of a curve

We know how to find the gradient of a straight line.
What do we mean, however, by the gradient of a curve?

The *steepness* of a curve is always changing – therefore we can only talk about the gradient *at a particular point* on a curve.

We say that the gradient at a particular point on a curve is the same as if the curve were replaced at that point by the closest straight line to it.

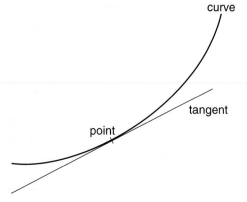

This line is called the *tangent* to the curve. The tangent is the straight line that just *touches* the curve at the particular point. It doesn't cut the curve at all – *but it has the same gradient as the curve at that point.*

Hence – to find the gradient at a particular point on a curve:

1 Draw the curve.

2 Draw the tangent to the curve at the required point.
   This is quite difficult to do accurately and some practice is needed.

The accuracy of the answer depends on the accuracy of the drawing of the tangent!

To draw the tangent lie a ruler along the curve at the angle you judge to be the same as the curve. Then draw a straight line just touching the curve at that particular point.

3 Calculate the gradient of the tangent – and hence the curve – by the methods shown earlier in the chapter.

Worked Example

Draw the graph of $y = x^3$. Draw tangents to the curve at the points $(-2, -8)$ and $(1, 1)$. Hence estimate the gradient of the curve at the points.

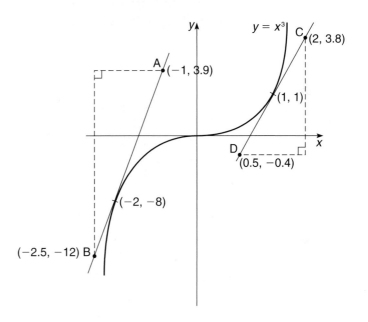

The diagram shows the graph of $y = x^3$.

It also shows tangents drawn at the points $(-2, -8)$ and $(1, 1)$.

Remembering how we found the gradients of straight lines earlier in the chapter we pick two suitable points on each tangent.

These are $A(-1, 3.9)$ and $B(-2.5, -12)$ for the tangent drawn at $(-2, -8)$ and $C(2, 3.8)$ and $D(0.5, -0.4)$ for the tangent drawn at $(1, 1)$.

The gradient of the curve at $(-2, -8)$ is calculated as:
$$\frac{3.9 - (-12)}{-1 - (-2.5)} = \frac{15.9}{1.5} = 10.6$$

The gradient of the curve at $(1, 1)$ is calculated as:
$$\frac{3.8 - (-0.4)}{2 - (0.5)} = \frac{4.2}{1.5} = 2.8$$

(The exact values are 12 and 3 respectively.)

NOTE

A calculator is necessary to do some parts of this example.

PRACTICE 8.7.2   Try these questions with a calculator

1   Draw the following curves and estimate the gradients at the given
points:
   a $y = x^2$ at $(-2, 4)$ and $(1, 1)$
   b $y = x^3 + 2$ at $(-1, 1)$ and $(3, 29)$
   c $y = x^2 - 2x - 8$ at $(-3, 7)$ and $(3, -5)$
   d $y = 4 + x - x^2$ at $(-1, 2)$ and $(2, 2)$

2   Draw, on the same paper, the graphs of $y = x^2$ and $y = 3x$ for $0 \leqslant x \leqslant 4$.
Using the straight line as a guide draw a tangent to the curve which is
parallel to the line $y = 3x$.
   a   What is the gradient of the curve at the point where you have drawn
   your tangent?
   b   What is the value of x at the point where this tangent touches the
   curve?

Further work on gradients

When we measure gradients on an x, y graph, we are measuring how much the
value of y changes compared with how much the value of x changes.

Mathematicians call this the *rate of change* of y compared with x.
Hence a gradient is a *rate of change*.
If the variables for x and y are actually physical units then there is a real
meaning to the gradient.

For example, if a graph shows how far a body has travelled over a time period
then

$$\frac{\text{change in } y}{\text{change in } x} \text{ becomes } \frac{\text{distance travelled}}{\text{time taken}}.$$

This is a measure of the speed, or velocity, of the body.
Hence the gradient of a distance/time graph measures the velocity.
Similarly the gradient of a velocity/time graph measures the acceleration of the
body.

Worked Example

A stone is dropped down a well. The distance, s, it has fallen after t seconds is
given by the equation $s = 5t^2$. Estimate its velocity after   **a** 1 second
b 8 seconds.

1   Draw up a table of values for $s = 5t^2$.

t	0	1	2	3	4	5	6	7	8	9	10
s	0	5	20	45	80	125	180	245	320	405	500

2 Draw the graph of the above table.

3 Draw tangents at $t = 1$ and $t = 8$.

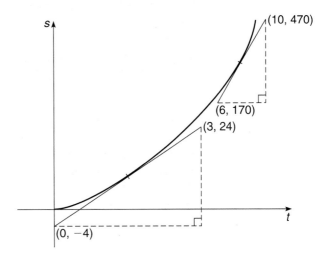

4 From the tangents shown:

   i when $x = 1$, gradient $= \dfrac{24 - (-4)}{3 - 0} = \dfrac{28}{3} = 9.33$

   (actual value $= 10$).

   ii When $x = 8$, gradient $= \dfrac{470 - 170}{10 - 6} = \dfrac{300}{4} = 75$

   (actual value $= 80$).

PRACTICE 8.7.3   Try these questions with a calculator

1 The distance a car has moved, t seconds after it has passed a set of traffic lights, is given by the equation $s = t^2 + 2t + 3$. Draw the graph of the car's motion up to 8 seconds after it has passed the lights. Use your graph to estimate the speed of the car after   **a** 3 seconds   **b** 6 seconds.

2 Ian Botham throws a cricket ball vertically upwards after making a catch. The height, h metres, above the ground, t seconds later, is given by the equation $h = 2 + 30t - 5t^2$.
   a Draw up a table of values for the first 6 seconds and draw the graph.
   b Use your graph to estimate:
      i the velocity with which Ian throws the ball,
      ii the velocity after 2 seconds,
      iii the velocity after 5 seconds,
      iv the greatest height of the ball above the ground and the time at which this occurs,
      v the time at which the ball hits the ground.

3 The velocity of a moving body is given by the equation $v = 5t - t^2$.
  a Draw up a table of values and draw the graph for $0 \leqslant t \leqslant 7$.
  b Use your graph to find:
    i the maximum velocity and the time at which this occurs,
    ii the acceleration of the body when $t = 2$,
    iii the acceleration of the body when $t = 4$,
    iv when the body is next stationary.
  c What is the meaning of the section of the graph from $t = 5$ to $t = 7$?

4 Draw the velocity/time graph for a body which:
  a starts from rest,
  b travels with a constant acceleration of $4 \, \text{m/s}^2$ for 5 seconds,
  c travels for a further 3 seconds at the speed reached when $t = 5$,
  d decelerates at a constant rate until it comes to rest after a further 4 seconds.

5 A car is caught in traffic. It begins to move and accelerates at a constant $1 \, \text{m/s}^2$. When it reaches a velocity of $5 \, \text{m/s}$ it continues at that speed for a further 10 seconds. After this time its speed decreases to 0 at a constant acceleration of $-1.5 \, \text{m/s}^2$.
Draw the velocity/time graph for this motion.
When does its speed reach 0 again?

Area under a velocity/time graph

The area under a velocity/time graph represents the distance travelled.

Consider a man running at a constant $5 \, \text{m/s}$ for 6 seconds.

Clearly he has run $6 \times 5 = 30 \, \text{m}$.

This is also shown by the area of the rectangle.

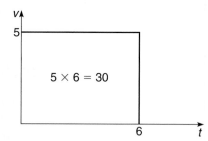

Now consider the solution to question 4 in Practice 8.7.3:

The area of triangle A $=$
$\frac{1}{2} \times 5 \times 20 = 50$

The area of rectangle B $=$
$(8 - 5) \times 20 = 60$

The area of triangle C $=$
$\frac{1}{2} \times (12 - 8) \times 20 = 40$

Total area $= 50 + 60 + 40 = 150$

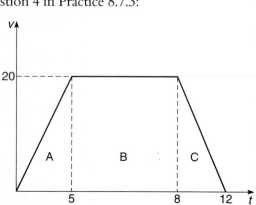

The body has travelled a total distance of $150 \, \text{m}$ during its motion.

PRACTICE 8.7.4

1 Find the distance travelled during the motion shown in the following velocity/time graphs.

a
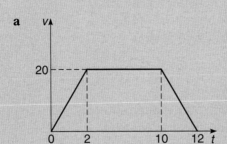

b
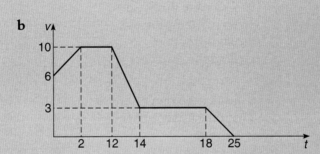

c
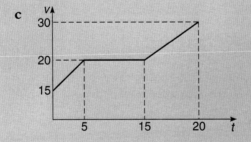

d
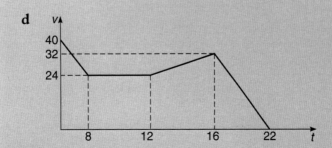

2 Find the distance travelled by the car in question 5 of Practice 8.7.3.

3 In the motion shown the distance travelled is 30 m. Find the maximum speed.

Does it matter when this maximum speed occurs? Explain your answer.

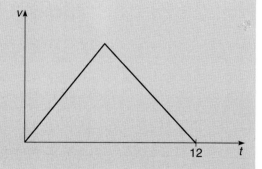

4 Consider the motion shown.
  a The initial acceleration is $8 \, \text{m/s}^2$.
    Find the value of t_1.
  b Calculate the distance travelled during the whole motion.
  c Find the final deceleration.

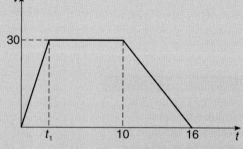

5 Consider the motion shown. The total distance travelled is 176 m.
Find the value of h.

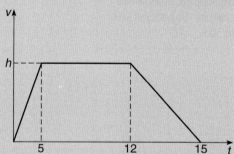

6 Consider the motion shown. The total distance travelled is 258 m.
Find the value of h.

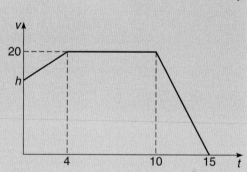

7 Consider the motion shown. The total distance travelled is 183 m.
Find the values of h and of T.

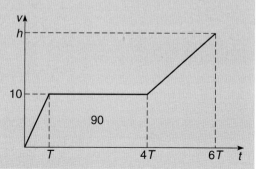

Finding the area under a curved graph

There are two simple methods we can use to estimate the area between a curved graph and the horizontal axis.

Both methods consist of dividing the required area up into a number of vertical *strips*. The area of each strip is then estimated and they are summed to find the total area.

The number of strips chosen depends on how accurate we need the final answer to be.

The more strips chosen the more accurate will be the estimate of the area but the more strips chosen the longer it will take to calculate.

The methods are best shown by the following examples.

Worked Examples

1 The **mid-ordinate rule**

This consists of considering each strip as a rectangle. The height of each rectangle is the height of the strip at its mid-point – as shown in the example below.

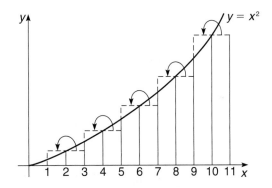

Find an approximate area under the curve $y = x^2$ from $x = 1$ to $x = 11$. Divide the area up into 5 strips.

Each strip has a width of 2 units.

The mid-points are at $x = 2, 4, 6, 8$ and 10.

Each strip is considered as a rectangle where the small section at the top on the right that is inside the curve but is *missed* from the rectangle is approximately replaced by the small section at the top on the left which is outside the curve but inside the rectangle.

The heights are found by calculating the y coordinates at the appropriate x values:

$$x = \quad 2 \quad 4 \quad 6 \quad 8 \quad 10$$
$$y = \quad 4 \quad 16 \quad 36 \quad 64 \quad 100$$

The total area is approximately $(4 \times 2) + (16 \times 2) + (36 \times 2) + (64 \times 2) + (100 \times 2)$ which is approximately equal to 440 square units.

2 The **trapezium rule**

This rule is very similar to the mid-ordinate rule, but each strip is taken to be a trapezium.

The part of the curve at the top of each strip is considered to be a straight line and so we only get an approximate answer.

The area of a trapezium is calculated as

$$\frac{\text{perpendicular height} \times \text{sum of parallel sides}}{2}$$

so on the graph we get the area as

$$\frac{\text{width of strip} \times \text{sum of } y \text{ coordinates at each side}}{2}$$

Hence:

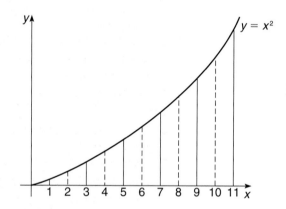

Find an approximate area under the curve $y = x^2$ from $x = 1$ to $x = 11$. Divide the area up into 5 strips.

Each strip has a width of 2 units.

The sides of each trapezium are at $x = 1, 3, 5, 7, 9$ and 11.

Each strip is considered as a trapezium where the curve at the top is replaced by a straight line. The heights are found by calculating the y coordinates at the appropriate x values:

$$x = \quad 1 \quad 3 \quad 5 \quad 7 \quad 9 \quad 11$$
$$y = \quad 1 \quad 9 \quad 25 \quad 49 \quad 81 \quad 121$$

The total area is now approximately

$$\frac{2 \times (1+9)}{2} + \frac{2 \times (9+25)}{2} + \frac{2 \times (25+49)}{2} + \frac{2 \times (49+81)}{2} + \frac{2 \times (81+121)}{2}$$

which is approximately equal to 450 square units.

We see that both rules give us slightly different estimates. The exact answer for this example is $444\frac{1}{3}$ square units.

PRACTICE 8.7.5   Try these questions with a calculator

1 Use both methods shown to find the area under the curve $y = x^3$ from
   $x = 2$ to $x = 8$. Divide the area up into   **a** 3 strips   **b** 6 strips.
   (Hint: the exact value for this area is 1020 square units.)

2 Use both methods shown to find the area under the curve
   $y = 6x - 5 - x^2$ from $x = 1$ to $x = 5$. Divide the area up into
   a 2 strips   **b** 4 strips.
   (Hint: the exact value for this area is $10\frac{2}{3}$ square units.)

3 Use the mid-ordinate rule to find the area between the curve $y = \dfrac{24}{x}$

   and the x-axis between the limits $x = 0$ and $x = 12$. Divide the area up
   into   **a** 3 strips   **b** 4 strips.

   Why can you *not* use the trapezium rule to answer this question?

4 The area shown is the quadrant
   (quarter) of a circle centre $(0, 0)$
   and radius 2 units.
   Its equation is given by
   $y = \sqrt{(4 - x^2)}$.
   a What is the exact area of the
   sector shown?
   b Divide the area up into 4 strips
   and use the trapezium rule to
   estimate the area.

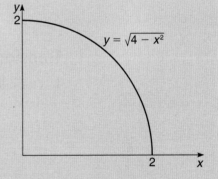

5

Scale 1 cm ≡ 10 m

The diagram above represents the cross section of a river at a certain
point. Divide the cross section up into 10 strips and measure the mid-
ordinate depths for each strip. Hence calculate an approximate area of
cross section of the river.

Assuming that the cross section remains constant, how many litres of
water are contained in a 10 metre stretch along the river bank? Give
your answer to an appropriate degree of accuracy.

6

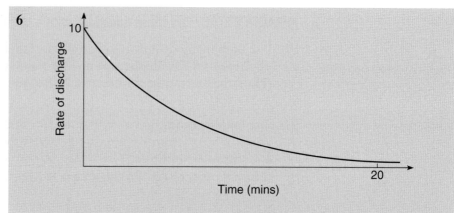

The diagram above shows the rate of discharge, in litres per minute, through a hole in a sewage tank. Use the trapezium rule to find the approximate area under the curve.

What physical quantity does the area represent?

Transformation of functions

1 Consider the graph of the function $y = x^2$. What happens if we add 3 on to the equation?

The equation now becomes $y = x^2 + 3$.

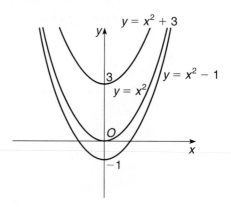

Drawing both graphs we can see that the original has been moved by 3 units in the positive y direction.

Similarly we can see that the graph of $y = x^2 - 1$ has translated $y = x^2$ by 1 unit in the negative y direction.

Hence we can see that $y = f(x) + a$ has the effect of moving (or translating – see Chapter 10) the equation $y = f(x)$ by a units in the direction of the y-axis, up or down depending on the sign of a.

2 Consider the graph of the function $y = x^2$. What happens if we add 3 on to x in the equation?

The equation now becomes $y = (x + 3)^2$.

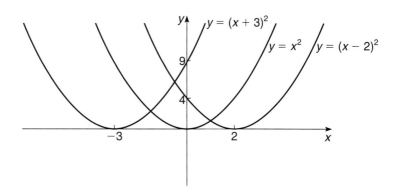

Drawing both graphs we can see that the original has been moved by 3 units in the negative x direction.

Similarly we can see that the graph of $y = (x - 2)^2$ has translated $y = x^2$ by 2 units in the positive x direction.

Hence we can see that $y = f(x + a)$ has the effect of moving (or translating – see Chapter 10) the equation $y = f(x)$ by a units in the direction of the x-axis, right or left depending on the sign of a.

3 Consider the graph of the function $y = x^2$. What happens if we multiply the equation by 3?

The equation now becomes $y = 3x^2$.

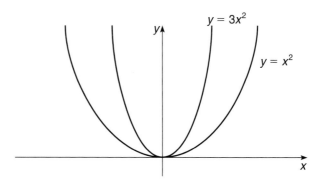

Drawing both graphs we can see that each y coordinate in the original has been multiplied by 3 units in the positive y direction.

Hence we can see that $y = kf(x)$ has the effect of multiplying the equation $y = f(x)$ by a factor of k units in the direction of the y-axis.

Combinations of these transformations can help in sketching the shape of the graph.

Consider, for example, the curve $y = x^2 - 4x + 7$.
We can rewrite this as $y = x^2 - 4x + 4 + 3$ and this can be written as $(x - 2)^2 + 3$.

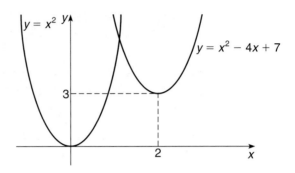

The $(x - 2)^2$ translates $y = x^2$ by 2 units in the positive x-direction.

The $+3$ translates $y = x^2$ by 3 units in the positive y-direction.

Hence $y = x^2 - 4x + 7$ translates $y = x^2$ by 2 units to the right and by 3 units up, as shown.

Worked Example

Find the transformation necessary to change $y = x^2$ into $y = 2x^2 + 12x + 13$.

$y = 2x^2 + 12x + 13$ can be rewritten as

$$y = 2(x^2 + 6x + 9) - 5$$
i.e. $\ y = 2(x + 3)^2 - 5$

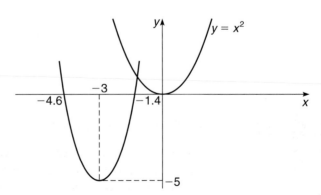

Hence we can see that $y = x^2$ must
  i be translated by 5 units in the negative y-direction,
 ii be translated by 3 units in the negative x-direction,
iii be multiplied by a scale factor 2 in the $(x + 3)^2$ term.

PRACTICE 8.7.6 **Try these questions without a calculator**

1 Sketch the graphs of $y = x^3$, $y = x^3 + 4$ and $y = x^3 - 2$.
State the transformation needed to change $y = x^3$ into each of the other two.

2 Sketch the graphs of $y = x^3$, $y = (x + 2)^3$ and $y = (x - 1)^3$.
State the transformation needed to change $y = x^3$ into each of the other two.

3 Sketch the graphs of $y = x^2$ and $y = x^2 - 4x + 4$.
Describe the transformation needed to change the first graph into the second.

4 Sketch the graphs of $y = x^2$ and $y = 2x^2 - 4x + 5$.
Describe the transformation needed to change the first graph into the second.

5 Rewrite $y = x^2 - 10x + 32$ in the form $y = (x + a)^2 + b$. Hence describe the transformation needed to change $y = x^2$ into $y = x^2 - 10x + 32$.

6 Rewrite $y = x^2 - 4x - 5$ in the form $y = (x + a)^2 + b$. Hence describe the transformation needed to change $y = x^2$ into $y = x^2 - 4x - 5$.

7 Graham wants to transform $y = x^2$ into a quadratic with a *minimum point* at $(-1, 3)$. Write down the transformation necessary. Hence write down the new equation. Confirm your results graphically.

8 Liz wants to transform $y = x^2$ into a quadratic with a *minimum point* at $(-4, -7)$. Write down the transformation necessary. Hence write down the new equation. Confirm your results graphically.

9 Find the transformation necessary to transform $y = x^2$ into $y = 2x^2 - 20x + 59$.

How to use coordinates

Coordinates are used to locate points on a graph.
The position of point P is written as the coordinates (a, b).
P is a units in the x-direction and b units in the y-direction.
The horizontal line is called the x-axis and the vertical line is called the y-axis, although any two variables can be used.
The point where the two axes cross is called the *origin*.
The coordinates of the origin are $(0, 0)$.
The axes can be extended both to the left and downwards in order to be able to plot the positions of points having negative coordinates.

Number patterns and sequences

A number pattern which is formed by some common rule is called a *sequence* or *series*.
Each number in the sequence is called a *term*.
Each term in the sequence is linked by a rule.
By studying the patterns that we see between the terms we are often able to work out the rule that generates the way the sequence is made up.

The Fibonacci sequence

The sequence is named after the mathematician Fibonacci.
The sequence occurs in science and natural history.
1, 1, 2, 3, 5, 8, 13, …
Each term is found by adding together the two previous terms.

Further sequences

Sometimes a formula generating a sequence is more than just linear.
We can show that a sequence is not linear by looking at the *differences* between successive terms.

Two-dimensional patterns

Grids, or arrays of numbers are often used in mathematics to generate patterns.
We can formulate and solve equations from them.

Drawing graphs

We always put the value of the x coordinate first.
The unit of measurement along each axis is called its *scale*.
The scales do not have to be the same on each axis but they must be the same on the positive and negative parts of the same axis.

Functions and graphs

A *function* is another name given to an algebraic expression.
A functional graph shows us a picture of this expression which connects two variables.
Usually these are called x and y but any pair of letters can be used.
The horizontal, or x-axis, is called the independent axis.
The vertical, or y-axis, is called the dependent.
This is because the function is written in the form $y =$ (some expression in x) and the values of y depend on whatever values x takes.

Linear graphs

Linear graphs are just another way of saying straight line graphs.
We know if a graph is linear just by looking at the equation.
If the powers of x and y are both one then the graph is linear or straight.
To draw a linear graph we find the coordinates of any two points that fit its equation and then plot them.
To make sure that we haven't made a mistake we usually plot three points and make sure that they lie on one straight line.
When we have plotted the points we can draw a straight line through them.
When calculating the coordinates it is best to *build up* the values in a table.

Solving simultaneous equations by using graphs

When we draw the graph of any straight line all the possible values of x and y which fit the equation of the graph must lie on the line.
Therefore, to solve a pair of simultaneous equations graphically;
plot the graphs of the two equations and find the coordinates of the point of intersection.

Gradient and intercept

Any linear (or straight line) graph, can be written in the form $y = mx + c$, where m and c are constants for each individual line.
c is called the *intercept* and is the place where the graph crosses the y-axis.
m is the coefficient of the x term and is the *gradient* of the line.
It measures how *steep* the line is compared to the x-axis.
If m is positive it means that the line slopes upward to the right.
If m is negative it means that the line slopes downwards to the right.

To find the gradient of a straight line

There are two main methods for calculating the gradient of a straight line.
From the equation of the line: the gradient is the coefficient of the x term.
From a plotted graph:
a   Choose *any two* convenient points on the line.
b   Calculate the vertical difference in y coordinates.
c   Calculate the horizontal difference in x coordinates.
d   The gradient $m = \dfrac{\text{the difference in } y \text{ coordinates}}{\text{the difference in } x \text{ coordinates}}$.

If the line slopes upward, both differences are positive and the line has a positive gradient.
If the line slopes downward from left to right, the x difference is positive and the y difference is negative (i.e. it decreases).
This means that the line has a negative gradient.

Interpreting graphs

We often see, in papers and magazines, a large variety of information presented in graphical form.

These graphs show a lot of data very easily and, with a little practice, we can find information very quickly.

Graphs from experimental data

Graphs can be used to find relationships in experimental data.

In an experiment we sometimes suspect that the variables are connected by a linear, or straight line, relationship.

By plotting the points and then drawing the straight line that *best fits* the points we can find out the equation that connects those variables.

The plotted points will probably not lie on an exact straight line.

This is because of slight inaccuracies in the reading of the apparatus or of taking measurements.

In this case we draw the straight line that most closely *fits* the plotted points.

Quadratic graphs

We can draw curves for any quadratic expression of the form $ax^2 + bx + c$.

All are smooth curves called *parabolas*.

All are symmetrical (i.e. they look the same on both sides) about a line parallel to the y-axis through the lowest, or highest, point on the curve.

When drawing quadratic graphs it is best to follow a certain order:

1 Calculate the values of y for a number of values of x.
2 Draw axes on a graph. Use suitable scales to fit the values from your table.
3 Plot all your calculated points.
4 Draw a *smooth* curve through your plotted points.
   The curve will be smooth – so if you have mis-calculated any values of y it will be apparent.
   If the x^2 term is positive the graph points downwards.
   If the x^2 term is negative the graph points upwards.
5 Make sure the curve is labelled with its equation. This is very important if more than one curve is to be drawn on the same graph.

Solving quadratic equations by using quadratic graphs

Drawing quadratic graphs enables us to solve quadratic equations.

On any graph, $y = 0$ anywhere along the x-axis.

Hence, the solution of $ax^2 + bx + c = 0$ lies on the graph where the curve cuts the x-axis.

Further graphs

We know how to draw quadratic graphs.
We can draw other sorts of curved graphs by building up the equation in the form of a table. Then we draw the graph as before.

The gradient of a curve (extension)

The *steepness*, or gradient, of a curve is always changing.
We can only talk about the gradient *at a particular point* on a curve.
We say that the gradient *at a particular point* on a curve is the same as if the curve were replaced at that point by the closest straight line to it.
This line is called the *tangent* to the curve.
The tangent is the straight line that just touches the curve at the particular point. It doesn't cut the curve at all – but it has the same gradient as the curve at that point.
To find the gradient at a particular point on a curve:

1   Draw the curve.
2   Draw the tangent to the curve at the required point.
3   Calculate the gradient of the tangent – and hence the curve.

Further work on gradients (extension)

When we measure gradients on an x, y graph, we are measuring how much the value of y changes compared with how much the value of x changes.
Mathematicians call this the *rate of change* of y compared with x.
Hence a gradient is a rate of change.
If the variables for x and y are actually physical units then there is a real meaning to the gradient.

Area under a velocity/time graph (extension)

The area under a velocity/time graph represents the distance travelled.

There are two simple methods we can use to estimate the area between a curved graph and the horizontal axis.

Both methods consist of dividing the required area up into a number of vertical *strips*. The area of each strip is then estimated and they are summed to find the total area.

The number of strips chosen depends on how accurate we need the final answer to be.

The more strips chosen the more accurate will be the estimate of the area but the more strips chosen the longer it will take to calculate.

a The *mid-ordinate rule* consists of considering each strip as a rectangle.
The height of each rectangle is the height of the strip at its mid-point.
The heights are found by calculating the y coordinates at the appropriate
x values.

b The *trapezium rule* consists of considering each strip as a trapezium.
The part of the curve at the top of each strip is considered to be a straight
line and so we only get an approximate answer.
The area of a trapezium is calculated as perpendicular height times sum of
parallel sides $\div 2$.
On the graph we get the area as width of strip times sum of y coordinates at
each side $\div 2$.

Transformation of functions (extension)

$y = f(x) + a$ has the effect of moving, or translating, the equation $y = f(x)$ by
a units in the direction of the y-axis, up or down depending on the sign of a.

$y = f(x + a)$ has the effect of moving, or translating, the equation $y = f(x)$ by
a units in the direction of the x-axis, right or left depending on the sign of a.

$y = kf(x)$ has the effect of multiplying the equation $y = f(x)$ by a factor of
k units in the direction of the y-axis.

Combinations of these transformations can help in sketching the shape of the
graph.

SECTION FOUR
Shape, space and measures (Module 3)

CONTENTS

CHAPTER 9
Properties of shape

In this chapter you will need to know that:

▶ a point measures the *position* of something

▶ a line can be curved or straight

▶ a straight line is the shortest distance between two points

▶ points on a line are marked as  and are often marked with letters as shown

▶ the straight line joining two points A and B is called the *line AB* or the *line segment AB*

▶ when two lines cross, or intersect, they meet at a point called a *vertex* (plural *vertices*)

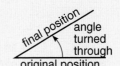
vertex

▶ when two lines meet at an *angle*, the lines are called the *arms* of the angle

arms

▶ an angle is measured by the amount of rotation that one arm has to turn through to coincide with the other; it is not governed by the lengths of the arms forming the angle

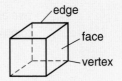
final position
angle turned through
original position

▶ a flat surface is called a *plane*
in theory it can extend in all its directions for an infinite distance

▶ shapes drawn in a plane are called *plane figures*

▶ the lines joining the vertices of plane figures are called its *sides*

▶ planes which form parts of three-dimensional figures are called *faces*

▶ in three-dimensional shapes, faces meet at edges and edges meet at vertices

▶ a *cube* is a solid containing
6 square faces
all its edges are equal in length

edge
face
vertex

▶ a *cuboid* is a solid containing
6 rectangular faces
it has a cross section which
is also a rectangle

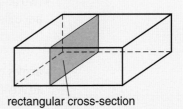
rectangular cross-section

▸ two lines which point in the same direction are called *parallel lines*; they are marked like this in diagrams:

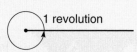

▸ when a line turns completely round until it points in the same direction it is said to have turned through *1 turn* or *1 revolution*

1 revolution

▸ 1 revolution is divided up into 360 small parts called *degrees* (°). thus 1 revolution = 360°

▸ angles are usually measured to decimals of a degree, e.g. 22.3°

▸ if a line rotates half a turn, i.e. 180°, it is called a *straight angle*

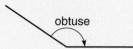

180°

▸ if a line rotates a quarter of a turn, i.e. 90°, it is called a *right angle*; right angles are marked like this:

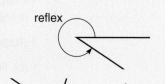

90°

▸ two lines which intersect at right angles are said to be *perpendicular*

▸ an angle less than 90° is called an *acute angle*

acute

▸ an angle between 90° and 180° is called an *obtuse angle*

obtuse

▸ an angle greater than 180° is called a *reflex angle*

reflex

▸ if a number of lines all meet at a point, the sum of all the angles is 360° (*angles at a point*)

total 360°

▸ two angles which add up to 90° are called *complementary angles*

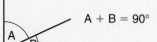

A + B = 90°

▸ two angles which add up to 180° are called *supplementary angles*

A + B = 180°

▸ angles next to one another, as shown in the last two examples, are said to be *adjacent angles*

Parallel lines

A line crossing one or more parallel lines is called a *transversal*.

On either side of a transversal angles marked A are equal. They are known as *alternate* angles, or sometimes, Z angles. The angles marked B are also equal.

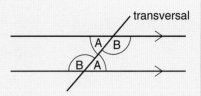

The angles marked C are equal. They are known as *corresponding* angles. The same applies to the angles marked D.

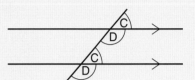

When two straight lines intersect, there are two pairs of equal angles. The angles marked E are equal as are the angles marked F and are called *vertically opposite* angles.

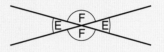

Each pair of angles shown in the diagram adds up to 180°. These are called *allied angles*.

Thus   G + H = 180°
and   I + J   = 180°

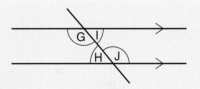

PRACTICE 9.1.1   Try these questions without a calculator

1   How many degrees are there in:

a $\frac{1}{3}$ of a revolution   e   2.1 revolutions

b $\frac{2}{5}$ of a revolution   f $\frac{1}{3}$ of a straight angle

c $1\frac{1}{2}$ revolutions   g $\frac{3}{5}$ of a right angle

d   0.3 of a revolution   h   0.55 of a right angle

2   A vinyl record revolves at 45 revolutions per minute. How many degrees per second is this?

3 Find the values of the marked angles in the following diagrams:

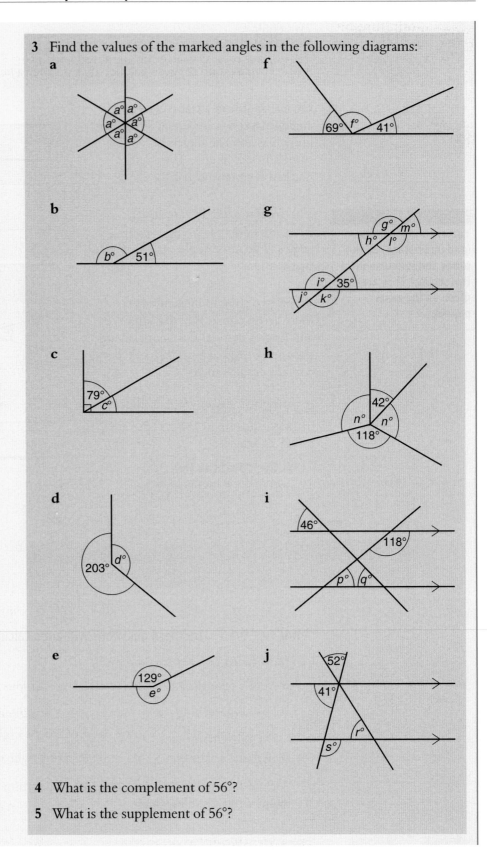

a

f

b

g

c

h

d

i

e

j

4 What is the complement of 56°?

5 What is the supplement of 56°?

Triangles

Triangle is the name given to any three sided plane figure.
Triangles which have certain properties have particular names:

1 A triangle with 3 acute angles is
    called an *acute angled* triangle.

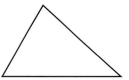

2 A triangle with one angle greater
    than 90° is called an *obtuse angled*
    triangle.

3 A triangle with an angle of 90° is
    called a *right angled* triangle.

4 A triangle with all sides different in
    length is called a *scalene* triangle.

5 A triangle with 2 sides equal is called
    an *isosceles* triangle.

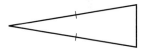

6 A triangle with all 3 sides equal is
    called an *equilateral* triangle.

Standard notation for triangles

Angles are sometimes marked with a letter inside them.

Another way of marking triangles is shown
here.

Angles are marked with capital letters and the
side opposite each angle is given the same letter
but in *lower case*.

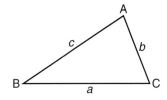

The angles are written either as A etc., or as $\angle$ABC (or $\angle$CBA), etc.

Properties of triangles

1 *In any triangle the sum of the three angles is 180°.*

This can easily be proved using our knowledge of parallel lines:

To do this we draw a line, XBY, through point B and parallel to side AC. (We call this a *construction* line.)

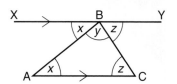

From our previous knowledge we can say:

$\angle$ BAC = $\angle$ XBA = x (alternate angles)
$\angle$ BCA = $\angle$ YBC = z (alternate angles)

Thus $\angle$ XBY = $x + y + z$

But we know that $\angle$ XBY = 180° since it is a straight angle.

Thus $x + y + z = 180°$

i.e. the sum of the three angles of any triangle equals 180°.

2 *In any triangle the largest side is opposite the largest angle and the smallest side is opposite the smallest angle.*

Also, *the sum of the lengths of any two sides is greater than the length of the third side.*
a is the largest side since it is opposite the largest angle. *b* is the shortest side.

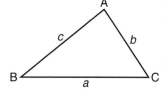

$b + c$ is greater than a
$c + a$ is greater than b
$a + b$ is greater than c

3 *When a side of a triangle is extended (we call this produced), the angle formed outside is called the exterior angle.*

We already know that
$\angle$A + $\angle$B + $\angle$C = 180° (see **1** above)

We also know that
$\angle$E + $\angle$C = 180° (straight angle)

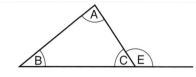

Therefore $\angle$E = $\angle$A + $\angle$B

i.e. the exterior angle is equal to the sum of the two opposite interior angles.

4 *Properties of the isosceles triangle.*

  i It has two equal sides (AB = AC).

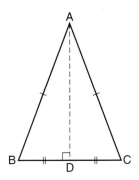

ii The *unequal* side is called the *base*, even though it doesn't always appear at the bottom of the triangle.

iii The angle between the two equal sides (∠A) is called the *vertical* angle.

iv The other two angles are called the *base angles* and are equal. Hence ∠B = ∠C.

v A line drawn from the vertical angle to meet the base at 90° (line AD), bisects the base. Hence BD = DC.

5 *Properties of the equilateral triangle.*

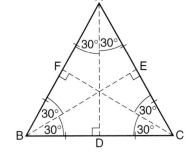

i It has three equal sides. Thus AB = BC = CA.

ii It has three equal angles. Since the sum is 180° then each angle is 60°.

iii The line drawn from any of the vertices A, B, C to meet the opposite side at 90°, bisects the opposite side.

Hence AE = EC = CD = DB = BF = FA.

Altitude and median

Any line drawn from any vertex of any triangle to meet the opposite side at right angles, is called an *altitude*.

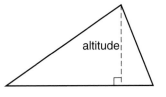

Any line drawn from any vertex of any triangle to the mid-point of the opposite side, is called a *median*.

Worked Examples

1 Find *a*

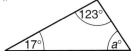

$a° + 123° + 17° = 180°$
Thus $a° + 140° = 180°$
Thus $a° = 40°$

2 Find *b*

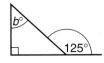

$b° + 90° = 125°$
$b° = 35°$

3 Find *c* and *d*

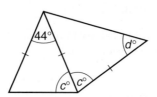

In the left-hand triangle
$$2c^\circ = 180^\circ - 44^\circ$$
i.e. $2c^\circ = 136^\circ$
i.e. $c^\circ = 68^\circ$

In the right-hand triangle
$$2d^\circ = 180^\circ - 68^\circ$$
i.e. $2d^\circ = 112^\circ$
i.e. $d^\circ = 56^\circ$

4 A triangle has angles x°, $2x^\circ$ and $x - 20^\circ$. Find x.

The sum of the three angles in any triangle is 180°.
Thus $x + 2x + x - 20 = 180$
i.e. $4x - 20 = 180$
i.e. $4x = 200$
i.e. $x = 50$

PRACTICE 9.2.1   Try these questions without a calculator

1 Calculate the values of the angles marked:

a

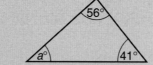

e

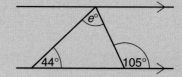

b

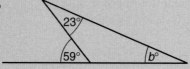

f

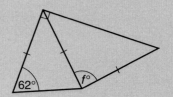

c

g

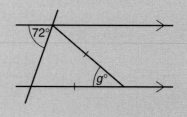

d

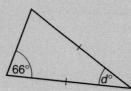

h

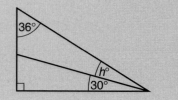

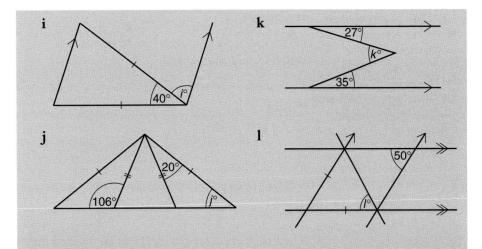

2 A triangle has angles x, $x + 30$, $x - 10$. Find the value of x.

3 An isosceles triangle has a vertical angle of 40°. How big are the base angles?

4 A triangle has sides of length 6 cm and 14 cm. The third side is also an integer number of cm. Find the minimum and maximum lengths of the third side.

5 Two angles of a triangle are $(3x - 10)°$ and $(4x + 20)°$. What is the value of the third angle?

Polygons

Polygon is the general name for a plane shape.
Some polygons have special names – square, rectangle, etc.

> 3-sided polygon is called a *triangle*
> 4-sided polygon is called a *quadrilateral*
> 5-sided polygon is called a *pentagon*
> 6-sided polygon is called a *hexagon*
> 8-sided polygon is called a *octagon*
> 10-sided polygon is called a *decagon*

Just as any triangle contains 180°, there are fixed sums for the interior angles of other polygons. For example:

i *Quadrilateral*
As we can see a quadrilateral can be divided into two triangles; A and B.

Each triangle contains 180°.

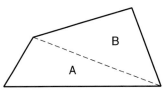

Therefore the angle sum of the interior angles of any quadrilateral
$= 2 \times 180° = 360°$.

ii *Pentagon*

As we can see a pentagon can be divided into 3 triangles; A, B and C.

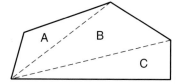

Each triangle contains 180°.

Therefore the angle sum of the interior angles of any pentagon
$= 3 \times 180° = 540°$.

iii *Any polygon*

A *quadrilateral* (4 sides) can be divided into 2 triangles.

A *pentagon* (5 sides) can be divided into 3 triangles.

Therefore a *hexagon* (6 sides) can be divided into 4 triangles, and so on.

Therefore a polygon (n sides) can be divided into n − 2 triangles.

Look at the polygon shown, with *n* sides.

The dotted lines indicate that the number of sides is not fixed.

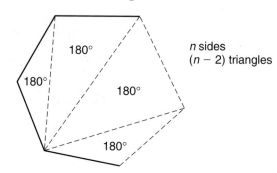

We can see that there are $n - 2$ triangles.

Each triangle contains 180°.

Therefore the angle sum of the interior angles of an n sided polygon is (n − 2) × 180°.

The exterior angle of a polygon

As in triangles, producing the sides of a polygon reveals *n* exterior angles when there are *n* sides.

At *each* vertex the sum of the interior and exterior angles = 180°.

Therefore the total sum of all interior and exterior angles
$= 180° \times n$.

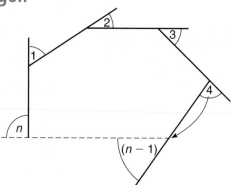

But we know that the sum of the interior angles $= (n - 2) \times 180°$
$$= 180n° - 360°.$$

Therefore the sum of the exterior angles $= 180n° - (180n° - 360°)$
$$= 180n° - 180n° + 360°$$
$$= 360°.$$

The sum of the exterior angles of any polygon = 360°.

Worked Examples

1 A polygon has 12 sides. What is its angle sum?

In this example $n = 12$.
Therefore the angle sum $= (12 - 2) \times 180° = 10 \times 180° = 1800°$.

2 In a pentagon, four of the exterior angles are 60°, 72°, 110° and 78°. How big is the fifth exterior angle?

The fifth angle is $360° - (60° + 72° + 110° + 78°) = 40°$.

Regular polygons

A regular polygon has all its sides and angles equal.
For example:

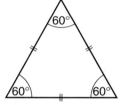 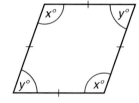

An equilateral triangle has 3 equal angles. All the sides and angles are equal for each triangle.

A rhombus has 4 equal sides. All the sides are equal but not the angles.

Since the angle sum of the interior angles is $(n - 2) \times 180°$, and there are n angles, we can say:

The size of the interior angle of a regular polygon $= \dfrac{(n - 2) \times 180°}{n}$

We know that the angle sum of the exterior angles $= 360°$

Therefore the size of the exterior angle of a regular polygon $= \dfrac{360°}{n}$

For example, if we know a regular polygon has 12 sides, we can say:

$$\text{exterior angle} = \frac{360°}{12} = 30°$$

thus interior angle $= 180° - 30° = 150°$.

Worked Examples

1 A regular polygon has exterior angles of 36°. How many sides does it have?

The exterior angle of a regular polygon $= \dfrac{360°}{n}$

Thus $36° = \dfrac{360°}{n}$

i.e. $n = \dfrac{360°}{36°} = 10$

The polygon has 10 sides.

2 Find the interior angle of a regular octagon.

For an octagon $n = 8$.

Thus interior angle $= (8 - 2) \times \dfrac{180°}{8} = \dfrac{1080°}{8} = 135°$.

(Alternatively, exterior angle $= \dfrac{360°}{8} = 45°$, interior $= 180° - 45° = 135°$.)

3 The interior angle of a regular polygon is 90°. How many sides does it have?

$$(n - 2) \times \dfrac{180°}{n} = 90°$$

i.e. $180n - 360 = 90n$

i.e. $90n = 360$

hence $n = 4$

The regular polygon has four sides and is a square.

PRACTICE 9.2.2   Try these questions without a calculator

1 Find the angle sum of polygons containing   **a** 7   **b** 11   **c** 22 sides.

2 The interior angles of two regular polygons are 108° and 140°. How many sides does each one have?

3 Find the interior angle of a regular hexagon.

4 In a pentagon, one angle is 100°. The other four angles are equal. How big is each one?

5 In a regular polygon each exterior angle is 120°. How many sides does it have?

6 In a regular polygon each interior angle is 100° more than the exterior angle. How many sides does the polygon have?

7 In a regular polygon each interior angle is four times the size of the exterior angle. How many sides does the polygon have?

8 One regular polygon has n sides. Another has $3n$ sides. The exterior angle of the first is 24° more than the exterior angle of the second. How many sides does each polygon have and what are the sizes of the interior and exterior angle in each case?

Properties of quadrilaterals

A **quadrilateral** is a plane figure with four sides.
Different types of quadrilaterals have special names:

1 The regular quadrilateral is called a **square**.

2 The quadrilateral with both pairs of opposite sides parallel is called a **parallelogram**.

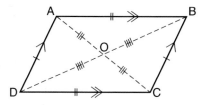

In every parallelogram:

  a each pair of opposite sides is equal i.e. AB = DC, AD = BC,
  b opposite angles are equal i.e. ∠A = ∠C, ∠B = ∠D,
  c the diagonals bisect each other i.e. AO = OC, DO = OB.

3 The parallelogram with four equal sides is called a **rhombus**.

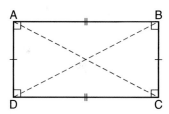

The rhombus has all the properties of the parallelogram above but:

all four sides are equal so the diagonals divide the rhombus up into four *identical* triangles,

therefore all the angles at O are equal,

thus: *the diagonals of a rhombus are perpendicular, and also bisect the angles,*

hence ∠DAO = ∠BAO = ∠DCO = ∠BCO
and ∠ABO = ∠CBO = ∠ADO = ∠CDO.

4 The parallelogram with all angles equal to 90° is called a **rectangle**.

The rectangle has all the properties of the parallelogram stated above, but in addition, the diagonals are equal in length i.e. AC = BD.

Note that the square can also be thought of as a special case of a rectangle with all four sides equal – or as a special case of a rhombus with all angles equal.

5 The quadrilateral with *one* pair of opposite sides parallel but *not* equal is called a **trapezium**.

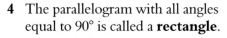

An isosceles trapezium is one which has its two non-parallel sides equal in length.

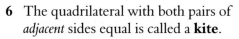

6 The quadrilateral with both pairs of *adjacent* sides equal is called a **kite**.

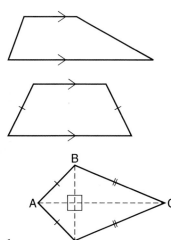

In every kite:

  a ∠B = ∠D
  b The diagonals AC and BD are perpendicular.

Worked Examples

1 Calculate the marked lengths and angles shown on the diagram. Explain your answers.

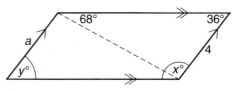

$a = 4$ (opposite sides)

$y = 36°$ (opposite angles)

$p = 180° - (68° + 36°)$

   $= 76°$ (angle sum of triangle)

$q = 68°$ (alternate angles)

Hence $x = 76° + 68° = 144°$.

NOTE

We could have said, more simply, that, using allied angles
$x = 180 - 36 = 144°$.

2 In the kite shown find angles a, b and c.

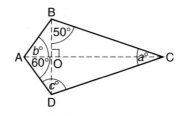

In triangle BOC

$\angle BCO = 180° - 90° - 50° = 40°$

Hence $a = 2 \times 40° = 80°$.

Since $\angle B = \angle D$ then $\angle ABO = \angle ADO = 30°$.

Thus $b = 180° - 90° - 30° = 60°$.

Clearly $c = 30° + 50° = 80°$.

PRACTICE 9.2.3   Try these questions without a calculator

1 Find the values of the marked angles in the following diagrams.

a

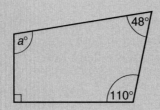

b

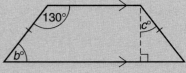

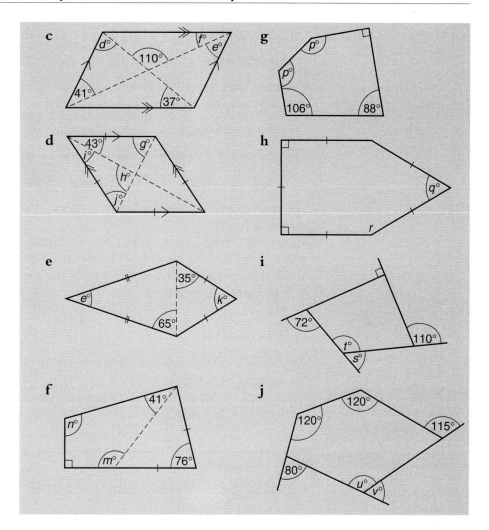

The circle

Reminder: We should already know the main terms associated with circles.

The diagram illustrates them.

▸ The total perimeter is called the *circumference*.

▸ The distance from any point on the circumference to the centre is constant and is called the *radius*.

▸ Any straight line through the centre is twice the radius and is called the *diameter*.

▸ A *chord* is any straight line across the circle not passing through the centre.

▸ Part of the circumference is called an *arc*.

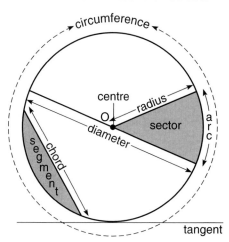

Circumference and area of the circle

The circumference

Centuries ago Greek mathematicians measured the circumferences and diameters of many circles.

They discovered that, for all circles, the ratio $\dfrac{C}{D}$ was a constant and just over 3.

They called it π. (π (pi) is a letter in the Greek alphabet.)

Hence: $\dfrac{C}{D} = \pi$ or $C = \pi D$ or $C = 2\pi r$ (r is the radius).

The exact value for π cannot be worked out – even by a computer, and it is an *irrational number*.

Most calculators now have a π button on them which gives $\pi = 3.141\,592\,654$ (depending on how many digits it has on its display).

In calculations we usually use $\pi = 3.14$ or else the π button on our calculators. A good fractional equivalent is $\pi = \frac{22}{7}$.

The area

The area of the circle was also discovered by the Greeks – and it involves π !!

The area for any circle, $A = \pi r^2$.

For example, the area of a circle of radius 3 m is $3.14 \times 3 \times 3 = 28.26$, i.e. the area $= 28.3\,\text{m}^2$ (3 sf).

> **NOTE**
> We always square r first – and then multiply by π.

> **NOTE**
> You need to memorise (and understand) these formulae:
> $C = \pi D$ or
> $C = 2\pi r$ and
> $A = \pi r^2$.

Worked Examples

1 Find the circumference of a circle of diameter 12.6 cm (take $\pi = 3.14$).

$D = 12.6$, therefore $r = 6.3$
$C = 2 \times 3.14 \times 6.3 = 39.564$
i.e. the circumference is 39.6 cm (3 sf).

2 Find the area of a circle of diameter 10.4 m.

$D = 10.4$, therefore $r = 5.2$
$A = 3.14 \times 5.2^2 = 3.14 \times 27.04 = 84.9056$
i.e. the area is 84.9 cm² (3 sf).

3 A circle has a circumference of 1 m. Find its area.

$C = \pi \times D$

i.e. $D = \dfrac{100}{3.14} = 31.85$ cm.

Hence $r = \dfrac{31.85}{2} = 15.925$ cm.

Thus area, $A = 3.14 \times 15.925^2$
$= 796.32$
$= 796\,\text{cm}^2$ (3 sf)

PRACTICE 9.2.4   Try these questions with a calculator

Take $\pi = 3.14$ or use the π button on your calculator.

1 Use $\pi = 3.14$ or use the π button on your
calculator to find:
  a the circumference of a circle of diameter 21 m,
  b the circumference of a circle of radius 8.9 cm,
  c the area of a circle of radius 4.3 in,
  d the area of a circle of diameter 15.8 in,
  e the complete perimeter of a semicircle of radius 14.6 ft.

2 The tile shown has the shape of a *quadrant*
(quarter) of a circle of radius 10 cm.
  a Find its area.
  b Calculate the perimeter.

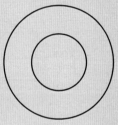

3 The washer shown has an outer radius of 3.6 cm and a hole of radius
0.4 cm.

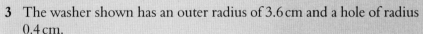

Calculate the area of the face of the washer.

4 Calculate the shaded area in each diagram.

a
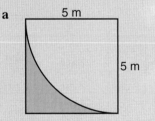

c
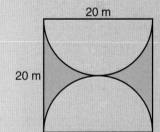

b
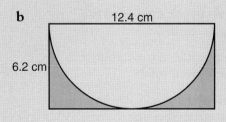

d
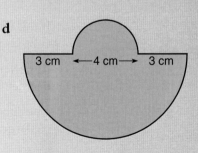

5 Three thin silver discs, of radii 4 cm, 7 cm and 10 cm are melted down
and recast into another disc of the same thickness.
Find the radius of this disc (ignore the thickness of the discs).

6 A vinyl disc of diameter 12 in. turns at $33\frac{1}{3}$ revolutions per minute.
  a Find the circumference of the disc.
  b Calculate how far a point on the rim of the disc travels in 1 minute.
  c Hence calculate the speed of the point on the rim in inches per sec.

7 A reel contains 30 m of garden hose. The reel has a diameter of 20 cm. Ignoring the thickness of the hose, calculate the number of times the reel rotates when the complete length of the hose is unwound.

Nets

A **net** is a pattern which can be cut out and then folded into a solid shape. For example, suppose we want to construct the cuboid shown.

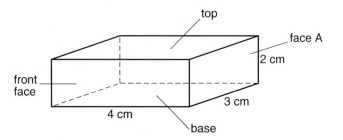

If all the faces are opened out we would have a *net* shaped like this:

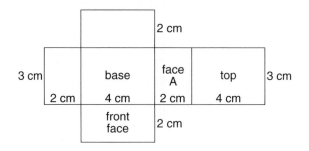

If this *net* is cut out and folded the cuboid can be made.

It is often possible to make more than one net for a given solid.

The cuboid above could also be constructed from this net:

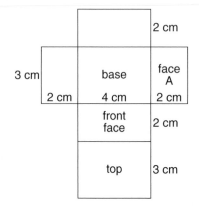

Worked Examples

1 Draw the net for the closed cylinder shown.

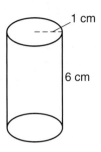

The curved sides, when opened out, would be a rectangle in which one side was the height of the cylinder and the other side the circumference of the circular ends.

Using $C = 2\pi r$ we get $C = 2 \times 3.14 \times 1 = 6.28$ cm.

Hence the required net is:

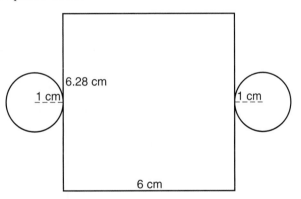

2 Illustrate the solid figure formed when the net shown is folded into a three-dimensional shape.

We can see that the final shape has 3 rectangular faces and 2 ends which are equilateral triangles.

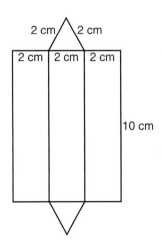

Hence we can see that the final figure is a triangular prism.

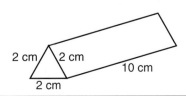

PRACTICE 9.2.5

1 The diagram shows a net.

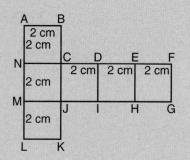

a What mathematical name is given to the solid formed when the net is folded?

b Name the pairs of points that will *meet* when the solid is made.

2 The diagrams below show some nets. Name the ones which would form cubes.

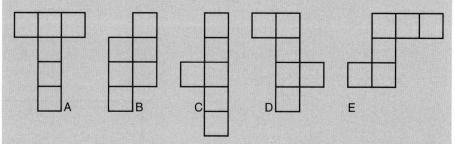

3 What solids are formed by the following nets?

a   **b**   **c**

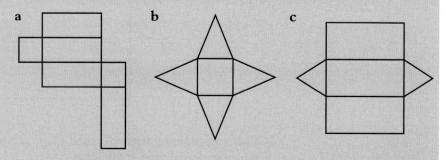

4 Draw accurate nets for the following solids.

a   **b**

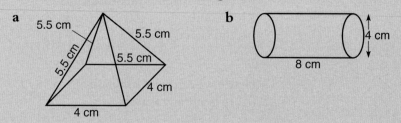

c A cuboid, 3 cm long, 2 cm wide and 1 cm high.

d A tetrahedron with the base an equilateral triangle of side 4 cm and each sloping face having a slant height of 6 cm.

Representing 3-dimensional objects in 2 dimensions

Three-dimensional objects can be represented in two dimensions using dotted or lined paper which is set out in equilateral triangles. This is known as *isometric paper*.

Worked Example

Illustrate the cuboid shown on isometric paper.

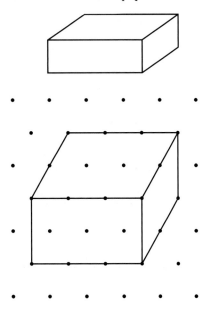

PRACTICE 9.2.6

1 Represent the following three-dimensional objects on isometric paper.

a

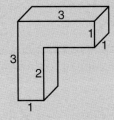

c
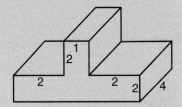

b
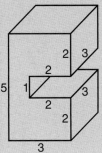

d
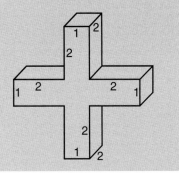

There are three types of symmetry.

2-dimensional shapes can have either **line symmetry** (reflection) or **rotational symmetry**.

3-dimensional solids can have **plane symmetry**.

Line symmetry

If a shape is identical on each side of a line drawn through it then it is said to possess *line symmetry*.

The kite shown has one line of symmetry along its longer diagonal.

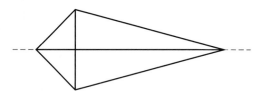

Each side of a line of symmetry is said to be a *mirror image* of the other.

We can show that a shape has line symmetry by placing a mirror along the mirror line and seeing that the reflected half is identical to the part of the shape behind the mirror.

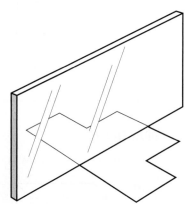

We can also show a shape possesses line symmetry by *tracing* the shape onto tracing paper and then folding it to show two identical halves.

Some shapes have no symmetry, for example, the parallelogram.

Others have several lines, for example, the square has four lines of symmetry:

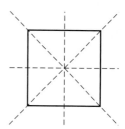

Rotational symmetry

As stated above, the parallelogram has no lines, or axes, of symmetry.

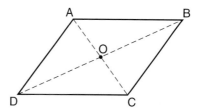

However, if we rotate any parallelogram through 180° about the centre O, it will look identical to its original position.

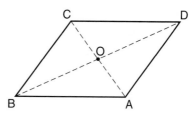

This is known as *rotational*, or *point, symmetry*.
The point about which the shape rotates is called the *centre*, or *point, of symmetry*.
Because there are two identical positions for a parallelogram, it is said to possess *rotational symmetry of order 2*.
Different shapes have different orders of symmetry.
The equilateral triangle has rotational symmetry of order 3:

The square has rotational symmetry of order 4.

Plane symmetry

If a three-dimensional solid can be cut into two identical halves the solid is said to possess *plane symmetry*.

If we imagine the plane of symmetry was a mirror, the reflection together with the intact half would look just like the complete solid.

The cuboid, for example, has three planes of symmetry:

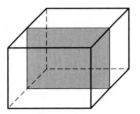 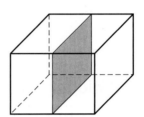 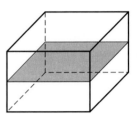

PRACTICE 9.3.1

1 Copy the following shapes and draw in the axes of symmetry.

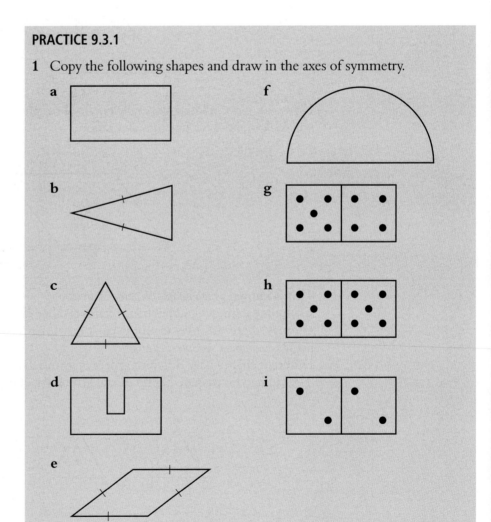

2 Write down a letter of the alphabet which could have
   a 2 lines of symmetry,
   b 4 lines of symmetry,
   c an infinite number of lines of symmetry,
   d rotational symmetry of order 2,
   e rotational symmetry of order 4,
   f infinite rotational symmetry,
   g rotational symmetry of order 2 but no line symmetry.

3 Copy and complete the following diagrams so that each figure is
symmetrical about all the marked lines:

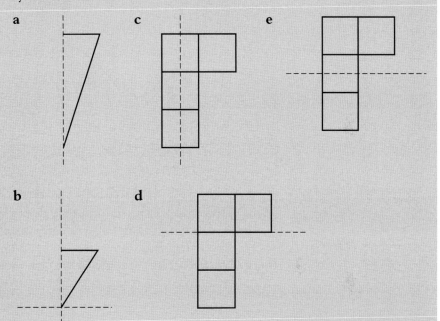

4 Copy and complete the following diagrams so that they have rotational
symmetry. O is the centre of symmetry in each case.

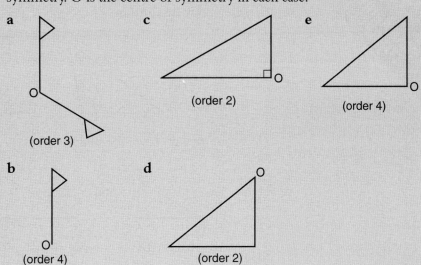

5 State the number of axes of symmetry and/or the order of rotational symmetry of the following

a

c

b

d

6 a How many planes of symmetry does a sphere have?
  b A cube has 12 planes of symmetry. Illustrate these by means of sketch diagrams.
  c Draw diagrams to show all the planes of symmetry of a prism with a cross sectional area of an equilateral triangle.

9.4 SIMILARITY AND CONGRUENCE

Similar triangles

If the three angles of one triangle match the three angles of another triangle, they are said to be **similar**.

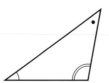

However, they do have one other property – *corresponding sides are in the same ratio.*

Hence, if 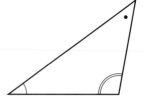 and are similar

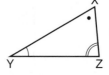

then $\dfrac{AB}{XY} = \dfrac{AC}{XZ} = \dfrac{BC}{YZ}$ or $\dfrac{XY}{AB} = \dfrac{XZ}{AC} = \dfrac{YZ}{BC}$

Worked Examples

1 Find x and y.

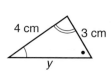 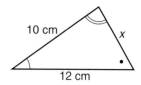

The triangles are similar, hence $\dfrac{4}{10} = \dfrac{3}{x} = \dfrac{y}{12}$

Since $\dfrac{4}{10} = \dfrac{3}{x}$ then $x = 3 \times \dfrac{10}{4} = 7.5\,\text{cm}$.

Since $\dfrac{4}{10} = \dfrac{y}{12}$ then $y = 4 \times \dfrac{12}{10} = 4.8\,\text{cm}$.

2 Prove that triangles OAB and ODC are similar.
Hence find the values of p, q and r.

$\angle$O is common to both triangles.

$\angle$OAB = $\angle$ODC and
$\angle$OBA = $\angle$OCD
(corresponding angles)

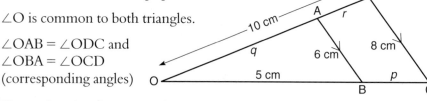

Hence the triangles are similar.

> **NOTE**
> To prove two triangles are similar, we only need to prove that *two* pairs of angles are equal.
> Since the angle sum in any triangle is 180° the third pair *must* then be equal.

Since the triangles are similar then $\quad \dfrac{8}{6} = \dfrac{10}{q} = \dfrac{5+p}{5}$

i.e. $\qquad \dfrac{8}{6} = \dfrac{10}{q}$

i.e. $\qquad 8 \times q = 10 \times 6$
$\qquad\qquad 8q = 60$
$\qquad\qquad q = 7\tfrac{1}{2}\,\text{cm}$

Similarly $\qquad\qquad \dfrac{8}{6} = \dfrac{5+p}{5}$

i.e. $\qquad 8 \times 5 = 6 \times (5+p)$
$\qquad\qquad 40 = 30 + 6p$
$\qquad\qquad 10 = 6p$
$\qquad 1\tfrac{2}{3}\,\text{cm} = p$

Finally, since $\qquad\qquad q + r = 10$
$\qquad\qquad 7.5 + r = 10$
$\qquad\qquad r = 2.5\,\text{cm}$

PRACTICE 9.4.1   Try these questions without a calculator

1 Find a and b.

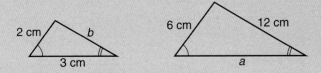

2 Find c and d.

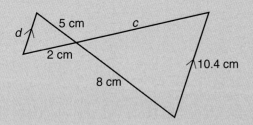

3 Find d, e and f.

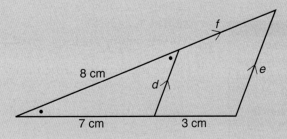

4 Find g and h.

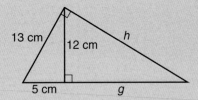

5 Find two similar triangles.
Hence find m and n.

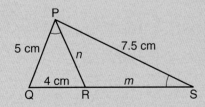

Other similar shapes

Shapes other than triangles are similar if:

a the angles in one shape are equal to corresponding angles in the other,
b all pairs of corresponding sides are in the same ratio.

For triangles, *one* of the above statements implies that the other is true.
For other shapes this is not so.
For example:

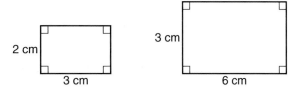

The angles match in these rectangles but their sides are not in the same ratio.
However, these rectangles are similar:

PRACTICE 9.4.2   Try these questions without a calculator

1 State whether the following pairs of shapes are similar. Explain your
answers.

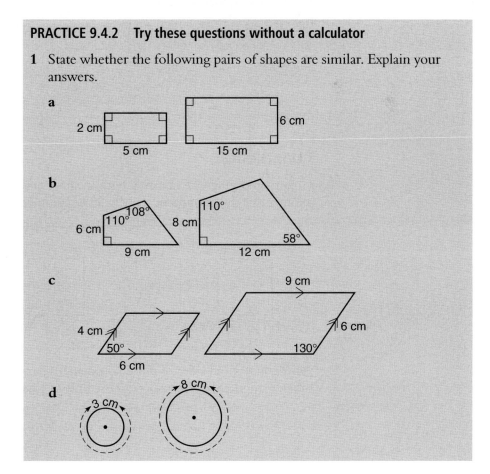

2 A door, 6 ft high and 2 ft 6 in. wide has a letter box of length 9 in. in it.
The letter box is similar in shape to the door.
Calculate the height of the letter box.

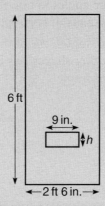

3 State whether the following shapes must be similar:

a two parallelograms	**f** two isosceles trapezia
b two squares	**g** two semicircles
c two rhombuses	**h** two regular hexagons
d two isosceles triangles	**i** two right angled triangles
e two equilateral triangles	**j** two right angled isosceles triangles.

4 Two wheels are rolled along a road side by side. The radius of one wheel equals the diameter of the other. The smaller wheel rotates 20 times. How many times does the larger wheel rotate?

Congruence

Congruent figures are identical both in shape and size and would *fit* over one another exactly. Congruent shapes can be 2-dimensional or 3-dimensional.

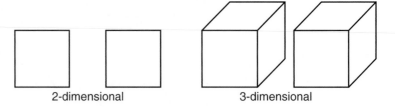

2-dimensional   3-dimensional

All the angles and sides of one shape match a *corresponding* angle or side in the other. Congruence is developed more fully in Chapter 10 on Transformations.

The Greek mathematician, Pythagoras, discovered a very useful property about right angled triangles.

He found out that if squares are drawn on the three sides, as shown, then the sum of the two smallest areas was equal to the largest area.

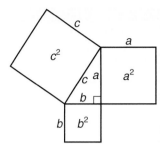

The longest side, c, of the right angled triangle, is called the **hypotenuse**.
Hence, from the diagram:

The square on the hypotenuse is equal to the sum of the squares on the other two sides
or, using algebra: $a^2 + b^2 = c^2$

We can use **Pythagoras' theorem** to find the length of any side in a right angled triangle if we know the lengths of the other two.

Also, if we know all three sides of the triangle and they fit the equation above, then it proves that the triangle is right angled.

Pythagorean triples

There are some well known right angled triangles that have lengths of sides that are whole numbers (integers). These are called **Pythagorean triples**.
The most well known of all is the 3, 4, 5 triangle since $3^2 + 4^2 = 5^2$,
i.e. $9 + 16 = 25$.
Some other well known triples are:

$$5, 12, 13 \text{ since } 5^2 + 12^2 = 13^2 \quad \text{i.e. } 25 + 144 = 169$$
$$8, 15, 17 \text{ since } 8^2 + 15^2 = 17^2 \quad \text{i.e. } 64 + 225 = 289$$
$$7, 24, 25 \text{ since } 7^2 + 24^2 = 25^2 \quad \text{i.e. } 49 + 576 = 625, \text{ etc.}$$

Any multiples of the above are also Pythagorean triples and thus sides of right angled triangles. Hence:

3, 4, 5	6, 8, 10	9, 12, 15, etc.
5, 12, 13	10, 24, 26	15, 36, 39, etc.

Use of Pythagoras' theorem in circles

Chords

There is a useful property associated with chords in a circle.

In any circle the line bisecting any chord at right angles, passes through the centre of the circle.

This line also divides the triangle formed by the chord and the two radii at the ends of the chord into two identical (congruent) right angled triangles.

The semicircle

Any diameter cuts a circle into two semicircles.

In any circle the triangle formed by a diameter joined to any other point on the circumference is right angled.

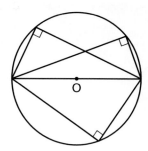

Worked Examples

1 Find the lengths x and y in the triangles shown:

a

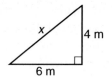

b

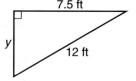

    a Using Pythagoras' theorem: $\quad 4^2 + 6^2 = x^2$
$$16 + 36 = x^2$$
$$52 = x^2$$
      i.e. $x = \sqrt{52} = 7.21\,\text{m}$ (3 sf)

    b Using Pythagoras' theorem: $y^2 + 7.5^2 = 12^2$
$$y^2 + 56.25 = 144$$
$$y^2 = 144 - 56.25 = 87.75$$
      i.e. $y = \sqrt{87.75} = 9.37\,\text{ft}$ (3 sf)

2 The line from the centre of a circle to the mid-point of a chord is 6.6 cm long. The chord is of length 17.6 cm.
Find the radius of the circle.

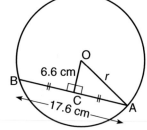

AB = 17.6 cm so therefore
AC = 8.8 cm

Using Pythagoras:
$r^2 = 8.8^2 + 6.6^2$
$r^2 = 77.44 + 43.56 = 121.0$

Hence the radius, $r = 11$ cm.

3 In a circle of radius 14.3 cm, the line joining the centre to the mid-point of a chord is 5.5 cm long.
Find the length of the chord.

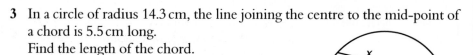

Using Pythagoras:
$14.3^2 = 5.5^2 + x^2$
$204.49 = 30.25 + x^2$
$174.24 = x^2$
$x = 13.2$ cm

Hence the length of the chord is $2 \times 13.2 = 26.4$ cm.

4 A right angled triangle is inscribed in a semicircle as shown.
Calculate the radius of the circle.

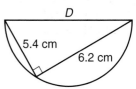

If the diameter = D and by
using Pythagoras

$D^2 = 6.2^2 + 5.4^2$
$D^2 = 38.44 + 29.16$
$D^2 = 67.6$
$D = 8.22$ cm

Hence the radius of the circle = $\dfrac{D}{2} = \dfrac{8.22}{2} = 4.11$ cm.

PRACTICE 9.5.1a   Try these questions without a calculator

1 Find the marked lengths in the following diagrams.

a

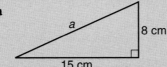

b

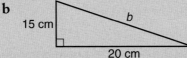

c

2 A kite is 48 m above the ground and has a string of length 80 m. How far is it horizontally from the holder?

3 A tangent, PT, is drawn to a circle of radius 2 m.

P is 5.2 m from the centre of the circle.

How far is P from the point of contact of the tangent and the circle?

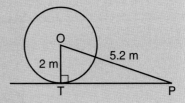

4 Arthen draws five triangles with the following sides:
   a 6, 8, 10 cm   **c** 7, 24, 25 in.   **e** 12, 21, 24 ft
   b 10, 15, 18 m   **d** 12, 18, 22 cm

Which of these are right angled triangles? Explain your answers.

5 In a circle of radius 17 m, a chord of length 30 m is drawn.
How far is it from the centre of the circle to the mid-point of the chord?

PRACTICE 9.5.1b   Try these questions with a calculator

1 Find the marked lengths in the following diagrams.

a

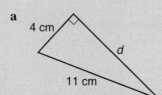

c

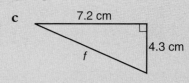

b

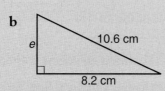

2 A ladder, 5 m long, is resting against a wall as shown.

The base of the ladder is 1.5 m from the wall.

How far up the wall does the ladder reach?

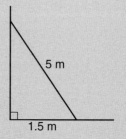

3 Darshna goes walking on Dartmoor. She walks 2 km due South and then 5 km due West. How far is she now from her starting position?

4 What is the length of a diagonal of a rectangle with sides 4 yd and 7 yd?

5 A plane is coming in to land. It is flying at 4000 ft and is currently 2 miles south of the runway. What is the actual distance the plane has left to fly before it lands (take 1 mile = 5280 ft)?

6 A square has a diagonal 14.14 cm long. How long is each side of the square?

7 John and Allan are playing conkers.

Allan's conker, C, is tied to the end of a string 20 in. long.

He pulls it back from the vertical until it is 9 in. horizontally from its original position.

Calculate the vertical distance, h, that the conker has risen.

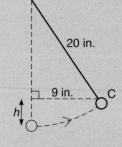

8 A chord, AB, is drawn in a circle of radius 10 cm.

The centre is 4.3 cm from M, the centre of the chord.

How long is the chord?

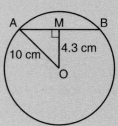

9　A road has a gradient of 1 in 10 as shown in the diagram.

Alicia drives up the hill rising
200 yds vertically. How far

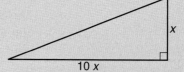

　a　has Alicia travelled horizontally,
　b　has Alicia driven ?

10　Find the distances between:
　　a　$(0, 0)$ and $(4, 2)$　　　**c**　$(^-3, 2)$ and $(5, 9)$
　　b　$(2, 3)$ and $(6, 7)$　　　**d**　$(^-4, ^-5)$ and $(4, ^-1)$
　　on a piece of graph paper with a unit distance of 1 cm.

11　In the diagram M is the mid-point of AB, AC = 17.5 cm and
　　BC = 11.4 cm. Calculate the length of MC.

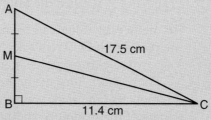

12　A semicircle is drawn with diameter AB = 28.6 m. A point C is marked
　　on the circumference and the triangle ABC drawn, where AC = 17.3 m.
　　Find the length of BC.

Trigonometry is the name given to the mathematics of triangles – it literally
means *triangle measurement*.

　　We use trigonometry with similar right angled triangles to calculate sides
and angles.

　　For example, suppose a post casts a shadow of 9 m and at the same time a
man, 2 m tall, casts a shadow 1.5 m long.

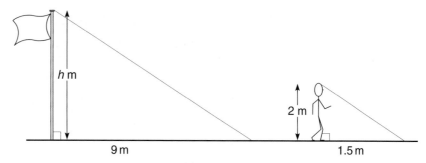

Because the two triangles are similar we can find the height of the post by
writing:

$$\frac{h}{9} = \frac{2}{1.5}$$

Hence　　$h = \dfrac{2 \times 9}{1.5}$

　　　　　　$h = 12$ m.

NOTE
Revise your work on
similar triangles before
reading this. See page
398.

Using this ratio, $\dfrac{O}{A}$, we can calculate the height of

any object if we know the length of its shadow at this time.

But, as the angle of the sun changes, the ratio changes.

However, if we know the ratio $\dfrac{O}{A}$

for different angles of the sun we could do any calculation we needed at any time.

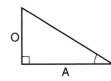

The tan ratio

The ratio $\dfrac{O}{A}$ is called the **tangent ratio** or **tan ratio**.

Its numerical value can be found on a scientific calculator, using the key marked TAN. Different calculators have different logic so we need to refer to our own calculators to see how to find the tan ratio for a particular angle.

For instance, imagine in the above example that the angle was now 58° and the length of the shadow of another pole was 10 m. We would write:

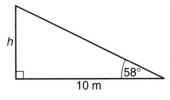

$$\tan 58° = \frac{h}{10}$$

Using our calculators we find that the tan ratio for 58° is 1.600 (4 sf).

Hence we would write: $1.600 = \dfrac{h}{10}$

$$\text{i.e. } 10 \times 1.600 = h$$

Hence the height of the object is 16.0 m (3sf).

The three trigonometrical ratios

When we consider a particular angle in a right angled triangle the side opposite the angle is called the **opposite** (O). The side next to the angle is called the **adjacent** (A). Remember that the side opposite the right angle is called the **hypotenuse** (H).

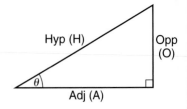

We already know from the previous section that the tan ratio is $\dfrac{O}{A}$.

$$\text{i.e. we could write} \quad \tan \theta = \frac{\text{opposite side}}{\text{adjacent side}}$$

There are two more ratios in common use and on your calculator:

the sin ratio is $\dfrac{O}{H}$, i.e. $\sin \theta = \dfrac{\text{opposite side}}{\text{hypotenuse}}$

the cos ratio is $\dfrac{A}{H}$, i.e. $\cos \theta = \dfrac{\text{adjacent side}}{\text{hypotenuse}}$

These ratios are really called sine, cosine and tangent, but we always use sin, cos and tan for short.

An easy way to remember these ratios is the made up word:

SOHCAHTOA

NOTE

The ratios *only apply* to right angled triangles.

i.e. $\sin \theta = \dfrac{O}{H}$ $\cos \theta = \dfrac{A}{H}$ $\tan \theta = \dfrac{O}{A}$

All three ratios can be found – for any particular angle – using the sin, cos and tan buttons on a scientific calculator.

Worked Examples

1   Find the sin, cos and tan ratios of   **a** 27°   **b** 73.8°

2   Find the angle whose   **a** sine is 0.361   **b** cosine is 0.243   **c** tangent is 1.75

Using our calculators we should obtain the following results:

1   **a**   sin 27° = 0.4540 (4 sf)   **b**   sin 73.8° = 0.9603 (4 sf)
         cos 27° = 0.8910 (4 sf)   cos 73.8° = 0.2790 (4 sf)
         tan 27° = 0.5095 (4 sf)   tan 73.8° = 3.442 (4 sf)

2   There is an *inverse* key on our calculators which enable us to use them *in reverse* to find the angles with a particular value of the sin, cos or tan ratio.
   Using this inverse key we should obtain these results:
   a   The angle whose sine is 0.361 is 21.2° (to the nearest 0.1°).
   b   The angle whose cosine is 0.243 is 75.9° (to the nearest 0.1°).
   c   The angle whose tangent is 1.75 is 60.3° (to the nearest 0.1°).

Using the trigonometrical ratios to solve problems in right angled triangles

Using our calculators we can now find any of the ratios we require and solve problems.

Be careful to:
   i draw a diagram and mark the sides O, A and H on it,
   ii write on the diagram what information is known,
   iii mark on the diagram what information is needed,
   iv pick the right ratio,
   v write down the correct equation(s) and solve it/them.

The following worked examples show the method.

Worked Examples

1   Find p and q using the values shown
    and without using a calculator.

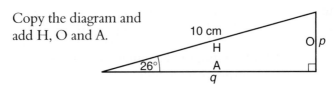

    sin 26 = 0.4384
    cos 26 = 0.8988
    tan 26 = 0.4877

    Copy the diagram and
    add H, O and A.

    We need p and know H = 10 cm;

    Opp and Hyp are connected by sin as $\sin \theta = \dfrac{O}{H}$

    hence $\sin 26° = \dfrac{p}{10}$

    (multiply by 10) $\sin 26° \times 10 = p$
    (obtain sin 26° from calculator) $0.4384 \times 10 = p$
    (multiplying out) $4.38 \text{ cm} = p$

    We need q and know H = 10;

    Adj and Hyp are connected by cos as $\cos \theta = \dfrac{A}{H}$

    hence $\cos 26° = \dfrac{q}{10}$

    (multiply by 10) $\cos 26° \times 10 = q$
    (obtain cos 26° from calculator) $0.8988 \times 10 = q$
    (multiplying out) $8.99 \text{ cm} = q$

2   Find r and s using a calculator.

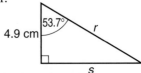

    Copy the diagram and
    add H, O and A.

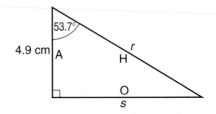

    We need r and know A = 4.9 cm;

    Adj and Hyp are connected by cos as $\cos \theta = \dfrac{A}{H}$

    hence $\cos 53.7° = \dfrac{4.9}{r}$

(multiply by r) $\cos 53.7° \times r = 4.9$

(divide by $\cos 53.7°$) $r = \dfrac{4.9}{\cos 53.7°}$

(obtain $\cos 53.7°$ from calculator) $r = \dfrac{4.9}{0.5920}$

(divide) $r = 8.28\,\text{cm}$ (3 sf)

We need s and know A $= 4.9$ cm;

 Adj and Opp are connected by tan as $\tan \theta = \dfrac{\text{O}}{\text{A}}$

      hence $\tan 53.7° = \dfrac{s}{4.9}$

(multiply by 4.9) $\tan 53.7° \times 4.9 = s$

(obtain $\tan 53.7°$ from calculator) $1.3613 \times 4.9 = s$

(multiplying out) $s = 6.67\,\text{cm}$ (3 sf)

3 Find angle θ and t.

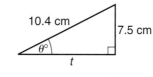

Copy the diagram and
add H, O and A.

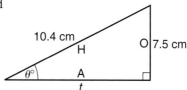

We need $\theta°$ and know H $= 10.4$ cm and O $= 7.5$ cm;

 Opp and Hyp are connected by sin as $\sin \theta° = \dfrac{\text{O}}{\text{H}}$

      hence $\sin \theta° = \dfrac{7.5}{10.4}$

      $\sin \theta° = 0.7212$

    Hence $\theta° =$ the angle whose sin is 0.7212

        $= 46.15$ (we need more accuracy for
           subsequent working)

     i.e. $\theta° = 46.1°$ (nearest 0.1°)

We need t and know H $= 10.4$ cm;

 Adj and Hyp are connected by cos as $\cos \theta° = \dfrac{\text{A}}{\text{H}}$

      hence $\cos 46.15° = \dfrac{t}{10.4}$

(multiply by 10.4) $\cos 46.15° \times 10.4 = t$

(obtain $\cos 46.15°$ from calculator) $0.6928 \times 10.4 = t$

        i.e. $t = 7.20\,\text{cm}$ (3 sf)

It is important to use enough figures in your working to ensure that your answer is accurate enough. A good *rule of thumb* is to use *at least* 4 figures in working (our calculators give us more than that), and to write answers to 3 figure accuracy.

PRACTICE 9.6.1a   Try this question without using a calculator

1   A ladder, 7 m long, rests on horizontal ground against a vertical wall. The angle between the ladder and the ground is 75°. How far up the wall does the ladder reach? Use one of the values given below to help you.

sin 75 = 0.9659   cos 75 = 0.2588   tan 75 = 3.7321

PRACTICE 9.6.1b   Try these questions using a calculator

1   Use a calculator to evaluate:
   a   sin 26°   **c**   tan 42°   **e**   cos 6.14°
   b   cos 33°   **d**   sin 71.23°   **f**   tan 88.41°

2   Find the angle:
   a   whose sin is 0.5   **d**   whose sin is 1
   b   whose cos is 0.8660   **e**   whose cos is 1
   c   whose tan is 3.142   **f**   whose tan is 3

3   Find the marked sides in the following diagrams:

   a 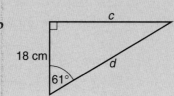   **c**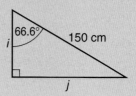

   b 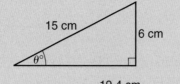   **d**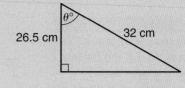

4   Find the marked angles in the following diagrams:

   a 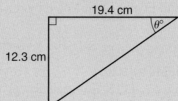   **c**

   b

5 In the isosceles triangle shown calculate the length of the base AB and the vertical height ON.

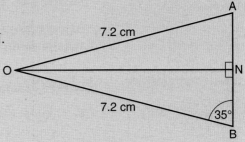

6 A ladder, 7 m long, rests on horizontal ground against a vertical wall. The angle between the ladder and the ground is 75°. How far up the wall does the ladder reach?

Bearings

Directions are given by using **bearings**.

Bearings are angles measuring the direction of an object *from due north and in a clockwise direction*. They are usually given as three figures before the decimal point. Some examples are:

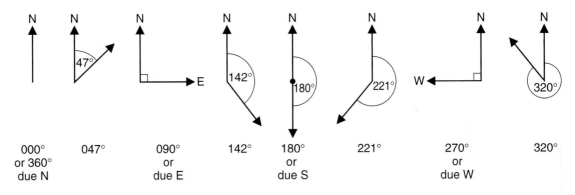

| 000°
or 360°
due N | 047° | 090°
or
due E | 142° | 180°
or
due S | 221° | 270°
or
due W | 320° |

Worked Example

Shaheed walks 8 km on a bearing of 141°. How far south is he from his starting point?

The angle in the triangle shown
$= 180° - 141°$
$= 39°$.

We need s and know H = 8 km.

Adj and Hyp are connected by cos.

Hence $\cos 39° = \dfrac{s}{8}$

$\cos 39° \times 8 = s$
i.e. $s = 6.22$ km (3 sf)

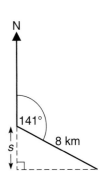

Thus Shaheed is 6.22 km south of his starting point.

Angles of elevation and depression

Angles measured from the horizontal upwards are called **angles of elevation** and if measured downwards **angles of depression**.

Worked Examples

1 Douglas is standing on a cliff top and sees a yacht out to sea at an angle of depression of 35°. The cliff is 250 m high. How far is the yacht from the base of the cliff? Ignore Douglas' height.

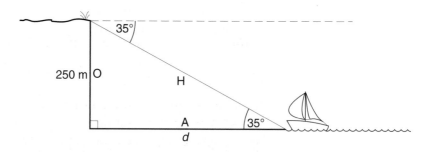

Using alternate angles in parallel lines we can see that the angle in the triangle is also 35°.

We need d and we know Opp = 250 m.
Opp and Adj are connected by tan.
Hence $\tan 35° = \dfrac{250}{d}$

$\tan 35° \times d = 250$

$$d = \frac{250}{\tan 35°}$$

$$= \frac{250}{0.7002}$$

$$d = 357.037 \text{ m (3 sf)}$$

The yacht is 357 m from the base of the cliff.

2 Marconi is looking at the top of a vertical radio mast. The angle of elevation of the top of the mast is 51.7° and Marconi is standing 200 ft from the base of the mast on horizontal ground. Marconi's eyes are 6 ft above ground level. Find the height of the mast.

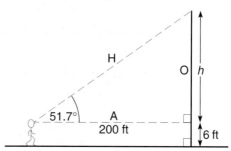

We need h and we know Adj $= 200$ ft.
Opp and Adj are connected by tan.

Hence $\tan 51.7° = \dfrac{h}{200}$

$$\tan 51.7° \times 200 = h$$
$$1.2662 \times 200 = h$$
$$253.24 \text{ ft} = h$$

But Marconi's eyes are 6 ft above ground level, i.e the height of the mast is $253 + 6 = 259$ ft (3 sf).

PRACTICE 9.6.2 Try these questions with a calculator

1 A TV mast, 1000 ft high, is held in place by ropes attached to the top of the mast and at an angle of elevation from the ground of 76.1°. How long are the ropes and how far from the base of the mast are they secured to the ground?

2 A plane flying at 30 000 ft is 10 miles horizontally from the airport. What is the angle of depression of the airport from the plane?

3 Whatley is orienteering on the moors. He hikes for 10 km on a bearing of 021° and then 5 km on a bearing of 111°. Calculate the distance and bearing that Whatley now is from his starting position.

4 An isosceles triangle has two sides of length 10.4 cm and a base of 7.25 cm. Find the vertical angle of the triangle.

5 Hannah is holding a kite string of length 100 feet. The angle of elevation of the kite from Hannah's eyes is 65.2°. Hannah's eyes are 5 ft above ground level. How high is the kite above ground level?

6 The diagram shows a triangular yacht course from Harbour P, round buoys Q and R and back to the harbour again.

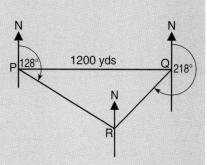

Q is 1200 yds due east of P, and R is on a bearing of 218° from Q and on a bearing of 128° from P.

Find the total length of the course.

7 The diagram shows the cross section of a shed attached to the wall of a house.

At what angle to the horizontal does the roof slope?

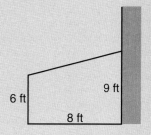

8 At a skating rink a bank of seats measures 100 ft from front to back and rises 15 ft vertically.

At what angle to the horizontal does the bank of seats slope?

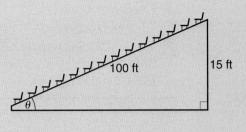

9 The diagram shows a crane with a load on it.

How high is the vertex above the ground? Ignore the width of the crane.

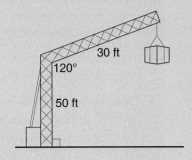

10 Matthew has a shadow 191 cm long. The sun is at an angle of elevation from the ground of 40°. How tall is Matthew?

11 The angles of elevation of the top and bottom of a hot air balloon are 65.5° and 37.1° respectively from an observation post O. The balloon is 16 ft horizontally from O. Calculate the height, h, of the balloon and basket.

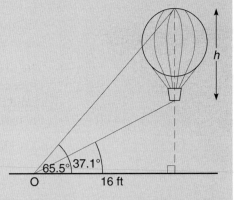

12 **a** Prove that the triangle is right angled.
    b Find the angle between BC and the y-axis.

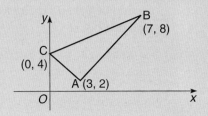

13 A rocket is fired from O at an
elevation of 78.5°. It travels for
7 miles to point A. It then
separates and the second stage
flies another 20 miles at an
elevation of 56.3° to point B.
Calculate the vertical height of B
above the launch pad and find
the distance, OC, that it has
travelled down range.

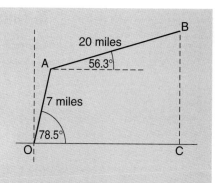

14 A mountain is 3500 m high. Find the angle of elevation of the top of
the mountain from a point level with the base of the mountain and
10 miles from the centre. (Take 1 mile ≡ 1.6 km.)

15 Debbie walks 10 m from A to B
towards a TV mast of height h.
The angles of elevation of the
top of the mast from A and B are
51.3° and 59° respectively. If the
distance BV = x,

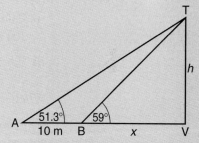

    a calculate x in terms of h,
    b calculate AV in terms of h,
    c hence calculate h to the nearest m.

9.7 EXTENSION MATERIAL

Three-dimensional trigonometry

Our knowledge of SOHCAHTOA and Pythagoras can be extended to three
dimensions, once we have decided what we mean by the angle between a line
and a plane and between two planes.

To find the angle between a line and a plane

  i Take any convenient point,
P, on the line and drop a
perpendicular to meet the
plane (PN).

  ii Identify the line, ON. This is
called the *projection* of the
line on the plane.

  iii The angle between the
line and the plane is taken
as angle $\theta° = \angle PON$.

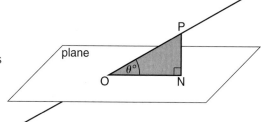

To find the angle between two planes

Any two planes meet in a straight line, called a *hinge*.

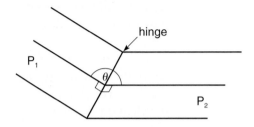

To find the angle between planes P_1 and P_2:

  i Locate the hinge.

 ii Take any convenient point on the hinge and find two lines *perpendicular* to the hinge – one in plane P_1 and one in plane P_2.

iii The angle between the two planes is the angle between these two lines.

When solving questions involving three dimensions:

- Choose sensible points and lines.

- Make right angled triangles if possible (see section on sine and cosine rules later).

- Draw separate diagrams for each calculation.

Worked Examples

1 A box has dimensions
   10 cm by 8 cm by 5 cm.
  a Find the angle between the
     diagonal BH and the base
     BCGF.
  b Find the length BH.
  c Find the angle between the
     planes BCGF and BDHF.

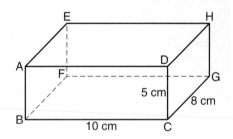

  a The diagonal BH cuts the plane at B and a suitable perpendicular is HG. However, we only know one length – GH – in this triangle. Thus we need to find another – and the best is BG across the base.

    By Pythagoras:
    $(BG)^2 = 8^2 + 10^2$
            $= 164$
    Hence BG = 12.81 cm.

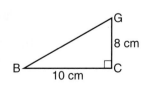

Now the angle required is ∠HBG and using SOHCAHTOA we can write

$$\tan B = \frac{5}{12.81}$$

$$= 0.3903$$

The angle between BH and BCGF is 21.3°.

b BH is found by Pythagoras: $(BH)^2 = 12.81^2 + 5^2$
$$(BH)^2 = 189$$
hence $BH = 13.75 \, cm$

c The hinge is the line BF.

We see that the required angle is ∠DBC.

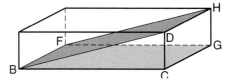

Using SOHCAHTOA we can write

$$\tan B = \frac{5}{10} = 0.5$$

Hence ∠DBC = 26.6°.

2 A rectangular pyramid with base 7 cm by 4 cm has a vertical height of 5 cm.

Find the angles between:
a The edge OC and the base ABCD.
b The face OBC and the base ABCD.

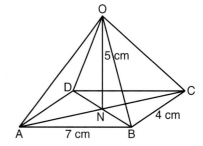

a O is vertically above N, the centre of the base. Thus CN is the projection of OC onto the base and the required angle is ∠OCN. As before we have only one length in triangle OCN so we need to find NC first.

By Pythagoras:
$(AC)^2 = 7^2 + 4^2$
$\qquad = 65$

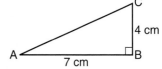

Hence $AC = 8.062 \, cm$
and $CN = \frac{1}{2}AC$
$\qquad\qquad = 4.031 \, cm$.

By SOHCAHTOA:

$$\tan C = \frac{5}{4.031}$$

$$= 1.240$$

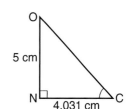

Hence the required angle, ∠OCN = 51.1°

b The hinge is BC and the
only point on it which gives
a suitable triangle is M – the
mid-point of BC.

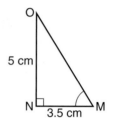

MO and MN are both
perpendicular to BC in
their respective planes –
so the required angle is
∠NMO.

We know that
NM = $\frac{1}{2}$AB = 3.5 cm.

Hence tan M = $\dfrac{5}{3.5}$

   = 1.4286

Hence the required angle, ∠NMO = 55.0° (3 sf)

PRACTICE 9.7.1   Try these questions with a calculator

1 From the diagram shown:
  a find the diagonals BD, BE, BG,
  b hence find BH,
  c find the angle between:
   i BD and the horizontal
   ii CH and the horizontal
   iii BH and the plane BFGC
   iv the planes BFGC and BEHC
   v the planes BFGC and BDHF
   vi the planes BEHC and ADGF.

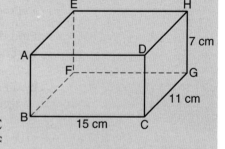

2 A roof is 20 m long and 5 m wide.
The height of the apex is 3 m above the base level.

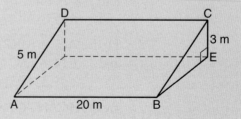

Calculate:
a the diagonal AC,
b the slope of the roof to the horizontal,
c the slope of the diagonal AC to the horizontal.

3 A flagpole stands at one
corner of a parade ground
100 m by 50 m.

The angle of elevation of the
top of the flagpole from the
corner at the end of the
shorter side is 26.6°.

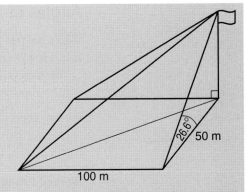

Calculate:
a the height of the flagpole,
b the angles of elevation of the top of the flagpole from the other two
corners.

4 A square pyramid of side 10 cm is 14 cm high. Calculate:
a the angle between one edge and the horizontal,
b the angle between one triangular face and the horizontal.

5 A lookout is 50 ft up the mast of a sailing boat. He sees another boat due
south at an angle of depression of 25.6°. A third boat is due west at an
angle of depression of 14.7°. Calculate the distances between the three
boats.

6 OPQR is a tetrahedron where
OP = PQ = QR = RP = 25 m.
O is vertically above P.

Calculate:
a the angle of elevation of
O from Q,
b OR,
c the angle between the planes
OQR and PQR.

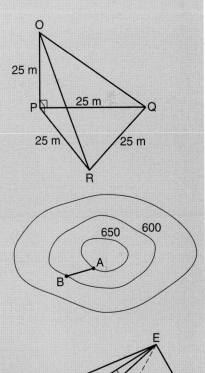

7 Contours on a map are 50 m
apart vertically.

AB is 76 m.

What is the slope of the line AB?

8 The triangular prism shown has
a cross sectional area ABC
which is an equilateral triangle
of side 2 in. The length of the
prism is 10 in.
Find ∠BEC.

Angles of any size

When we use SOHCAHTOA in right angled triangles, all the angles are 90° or less. However, sin, cos and tan of angles of any size do exist.

We can find out values for these ratios using a scientific calculator. We take some values of x from 0° to 360° and find the sin, cos and tan of them.

We can then plot the points obtained and draw their graphs.

Worked Example

Use your calculator to find values of sin x, cos x and tan x for values of x every 10° from 0° to 360°. Write your answer to 3 significant figures.
Plot these points as accurately as you can on graph paper and draw the graphs of $y = \sin x$, $y = \cos x$ and $y = \tan x$.

x	0°	10°	20°	30°	40°	50°	60°	70°	80°	90°
sin x	0	0.174	0.342	0.5	0.643	0.766	0.866	0.940	0.985	1
cos x	1	0.985	0.940	0.866	0.766	0.643	0.5	0.342	0.174	0
tan x	0	0.176	0.364	0.577	0.840	1.19	1.73	2.75	5.67	∞

x	100°	110°	120°	130°	140°	150°	160°	170°	180°
sin x	0.985	0.940	0.866	0.766	0.643	0.5	0.342	0.174	0
cos x	−0.174	−0.342	−0.5	−0.643	−0.766	−0.866	−0.940	−0.985	−1
tan x	−5.67	−2.75	−1.732	−1.19	−0.840	−0.577	−0.364	−0.176	0

x	190°	200°	210°	220°	230°	240°	250°	260°	270°
sin x	−0.174	−0.342	−0.5	−0.643	−0.766	−0.866	−0.940	−0.985	−1
cos x	−0.985	−0.940	−0.866	−0.766	−0.643	−0.5	−0.342	−0.174	0
tan x	0.176	0.364	0.577	0.840	1.19	1.73	2.75	5.67	∞

x	280°	290°	300°	310°	320°	330°	340°	350°	360°
sin x	−0.985	−0.940	−0.866	−0.766	−0.643	−0.5	−0.342	−0.174	0
cos x	0.174	0.342	0.5	0.643	0.766	0.866	0.940	0.985	1
tan x	−5.67	−2.75	−1.732	−1.19	−0.840	−0.577	−0.364	−0.176	0

Plotting these points and drawing the graphs we get the following results:

$y = \sin x$

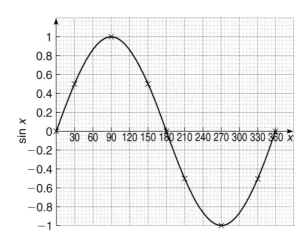

$y = \cos x$

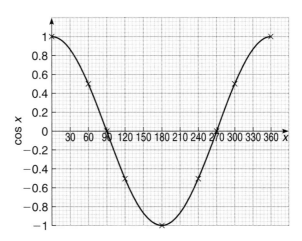

$y = \tan x$

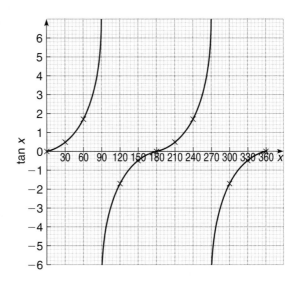

Notice that:

the graphs of sin x and cos x are the same shape but they are 90° *out of phase,*

if the graph of $y = \cos x$ is translated (see Chapter 10) 90° to the right it will fit exactly on the graph of $y = \sin x$,

the maximum value of both sin x and cos x is 1,

the minimum value of both sin x and cos x is -1,

$y = \sin x$ is symmetrical about $x = 90°$ and $x = 270°$,
$y = \cos x$ is symmetrical about $x = 180°$.

The 360° are divided into four *quadrants*:

in the *first* quadrant (0° to 90°)
sin x increases from 0 to 1
cos x decreases from 1 to 0   *All the ratios are positive.*
tan x increases from 0 to ∞ (infinity)

in the *second* quadrant (90° to 180°)
sin x decreases from 1 to 0
cos x decreases from 0 to -1 *Only sin x is positive.*
tan x increases from $-\infty$ to 0

All the angles are the same as those measured to the x-axis,
e.g. sin 140° = sin 40°, cos 130° = $-$cos 50° and tan 120° = $-$tan 60°.

In the *third* quadrant (180° to 270°)
sin x decreases from 0 to -1
cos x increases from -1 to 0   *Only tan x is positive.*
tan x increases from 0 to ∞

All the angles are the same as those measured to the x-axis,
e.g. sin 240° = $-$sin 60°, cos 230° = $-$cos 50° and tan 220° = tan 40°

In the *fourth* quadrant (270° to 360°)
sin x increases from -1 to 0
cos x increases from 0 to 1   *Only cos x is positive.*
tan x increases from $-\infty$ to 0

All the angles are the same as those measured to the x-axis,
e.g. sin 340° = $-$sin 20°, cos 330° = cos 30° and tan 320° = $-$tan 40°.

There is an easy way to remember which quadrant has the positive ratio:

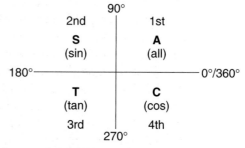

The letters spell the word **CAST** in order, starting from the fourth quadrant.

Worked Examples

Decide what angles in the range 0° to 90° have the same numerical value as:

1 cos 133°   **3** sin 127°   **5** sin 199°   **7** sin 333.3°   **9** tan 301.1°
2 tan 159°   **4** tan 256°   **6** cos 222.2°   **8** cos 275°

Calculate your answers correct to 4 sf.

1 cos 133°   = (second quadrant) = −cos(180° − 133°)   = −cos 47°
        = −0.6820

2 tan 159°   = (second quadrant) = −tan(180° − 159°)   = −tan 21°
        = −0.3839

3 sin 127°   = (second quadrant) = sin(180° − 127°)   = sin 53°
        = 0.7986

4 tan 256°   = (third quadrant)   = tan(256° − 180°)   = tan 76°
        = 4.011

5 sin 199°   = (third quadrant)   = −sin(199° − 180°)   = −sin 19°
        = −0.3256

6 cos 222.2° = (third quadrant)   = −cos(222.2° − 180°) = −cos 42.2°
        = −0.7408

7 sin 333.3° = (fourth quadrant) = −sin(360° − 333.3°) = −sin 26.7°
        = −0.4493

8 cos 275°   = (fourth quadrant) = cos(360° − 275°)   = cos 85°
        = 0.0872

9 tan 301.1° = (fourth quadrant) = −tan(360° − 301.1°) = −tan 58.9°
        = −1.6577

PRACTICE 9.7.2   Try these questions with a calculator

In questions 1 to 18 find the angles in the range 0° to 90° which have the same positive numerical value as:

1 sin 130°	**6** sin 180.1°	**11** sin 291.3°	**16** sin 346.1°
2 cos 141.2°	**7** tan 271.3°	**12** cos 355°	**17** cos 263°
3 tan 111.1°	**8** sin 265.7°	**13** tan 326.1°	**18** cos 99.9°
4 cos 231°	**9** cos 298°	**14** sin 161.2°	
5 tan 192.3°	**10** tan 166°	**15** tan 243.7°	

19 Find an angle $x°$ in the second quadrant where $\sin x° = 0.2714$
20 Find an angle $x°$ in the third quadrant where $\tan x° = 4.123$
21 Find an angle $x°$ in the fourth quadrant where $\cos x° = 0.5555$
22 Find an angle $x°$ in the second quadrant where $\cos x° = -0.1234$
23 Find an angle $x°$ in the third quadrant where $\cos x° = -0.1234$
24 Find an angle $x°$ in the third quadrant where $\sin x° = -0.6713$
25 Find an angle $x°$ in the fourth quadrant where $\sin x° = -0.6713$
26 Find an angle $x°$ in the second quadrant where $\tan x° = -0.5$
27 Find an angle $x°$ in the fourth quadrant where $\tan x° = -0.5$

Further trigonometry

If the triangle does not have a right angle in it, we cannot solve it using the basic sin, cos and tan ratios.

However, there are two formulae we can use to solve trigonometry problems in such triangles. These are called the **sine rule** and the **cosine rule**.

The sine rule

Using the standard notation for the triangle, the sine rule states:
In any triangle ABC:

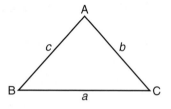

$$\frac{a}{\sin A} = \frac{b}{\sin B} = \frac{c}{\sin C} \quad \text{or} \quad \frac{\sin A}{a} = \frac{\sin B}{b} = \frac{\sin C}{c}$$

Notice that:

  i   the rule connects each side of the triangle with the angle opposite,
  ii   each of the above is really three equations in one,
  iii   each single equation has four terms in it – of which any three must be known,
  iv   if the unknown required is a side, use the first set of equations; if it is an angle, use the second set of equations.

Worked Example

Solve the triangle shown.

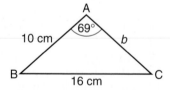

Using the sine rule: $\dfrac{16}{\sin 69°} = \dfrac{b}{\sin B} = \dfrac{10}{\sin C}$ or $\dfrac{\sin 69°}{16} = \dfrac{\sin B}{b} = \dfrac{\sin C}{10}$

The only equation with one unknown is for angle C. Hence

$$\frac{\sin C}{10} = \frac{\sin 69°}{16}$$

i.e. $\sin C = \dfrac{\sin 69° \times 10}{16} = 0.5835$

Hence $\angle C = 35.7°$

Since $\angle A + \angle B + \angle C = 180°$, then $\angle B = 180° - 69° - 35.7° = 75.3°$.

Hence we can now write $\dfrac{16}{\sin 69°} = \dfrac{b}{\sin 75.3°}$

i.e. $b = \dfrac{\sin 75.3° \times 16}{\sin 69°} = 16.577 = 16.6\,\text{cm}$ (3 sf)

We have now found *all* the angles and sides:

$\angle A = 69°$ $\angle B = 75.3°$ $\angle C = 35.7°$ $a = 16\,\text{cm}$ $b = 16.6\,\text{cm}$ $c = 10\,\text{cm}$.

NOTE
Do not forget the angle sum of a triangle when calculating using the sine rule.

PRACTICE 9.7.3   Try these questions with a calculator

Taking the standard notation for triangles, solve the following triangles.

1 $\angle A = 42°$, $\angle B = 69°$, $b = 42.3\,\text{m}$

2 $\angle B = 61°$, $\angle C = 58°$, $a = 4.7\,\text{ft}$

3 $\angle B = 80°$, $a = 17.3\,\text{in.}$, $b = 19.2\,\text{in.}$

4 $\angle C = 106°$, $b = 12.1\,\text{yd}$, $c = 14.3\,\text{yd}$

The cosine rule

Consider the triangle ABC:
Using the sine rule we get

$$\frac{a}{\sin 68°} = \frac{4.3}{\sin B} = \frac{5.6}{\sin C}$$

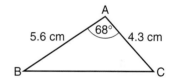

We can see that, whatever equation we take, we get one that contains two unknown quantities, and we cannot solve such an equation.

Hence, the sine rule is no help in a situation where we know two sides and the included angle. We need another rule – and this is the cosine (or cos) rule. This states that in any triangle ABC:

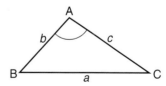

$$a^2 = b^2 + c^2 - (2bc \cos A)$$

i   The above formula gives the solution for unknown side a. However, if the unknown side is b or c the formula has to be adapted into $b^2 = c^2 + a^2 - (2ca \cos B)$ or $c^2 = a^2 + b^2 - (2ab \cos C)$. Once the form of the equation is learned it is not difficult to remember it for whichever side is needed.

ii The brackets are not strictly necessary in the formula but they do remind us that we have to multiply out all of the terms in them *before* subtracting. **This is a common error in examinations**.

iii If we know all three sides, the sine rule would not work, but we can use the cosine rule to find an angle. This is shown in the following worked examples.

Worked Examples

1 Find b.

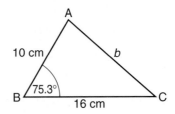

The unknown side is b: i.e. $b^2 = c^2 + a^2 - (2ca \cos B)$

i.e. $b^2 = 10^2 + 16^2 - (2 \times 10 \times 16 \times \cos 75.3°)$
$= 100 + 256 - (320 \times 0.2538)$
$= 356 - 81.2$

i.e. $b^2 = 274.8$ and hence $b = 16.6 \, \text{cm}$ (3 sf)
(as we obtained in the last worked example).

2 Find the smallest angle in the triangle.

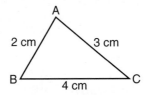

The smallest angle is opposite the smallest side, i.e. $\angle C$.
Hence $2^2 = 4^2 + 3^2 - (2 \times 4 \times 3 \times \cos C)$
$4 = 16 + 9 - (24 \times \cos C)$
$24 \cos C = 21$
$\cos C = \frac{21}{24} = 0.875$
i.e. $\angle C = 29.0°$ (1 dp)

> **NOTE**
> If asked to completely solve a triangle, after first applying the cosine rule, it is generally easier and quicker to use the sine rule subsequently.

PRACTICE 9.7.4   Try these questions with a calculator

1 Find the marked sides.

a

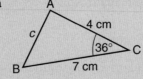

c

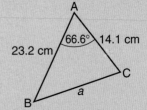

b

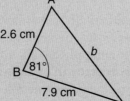

2 Find the smallest angles in:

a

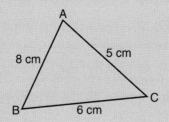

b

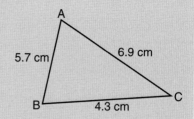

3 a Find *a*.

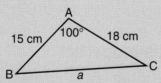

b Find ∠B.

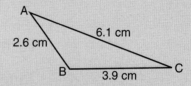

(Don't forget that the cosine of an obtuse angle is negative!)

4 Solve the following triangles completely.

a

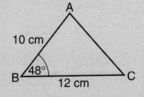

c

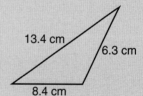

b

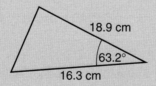

d

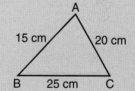

5 Find ∠D.

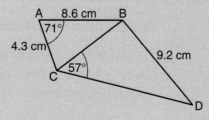

6 A yacht sails 5 km on a bearing of 129°. It then sails a further 8 km on a bearing of 240°. Find its distance and bearing from its starting position.

7 Nick Faldo drives toward the green on a 375 yd hole. He drives for 340 yds but at an angle of 2° away from the correct line. How far is his ball from the hole now?

8 A is 4 miles from O on a bearing of 021°. B is 7 miles from O on a
bearing of 104°. Calculate the distance and bearing of A from B.

9 A plane is descending to land at Birmingham International. It is first
recorded from an observation post 4000 ft away at an angle of elevation
of 51°. After passing directly over the observation post it is next
recorded, flying away from the post, 2500 ft away and at an elevation of
32°. At what angle to the horizontal is the plane descending?

Further circle properties

Tangents

There are some properties of tangents and circles that should be known.

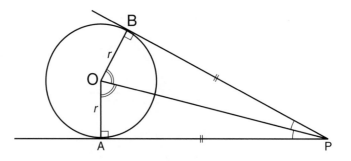

1 In any circle a tangent is perpendicular to the radius drawn to the point of
contact
i.e. ∠OAP = ∠OBP = 90°

2 Two tangents can be drawn from any external point, P, to a circle. The
distances from P to the points of contact are equal. i.e. PA = PB

3 The line PO bisects both the angle at P *and* the angle at O.
Hence ∠APO = ∠BPO and ∠POA = ∠POB. This can be proved by the
congruency of triangles OPA and OPB.

Further angle properties

We saw in Topic 9.5 that the angle made by a diameter joined to any other point
on the circumference is 90°.

We need to know four other angle properties.

i Take any arc, or chord, AB, in a circle. This arc, or chord, can subtend angles anywhere along the remainder of the circumference – like C for example.

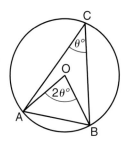

In any circle with any arc: $\angle AOB = 2 \times \angle ACB$

The angle subtended by any arc, or chord, at the centre of a circle, is twice the angle subtended by the arc, or chord, at any other point on the remainder of the circumference.

Worked Examples

Find the angle $\theta°$ in each case.

a

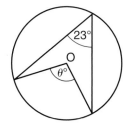

b

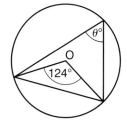

a $\theta° = 2 \times 23° = 46°$

b $\theta° = \dfrac{124°}{2} = 62°$

ii Take any arc, or chord, AB, in a circle.

Let it subtend angles at points C, D, E, F, etc. on the remainder of the circumference.

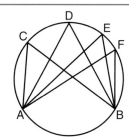

In all cases, $\angle ACB = \angle ADB = \angle AEB = \angle AFB$.

The angles subtended by an arc, or chord, at all points on the remainder of the circumference are equal.

Worked Example

Find angles A, B, C and D.

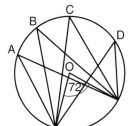

The angle at the centre is 72°.

Therefore $\angle A = \angle B = \angle C = \angle D = \dfrac{72°}{2} = 36°$.

iii ABCD is a quadrilateral inscribed in a circle.

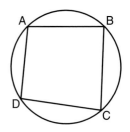

In any such quadrilateral:

$\angle A + \angle C = 180°$ and $\angle B + \angle D = 180°$.

i.e. *opposite angles are supplementary*.

Not all quadrilaterals are cyclic. We cannot draw a circle through the four vertices of a parallelogram for instance.

However, if they *are* cyclic, their opposite angles will add up to 180°.

Worked Example

Calculate angles C and D.

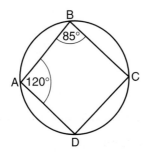

$\angle A + \angle C = 180°$ Thus $\angle C = 180° - 120° = 60°$

$\angle B + \angle D = 180°$ Thus $\angle D = 180° - 85° = 95°$

---

iv TCV is a tangent to a circle.

AC is *any* chord through the point of contact, C.

AC divides the circle into two segments, ABC and ADC.

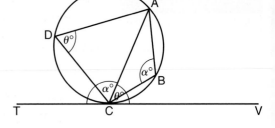

AC subtends equal angles anywhere along arc ADC (see **ii** above) and equal angles anywhere along arc ABC.

For any such chord, the angle between a tangent and any chord through the point of contact is equal to the angle the chord subtends anywhere in the *alternate* (opposite) segment.

i.e. $\angle TCA = \angle ABC \, (= \alpha)$ and $\angle VCA = \angle ADC \, (= \theta)$.

We call this the *alternate segment theorem*.

Worked Examples

1 What angle(s) are equal to:

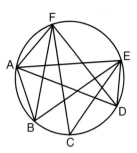

   a ∠AFC

   b ∠AFD

   c ∠FAE

   d ∠CFD

    a ∠AEC **b** ∠AED **c** ∠FBE, ∠FCE, ∠FDE **d** ∠CED
    All reasons are the same, i.e. *same segment*.

2 Find ∠A, ∠B, ∠D.

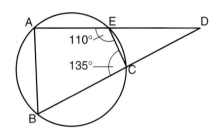

   ∠A = 180° − 135° = 45° (opposite angles of a cyclic quadrilateral)

   ∠B = 180° − 110° = 70° (same reason)

   ∠D = 180° − 70° − 45° = 65° (angle sum of triangle)

3 Find ∠ABC, ∠ADC, ∠COD.

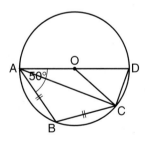

   ∠BCD = 180° − 50° = 130° (cyclic quadrilateral)

   ∠ACD = 90° (angle in a semicircle), ∠ACB = 40°

   But triangle ABC is isosceles (AB = BC).
   Thus,   ∠CAB = 40° also (base angles),
   therefore ∠ABC = 180° − 40° − 40° = 100°,
   hence,   ∠ADC = 180° − 100° = 80° (cyclic quadrilateral)

   ∠DAB = 50° (given) and ∠CAB = 40° (proved)

   Therefore ∠CAD = 50° − 40° = 10° and
   ∠COD = 20° (angle at centre = twice angle at circumference)

PRACTICE 9.7.5   Try these questions without a calculator

In each of the following diagrams calculate the marked angles.
You may have to draw some extra lines in to help you solve the problem.
These are called *construction* lines.

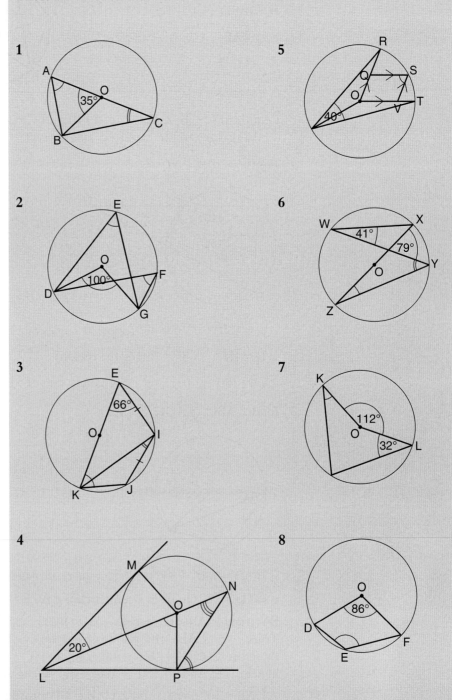

1

5

2

6

3

7

4

8

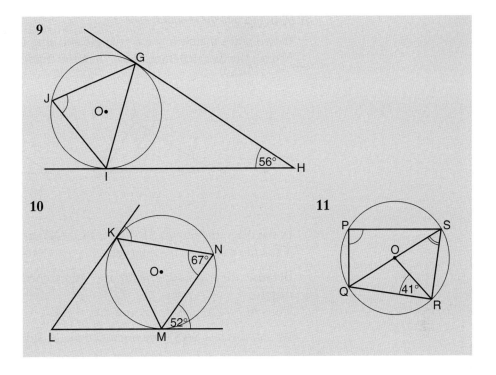

Congruent triangles

There are six pieces of information we can know when we draw a triangle – its three sides and three angles.

However, to prove two triangles are congruent, we *don't* have to know all six. We can prove two triangles are congruent sometimes by knowing only three pieces of information about them. These are called the *tests for congruency* and are:

i *Three sides*

If the three sides of triangle A match the three sides of triangle B then the triangles must be congruent.

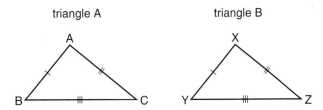

In the diagrams shown AB = XY, BC = YZ and CA = ZX.

Thus the triangles are congruent.

Because they are congruent we can also say that the angles match.

Thus ∠A = ∠X, ∠B = ∠Y and ∠C = ∠Z.

We call this test **SSS** (3 sides).

ii *Two sides and the included angle*

If two sides match in each triangle and the included angle, i.e. the angle *between* the two matching sides, then the triangles must be congruent.

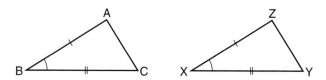

In the diagrams shown AB = ZX, BC = XY and ∠B = ∠X.
Thus the triangles are congruent.

Because they are congruent, the other corresponding sides and angles match.
Thus AC = ZY, ∠A = ∠Z and ∠C = ∠Y.

We call this test **SAS** (side, included angle, side).

iii *Two angles and the corresponding side*

If two angles match in each triangle and a *corresponding* side matches, i.e. the side in the same position in each triangle, then the triangles must be congruent.

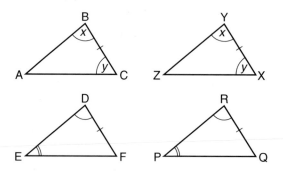

In the diagrams shown   ∠B = ∠Y, ∠C = ∠X and BC = YX
                        ∠D = ∠R, ∠E = ∠P and DF = RQ.
Thus each pair of triangles is congruent.

Because they are congruent, the other corresponding sides and angles match.
Thus AC = ZX, AB = ZY and ∠A = ∠Z
and   DE = RP, EF = PQ and ∠F = ∠Q.
We call this test **ASA** (first pair) or **AAS** (second pair) (2 angles and corresponding side).

iv *Right angled triangle*

If two triangles each have a right angle, the hypotenuse and another side in common, then the triangles are congruent.

The hypotenuse is the side opposite the right angle.

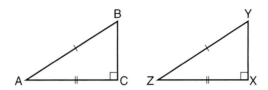

In the diagrams shown $\angle C = \angle X = 90°$, AB = ZY and AC = ZX. Thus the triangles are congruent.

Because they are congruent $\angle A = \angle Z$, $\angle B = \angle Y$ and BC = YX.

We call this test **RHS** (right angle, hypotenuse and another side).

Worked Examples

In the following three pairs of triangles, one pair is congruent, one pair is not congruent and in one pair it is not possible to tell. Identify each pair and explain.

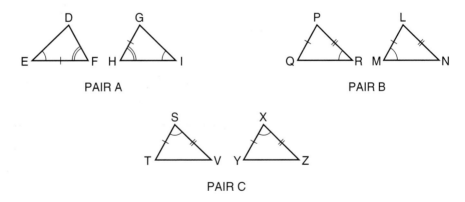

Pair A: We have 2 angles and 1 side – hence test ASA or AAS.
The side is *not* corresponding, but if D were to equal I then the two triangles would be isosceles and the angles would be corresponding and equal. However we don't know whether these angles are equal or not – hence in this pair *we cannot tell*.

Pair B: We have 2 sides and 1 angle – hence test SAS. The angle is *not* the included angle – hence the triangles are *not congruent*.

Pair C: We have 2 sides and 1 angle – hence test SAS. The angle *is* the included angle – hence the triangles *are congruent*.

PRACTICE 9.7.6

1 In the following pairs of triangles, find which are definitely congruent and state the test, and which are definitely not congruent and say why.

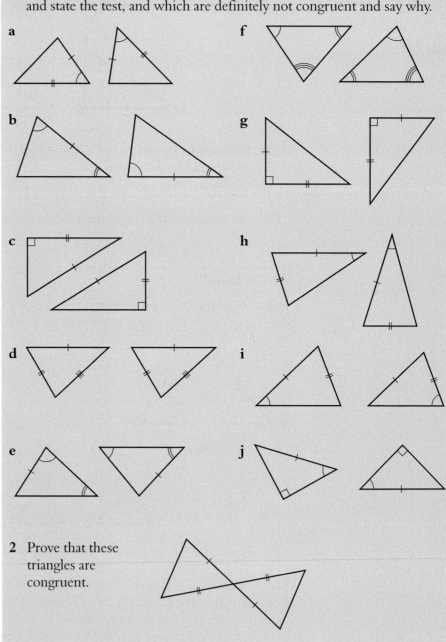

a   f

b   g

c   h

d   i

e   j

2 Prove that these triangles are congruent.

3 Prove that either diagonal divides a parallelogram into two congruent triangles.

4 Prove that the longer diagonal of a kite divides it into two congruent triangles and that the shorter diagonal does not.

5 Prove that the two diagonals divide a rhombus into four congruent triangles.

Properties of shape

A point measures the *position* of something.

A line can be curved or straight.

A straight line is the shortest distance between two points.

The straight line joining two points A and B is called the *line AB* or the *line segment AB*.

When two lines cross, or intersect, they meet at a point called a *vertex* (plural *vertices*).

When two lines meet at an *angle*, the lines are called the *arms* of the angle.

An angle is measured by the amount of rotation that one arm has to turn through to coincide with the other. It is not governed by the lengths of the arms forming the angle.

A flat surface is called a *plane*.

Shapes drawn in a plane are called *plane figures*.

The lines joining the vertices of plane figures are called its *sides*.

Planes which form parts of three-dimensional figures are called *faces*.

In three-dimensional shapes, faces meet at edges and edges meet at vertices.

A *cube* is a solid containing 6 square faces. All its edges are equal in length.

A *cuboid* is a solid containing 6 rectangular faces. It has a cross section which is also a rectangle.

Two lines which point in the same direction are called *parallel lines*.

When a line turns completely round until it points in the same direction it is said to have turned through 1 *turn* or 1 *revolution*.

1 revolution = 360°.

Angles are usually measured to decimals of a degree.

If a line rotates half a turn it is called a *straight angle*.

If a line rotates a quarter of a turn it is called a *right angle*.

Two lines which intersect at right angles are said to be *perpendicular*.

An angle less than 90° is called an *acute angle*.

An angle between 90° and 180° is called an *obtuse angle*.

An angle greater than 180° is called a *reflex angle*.

If a number of lines all meet at a point, the sum of them is 360°.

Two angles which add up to 90° are called *complementary angles*.

Two angles which add up to 180° are called *supplementary angles*.

Angles next to one another are said to be *adjacent angles*.

Parallel lines

A line crossing one or more parallel lines is called a *transversal*.

On either side of a transversal, *alternate* angles are equal.

Corresponding angles are also equal.

When two straight lines intersect, there are two pairs of equal angles.

These are called *vertically opposite* angles.

Triangles

Triangle is the name given to any three sided plane figure.

Triangles which have certain properties have particular names:

a triangle with 3 acute angles is called an *acute angled* triangle,

a triangle with one angle greater than 90° is called an *obtuse angled* triangle,

a triangle with an angle of 90° is called a *right angled* triangle,

a triangle with all sides different in length is called a *scalene* triangle,

a triangle with 2 sides equal is called an *isosceles* triangle,

a triangle with all 3 sides equal is called an *equilateral* triangle.

Standard notation for triangles

Angles are marked with capital letters and the *side opposite each angle* is given the same letter but in *lower case*.

Properties of triangles

In any triangle the sum of the three angles is 180°.

In any triangle the largest side is opposite the largest angle and the smallest side is opposite the smallest angle.

The sum of the lengths of any two sides is greater than the length of the third side.

The exterior angle is equal to the sum of the two opposite interior angles.

Properties of the isosceles triangle

1 It has two equal sides.
2 The *unequal* side is called the *base*, even though it doesn't always appear at the bottom of the triangle.
3 The angle between the two equal sides is called the *vertical* angle.
4 The other two angles are called the *base angles* and are equal.
5 A line drawn from the vertical angle to meet the base at 90° bisects the base.

Properties of the equilateral triangle

1 It has three equal sides.
2 It has three equal angles. Since the sum is 180° then each angle is 60°.
3 The line drawn from any of the vertices to meet the opposite side at 90°, bisects the opposite side.

  Any line drawn from any vertex of any triangle to meet the opposite side at right angles, is called an *altitude*.

  Any line drawn from any vertex of any triangle to the mid-point of the opposite side, is called a *median*.

Polygons

Polygon is the general name for a plane shape.

3-sided polygon – *triangle*

4-sided polygon – *quadrilateral*

5-sided polygon – *pentagon*
6-sided polygon – *hexagon*
8-sided polygon – *octagon*
10-sided polygon – *decagon*
The angle sum of the interior angles of any quadrilateral $= 360°$.
The angle sum of the interior angles of any pentagon $= 540°$.
The angle sum of the interior angles of an *n* sided polygon is $(n - 2) \times 180°$.

The exterior angle of a polygon

The sum of the exterior angles of any polygon $= 360°$.

Regular polygons

A regular polygon has all its sides and angles equal.
Equal sides does not imply equal angles – and vice versa.

Properties of quadrilaterals

A *quadrilateral* is a plane figure with four sides.
Different types of quadrilaterals have special names:
the regular quadrilateral is called a *square*,
the quadrilateral with both pairs of opposite sides parallel is called a *parallelogram*.

In every parallelogram:

a each pair of opposite sides is equal,
b opposite angles are equal,
c the diagonals bisect each other.

The parallelogram with four equal sides is called a *rhombus*.
The rhombus has all the properties of the parallelogram above but:
all four sides are equal so the diagonals divide the rhombus up into four identical triangles.
The diagonals of a rhombus are perpendicular, and also bisect the angles.
The parallelogram with all angles equal to 90° is called a *rectangle*.
The rectangle has all the properties of the parallelogram stated above, but in addition, the diagonals are equal in length.
The quadrilateral with *one* pair of opposite sides parallel but *not* equal is called a *trapezium*.
An isosceles trapezium is one which has its two non-parallel sides equal in length.
The quadrilateral with both pairs of *adjacent* sides equal is called a *kite*.
In every kite the diagonals are perpendicular.

The circle

The total perimeter is called the *circumference*.
The distance from any point on the circumference to the centre is constant and is called the *radius*.

Any straight line through the centre is twice the radius and is called the *diameter*.

A *chord* is any straight line across the circle not passing through the centre.

Part of the circumference is called an *arc*.

Circumference and area of the circle

The circumference for any circle, $C = 2\pi r$ (r is the radius).

The exact value for π cannot be worked out.

Most calculators now have a π button on them which gives $\pi = 3.141\,592\,654$.

In calculations we usually use $\pi = 3.14$ or else the π button on our calculators.

A good fractional equivalent is $\pi = \frac{22}{7}$.

The area for any circle, $A = \pi r^2$.

We always square r first and then multiply by π.

Nets

A *net* is a pattern which can be cut out and then folded into a solid shape.

If all the faces are opened out we have a net shape.

It is often possible to make more than one net for a given solid.

Representing 3-dimensional objects in 2 dimensions

Three-dimensional objects can be represented in two dimensions using dotted or lined paper which is set out in equilateral triangles.

This is known as *isometric paper*.

Symmetry

There are three types of symmetry.

2-dimensional shapes can have either *line* (reflection) or *rotational symmetry*.

3-dimensional solids can have *plane symmetry*.

Line symmetry

If a shape is identical on each side of a line drawn through it then it is said to possess *line symmetry*.

A line of symmetry is also called an *axis of symmetry*, or a *mirror line*.

Each side of a line of symmetry is said to be a *mirror image* of the other.

We can show that a shape has line symmetry by placing a mirror along the mirror line and seeing that the reflected half is identical to the part of the shape behind the mirror.

We can also show a shape possesses line symmetry by *tracing* the shape onto tracing paper and then folding it to show two identical halves.

Some shapes have no symmetry, others have several lines.

Rotational symmetry

The parallelogram has no lines, or axes, of symmetry. However, if we rotate any parallelogram through 180° about the centre O, it will look identical to its original position.

This is known as *rotational*, or *point*, *symmetry*.

The point about which the shape rotates is called the *centre*, or *point*, *of symmetry*. Because there are two identical positions for a parallelogram, it is said to possess *rotational symmetry of order 2*.

Different shapes have different orders of symmetry.

The equilateral triangle has rotational symmetry of order 3; the square has rotational symmetry of order 4.

Plane symmetry

If a three-dimensional solid can be cut into two identical halves the solid is said to possess *plane symmetry*.

If we imagine the plane of symmetry was a mirror, the reflection together with the intact half would look just like the complete solid.

Similar triangles

If the three angles of one triangle match the three angles of another triangle, they are said to be *similar*.

They have another property – *corresponding sides are in the same ratio*.

To prove two triangles are similar, we only need to prove that *two* pairs of angles are equal.

Other similar shapes

Shapes other than triangles are similar if:

a the angles in one shape are equal to corresponding angles in the other,
b all pairs of corresponding sides are in the same ratio.

For triangles, *one* of the above statements implies that the other is true.
For other shapes this is not so.

Congruence

Congruent figures are identical both in shape and size and would *fit* over one another exactly.

Pythagoras' theorem

The square on the hypotenuse is equal to the sum of the squares on the other two sides.
We can use Pythagoras' theorem to find the length of any side in a right angled triangle if we know the lengths of the other two.

Also, if we know all three sides of the triangle and they fit Pythagoras' theorem, then it proves that the triangle is right angled.

Pythagorean triples

There are some well known right angled triangles that have lengths of sides that are whole numbers (integers). These are called *Pythagorean triples*.
The most well known of all is the 3, 4, 5 triangle since $3^2 + 4^2 = 5^2$.
Some other well known triples are:

5, 12, 13 since $5^2 + 12^2 = 13^2$ i.e. $25 + 144 = 169$
8, 15, 17 since $8^2 + 15^2 = 17^2$ i.e. $64 + 225 = 289$
7, 24, 25 since $7^2 + 24^2 = 25^2$ i.e. $49 + 576 = 625$, etc.

Any multiples of the above are also Pythagorean triples and thus sides of right angled triangles.

Use of Pythagoras' theorem in circles

In any circle the line bisecting any chord at right angles, passes through the centre of the circle.
This line also divides the triangle formed by the chord and the two radii at the ends of the chord into two identical (congruent) right angled triangles.
In any circle the triangle formed by a diameter joined to any other point on the circumference is right angled.

Trigonometry

Trigonometry is the name given to the mathematics of triangles.
We use trigonometry with similar right angled triangles to calculate sides and angles.

The three trigonometrical ratios

When we consider a particular angle in a right angled triangle the side opposite the angle is called the *opposite* (O).
The side next to the angle is called the *adjacent* (A).
The side opposite the right angle is called the *hypotenuse* (H).

The tan ratio is $\dfrac{O}{A}$.

The sin ratio is $\dfrac{O}{H}$.

The cos ratio is $\dfrac{A}{H}$.

An easy way to remember these ratios is the made up word: SOHCAHTOA.
All three ratios can be found for any particular angle using the sin, cos and tan buttons on a scientific calculator.
The above ratios *only apply* to right angled triangles.

Using the trigonometrical ratios to solve problems in right angled triangles

Using our calculators we can now find any of the ratios we require and solve problems. Be careful to:

1 Draw a diagram and mark the sides O, A and H on it.
2 Write on the diagram what information is known.
3 Mark on the diagram what information is needed.
4 Pick the right ratio.
5 Write down the correct equation(s) and solve it/them.

Bearings

Directions are given by using *bearings*.
Bearings are angles measuring the direction of an object *from due north and in a clockwise direction*. They are usually given as three figures before the decimal point.

Angles of elevation and depression

Angles measured from the horizontal upwards are called *angles of elevation* and if measured downwards *angles of depression*.

Three-dimensional trigonometry (extension)

Our knowledge of SOHCAHTOA and Pythagoras can be extended to three dimensions, once we have decided what we mean by the angle between a line and a plane and between two planes.

To find the angle between a line and a plane

   i Take any convenient point, P, on the line and drop a perpendicular to meet the plane (PN).
   ii Identify the line, ON. This is called the *projection* of the line on the plane.
  iii The angle between the line and the plane is taken as angle $\theta = \angle$PON.

To find the angle between two planes

Any two planes meet in a straight line, called a *hinge*.
To find the angle between planes P_1 and P_2:
   i Locate the hinge.
   ii Take any convenient point on the hinge and find two lines *perpendicular* to the hinge – one in plane P_1 and one in plane P_2.
  iii The angle between the two planes is the angle between these two lines.

When solving questions involving three-dimensions:
- Choose sensible points and lines.
- Make right angled triangles if possible.
- Draw separate diagrams for each calculation.

Angles of any size (extension)

When we use SOHCAHTOA in right angled triangles, all the angles are 90° or less.

Sin, cos and tan of angles of any size do exist.

We can find out values for these ratios using a scientific calculator.

The graphs of $\sin x$ and $\cos x$ are the same shape but they are 90° *out of phase*.

The maximum value of both $\sin x$ and $\cos x$ is 1.

The minimum value of both $\sin x$ and $\cos x$ is -1.

$y = \sin x$ is symmetrical about $x = 90°$ and $x = 270°$.

$y = \cos x$ is symmetrical about $x = 180°$.

The 360° are divided into four *quadrants*:

In the first quadrant (0° to 90°), *all the ratios are positive*.

In the second quadrant (90° to 180°), *only sin x is positive*.

In the third quadrant (180° to 270°), *only tan x is positive*.

In the fourth quadrant (270° to 360°), *only cos x is positive*.

There is an easy way to remember which quadrant has the positive ratio:

The letters spell the word *CAST* in order, starting from the fourth quadrant.

Further trigonometry (extension)

If the triangle does not have a right angle in it, we cannot solve it using the basic sin, cos and tan ratios.

However, there are two formulae we can use to solve trigonometry problems in such triangles.

These are called the *sine rule* and the *cosine rule*.

The sine rule

In any triangle ABC:

$$\frac{a}{\sin A} = \frac{b}{\sin B} = \frac{c}{\sin C} \quad \text{or} \quad \frac{\sin A}{a} = \frac{\sin B}{b} = \frac{\sin C}{c}$$

The rule connects each side of the triangle with the angle opposite.

Each of the above is really three equations in one.

Each single equation has four terms in it – of which any three must be known.

If the unknown required is a side, use the first set of equations; if it is an angle, use the second set of equations.

The cosine rule

In any triangle ABC:
$$a^2 = b^2 + c^2 - (2bc \cos A)$$
The above formula gives the solution for unknown side a.
If the unknown side is b or c the formula becomes
$$b^2 = c^2 + a^2 - (2ca \cos B) \quad \text{or} \quad c^2 = a^2 + b^2 - (2ab \cos C).$$
The brackets are not strictly necessary in the formula but they do remind us that we have to multiply out all of the terms in them before subtracting. **This is a common error in examinations.**
If we know all three sides, the sine rule would not work, but we can use the cosine rule to find an angle.

Further circle properties (extension)

Tangents

In any circle a tangent is perpendicular to the radius drawn to the point of contact.
Two tangents can be drawn from any external point, P, to a circle. The distances from P to the points of contact are equal.
The line PO bisects both the angle at P *and* the angle at O.

Further angle properties

The angle subtended by any arc (or chord) at the centre of a circle, is twice the angle subtended by the arc (or chord) at any other point on the remainder of the circumference.
The angles subtended by an arc (or chord) at all points on the remainder of the circumference are equal.
Opposite angles of a cyclic quadrilateral are supplementary.
Not all quadrilaterals are cyclic.
The angle between a tangent and any chord through the point of contact is equal to the angle the chord subtends anywhere in the *alternate* (opposite) segment.
We call this the *alternate segment theorem*.

Congruent triangles

There are six pieces of information we can know when we draw a triangle - its three sides and three angles.
To prove two triangles are congruent, we *don't* have to know all six.
We can prove two triangles are congruent sometimes by knowing only three pieces of information about them.
These are called the *tests for congruency* and are:

i *Three sides*

If the three sides of triangle A match the three sides of triangle B then the triangles must be congruent.

We call this test SSS (3 sides).

ii *Two sides and the included angle*

If two sides match in each triangle and the included angle, i.e. the angle between the two matching sides, then the triangles must be congruent.

We call this test SAS (side, included angle, side).

iii *Two angles and the corresponding side*

If two angles match in each triangle and a corresponding side matches, i.e. the side in the same position in each triangle, then the triangles must be congruent.

We call this test ASA or AAS (2 angles and corresponding side).

iv *Right angled triangle*

If two triangles each have a right angle, the hypotenuse and another side in common, then the triangles are congruent.

We call this test RHS (right angle, hypotenuse and another side).

CHAPTER 10
Transformations

In this chapter you will need to:
▸ be able to plot points on graphs by using coordinates (see Topic 8.1)
▸ know about coordinates in all four quadrants (see Topic 8.3)
▸ know about bearings (see Topic 9.6)

Vectors are quantities that have both a size *and* a direction, for example, a velocity of 20 km/h due north.

Three examples of vector quantities are: acceleration, velocity and displacement. (Displacement means distance in a particular direction.)

For example, we could say that Town B was 3 miles due east and 4 miles due north of Town A.

This displacement vector is represented as $AB = \begin{pmatrix} 3 \\ 4 \end{pmatrix}$.

By Pythagoras, we know that the distance AB is 5 miles, and trigonometry tells us that the angle $\theta°$ is 36.9°.

Thus, the **magnitude**, or size, or length, of the vector is 5 miles.

The **direction** of the vector is 036.9° (in this example, the direction of the vector is a bearing).

This is represented diagrammatically as:

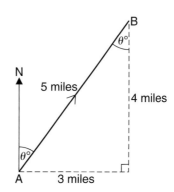

We can think of coordinates of points on graphs as displacement vectors from the origin. These are called *position vectors*.

Thus P(3, 2) could be written as P$\begin{pmatrix} 3 \\ 2 \end{pmatrix}$ and drawn:

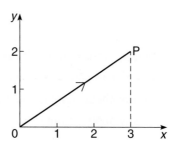

Transformations

The word **transformation** means *change*.

All transformations change a diagram - by altering its position, size or shape. In the GCSE syllabus we have to know about four types of transformation:

▶ Translation
▶ Reflection
▶ Rotation
▶ Enlargement

Translation is the simplest of the four transformations.

In a translation every point on a shape is moved by the same displacement – i.e. by equal distances and in the same direction.

We can think of a translation as *sliding* the shape from its object position to its image position.

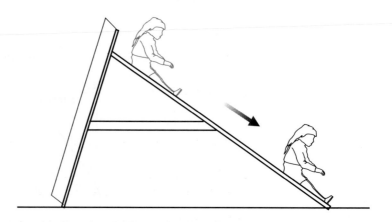

A translation is described by a column vector.

NOTE
The translation vector does not just apply to the four vertices calculated. We can see from the diagram that it applies to *all* pairs of corresponding points.

For example, if the rectangle $A(1, 3)$, $B(4, 3)$, $C(4, 2)$, $D(1, 2)$ has the translation vector $\begin{pmatrix} 5 \\ 3 \end{pmatrix}$ applied to it we can calculate its image position $A_1B_1C_1D_1$ as

$$A_1 = \begin{pmatrix} 1 \\ 3 \end{pmatrix} + \begin{pmatrix} 5 \\ 3 \end{pmatrix} = \begin{pmatrix} 6 \\ 6 \end{pmatrix} \qquad C_1 = \begin{pmatrix} 4 \\ 2 \end{pmatrix} + \begin{pmatrix} 5 \\ 3 \end{pmatrix} = \begin{pmatrix} 9 \\ 5 \end{pmatrix}$$

$$B_1 = \begin{pmatrix} 4 \\ 3 \end{pmatrix} + \begin{pmatrix} 5 \\ 3 \end{pmatrix} = \begin{pmatrix} 9 \\ 6 \end{pmatrix} \qquad D_1 = \begin{pmatrix} 1 \\ 2 \end{pmatrix} + \begin{pmatrix} 5 \\ 3 \end{pmatrix} = \begin{pmatrix} 6 \\ 5 \end{pmatrix}$$

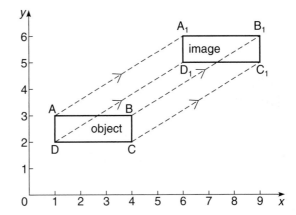

Properties of translation

1   Translations are usually written in two parts and are written in the form $\begin{pmatrix} x \\ y \end{pmatrix}$.

2   This means that the number in the top row is the translation in the x-direction and the number in the bottom row is the translation in the y-direction.

   For example, $\begin{pmatrix} 4 \\ 3 \end{pmatrix}$ means an increase of 4 units to the right (or in the positive x-direction) and 3 units upwards (or in the positive y-direction), whereas $\begin{pmatrix} -2 \\ -7 \end{pmatrix}$ means an increase of 2 units to the left (or in the negative x-direction) and 7 units downwards (or in the negative y-direction).

3   Translation does not affect the size or shape of the object. It only changes the position.

4   The image is *congruent* to the object. (See Topic 9.4.)

5   *All* the lines drawn between any pair of corresponding object and image points are equal and parallel.

6   Any image point is found by adding the translation vector to the corresponding object point.

Worked Examples

Calculate and draw the image points obtained by applying the translations given to the object shape shown.

a $\begin{pmatrix} 4 \\ 6 \end{pmatrix}$ **c** $\begin{pmatrix} -7 \\ 2 \end{pmatrix}$

b $\begin{pmatrix} 5 \\ -6 \end{pmatrix}$ **d** $\begin{pmatrix} -3 \\ -5 \end{pmatrix}$

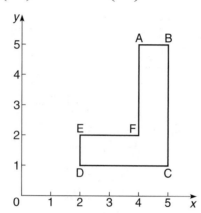

Calculating the image points:

a $A_1 \begin{pmatrix} 4 \\ 5 \end{pmatrix} + \begin{pmatrix} 4 \\ 6 \end{pmatrix} = \begin{pmatrix} 8 \\ 11 \end{pmatrix}$ $C_1 \begin{pmatrix} 5 \\ 1 \end{pmatrix} + \begin{pmatrix} 4 \\ 6 \end{pmatrix} = \begin{pmatrix} 9 \\ 7 \end{pmatrix}$ $E_1 \begin{pmatrix} 2 \\ 2 \end{pmatrix} + \begin{pmatrix} 4 \\ 6 \end{pmatrix} = \begin{pmatrix} 6 \\ 8 \end{pmatrix}$

    $B_1 \begin{pmatrix} 5 \\ 5 \end{pmatrix} + \begin{pmatrix} 4 \\ 6 \end{pmatrix} = \begin{pmatrix} 9 \\ 11 \end{pmatrix}$ $D_1 \begin{pmatrix} 2 \\ 1 \end{pmatrix} + \begin{pmatrix} 4 \\ 6 \end{pmatrix} = \begin{pmatrix} 6 \\ 7 \end{pmatrix}$ $F_1 \begin{pmatrix} 4 \\ 2 \end{pmatrix} + \begin{pmatrix} 4 \\ 6 \end{pmatrix} = \begin{pmatrix} 8 \\ 8 \end{pmatrix}$

b $A_2 \begin{pmatrix} 4 \\ 5 \end{pmatrix} + \begin{pmatrix} 5 \\ -6 \end{pmatrix} = \begin{pmatrix} 9 \\ -1 \end{pmatrix}$ $C_2 \begin{pmatrix} 5 \\ 1 \end{pmatrix} + \begin{pmatrix} 5 \\ -6 \end{pmatrix} = \begin{pmatrix} 10 \\ -5 \end{pmatrix}$ $E_2 \begin{pmatrix} 2 \\ 2 \end{pmatrix} + \begin{pmatrix} 5 \\ -6 \end{pmatrix} = \begin{pmatrix} 7 \\ -4 \end{pmatrix}$

    $B_2 \begin{pmatrix} 5 \\ 5 \end{pmatrix} + \begin{pmatrix} 5 \\ -6 \end{pmatrix} = \begin{pmatrix} 10 \\ -1 \end{pmatrix}$ $D_2 \begin{pmatrix} 2 \\ 1 \end{pmatrix} + \begin{pmatrix} 5 \\ -6 \end{pmatrix} = \begin{pmatrix} 7 \\ -5 \end{pmatrix}$ $F_2 \begin{pmatrix} 4 \\ 2 \end{pmatrix} + \begin{pmatrix} 5 \\ -6 \end{pmatrix} = \begin{pmatrix} 9 \\ -4 \end{pmatrix}$

c $A_3 \begin{pmatrix} 4 \\ 5 \end{pmatrix} + \begin{pmatrix} -7 \\ 2 \end{pmatrix} = \begin{pmatrix} -3 \\ 7 \end{pmatrix}$ $C_3 \begin{pmatrix} 5 \\ 1 \end{pmatrix} + \begin{pmatrix} -7 \\ 2 \end{pmatrix} = \begin{pmatrix} -2 \\ 3 \end{pmatrix}$ $E_3 \begin{pmatrix} 2 \\ 2 \end{pmatrix} + \begin{pmatrix} -7 \\ 2 \end{pmatrix} = \begin{pmatrix} -5 \\ 4 \end{pmatrix}$

    $B_3 \begin{pmatrix} 5 \\ 5 \end{pmatrix} + \begin{pmatrix} -7 \\ 2 \end{pmatrix} = \begin{pmatrix} -2 \\ 7 \end{pmatrix}$ $D_3 \begin{pmatrix} 2 \\ 1 \end{pmatrix} + \begin{pmatrix} -7 \\ 2 \end{pmatrix} = \begin{pmatrix} -5 \\ 3 \end{pmatrix}$ $F_3 \begin{pmatrix} 4 \\ 2 \end{pmatrix} + \begin{pmatrix} -7 \\ 2 \end{pmatrix} = \begin{pmatrix} -3 \\ 4 \end{pmatrix}$

d $A_4 \begin{pmatrix} 4 \\ 5 \end{pmatrix} + \begin{pmatrix} -3 \\ -5 \end{pmatrix} = \begin{pmatrix} 1 \\ 0 \end{pmatrix}$ $C_4 \begin{pmatrix} 5 \\ 1 \end{pmatrix} + \begin{pmatrix} -3 \\ -5 \end{pmatrix} = \begin{pmatrix} 2 \\ -4 \end{pmatrix}$ $E_4 \begin{pmatrix} 2 \\ 2 \end{pmatrix} + \begin{pmatrix} -3 \\ -5 \end{pmatrix} = \begin{pmatrix} -1 \\ -3 \end{pmatrix}$

    $B_4 \begin{pmatrix} 5 \\ 5 \end{pmatrix} + \begin{pmatrix} -3 \\ -5 \end{pmatrix} = \begin{pmatrix} 2 \\ 0 \end{pmatrix}$ $D_4 \begin{pmatrix} 2 \\ 1 \end{pmatrix} + \begin{pmatrix} -3 \\ -5 \end{pmatrix} = \begin{pmatrix} -1 \\ -4 \end{pmatrix}$ $F_4 \begin{pmatrix} 4 \\ 2 \end{pmatrix} + \begin{pmatrix} -3 \\ -5 \end{pmatrix} = \begin{pmatrix} 1 \\ -3 \end{pmatrix}$

Drawing these image points, we get:

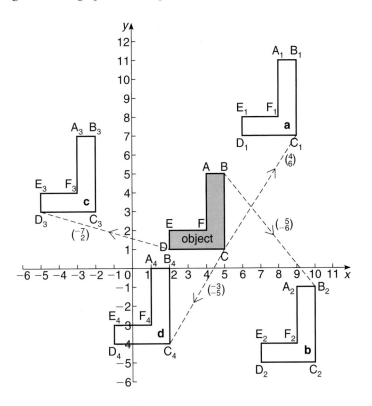

PRACTICE 10.3.1

1 Write down the coordinates of the images of each point by applying the given translations.

Object	Translation
$(2, 7)$	$\begin{pmatrix} 2 \\ 1 \end{pmatrix}$
$(-3, 9)$	$\begin{pmatrix} 4 \\ -3 \end{pmatrix}$
$(2, -7)$	$\begin{pmatrix} -5 \\ -1 \end{pmatrix}$
$(-4, -6)$	$\begin{pmatrix} -6 \\ 2 \end{pmatrix}$

2 A triangle has coordinates A$(-4, -2)$, B$(-1, -1)$ and C$(-3, 3)$. The triangle is transformed by a translation of $\begin{pmatrix} 4 \\ -1 \end{pmatrix}$. Calculate its image position.

3 After a translation of $\begin{pmatrix} -3 \\ 4 \end{pmatrix}$, the coordinates of a rectangle are $(4,3)$, $(-1,3)$, $(4,-2)$ and $(-1,-2)$. Calculate the coordinates of the object position.

4 What translation transforms
   a $(3,0)$ into $(7,-2)$
   b $(5,-2)$ into $(2,4)$
   c $(-4,-7)$ into $(4,7)$
   d $(-2,3)$ into $(2,3)$?

5 What is noticeable about the translations: a $\begin{pmatrix} 3 \\ 0 \end{pmatrix}$ and b $\begin{pmatrix} 0 \\ -2 \end{pmatrix}$?

6 A flag and its pole are represented by the points $(-3,-1)$, $(-3,4)$, $(-3,5)$, $(-1,5)$ and $(-1,4)$.
   a Draw this shape on graph paper.
   b Calculate and draw the image positions of the object under the following translations:

   i $\begin{pmatrix} -3 \\ 3 \end{pmatrix}$ ii $\begin{pmatrix} 2 \\ 4 \end{pmatrix}$ iii $\begin{pmatrix} 3 \\ -1 \end{pmatrix}$ iv $\begin{pmatrix} -2 \\ -2 \end{pmatrix}$

7 Calculate the translation vectors for the translations shown below:

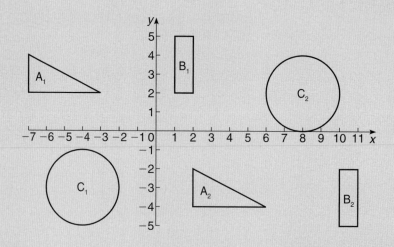

8 $A(3,5)$ is mapped onto $A_1(8,4)$. Find the image of $(2,-1)$ under the same translation.

We first met the idea of **reflection** when we studied symmetry (see Topic 9.3). Reflection occurs when a shape has a line of symmetry – one half of the shape can be *reflected* or *folded* along the mirror line on to the other half.

Each half is congruent (see Topic 9.4) and said to be the *mirror image* of the other.

Properties of reflection

1 Reflection has no effect on the size and shape of the object. It only changes the position.

2 The effect on position is that the object is *folded* over a mirror line.

3 The image of any point is the same distance behind the mirror line that the corresponding object point is in front.

4 The mirror line is called the perpendicular bisector of the line joining the object and image points. (For more on perpendicular bisectors see Topic 10.8 later.)

NOTE

When finding the image of object shapes on graph paper the mirror line is often written as an equation. (To revise equations of straight lines see Topic 8.3.)

5 If an object point lies on the mirror line the image is the same point.

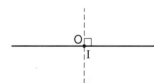

6 Reflections can easily be shown using tracing paper. One side of the mirror line is drawn and, when turned over, it can easily be seen to *fit* the other side of the mirror line.

Worked Examples

Find the positions of the image shapes for the triangle shown, in the following mirror lines:

a $x = 0$
b $y = 0$
c $y = x$
d $y = -x$

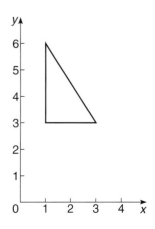

It is not easy to calculate the image positions for any object point. The best way is to:

  i Draw the object.
  ii Draw the mirror line.
  iii Find the reflection of each vertex in turn by measuring and marking the image points.

Using these techniques:

a $x = 0$ is the y-axis.

b $y = 0$ is the x-axis.

c $y = x$ is a line through the origin at 45° to the axes.

d $y = -x$ is a line through the origin at −45° to the axes.

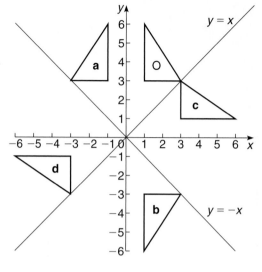

PRACTICE 10.4.1

1 Reflect the given shape
   a in the y-axis,
   b in the x-axis.

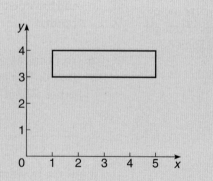

2 Reflect the given shape
   a in the line $y = x$,
   b in the line $y = -x$.

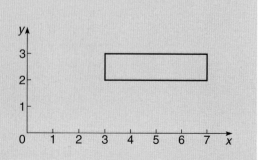

3 Reflect the given shape
in the line $y = x$.

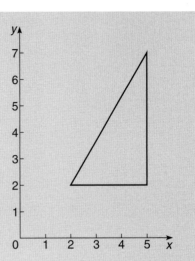

4 Reflect the given object in the line A.
Reflect the image in the line B.
What do you notice?

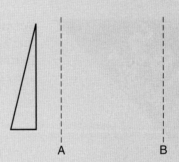

5 Reflect the object in the y-axis.
Reflect the image in the x-axis.

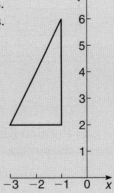

6 Reflect the object shown in the lines:
  a $x = 0$
  b $y = 0$
  c $y = x$
  d $y = -x$

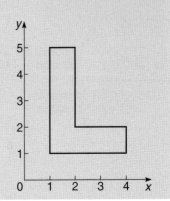

7 Reflect the object shown in the lines:
  a $x = 1$
  b $y = 2$
  c $y = x$
  d $y = -x$

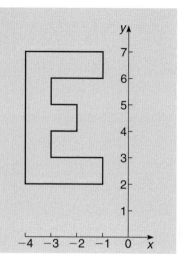

We met **rotation** when we learned about angles. An angle is a rotation of one line on to another.

In rotation, every point on the object shape turns through the same angle about a fixed point. Some examples are:

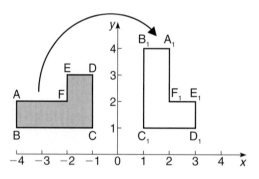

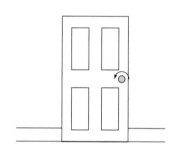

Properties of rotation

1 Rotation has no effect on the size and shape of the object. It only changes the position.

2 Every point on the shape is turned through the same angle about a certain fixed point. This amount of turning is called the *angle of rotation*.

3 The fixed point is called the *centre of rotation*. It is the only point that does not change in the rotation. It can be either inside or outside the object shape.

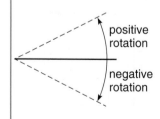

4 The direction of rotation must be specified.
Anticlockwise is taken as positive and clockwise as negative.
Thus $^-90°$ means a rotation of 90° clockwise.

5 The object and image are congruent shapes.

6 Rotations can easily be shown using tracing paper. The object is drawn, together with the axes and fixed point. The tracing paper can then easily be turned through the required angle and the image drawn in the correct position.

Worked Examples

1   Rotate the object shown through:
    a   90° anticlockwise,
    b   90° clockwise, about
          i point A,   **ii** point B.

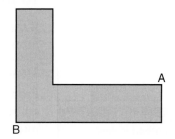

As in reflection, it is not easy to calculate image positions. The best way
to find the image under rotation is to:
● join each vertex to the centre of rotation
● rotate these lines through the required angle in the required
   direction
● draw the image shape from the points obtained.

i

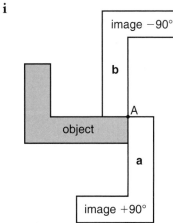

ii

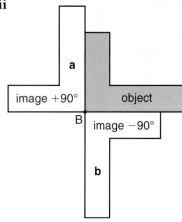

2   Rotate the given shape, about the origin, by
    a   +90°
    b   −90°
    c   180°

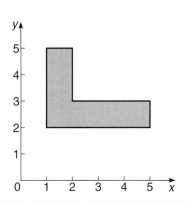

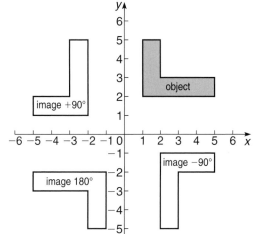

To find the angle of rotation

If the positions of the object and image are known the angle of rotation can be found.

Method one

Produce two corresponding lines on the diagrams back until they intersect. (Corresponding lines are lines that are in the *same place* in each diagram.)

The angle between them is the angle of rotation, $\theta°$.

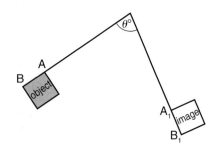

Method two

Draw lines from any two corresponding points on the object and image back to the centre of rotation.

The angle between them is the angle of rotation, $\theta°$.

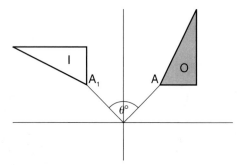

To find the centre of rotation

  i Draw a line between any pair of corresponding points.
 ii Draw the perpendicular bisector of this line.
iii Repeat **i** and **ii** for another pair of corresponding points.
 iv The centre of rotation is the point where these two lines intersect.

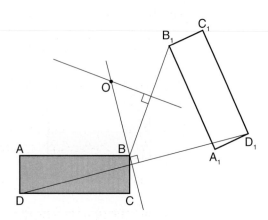

PRACTICE 10.5.1

1 Copy the following diagrams onto squared paper. In each case draw the image obtained by rotating the shape

a 90° anticlockwise, about the given point,

b 90° clockwise, about the given point.

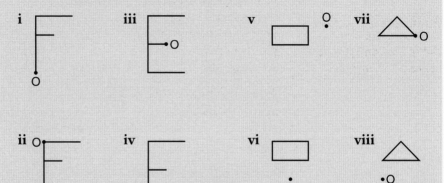

2 Find the images of the given shape after rotations about the origin of:

a +90°,

b −90°,

c $\frac{3}{4}$ of a turn anticlockwise.

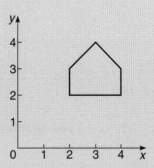

3 Join the following points to draw a flag and pole: A(2, ⁻6), B(2, ⁻3), C(2, ⁻2), D(4, ⁻2) and E(4, ⁻3).

Find the images of the diagram after the following rotations about the origin:

a 180°   **b** $\frac{3}{4}$ of a turn clockwise   **c** −90°

4 A square is formed by the points A(2, 2), B(4, 2), C(4, 4) and D(2, 4).

a Rotate this square through +90° about the origin.

b Apply the translation vector $\begin{pmatrix} -6 \\ 0 \end{pmatrix}$ to the original square.

c Are the solutions to **a** and **b** the same? Explain your answer.

5 Find the angles of rotation in the following diagrams:

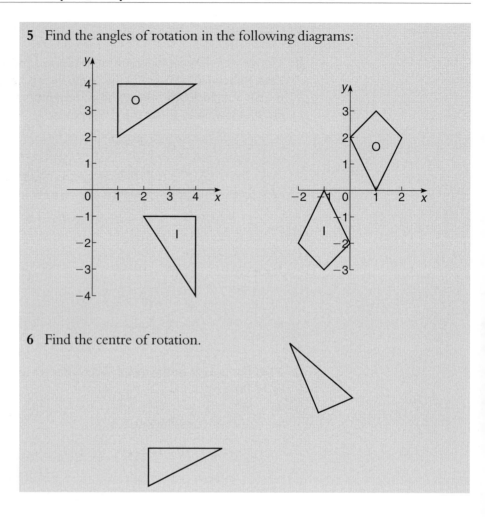

6 Find the centre of rotation.

The word **enlargement** is used when the size of an object is changed.
For example:

Properties of enlargement

1 Enlargement affects both the position and the size of the object.

2 Enlargement has no effect on shape – the image is exactly the same shape as the object. Such figures are called *similar figures*, i.e. exactly the same shape but differing in size (see Topic 9.4).

3 Any pair of corresponding lengths on the object and image are *in the same ratio*. This ratio is called the *scale factor* of the enlargement.

4 If the scale factor is numerically greater than one, the image is larger than the object. If it is numerically less than one, it is smaller than the object.

Worked Examples

1 Draw an enlargement of the given shape with a scale factor 3.

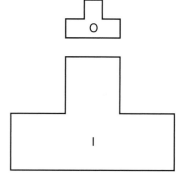

Each corresponding side on the image is 3 times the corresponding length on the object.

2 Shape A is mapped onto shape B. Calculate the scale factor of this enlargement.

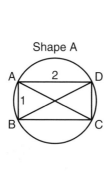
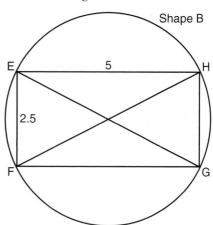

Comparing some of the corresponding sides, we get:

$$\frac{FG}{BC} = \frac{5}{2} = 2.5 \qquad \frac{EF}{AB} = \frac{2.5}{1} = 2.5, \text{ etc.}$$

Hence the scale factor is 2.5.

(Any pair of corresponding sides can be used – note the radii of the circles are 1.1 and 2.75 ; and $\frac{2.75}{1.1} = 2.5$.)

Constructing enlargements

Enlargements are constructed *from a particular point.*
This point is called the *centre of enlargement.*
It can be either inside or outside the shape.

The method is as follows:

  i Draw straight lines from the centre of enlargement (O) through each vertex of the object.
  ii Measure the distance from O to each vertex.
  iii Multiply each of these distances by the scale factor for the enlargement.
  iv Mark off these new distances from O through each vertex.
  v Join up these points to form the image.

Worked Examples

Construct enlargements of the given shapes with given scale factors from the centres marked O.

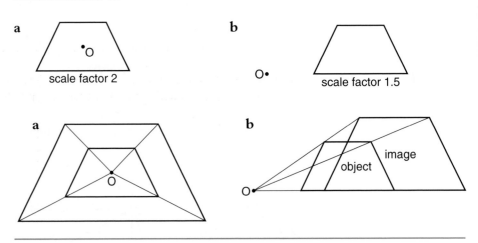

a
scale factor 2

b
scale factor 1.5

a

b
object
image

PRACTICE 10.6.1

1 Use squared paper to draw enlargements of the following shapes with the given scale factors.

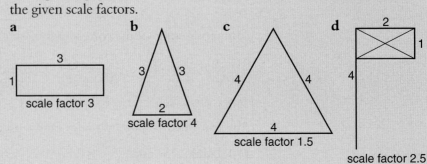

a
3
1
scale factor 3

b
3 / \ 3
2
scale factor 4

c
4 / \ 4
4
scale factor 1.5

d
2
1
4
scale factor 2.5

2 Find the scale factors in each of the following enlargements:

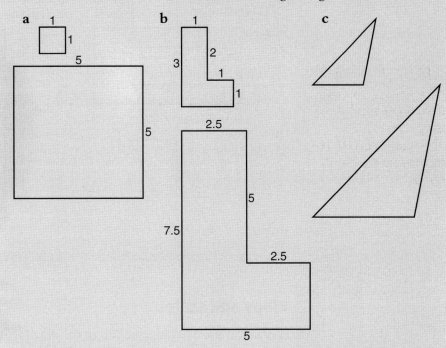

a **b** **c**

3 Use squared paper to copy and construct enlargements for each of the following shapes with given scale factors and from the marked centres:

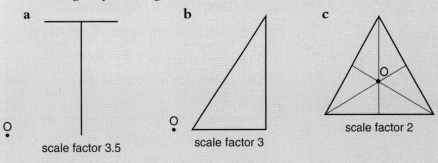

a **b** **c**

scale factor 3.5   scale factor 3   scale factor 2

4 Enlarge the given shape from centre O with scale factor $\frac{1}{2}$:

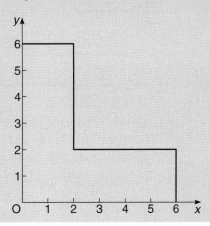

5 Find the centre of enlargement and scale factor of the following enlargements:

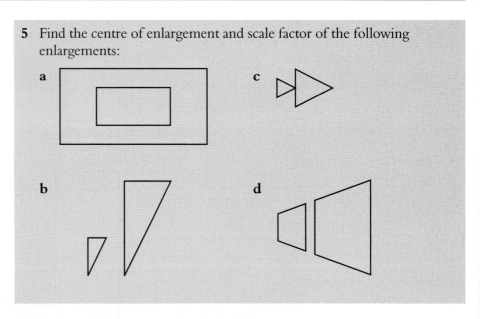

Maps and scales

A practical use of enlargement is in the drawing of maps.
A map is a scale drawing of a geographical area.
The *scale factor* is the ratio between a given length on the map and the corresponding length on the ground.

The map scale is shown in one of two ways:

  i A ratio, for example, 1 : 25 000.

    This means that one unit on the map represents 25 000 equal units on the ground.

    Note that   1 cm : 25 000 cm works out at 1 cm : $\frac{1}{4}$ km and
                   1 in. : 25 000 in. works out at 1 in. : 0.4 mile approx.

 ii A map scale, for example, 5 in. = 1 mile.

    This means that 1 inch on the map represents 0.2 mile or 352 yds.

    The scale is often shown as a diagram, for example,

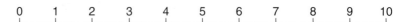

0   1   2   3   4   5   6   7   8   9   10

Worked Examples

1 On the Ordinance Survey Travelmaster 1 : 250 000 map of Northern Scotland, Inverness and Fort William are 14 inches apart. What is the real distance between the towns?

On this scale 1 inch represents 4 miles.
Thus 14 inches = 14 × 4
               = 56 miles.

NOTE

On the actual map
Inverness to Fort William
is marked as 65 miles and
Montrose to Aberdeen is
actually 8.5 inches apart.

The discrepancy is due to
the fact that we are
measuring straight
distances between points
and roads are never
exactly straight!

Hence the road distances
are actually greater than
the equivalent map
distances.

2 On the same map Montrose and Aberdeen are marked as being 38 miles apart. How far apart are they on the map?

4 miles = 1 in.
Therefore 38 miles = $\frac{38}{4}$ in.
= 9.5 in.

PRACTICE 10.6.2a   Try these questions without a calculator

1 On a map, the scale is 1 in. = 4 miles.
   a Stafford is 4.2 in. north of Wolverhampton. How far is Stafford from Wolverhampton?
   b Bristol airport is 2.2 in. from Bristol (Temple Meads) station on the map. How far will a taxi take Gryff and Dot on this journey?

2 On a map, the scale is 1 cm = 2.5 km.
   a From Manchester to Stockport is 10 km. How far apart are they on the map?
   b Cambridge is 88 km from London. How far apart are they on the map?

3 On a map of Europe, the scale is 1 in. = 20 miles. The Newhaven to Dieppe ferry route is 3.9 in. How far is Dieppe from Newhaven?

PRACTICE 10.6.2b   Try these questions with a calculator

1 On a map of Europe, the scale is 1 cm = 12.5 km. The Dover to Calais ferry route is marked as 41 km. How far is this on the map?

2 A set of town maps have a scale of 1 in. = $\frac{1}{4}$ mile.
   a The map is quoted as having a scale of $1 : x$. Find the value of x, writing your answer to 2 significant figures.
   b In Cardiff, the Arms Park is $1\frac{1}{4}$ in. from the station. How many yards is this?
   c In Edinburgh, St. Andrew's square is 1500 yards from the Albert Memorial. How far apart are they on the map?

3 A street map of London has a scale of $1 : 14\,000$.
   a On the map Nelson's Column is 8.6 cm from Buckingham Palace. How many metres apart are they?
   b Great Ormond Street Childrens' Hospital is 2.5 km from St. Thomas' Hospital. How far apart are they on the map?

A combined transformation occurs when one transformation is followed by another. Repeated transformations can often lead to interesting patterns. For example, the pattern below is made by repeated rotations:

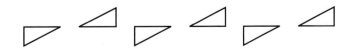

Often, two transformations which follow one another can be replaced by a single transformation.

For example, a reflection in the y-axis followed by a reflection in the x-axis is exactly the same as a single rotation of 180° about $(0,0)$.

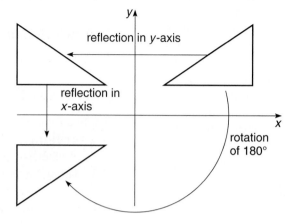

Worked Example

Triangle T, on the axes shown, can be transformed onto triangle S, by a combination of two transformations.

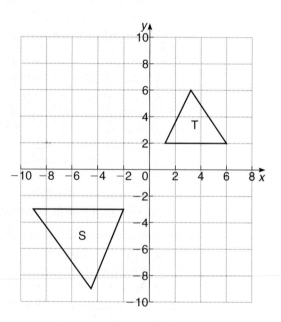

a Describe each transformation fully.
b Write down the *single* transformation which would replace the two original transformations.

 a i Rotation of 180° about $(0,0)$.
    ii Enlargement scale factor 1.5 centre $(0,0)$.
 b The single transformation would be: enlargement scale factor -1.5 centre $(0,0)$.

NOTE
It doesn't matter which transformation is done first in this case.

The following questions give examination practice in both general and combined transformations.

PRACTICE 10.7.1

1 A pentagon ABCDE is shown.

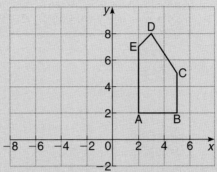

    a ABCDE is transformed into $A_1B_1C_1D_1E_1$ by the translation $\begin{pmatrix} 5 \\ -2 \end{pmatrix}$.

    On graph paper, draw and label the resulting pentagon.

    b ABCDE is transformed into $A_2B_2C_2D_2E_2$ by a rotation of 90° anticlockwise about $(0,0)$.

    Draw and label the resulting pentagon on the diagram.

2 Draw and label axes for values of x and y between -16 and 16.

    a On the graph draw a letter F by plotting and joining the points $A(2,1)$, $B(2,3)$, $C(2,5)$, $D(3,3)$ and $E(4,5)$.

    b Enlarge the letter by a scale factor 3 centre $(0,0)$.

    c Rotate your enlargement by $+90°$ about $(0,0)$.

    d The F drawn in **a** may be transformed into another F by a

    translation of $\begin{pmatrix} 6 \\ -8 \end{pmatrix}$.

    Draw the resulting image on your graph.

3 A flag is represented on graph paper by the points $A(1,0)$, $B(1,2)$, $C(1,4)$ and $D(4,3)$.

    a Taking axes for x from -8 to 8 and for y from -10 to 10, plot the above points and join with straight lines AC, CD and DB.

    b Enlarge the flag by scale factor 2 centre $(0,0)$.

    c Rotate the resulting enlargement by $-180°$ about $(0,0)$.

4   **a** Reflect the given figure in the x-axis, followed by a rotation of 90° about $(0,0)$.

    b Which single transformation is the equivalent of this?

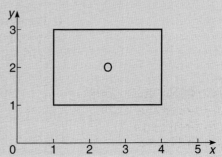

5 a Rotate the given figure by 180°
about (0, 0), followed by a
rotation of −90° about (0, 0).
b Which single transformation is
the equivalent of this?

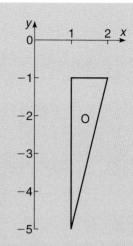

6 a Reflect the given figure in
the line $y = x$, followed by a
reflection in the line $y = -x$.
b Which single transformation
is the equivalent of this?

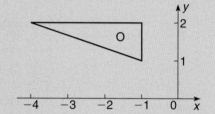

7 a Reflect the given figure
in the y-axis followed by a
rotation of 180° about (0, 0).
b Which single transformation
is the equivalent of this?

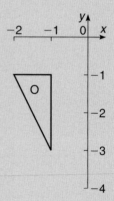

8 a Rotate the given figure by
−90° about (0, 0) followed by
a reflection in the x-axis.
b Which single transformation
is the equivalent of this?

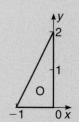

Tessellations

We can use our knowledge of transformations and of polygons and symmetry to devise tessellations.

A **tessellation** is a *tiling pattern*.

It is the arrangement of one or more shapes to completely fill a space, for example:

Properties of tessellations

1 There must be no gaps between the *tiles*.

2 No shape must overlap another shape.

3 At any vertex (point where shapes touch), all the angles must add up to 360°.

PRACTICE 10.7.2

1 The only regular polygons that tessellate on their own are those whose interior angles divide exactly into 360°.
   Use the information gained in Topic 9.2 to find which regular polygons tessellate on their own.

2 Will *any* parallelogram tessellate? Explain your answer.

3 Will *any* rhombus tessellate? Explain your answer.

4 *Investigation*
   Investigate, as an assignment, the use of tessellations that occur in one of the following areas:
   a nature   **b** wallpaper and floor coverings   **c** advertising.

Constructions

Sometimes we have to make accurate drawings, so we have to be able to use drawing instruments.

a To bisect a line AB:
- **i** Open a pair of compasses to more than half AB.
- **ii** With centre at A draw an arc P.
- **iii** With the compasses at the same setting and with centre B draw an arc Q to intersect arc P.
- **iv** Draw the line joining the points where the two arcs intersect.
  This line bisects AB at right angles. It is called the *perpendicular bisector* of AB. M is the mid-point of the line AB.

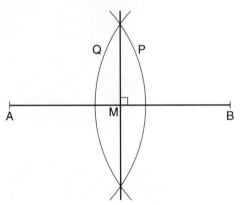

b To bisect an angle ABC:
- **i** With centre at B and any suitable radius, draw an arc intersecting the arms of the angle at P and Q.
- **ii** With centres P and Q and a radius more than half PQ, draw two arcs to intersect at R.
- **iii** Join RB. This line bisects ∠ABC.

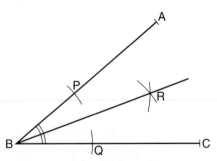

c To construct the perpendicular at a point on a line, use the same method as bisecting an angle, where ∠ABC is 180°. We bisect it to get 90°.

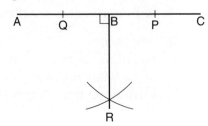

Worked Examples

1 Construct the triangle with sides 4 cm, 6 cm and 8 cm. Measure the largest angle.

   i Draw a line and mark A and B on it 8 cm apart.

   ii With radius 6 cm and centre A, (or B), draw arc P.

   iii With radius 4 cm and centre B, (or A), draw arc Q to intersect arc P. This is point C.

   iv Complete the triangle ABC.

   v Using a protractor measure the required angle, $\angle C = 104°$.

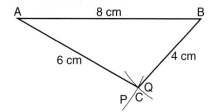

2 Construct the triangle where BC = 6 cm, $\angle B = 47°$ and $\angle C = 63°$. Bisect $\angle A$ and mark the point where this line intersects BC as D. Measure BD.

   i Draw a line and mark B and C on it 6 cm apart.

   ii Using a protractor draw a straight line at B at 47° to BC.

   iii Using a protractor draw a straight line at C at 63° to BC.

   iv Mark the point where these lines intersect as A.

   v Using compasses bisect $\angle A$ and mark D on BC.

   vi Measure BD.

The length BD was measured as 3.3 cm (2 sf).

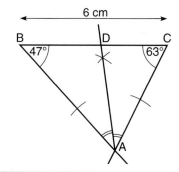

PRACTICE 10.8.1

1 Construct the following triangles:

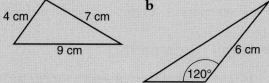

2 Draw a line and mark AB = 5 cm on it.
Construct a perpendicular to the line at B and mark C on this line
where BC = 4 cm.
Complete triangle ABC.
Measure and record the length AC.

3 Construct an isosceles triangle with sides 8 cm, 8 cm and 6 cm.
Bisect the vertical angle.
Show that it perpendicularly bisects the base.

4 Draw any triangle.
Bisect all three angles and show that the three bisectors all pass through
one point.

5 Draw any triangle.
Draw all three medians (lines joining any vertex to the mid-point of the
opposite side). Show that the three medians all pass through one point.
(This point is called the *centre of gravity* of the triangle.)

6 Draw any triangle.
Construct the perpendicular bisectors of all three sides.
Show that the three bisectors all pass through one point.
Using this point as the centre, draw the circle that passes through the
three vertices. Explain why this is so.

Locus

The word **locus** means *path*. A locus is the path traced out by a point when it
moves to obey a given law or laws.

For example, the locus of a point which is
always 2 cm from a fixed point O, is the
circumference of a circle, centre O, radius
2 cm:

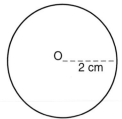

The plural of locus is **loci**.

When drawing a locus we sometimes have
to experiment by marking some points on a
diagram that obey the given law.

When we can see what the locus looks like we can complete the diagram.

A locus can sometimes be an area.

For instance, in the example above, the locus of points P such that
OP < 2 cm, would be the total area inside the circle (not including the
circumference). If OP ≤ 2 it would include the circumference.

Some common loci

1 The locus of a point which moves such that it is a fixed distance from a
given point is the circumference of a circle.

2 The locus of a point which moves such that it is a fixed distance from a given line is a pair of lines parallel to the given line and the fixed distance d from it.

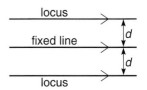

3 The locus of a point which moves such that it is always the same distance from two fixed points A and B is the perpendicular bisector of AB.

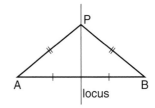

4 The locus of a point which moves such that it is always the same distance from two fixed straight lines is the angle bisector of the lines.

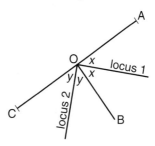

In the diagram shown, OA and OB are the fixed straight lines and locus 1 bisects the angle.

However, if AO or BO is produced the exterior $\angle AOB$ is formed and locus 2 bisects that angle.

Also, since AOC is a straight angle, i.e. 180°, then $2x + 2y = 180°$, so $x + y = 90°$.

But, $x + y$ is the angle between the two loci. Thus:

the bisectors of the interior and exterior angles formed by two straight lines are perpendicular.

Worked Examples

1 A and B are fixed points 8 inches apart.
Find the locus of a point which moves such that it is always equidistant from A and B and never further than 5 inches from either point.

As shown before the initial locus is the perpendicular bisector of AB, but, using Pythagoras, we can see that it can only extend for 3 inches on each side of the line AB.

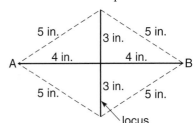

2 A goat is tethered to one corner of a square post of side 2 m in the middle
   of one wall of a large field. Its rope is 5 m long.
   Indicate the locus of the grass from which the goat can feed.

At first the goat can feed within a
circle of radius 5 m, but after
turning the first corner the radius
becomes 3 m and then 1 m after it
turns the second corner.

The diagram shows the area that
is available to it.

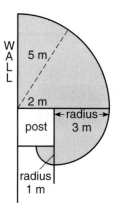

PRACTICE 10.8.2

1 ∠ABC is 90° and BC = 10 cm. Find the locus of points which are
   equidistant from:
   a B and C,
   b AB and BC.
   Mark the point D which satisfies both loci and measure the length DB.

2 AB is a line 5 cm long and is the hypotenuse of a right angled triangle
   ABC. Draw the locus of point C.

3 A rectangular room 6 m by 4 m has power points at both ends of one of
   the longer sides. Truda has a vacuum cleaner of combined length, with
   cable, of 4.5 m.
   Show the locus of all points in the room which Truda cannot reach.

4 AC is the hypotenuse of a right angled triangle ABC. AB = 5 cm and
   BC = 12 cm.
   Show the locus of all points inside the triangle which are closer to A
   than B but less than 10 cm from C.

5 In triangle ABC, AC = 4 in., BC = 8 in. and ∠ACB = 64°. Draw the
   following loci:
   a the locus of all points equidistant from AC and BC,
   b the locus of all points 2.25 in. from A.
   Mark and label any points which are common to both loci.

6   X, Y and Z are three observation posts at the vertices of an equilateral triangle of side 20 miles.
     Observers at X and Y simultaneously record a UFO equidistant from them and moving along their perpendicular bisector towards Z.
     Ten seconds later it is recorded as being equidistant from all three observation posts.
     a Draw the locus accurately and find the distance the UFO has moved.
     b Calculate:
        i the speed of the UFO in mph,
        ii how long it will take, flying at its present speed and course, to appear directly over Z.

7   **a** Draw a circle of radius 5 in.
     b Draw a number of chords of this circle each 8 in. long and mark their mid-points.
     c Deduce the locus of the mid-points of all such chords. Explain your answer.

Enlargement with negative scale factor

We have already seen how a shape is enlarged by a given scale factor. This scale factor can, however, be negative.

The following example shows the effect that a negative scale factor has on an object.

Worked Example

Enlarge the given shape from O with a scale factor -2.

We can find the coordinates of the vertices of the image by multiplying the object vertices by the scale factor:

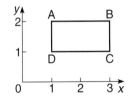

$$A' = -2 \begin{pmatrix} 1 \\ 2 \end{pmatrix} = \begin{pmatrix} -2 \\ -4 \end{pmatrix}$$

$$B' = -2 \begin{pmatrix} 3 \\ 2 \end{pmatrix} = \begin{pmatrix} -6 \\ -4 \end{pmatrix}$$

$$C' = -2 \begin{pmatrix} 3 \\ 1 \end{pmatrix} = \begin{pmatrix} -6 \\ -2 \end{pmatrix}$$

$$D' = -2 \begin{pmatrix} 1 \\ 1 \end{pmatrix} = \begin{pmatrix} -2 \\ -2 \end{pmatrix}$$

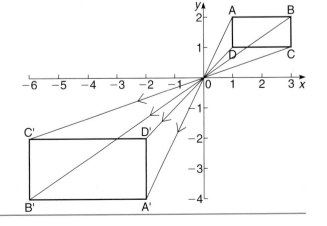

Further vectors

Notation

We have already met the matrix method of representing a vector i.e. $\begin{pmatrix} 3 \\ -1 \end{pmatrix}$.

Vectors can also be represented on diagrams by line segments where:

a the length of the line represents the size, or *magnitude*, of the vector,
b the direction of the line shows the *direction* of the vector.

Algebraically the line is given a
letter or else the ends are labelled

i.e. vector $\overrightarrow{AB}$ or **a**.

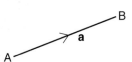

Some important points about vector notation are listed below.

1 The arrow is important. It shows the direction of the vector.

2 $\overrightarrow{AB}$ and $\overrightarrow{BA}$ are different vectors. They have the same magnitude but are *opposite* in direction. Hence $\overrightarrow{AB} = -\overrightarrow{BA}$.

3 The magnitude of $\overrightarrow{AB}$ is written either as AB (i.e. the length of the line AB) or as $|\overrightarrow{AB}|$. Similarly we have a or $|\mathbf{a}|$.
$|\overrightarrow{AB}|$ and $|\mathbf{a}|$ are called the *modulus* of the vector.

4 A vector printed **a** in the book cannot easily be written by hand. It is often written either as $\overrightarrow{a}$ or as $\underline{a}$.

5 If two vectors are equal they must be
a equal in magnitude,
b in the same direction.
Hence $\overrightarrow{AB} = \overrightarrow{PQ}$.

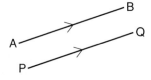

The modulus of a vector

The modulus of a vector is just another name for its size, or *magnitude*.

The diagram shows a displacement vector

$$= \begin{pmatrix} 2 \\ 4 \end{pmatrix}:$$

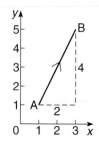

We can see that the triangle is right angled.
In Topic 9.5 we studied Pythagoras' theorem
and applying this, we can say:

$$(AB)^2 = 2^2 + 4^2$$
$$= 4 + 16$$
$$= 20$$

Hence AB $= \sqrt{20} = 4.47$ units (3 sf).

Thus the length 4.47 units, is the *magnitude*, or *modulus* of the vector.

In general the modulus of the vector $\begin{pmatrix} x \\ y \end{pmatrix}$ is given by $\sqrt{(x^2 + y^2)}$.

Vectors written as $\begin{pmatrix} x \\ y \end{pmatrix}$ are called *column vectors*.

Quantities which are *not* vectors are called *scalar quantities*. Three examples are mass, area and capacity (volume).

PRACTICE 10.9.1a   Try these questions without a calculator

1 Find the modulus (plural moduli) of each of the following vectors.

a $\begin{pmatrix} 3 \\ 4 \end{pmatrix}$ **b** $\begin{pmatrix} -5 \\ 12 \end{pmatrix}$ **c** $\begin{pmatrix} 7 \\ -24 \end{pmatrix}$

2 A point is moved along the vector $\begin{pmatrix} 6 \\ -8 \end{pmatrix}$. How far has it moved?

PRACTICE 10.9.1b   Try these questions with a calculator

1 Find the modulus (plural moduli) of each of the following vectors.

a $\begin{pmatrix} 2 \\ 6 \end{pmatrix}$ **b** $\begin{pmatrix} -2 \\ -5 \end{pmatrix}$

2 The following table gives the starting and finishing positions of several vectors. Calculate which vector has the largest modulus.

start	finish
$(1, 2)$	$(5, 7)$
$(-3, 7)$	$(-8, 10)$
$(-6, -4)$	$(-7, -8)$
$(3, -1)$	$(10, -2)$

Components of a vector

The vector $\overrightarrow{AB}$ is written as $\begin{pmatrix} \mathbf{a} \\ \mathbf{b} \end{pmatrix}$.

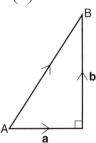

This means *a units* in the *x*-direction followed by *b units* in the *y*-direction.

Hence **a** and **b** are vectors themselves and are called *components* of the vector $\overrightarrow{AB}$.

NOTE

Components do not have to be at right angles. Any set of vectors that started at A and finished at B above, would be components of $\overrightarrow{AB}$.

Worked Example

Write down the vectors $\overrightarrow{AB}$ and $\overrightarrow{CD}$ in component form.

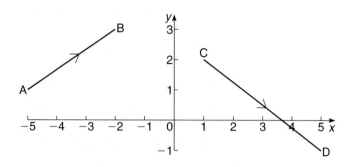

$\overrightarrow{AB}$ is 3 units in the x-direction and 2 units in the y-direction, hence $\begin{pmatrix} 3 \\ 2 \end{pmatrix}$.

$\overrightarrow{CD}$ is 4 units in the x-direction and 3 units in the $-y$-direction, hence $\begin{pmatrix} 4 \\ -3 \end{pmatrix}$.

PRACTICE 10.9.2

1 a Write down, in matrix component form, each of the vectors shown.

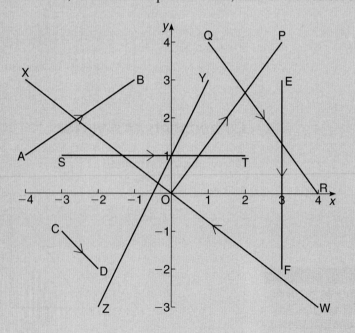

b Find the magnitudes of $\overrightarrow{QR}$ (without a calculator) and $\overrightarrow{YZ}$ (with a calculator).

Vector arithmetic

Vectors can be added or subtracted.

Algebraically, this is easy, for example:

$$\begin{pmatrix} 2 \\ 6 \end{pmatrix} + \begin{pmatrix} 3 \\ 1 \end{pmatrix} = \begin{pmatrix} 5 \\ 7 \end{pmatrix} \text{ and } \begin{pmatrix} 2 \\ 6 \end{pmatrix} - \begin{pmatrix} 3 \\ 1 \end{pmatrix} = \begin{pmatrix} -1 \\ 5 \end{pmatrix}$$

However, *in diagrams* we do the following:

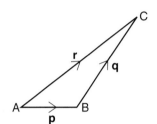

a Draw one vector.
b Add the second vector on to the
   end of the first – like a *nose to tail*
c Draw the vector from the start of
   the first vector to the end of the
   second. This vector is the sum of
   the other two vectors.

   i.e. $\overrightarrow{AC} = \overrightarrow{AB} + \overrightarrow{BC}$ or $\mathbf{p} + \mathbf{q} = \mathbf{r}$

1 The vector $\overrightarrow{AC}$ is called the **resultant** of the vectors $\overrightarrow{AB}$ and $\overrightarrow{BC}$.

2 It does not matter in which order the
   vectors are added – the result is the
   same.

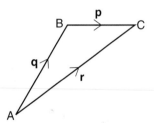

3 Although it *is* true that $\overrightarrow{AC} = \overrightarrow{AB} + \overrightarrow{BC}$, it is *not* true that AC = AB + BC.

   This is saying that length AC is the sum of lengths AB and BC.

To *subtract* two vectors diagrammatically, we reverse the second vector and add.

For instance, if $\mathbf{a} = $ and $\mathbf{b} = $

then $-\mathbf{b} = $

and $\mathbf{a} - \mathbf{b} = \mathbf{a} + -\mathbf{b}$

i.e. $\mathbf{c} = \mathbf{a} - \mathbf{b}$.

More than two vectors can be added in
the same way – by adding them all, or
by placing the vectors in a diagram
using the *nose to tail* method.

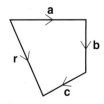 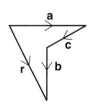

Again, the order does not matter, as
the diagrams show:

i.e. $\mathbf{r} = \mathbf{a} + \mathbf{b} + \mathbf{c} = \mathbf{a} + \mathbf{c} + \mathbf{b}$, etc.

Multiplying a vector by a constant

Any vector can be multiplied by a constant, k.
The result is another vector *in the same direction* as the first but k *times as long*.

For example if $\mathbf{a} = $ ———→—— then $3\mathbf{a} = $ ——————————→———

Worked Examples

1 Each parallelogram in the grid shown has sides with vectors $\mathbf{a}$ and $\mathbf{b}$.

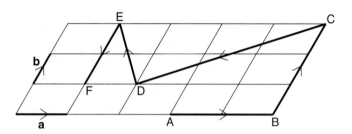

Write down the vectors $\overrightarrow{AB}$, $\overrightarrow{BC}$, $\overrightarrow{CD}$, $\overrightarrow{DE}$ and $\overrightarrow{EF}$.

$\overrightarrow{AB} = 2\mathbf{a}$ $\overrightarrow{BC} = 3\mathbf{b}$ $\overrightarrow{CD} = -3\mathbf{a} - 2\mathbf{b}$ $\overrightarrow{DE} = -\mathbf{a} + 2\mathbf{b}$ $\overrightarrow{EF} = -2\mathbf{b}$

2 In the parallelogram shown $\overrightarrow{AB} = \mathbf{a}$ and $\overrightarrow{BC} = \mathbf{b}$.

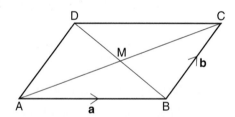

Write down vectors for:

  a $\overrightarrow{AD}$ **b** $\overrightarrow{DC}$ **c** $\overrightarrow{AC}$ **d** $\overrightarrow{DB}$ **e** $\overrightarrow{AM}$ **f** $\overrightarrow{DM}$

  a $\overrightarrow{AD} = \mathbf{b}$ **b** $\overrightarrow{DC} = \mathbf{a}$ **c** $\overrightarrow{AC} = \mathbf{a} + \mathbf{b}$ **d** $\overrightarrow{DB} = \mathbf{a} - \mathbf{b}$

  e $\overrightarrow{AM} = \frac{1}{2}\overrightarrow{AC} = \frac{1}{2}(\mathbf{a} + \mathbf{b}) = \frac{1}{2}\mathbf{a} + \frac{1}{2}\mathbf{b}$

  f $\overrightarrow{DM} = \frac{1}{2}\overrightarrow{DB} = \frac{1}{2}(\mathbf{a} - \mathbf{b}) = \frac{1}{2}\mathbf{a} - \frac{1}{2}\mathbf{b}$

3 In the triangle shown, $\overrightarrow{AB} = \mathbf{a}$ and $\overrightarrow{AC} = \mathbf{b}$. BD is one third of BC.

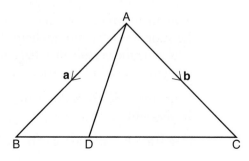

Calculate vectors for:

a $\overrightarrow{BC}$ **b** $\overrightarrow{BD}$ **c** $\overrightarrow{AD}$

a Using the triangular law of addition, we can say $\overrightarrow{AB} + \overrightarrow{BC} = \overrightarrow{AC}$.

Hence $\mathbf{a} + \overrightarrow{BC} = \mathbf{b}$ i.e. $\overrightarrow{BC} = \mathbf{b} - \mathbf{a}$

b $\overrightarrow{BD} = \frac{1}{3}\overrightarrow{BC} = \frac{1}{3}(\mathbf{b} - \mathbf{a}) = \frac{1}{3}\mathbf{b} - \frac{1}{3}\mathbf{a}$

c Using the triangular law of addition, we can say $\overrightarrow{AB} + \overrightarrow{BD} = \overrightarrow{AD}$.

Hence $\mathbf{a} + \frac{1}{3}\mathbf{b} - \frac{1}{3}\mathbf{a} = \overrightarrow{AD}$ i.e. $\overrightarrow{AD} = \frac{2}{3}\mathbf{a} + \frac{1}{3}\mathbf{b}$.

4 $\mathbf{a} = \begin{pmatrix} 2 \\ 4 \end{pmatrix}$ $\mathbf{b} = \begin{pmatrix} -3 \\ 1 \end{pmatrix}$ $\mathbf{c} = \begin{pmatrix} -2 \\ -3 \end{pmatrix}$

Calculate **a** $\mathbf{a} + \mathbf{b} + \mathbf{c}$ **b** $2\mathbf{a} + \mathbf{b}$ **c** $3\mathbf{c} - 2\mathbf{b}$ **d** $3\mathbf{a} + 4\mathbf{b} - 2\mathbf{c}$.

a $\mathbf{a} + \mathbf{b} + \mathbf{c} = \begin{pmatrix} 2 \\ 4 \end{pmatrix} + \begin{pmatrix} -3 \\ 1 \end{pmatrix} + \begin{pmatrix} -2 \\ -3 \end{pmatrix} = \begin{pmatrix} -3 \\ 2 \end{pmatrix}$

b $2\mathbf{a} + \mathbf{b} = 2\begin{pmatrix} 2 \\ 4 \end{pmatrix} + \begin{pmatrix} -3 \\ 1 \end{pmatrix} = \begin{pmatrix} 4 \\ 8 \end{pmatrix} + \begin{pmatrix} -3 \\ 1 \end{pmatrix} = \begin{pmatrix} 1 \\ 9 \end{pmatrix}$

c $3\mathbf{c} - 2\mathbf{b} = 3\begin{pmatrix} -2 \\ -3 \end{pmatrix} - 2\begin{pmatrix} -3 \\ 1 \end{pmatrix} = \begin{pmatrix} -6 \\ -9 \end{pmatrix} - \begin{pmatrix} -6 \\ 2 \end{pmatrix} = \begin{pmatrix} 0 \\ -11 \end{pmatrix}$

d $3\mathbf{a} + 4\mathbf{b} - 2\mathbf{c} = 3\begin{pmatrix} 2 \\ 4 \end{pmatrix} + 4\begin{pmatrix} -3 \\ 1 \end{pmatrix} - 2\begin{pmatrix} -2 \\ -3 \end{pmatrix}$

$= \begin{pmatrix} 6 \\ 12 \end{pmatrix} + \begin{pmatrix} -12 \\ 4 \end{pmatrix} - \begin{pmatrix} -4 \\ -6 \end{pmatrix} = \begin{pmatrix} -2 \\ 22 \end{pmatrix}$

PRACTICE 10.9.3   Use a calculator in this practice where necessary

1 Enlarge shape A in the diagram shown by scale factor -3 and shape B by scale factor $-\frac{1}{2}$ both with centre of enlargement the origin.

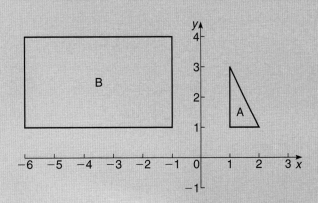

2 All the small parallelograms in the grid are congruent and formed by the vectors **a** and **b** as shown.

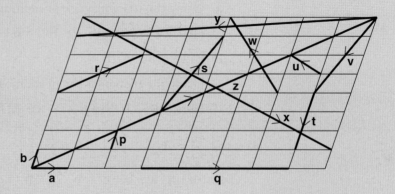

Write down, in terms of **a** and **b**, the vectors **p** to **z** marked in the diagram.

3 $p = \begin{pmatrix} 2 \\ -1 \end{pmatrix}$

    a Draw this on squared paper.
    b $q = 2p$. Write down and draw **q**.
    c Find the moduli of **p** and **q**. What do you notice?

4 $p = \begin{pmatrix} -1 \\ -2 \end{pmatrix}$ $q = \begin{pmatrix} 4 \\ -3 \end{pmatrix}$ $r = \begin{pmatrix} -2 \\ 8 \end{pmatrix}$ $s = \begin{pmatrix} 3 \\ 7 \end{pmatrix}$

    a Calculate the vectors:
      i $p + q + r + s$ **ii** $2p + 3s$ **iii** $2r - q$ **iv** $2p + \frac{1}{2}r$ **v** $-3q + 5s$
    b Find the vectors $q - p$ and $r - s$. What do you notice about them?
    c Calculate $|p + q|$, the modulus of the vector $p + q$. Is this the same as $|p| + |q|$?

5 The trapezium shows vectors for three of its four sides Calculate the vector which represents the fourth side.

6 In a triangle ABC, $\vec{AB} = \mathbf{x}$ and $\vec{AC} = \mathbf{y}$. P lies on AB such that $BP = \frac{1}{3}BA$ and Q lies on $\vec{AC}$ such that $\vec{AQ} = \frac{1}{4}\vec{AC}$.
Find vector expressions for:
    a $\vec{AP}$ **b** $\vec{AQ}$ **c** $\vec{PQ}$ **d** $\vec{CP}$ **e** $\vec{BQ}$.

7 In an equilateral triangle ABC, $\vec{AB} = \mathbf{c}$ and $\vec{AC} = \mathbf{d}$. M, N and P are the mid-points of AB, BC and CA. Find the vectors $\vec{MN}$, $\vec{NP}$ and $\vec{PM}$.

8 P and Q are the mid-points of the sides DC and BC of a rectangle ABCD where $\vec{AB} = \mathbf{s}$ and $\vec{AD} = \mathbf{t}$. Find vector $\vec{PQ}$ in terms of $\mathbf{s}$ and $\mathbf{t}$.

9 M is the mid-point of the diagonals of a parallelogram ABCD where $\vec{MA} = \mathbf{f}$ and $\vec{MD} = \mathbf{g}$. Find vectors, in terms of $\mathbf{f}$ and $\mathbf{g}$, for the sides of the parallelogram.

10 In the diagram shown, M is the mid-point of AB and $\vec{AM} = \mathbf{a}$. $\vec{BC} = \mathbf{b}$ and $\vec{CD} = 3\vec{BC}$.

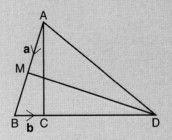

Calculate vectors for

a $\vec{AB}$,   **d** $\vec{MC}$,

b $\vec{BD}$,   **e** $\vec{DM}$,

c $\vec{AC}$,   **f** $\vec{DA}$.

Notation for combined transformations

1 If we apply a transformation A to an object O, the A(O) means *the transformation A applied to object shape O*.

2 If we now apply a second transformation B to the result, we would write BA(O).

Hence BA means *apply transformation A first followed by transformation B to the object shape O*.

3 Similarly AB would mean *apply transformation B first followed by transformation A to the object shape O*.

4 Sometimes AB can result in a single transformation that could have been applied. For example, a reflection in the *y*-axis followed by a reflection in the *x*-axis is exactly the same as a single rotation of 180°.

5 A transformation A applied to an object O and then repeated is written AA(O) or A^2(O). Similarly A^3(O) means a transformation applied three times.

6 A transformation which changes the image back to its original object is called an *inverse* and is written A^{-1}.

Worked Examples

1 Show that the result in statement 4 above is true for the given shape.

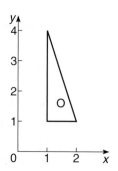

Doing these two transformations in order we get:

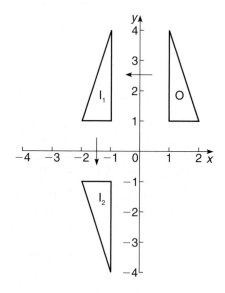

Clearly we can see that the final image I_2 is a rotation about 0 of 180°.

2 A is an enlargement, scale factor 2, centre 0. B is a reflection in the line $x = 3$ and C is the translation $\begin{pmatrix} 4 \\ -1 \end{pmatrix}$.

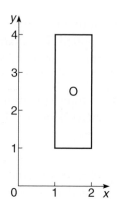

Perform the combined transformation CAB on the object shown.

The following diagram shows the stages in the solution:

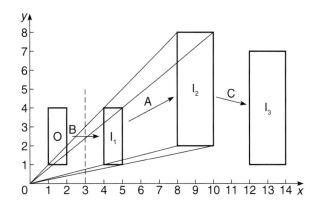

PRACTICE 10.9.4

In questions **1** and **2** use the following transformations:

A is a reflection in the x-axis
B is a reflection in the y-axis
C is a reflection in the line $y = x$
D is a reflection in the line $y = -x$
E is a rotation of $+90°$ about the origin
F is a rotation of $-90°$ about the origin
G is a rotation of $180°$ about the origin.

1 a Apply the combined
transformation DCG on the
given figure.

  b Which single transformation
is the equivalent of this?

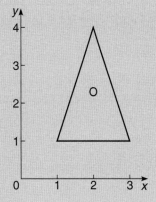

2 a Some of the transformations A to G above are *self-inverses*, i.e.
applying the transformation twice changes the image back into the
original object.
Which are these?

  b Is the single transformation that replaces a combined one the same if
the order of the combined transformations is reversed? Explain your
answer.

3 P is an enlargement, centre 0, scale factor 3; Q is the translation $\begin{pmatrix} -2 \\ 3 \end{pmatrix}$.

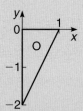

    a Apply the combination PQ to the given shape:
    b Apply the combination QP to the original shape.
    c Are the end results the same?

4 L is the translation $\begin{pmatrix} 4 \\ 2 \end{pmatrix}$.

G is an enlargement, scale factor 1.5, centre 0.

Apply the combination L^2G to:

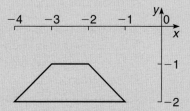

5 a
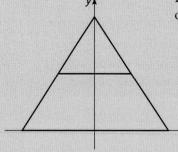
In the figure what transformation maps one half on to the other?

b
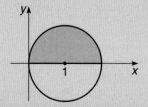
Give two possible transformations that map the shaded area on to the other.

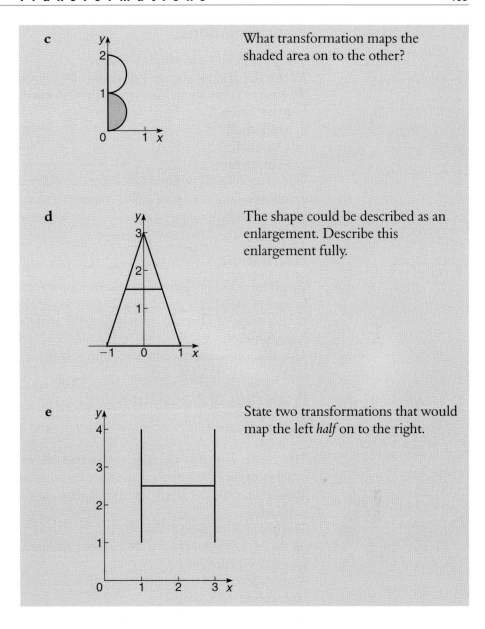

c   What transformation maps the shaded area on to the other?

d   The shape could be described as an enlargement. Describe this enlargement fully.

e   State two transformations that would map the left *half* on to the right.

Vectors

Vectors are quantities that have both a size *and* a direction.
Displacement means distance in a particular direction.
The *magnitude* of a vector is its size, or length.
The *direction* of a vector is its direction, or bearing.
We can think of coordinates of points on graphs as displacement vectors from the origin. These are called *position vectors*.

Transformations

The word *transformation* means *change*.
All transformations change a diagram – by altering its position, size or shape.
We have to know about four types of transformation:
- ▸ translation
- ▸ reflection
- ▸ rotation
- ▸ enlargement.

We call the original position of a shape the *object* and the final position the *image*.
Transformations are often called *mappings* and the object is said to be *mapped onto* the image.

Translation

Translation is the simplest of the four transformations.
In a translation every point on a shape is moved by the same displacement.
We can think of a translation as sliding the shape from its object position to its image position.
A translation is described by a column vector.

Properties of translation

Translations are usually written in two parts and are written in the form $\begin{pmatrix} x \\ y \end{pmatrix}$.

The number in the top row is the translation in the *x*-direction and the number in the bottom row is the translation in the *y*-direction.
Translation does not affect the size or shape of the object. It only changes the position.
The image is *congruent* to the object.
All the lines drawn between any pair of corresponding object and image points are equal and parallel.
Any image point is found by adding the translation vector to the corresponding object point.

Reflection

Reflection occurs when a shape has a line of symmetry – one half of the shape can be *reflected* or *folded* along a mirror line on to the other half.
Each half is congruent and said to be the *mirror image* of the other.

Properties of reflection

Reflection has no effect on the size and shape of the object. It only changes the position.
The effect on position is that the object is *folded* over a mirror line.
The image of any point is the same distance behind the mirror line that the corresponding object point is in front.

The mirror line is called the perpendicular bisector of the line joining the object and image points.

If an object point lies on the mirror line the image is the same point.

Reflections can easily be shown using tracing paper.

One side of the mirror line is drawn and, when turned over, it can easily be seen to *fit* the other side of the mirror line.

When finding the image of object shapes on graph paper the mirror line is often written as an equation.

Rotation

An angle is a rotation of one line onto another.

Every point on the object shape turns through the same angle about a fixed point.

Properties of rotation

Rotation has no effect on the size and shape of the object. It only changes the position.

Every point on the shape is turned through the same angle about a certain fixed point.

This amount of turning is called the *angle of rotation*.

The fixed point is called the *centre of rotation*.

It is the only point that does not change in the rotation.

It can be either inside or outside the object shape.

The direction of rotation must be specified.

Anticlockwise is taken as positive and clockwise as negative.

The object and image are congruent shapes.

Rotations can easily be shown using tracing paper.

The object is drawn, together with the axes and fixed point. The tracing paper can then easily be turned through the required angle and the image drawn in the correct position.

To find the angle of rotation

If the positions of the object and image are known the angle of rotation can be found.

Method one

Produce two corresponding lines on the diagrams back until they intersect.

The angle between them is the angle of rotation.

This method is very useful if we do not know the centre of rotation.

Method two

Draw lines from any two corresponding points on the object and image back to the centre of rotation.

The angle between them is the angle of rotation.

To find the centre of rotation

i Draw a line between any pair of corresponding points.
ii Draw the perpendicular bisector of this line.
iii Repeat **i** and **ii** for another pair of corresponding points.
iv The centre of rotation is the point where these two lines intersect.

Enlargement

The word *enlargement* is used when the size of an object is changed.

Properties of englargement

Enlargement affects both the position and the size of the object.
Enlargement has no effect on shape – the image is exactly the same shape as the object.
Any pair of corresponding lengths on the object and image are *in the same ratio*.
This ratio is called the *scale factor* of the enlargement.
If the scale factor is numerically greater than one, the image is larger than the object.
If the scale factor is numerically less than one, it is smaller than the object.

Constructing enlargements

Enlargements are constructed from a particular point.
This point is called the *centre of enlargement*.
It can be either inside or outside the shape.
The method is:

i draw straight lines from the centre of enlargement (O) through each vertex of the object,
ii measure the distance from O to each vertex,
iii multiply each of these distances by the scale factor for the enlargement,
iv mark off these new distances from O through each vertex,
v join up these points to form the image.

If O is inside the object the diagram is called a *spider diagram*.
If O is outside the object the diagram is called a *ray diagram*.

Maps and scales

A practical use of enlargement is in the drawing of maps.
A map is a scale drawing of a geographical area.
The *scale factor* is the ratio between a given length on the map and the corresponding length on the ground.
The map scale is shown in one of two ways:

i A ratio, for example, 1 : 25 000.
This means that one unit on the map represents 25 000 equal units on the ground.

1 cm : 25 000 cm works out at 1 cm : $\frac{1}{4}$ km.

1 in. : 25 000 in. works out at 1 in. : 0.4 mile approx.

ii A map scale, for example, 5 in. = 1 mile.

This means that 1 inch on the map represents 0.2 mile or 352 yd.

Combined transformations

A combined transformation occurs when one transformation is followed by another.

Repeated transformations can often lead to interesting patterns.

Often, two transformations which follow one another can be replaced by a single transformation.

Tessellations

A *tessellation* is a tiling pattern.

It is the arrangement of one or more shapes to completely fill a space.

Properties of tessellations

There must be no gaps between the tiles.

No shape must overlap another shape.

At any vertex (point where shapes touch), all the angles must add up to 360°.

Constructions and loci

To bisect a line AB:

Open a pair of compasses to more than half AB.

With centre at A draw an arc P.

With the compasses at the same setting and with centre B draw an arc Q to intersect arc P.

Draw the line joining the points where the two arcs intersect.

This line bisects AB at right angles.

It is called the *perpendicular bisector* of AB.

To bisect an angle ABC:

With centre at B and any suitable radius, draw an arc intersecting the arms of the angle at P and Q.

With centres P and Q and a radius more than half PQ, draw two arcs to intersect at R.

Join RB.

This line bisects ∠ABC.

To construct the perpendicular at a point on a line:

This is the same as above where ∠ABC is 180°.

We bisect it to get 90°.

Locus

The word *locus* means path.
A locus is the path traced out by a point when it moves to obey a given law or laws.
The plural of locus is *loci*.
When drawing a locus we sometimes have to experiment by marking some points on a diagram that obey the given law.
When we can see what the locus looks like we can complete the diagram.
A locus can sometimes be an area.

Some common loci

The locus of a point which moves such that it is a fixed distance from a given point is the circumference of a circle.
The locus of a point which moves such that it is a fixed distance from a given line is a pair of lines parallel to the given line and the fixed distance from it.
The locus of a point which moves such that it is always the same distance from two fixed points A and B is the perpendicular bisector of AB.
The locus of a point which moves such that it is always the same distance from two fixed straight lines is the angle bisector of the lines.
The bisectors of the interior and exterior angles formed by two straight lines are perpendicular.

Enlargement with negative scale factor (extension)

The scale factor of an enlargement can be negative.

Further vectors (extension)

Vectors can be represented on diagrams by line segments where:
the length of the line represents the size, or *magnitude*, of the vector, and
the direction of the line shows the *direction* of the vector.
The arrow is important. It shows the direction of the vector.
$\overrightarrow{AB}$ and $\overrightarrow{BA}$ are different vectors. They have the same magnitude but are *opposite* in direction.
Hence $\overrightarrow{AB} = -\overrightarrow{BA}$.
The magnitude of $\overrightarrow{AB}$ is written either as AB (i.e. the length of the line AB) or as $|\overrightarrow{AB}|$. Similarly we have a or $|\mathbf{a}|$.
$|\overrightarrow{AB}|$ and $|\mathbf{a}|$ are called the *modulus* of the vector.
A vector printed **a** in the book cannot easily be written by hand. It is often written either as $\overrightarrow{a}$ or as $\underline{a}$.
If two vectors are equal they must be equal in magnitude and in the same direction.

The modulus of a vector (extension)

The modulus of a vector is just another name for its size, or *magnitude*.

In general the modulus of the vector $\begin{pmatrix} x \\ y \end{pmatrix}$ is given by $\sqrt{(x^2 + y^2)}$.

Vectors written as $\begin{pmatrix} x \\ y \end{pmatrix}$ are called *column vectors*.

Quantities which are not vectors are called *scalar quantities*. Three examples are mass, area and capacity (volume).

Components of a vector (extension)

The vector $\overrightarrow{AB}$ is written as $\begin{pmatrix} \mathbf{a} \\ \mathbf{b} \end{pmatrix}$.

This means *a units* in the *x*–direction followed by *b units* in the *y*–direction.
Hence **a** and **b** are vectors themselves and are called *components* of the vector $\overrightarrow{AB}$.

Components do not have to be at right angles. Any set of vectors that started at A and finished at B, would be components of $\overrightarrow{AB}$.

Vector arithmetic (extension)

Vectors can be added or subtracted.
In diagrams we do the following:

- Draw one vector.
- Add the second vector on to the end of the first – like a *nose to tail*.
- Draw the vector from the start of the first vector to the end of the second. This vector is the sum of the other two vectors.

The vector $\overrightarrow{AC}$ is called the *resultant* of the vectors $\overrightarrow{AB}$ and $\overrightarrow{BC}$.
It does not matter in which order the vectors are added – the result is the same.
Although it is true that $\overrightarrow{AC} = \overrightarrow{AB} + \overrightarrow{BC}$, it is not true that AC = AB + BC.
To subtract two vectors diagrammatically, we reverse the second vector and add.
More than two vectors can be added by placing the vectors in a diagram using the nose to tail method.

Multiplying a vector by a constant (extension)

Any vector can be multiplied by a constant, *k*.
The result is another vector in the same direction as the first but *k* times as long.

Notation for combined transformations (extension)

If we apply a transformation A to an object O, the A(O) means *the transformation A applied to object shape O*.

If we now apply a second transformation B to the result, we would write BA(O).

BA means *apply transformation A first followed by transformation B to the object shape O*.

AB means *apply transformation B first followed by transformation A to the object shape O*.

Sometimes AB can result in a single transformation that could have been applied.

A transformation A applied to an object O and then repeated is written AA(O) or $A^2(O)$. Similarly $A^3(O)$ means a transformation applied three times.

A transformation which changes the image back to its original object is called an *inverse* and is written A^{-1}.

CHAPTER 11
Measures

In this chapter you will need to:

▸ be able to use appropriate measuring and drawing instruments – including ruler, protractor, compasses, etc.

▸ know common equivalents i.e.
 1 kilogramme is approximately 2.2 pounds
 1 inch is approximately 2.5 centimetres
 1 foot is approximately 30 centimetres
 5 miles is approximately 8 kilometres
 1 gallon is approximately 4.5 litres

▸ understand the differences between discrete and continuous data (see Topic 4.1)

▸ understand decimal calculations (see Topic 1.4)

▸ understand the appropriate accuracy to use in a problem (see Topic 2.7) and understand that no answer is more accurate than the data it uses – or is possible

---

Worked Examples

1 Tricia has a rolling pin 40 cm long. What is the approximate length of the rolling pin in inches?

2.5 cm is approximately 1 inch, so 40 cm is approximately $\frac{40}{2.5} = 16$ inches.

2 Ruth buys 4 oz of jelly babies. How many grams is this approximately?

1 oz is approximately 28 g, thus 4 oz is approximately 112 g.

PRACTICE 11.1.1 Try these questions with a calculator

1 Hugo runs for 4.8 km. Approximately how many miles is this?

2 Margaret buys potatoes in a 25 lb bag. Approximately how many kg is this?

3 Bill drinks 3 litres of lager. Approximately how many pints does he drink?

4 Debbie has a 5 foot tape measure. Approximately how many cm is this?

5 Gary hits a golf ball 260 m. Approximately how many yards is this?

The **perimeter** is the distance around the edge of a shape.
For instance, the perimeter of a square of side x m is $4x$ m.

The perimeter of a circle is usually called the circumference (see Topic 9.2).

Worked Examples

1 Calculate the perimeters of the following shapes:

a 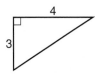 **b** 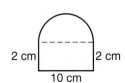 **c**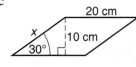

   a By Pythagoras' theorem the hypotenuse squared equals $3^2 + 4^2$ which is 25. Thus the hypotenuse is 5 and the perimeter $= 3 + 4 + 5 = 12$ units.

   b The curved line is half the circumference of a circle of radius 5 cm i.e. $3.14 \times 5 = 15.7$. Thus the perimeter $= 15.7 + 10 + 2 + 2 = 29.7$ cm.

   c Using SOHCAHTOA we can see that $\sin 30° = \dfrac{10}{x}$

$$\text{i.e. } 0.5 = \frac{10}{x}$$

Hence $x = \dfrac{10}{0.5} = 20$ cm.

Thus perimeter $= 4 \times 20 = 80$ cm.

NOTE
You may need to revise
Pythagoras' theorem,
circle circumference and
simple trigonometry to
work these questions out.

PRACTICE 11.2.1a   Try these questions without a calculator

1   Calculate the perimeters of the following shapes:

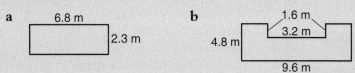

2   A rectangle has a perimeter of 48.6 cm and the longer side of length 14.5 cm. Find the length of the shorter side.

3   The two shortest sides of a right angled triangle are 5 in. and 12 in. respectively. Find the perimeter of the triangle.

4   A rhombus has diagonals of lengths 12 cm and 16 cm. Find its perimeter.

PRACTICE 11.2.1b   Try these questions with a calculator

1   Calculate the perimeters of the following shapes:

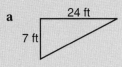

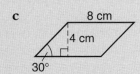   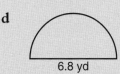

2   A coin is 5 cm in diameter. Calculate its perimeter.

An **area** measures the amount of space inside a plane shape. An area is measured in square units, for example:

1 square cm – written 1 cm^2

The rectangle contains an area of 6 cm^2.

Estimating areas

If the figure has curved sides, one way is to divide it up into small squares of known area and simply count them. Where there is less than a half a full square at the edge of the shape, do not count it. Where there is more than half a full square, count it as one full square.

Worked Example

Estimate the area of the given shape.

As we can see, each square more than half filled has been counted as a whole square and each one less than half has not been counted.

The area of the shape is estimated as 8 cm².

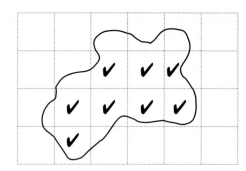

PRACTICE 11.3.1

1   The given shape is divided into centimetre squares. Estimate its area.

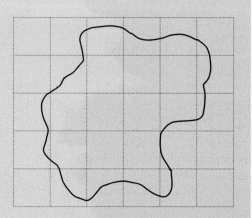

2   The diagram shows a map of Jersey.
    Each full square represents 1 square mile.
    Estimate the area of Jersey, to the nearest 10 square miles.

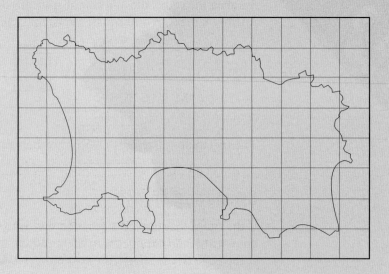

Areas of shapes

1 *The rectangle*

A rectangle *l* units long divides the rectangle into *l* vertical strips.
If it is *b* units broad, it divides the rectangle into *b* horizontal strips.
Hence the whole rectangle is cut into *l* lots of *b* squares = $l \times b$ squares.
Thus the area, *A*, of a rectangle is given by the formula, $A = lb$.

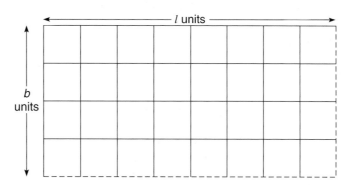

2 *The triangle*

a Right angled triangles

We can see that the right angled triangle of base *b* and height *h* units is exactly half of a rectangle.

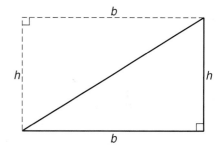

The area of the rectangle is *bh* so the area of the triangle is $\frac{1}{2} bh$.

b Any triangle

Imagine the triangle was enclosed in a rectangle ACDF as shown.

The breadth *h* of the rectangle is clearly the same as the perpendicular height from vertex B to the base of the triangle.

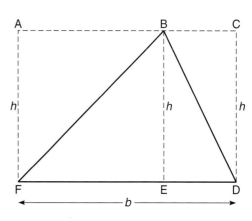

Using the result for right angled triangles above, we can see that the section BEF of the triangle is exactly half the rectangle ABEF.
Similarly, the section BED is exactly half the rectangle CBED.
Thus the whole triangle FBD is exactly half the area of the whole rectangle ACDF.

Hence, the area, A, of triangle FBD is given by $A = \frac{1}{2}bh$.

This is the same formula we obtained for the right angled triangle. In both cases h was the perpendicular height of the triangle.

Hence:
the area of a triangle $= \frac{1}{2}bh$
where b is the length of the base and h the perpendicular height down on to this base.

Notice that:

i The base need not necessarily be the *bottom* of the triangle, i.e.

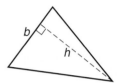

ii If the triangle is obtuse angled the height is measured as a perpendicular to the base produced.

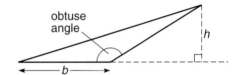

3 *The parallelogram*

We can see that the parallelogram ABDF can be made into the rectangle ABCE by translating (see Topic 10.3) the triangle AEF into BCD.

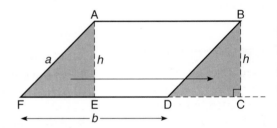

Area of parallelogram ABDF = base $\times$ perpendicular height = bh.

4 *The rhombus*

Let each side be a units and the vertical height AE be h.

The result here is the same as for the parallelogram.

The rhombus is a special case of the parallelogram. Thus:

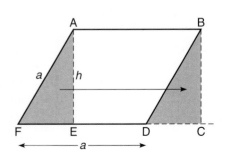

area of rhombus ABDF = area of rectangle ABCE = ah.

5 *The circle*

Imagine a circle divided into a large number of sections – as shown in the diagram.

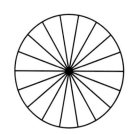

If these were cut out and reversed as shown, the area of the circle becomes *almost* the shape of a rectangle.

We know the area of a rectangle is length × breadth.

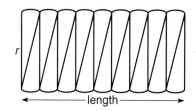

The length is approximately $\frac{1}{2}$ the circumference on each side, i.e. πr (see Topic 9.2), the breadth is approximately the radius r.

Thus, area is approximately $\pi r \times r = \pi r^2$.

In theory, if an infinite number of sections were taken, we would get a rectangle of exactly length πr and breadth r.

Hence an exact formula is area of circle, $A = \pi r^2$.

When doing a calculation, square r first then multiply by π.

6 *The trapezium*

Let the parallel sides be of length a and b units and the perpendicular height h be the distance between them.

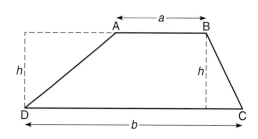

We can see that:

Area of trapezium ABCD
= area of triangle ABD + area of triangle BCD.
= $\frac{1}{2}ah + \frac{1}{2}bh$.

Hence area of trapezium = $\frac{1}{2}(a + b)h$
or (sum of parallel sides) × (perpendicular height divided by 2).

Worked Examples

Find the areas of the following shapes:

1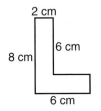

2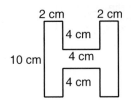

3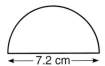

4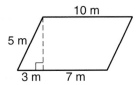

5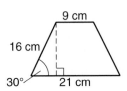

6

7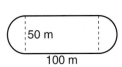

8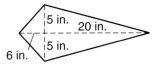

1 We can divide the shape into
    2 rectangles, A and B.

Area of A = 8×2 = $16\,\text{cm}^2$
Area of B = 4×2 = $8\,\text{cm}^2$
Total area   = $24\,\text{cm}^2$

2 Dividing the shape up into
    rectangles, A, B, C,

Area of A = $10 \times 2 = 20\,\text{cm}^2$
Area of B = $10 \times 2 = 20\,\text{cm}^2$
Area of C = 4×2 = $8\,\text{cm}^2$
Total area   = $48\,\text{cm}^2$

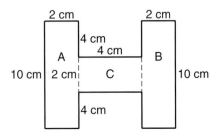

3   This is a semicircle with a diameter of 7.2 cm.

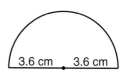

Hence radius, $r = \dfrac{7.2}{2} = 3.6$ cm

Area $= \frac{1}{2}$ area of circle $= \frac{1}{2} \times \pi \times 3.6^2$

Using $\pi = 3.14$ we get

$$A = \frac{3.14 \times 3.6 \times 3.6}{2}$$

$$= 20.35 \text{ cm}^2$$

Hence $A = 20.4$ cm^2 (3 sf).

NOTE
We can also use the value of π as given in our calculators.

4   We do not know the vertical height yet.
By the triangle shown, and using Pythagoras' theorem (see Topic 9.5)

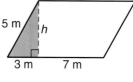

$h^2 + 3^2 = 5^2$
$h^2 + 9 \; = 25$
$\quad\; h^2 = 16$
i.e. $h = 4$

Thus perpendicular height $= 4$ m.

Hence area of parallelogram $=$ base $\times$ height $= 10 \times 4 = 40$ m^2

5   Again we do not know the vertical height.
However, using SOHCAHTOA from the triangle marked:

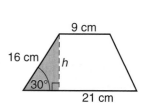

$\sin 30° = \dfrac{h}{16}$ (see Topic 9.6)

$0.5 = \dfrac{h}{16}$

$0.5 \times 16 = h$

$\quad\quad\; 8 = h$

i.e. perpendicular height $= 8$ cm.

Hence, $A = \dfrac{(\text{sum of parallel sides}) \times \text{perpendicular height}}{2}$

$$= \frac{(9 + 21) \times 8}{2} = \frac{30 \times 8}{2} = 120 \text{ cm}^2$$

6 Area of square $= 10^2 = 100\,\text{cm}^2$

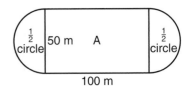

Area of circle

$= \pi r^2$

$= 3.142 \times 4^2$

$= 3.142 \times 16$

$= 50.272\,\text{cm}^2$

Hence required area

$= 100 - 50.272$

$= 49.728$

$= 49.7\,\text{cm}^2$ (3 sf)

7 In this case we have a rectangle A and the two ends which are half circles.

Area of A

$= 100 \times 50$

$= 5000\,\text{m}^2$

Radius of circle $= 25\,\text{m}$

Thus area of half circle

$= \frac{1}{2} \times \pi \times 25^2$

$= \frac{1}{2} \times 3.14 \times 625$

$= 981.25\,\text{m}^2$

Therefore total area $= 5000 + 2 \times 981.25\,\text{m}^2 = 6960\,\text{m}^2$ (3 sf).

NOTE
The area of the two half circles could have been calculated as the area of a full circle of radius 25 m.

8 In this case the two left hand triangles A can be rearranged to form a complete rectangle, as shown in the diagrams, as do the two rectangles B.

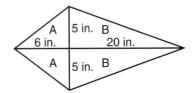

Hence area of 2A

$= 5 \times 6$

$= 30\,\text{in.}^2$

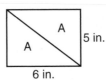

Hence area of 2B

$= 5 \times 20$

$= 100\,\text{in.}^2$

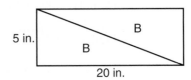

Total area of kite $= 130\,\text{in.}^2$

PRACTICE 11.3.2   Try these questions with a calculator

Find the areas of the following shapes.

1

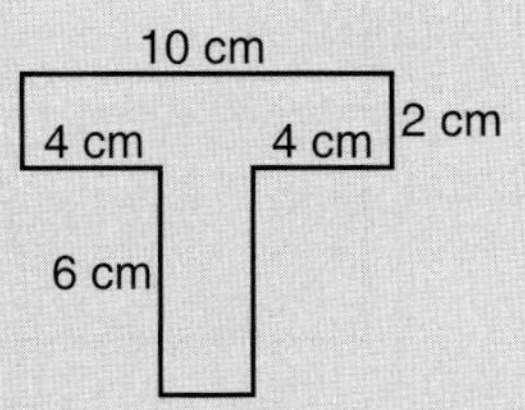

10 cm
4 cm   4 cm | 2 cm
6 cm

2

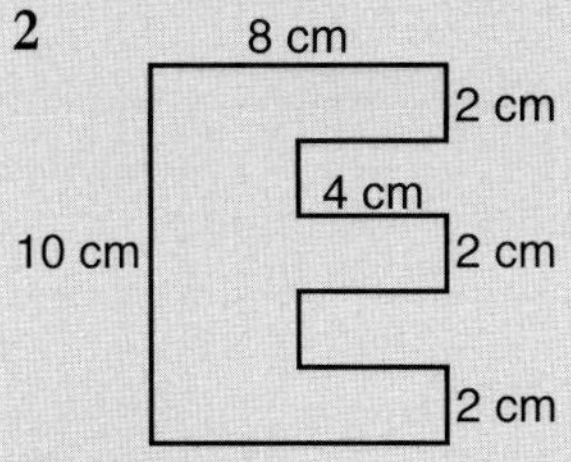

8 cm
2 cm
4 cm
10 cm
2 cm
2 cm

3

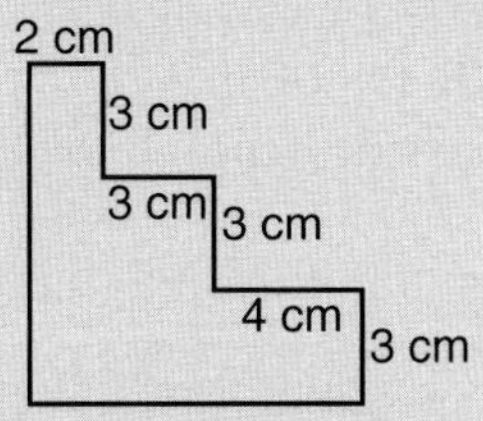

2 cm
3 cm
3 cm | 3 cm
4 cm
3 cm

4

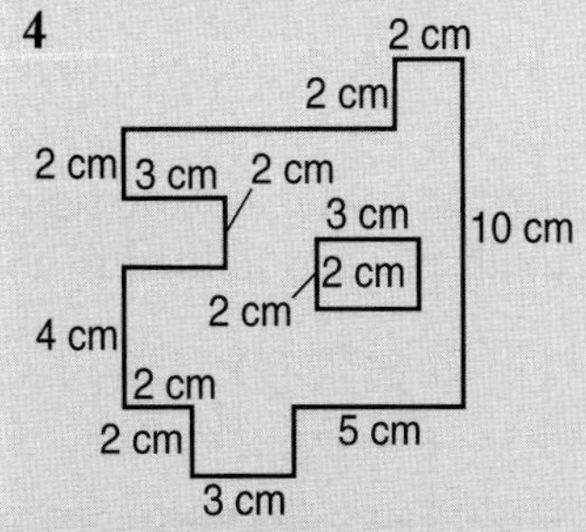

2 cm
2 cm
2 cm | 3 cm | 2 cm
3 cm
10 cm
2 cm
4 cm
2 cm
2 cm   5 cm
3 cm

5

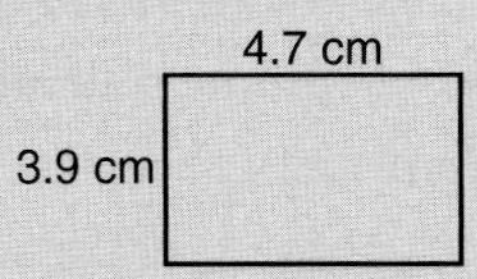

4.7 cm
3.9 cm

6

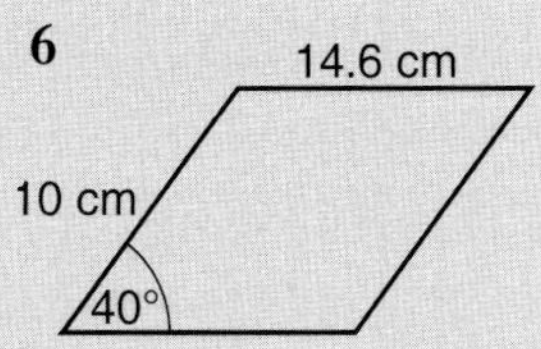

14.6 cm
10 cm
40°

7

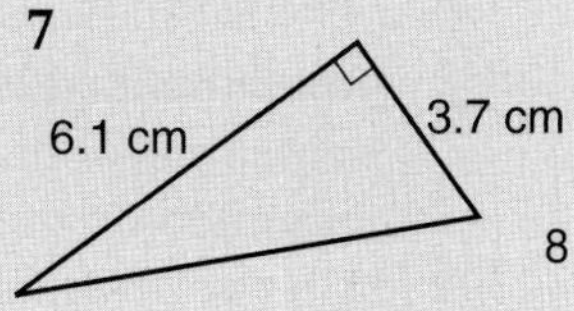

6.1 cm   3.7 cm

8

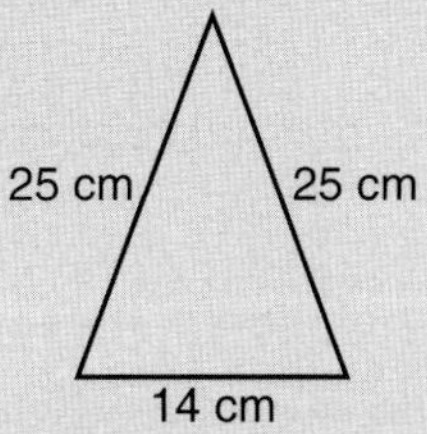

25 cm   25 cm
14 cm

9

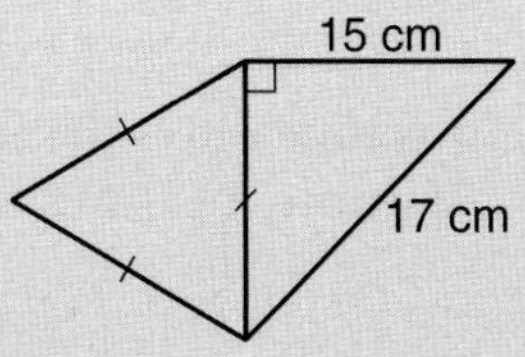

15 cm
17 cm

10

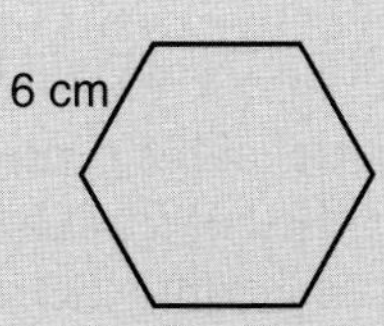

6 cm

11

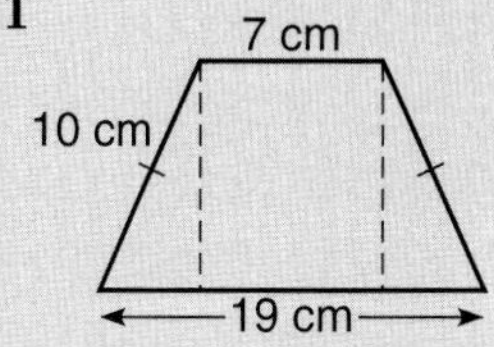

7 cm
10 cm
19 cm

12

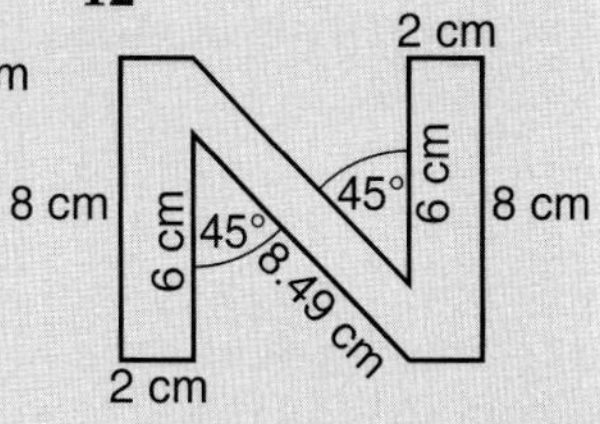

2 cm
6 cm
8 cm   45°   8 cm
6 cm   45°   8.49 cm
2 cm

13

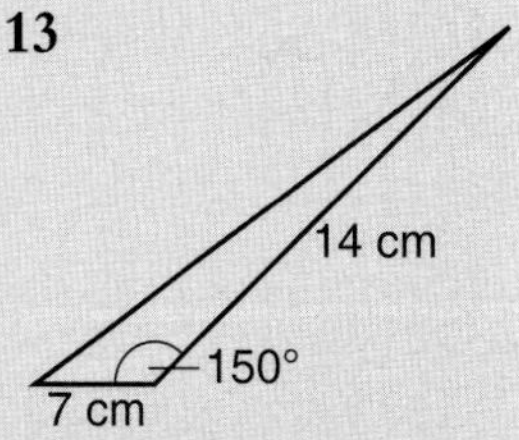

14 cm
150°
7 cm

14

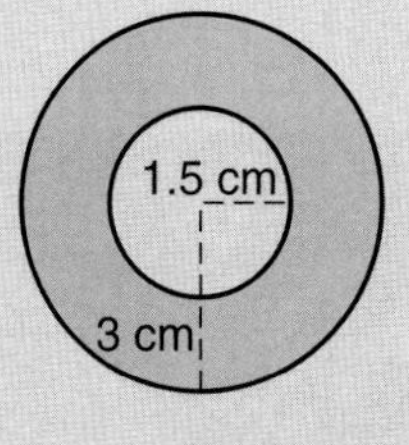

1.5 cm
3 cm

15

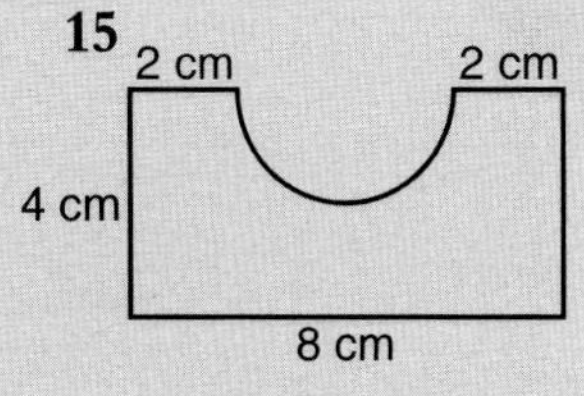

2 cm   2 cm
4 cm
8 cm

16

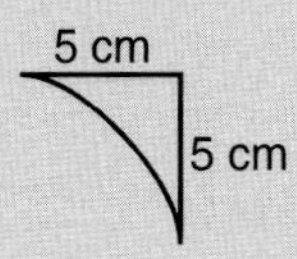

5 cm
5 cm

17 Find the area of the shaded section.

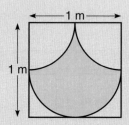

18 The metal head of a garden
implement consists of a sharp
semicircle of diameter 7.5 in.
mounted on the end of a rectangle
4 in. by 2.5 in.

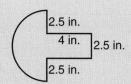

Find the area of the head.

19 The British Kite mark consists of
two semicircles at the top of an
equilateral triangle of side 4 in.
Find the area.

20 Find the area of a regular octagon of side 5 cm.

Area measures the flat surface inside a plane figure.
Volume measures the total space contained in a three-dimensional figure.

There are several basic units of volume – all *cubes*:

the cubic centimetre or cm^3
the cubic inch or in^3
the cubic metre or m^3
the cubic foot or ft^3

Thus, for example, a cuboid,
4 cm by 3 cm by 2 cm will contain
$4 \times 3 \times 2 = 24$ cubes each of side 1 cm.

Thus the volume of the cuboid is 24 cm^3.

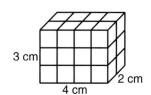

Volumes of figures

Many three-dimensional figures can be put into one of three types:

1 *The sphere*

The volume of a sphere (or ball) is given by the formula $V = \frac{4}{3}\pi r^3$, where r is the radius, (see Topic 9.2).

2 *Shapes with constant cross section*

The general name for any shape with a constant cross section is **prism**. Some prisms have special names:

a The square or rectangular cross section produces a *cube* (all sides equal) or *cuboid*. The volume of a cuboid is given by $V = lbh$, where l is the length, b the breadth and h the height of the cuboid.
Hence, volume of a cube, $V = l^3$.

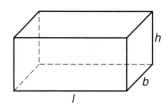

b The circular cross section produces a cylinder.

If the radius of the circular cross section is r and the height of the cylinder is h, the volume of the cylinder is given by $V = \pi r^2 h$.

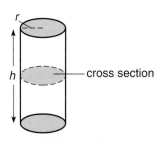

cross section

c Other shapes are called prisms, e.g.

triangular prisms

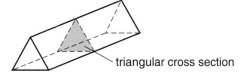

triangular cross section

octagonal prisms

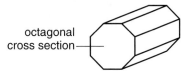

octagonal cross section

and so on …

However, there is an easy way to work out the volume of a prism whatever the shape of the cross section.

    i Work out the area of the cross section,
    ii multiply by the height,
    iii volume of prism = area of cross section × height
    (We have already seen that this is true for the cuboid and cylinder.)

3 *Shapes which come to a point*

The general name for any shape which comes to a point is **pyramid**. The point is called the **apex**.

As for the prism above, there is also a general formula for the volume, i.e.

volume of pyramid $= \frac{1}{3} \times$ base area × perpendicular height

$$= \tfrac{1}{3}Ah$$

Again, some pyramids have special names:

a The circular based pyramid is called a **cone**.

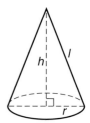

    Hence from above
    $V = \frac{1}{3} \times$ base area × perpendicular height
    $V = \frac{1}{3}\pi r^2 h$

NOTE
You will need to know the formula for the volume of a cone for the examination.

b The triangular based pyramid is called a **tetrahedron**.

    This comes from a Greek word which means *four faces*.

We can see that the tetrahedron does contain four triangular faces.

c Other shapes are called pyramids e.g. square-based pyramid.

As before, the easy way to work out the volume is:
    i work out the area of the base,
    ii multiply by the height,
    iii divide by 3.

Hence *volume of pyramid* $= \dfrac{base\ area \times perpendicular\ height}{3}$

Points to remember:

1 *Perpendicular height* means the distance from the apex vertically down on to the base.

2 *Slant height* means the *slanting distance* up the side of a pyramid (see the cone diagram).

3 In the cone, slant height (*l*), perpendicular height (*h*) and base radius (*r*) are all connected by Pythagoras' theorem.

4 If the apex is vertically above the centre of the base the shape is said to be *right*, i.e. we would have a *right circular cone*, or a *right square pyramid*, etc.

Density

We have all noticed that the same volume of different substances have different masses. This is because some materials are *denser* than others.

The **density** of a body is the mass contained in 1 unit volume.

Hence, density is quoted in grams per cubic centimetre (g/cm^3)
or kg per cubic metre (kg/m^3)
or pounds per cubic inch (lb/in^3), etc.

There is an easy formula;
if M is the mass, V is the volume and d is the density, then

$$M = V \times d \quad \text{or} \quad V = \frac{M}{d} \quad \text{or} \quad d = \frac{M}{V}$$

For example, if a $\frac{1}{2}$ kg block of a materials takes up $100\,\text{cm}^3$ of space, we can say

$$100 \times d = 500$$
$$\text{i.e.} \quad d = 5$$

the density of the material is $5\,\text{g/cm}^3$.

Worked Examples

Find the volumes of the following bodies.

1

5
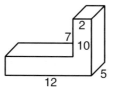

2

6
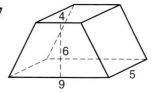

3
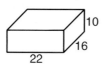

7
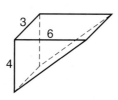

4
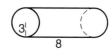

8

1 For a sphere $V = \frac{4}{3}\pi r^3$

$$= \frac{4}{3} \times 3.14 \times 4 \times 4 \times 4 = 268 \, \text{unit}^3$$

2 For a cuboid $V = 22 \times 16 \times 10$

$$= 3520 \, \text{unit}^3$$

3 The shape can be divided into 2 cuboids

A: $3 \times 12 \times 5 = 180$
B: $7 \times 2 \times 5 = 70$
Total volume $= 250 \, \text{unit}^3$

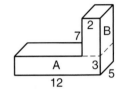

4 For a prism

the cross section is a right angled triangle

therefore area of cross section $= \frac{1}{2} \times \text{base} \times \text{height}$

$$= \frac{1}{2} \times 4 \times 6 = 12$$

volume $= \text{cross section} \times \textit{height}$

$$= 12 \times 3$$
$$= 36 \, \text{unit}^3$$

5 For a rectangular based pyramid, the base area is a rectangle

area $= l \times b = 4 \times 6$

$$= 24 \, \text{unit}^2$$

volume $= \frac{1}{3} \times \text{base area} \times \text{height}$

$$= \frac{1}{3} \times 24 \times 5$$
$$= 40 \, \text{unit}^3$$

6 For a cylinder, volume $= \text{base area} \times \text{height}$

$$= \pi r^2 h$$
$$= 3.14 \times 3^2 \times 8$$
$$= 3.14 \times 9 \times 8$$
$$= 226 \, \text{unit}^3$$

7 For a prism, with the cross section of a trapezium

area of cross section $= \dfrac{h(a+b)}{2}$

$$= \dfrac{6(4+9)}{2}$$

$$= \dfrac{6 \times 13}{2} = 39 \, \text{unit}^2$$

volume $= \text{cross-sectional area} \times \text{length}$

$$= 39 \times 5$$
$$= 195 \, \text{unit}^3$$

8 This is a cone on top a hemisphere.

volume of cone	$= \frac{1}{3}\pi r^2 h$
	$= \frac{1}{3} \times 3.14 \times 5^2 \times 8$
	$= 209.3\,\text{unit}^3$
volume of hemisphere	$= \frac{1}{2} \times \text{volume of sphere}$
	$= \frac{1}{2} \times \frac{4}{3} \times 3.14 \times 5 \times 5 \times 5$
	$= 261.7\,\text{unit}^3$
Therefore total volume	$= 209.3 + 261.7 = 471\,\text{unit}^3$

PRACTICE 11.4.1   Try these questions with a calculator

(Take $\pi = 3.14$ or use the π button on your calculator.)

Find the volumes of the following shapes.

1

4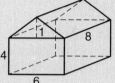

7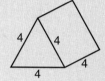

2

5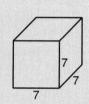

8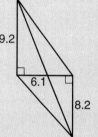

3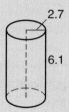

6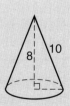

9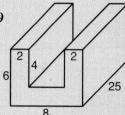

10 A toy consists of a cone sitting on top of a hemisphere.

The diameter of the hemisphere is 7.2 cm and the total height of the toy is 9.8 cm.

a Find the total volume of the toy.
b If the density of the material is 0.6 g/cm³, find the mass of the toy.

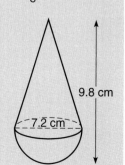

11 Pam takes a slice out of a slab of
butter, as shown in the diagram.

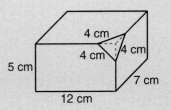

   a Calculate the volume of the slice
removed.

   b Calculate the volume of butter
remaining.

   c How many *slices* of the same
volume could Pat remove before
the butter is used?

12 A sphere has a volume of $2500 \, \text{m}^3$. Find its radius.

13 A ball bearing of radius $0.8 \, \text{cm}$ is dropped into a cylindrical beaker of
base radius $1.8 \, \text{cm}$ containing water. How much does the water level
rise?

14 The diagram shows a *frustum* of a cone.
(The top of a cone is cut off leaving a
frustum behind.) The radii of the circular
ends are $3 \, \text{in.}$ and $5 \, \text{in.}$ and are $4 \, \text{in.}$ apart.

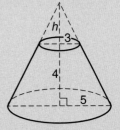

   a Use similar triangles to determine the
height, h, of the cone removed.

   b Hence, find the volume of the
frustum.

15 A lead cylinder, height $5 \, \text{cm}$ and base radius $1.5 \, \text{cm}$ is melted down
and recast into a number of lead spheres of radius $1 \, \text{cm}$. How many
spheres can be made?

16 An iron pipe is $2 \, \text{m}$ long and has an outer radius of $1 \, \text{cm}$ with a central
hole of radius $0.5 \, \text{cm}$.

   a Find the volume of iron in the pipe.
(The density of iron is $7.86 \, \text{g/cm}^3$.)

   b Find the mass of the pipe.

17 Assume the earth is a sphere of radius 3960 miles with mean density
$5.53 \, \text{lb/in}^3$.

   a Calculate the volume of the earth.

   b Calculate the approximate mass of the earth.

   c The surface area of a sphere is given by the formula $A = 4\pi r^2$.
Calculate the surface area of the earth.

   d A rampant virus kills every living thing in its tracks. It can infect
$5000 \, \text{miles}^2$ of the earth in 1 day. How long will life survive on earth?

18 An unsharpened wooden pencil
takes the form of a hexagonal
prism. Each side of the hexagon
is 0.15 in. and the pencil is 6 in.
long.

The graphite core is a cylinder
of radius 0.04 in.

  a Calculate:
    i the area of the hexagonal
      cross section,
    ii the total volume of the pencil
      and core,
    iii the volume of the graphite core,
    iv the volume of wood used in the pencil.
  b What percentage of the whole pencil is taken up by the core?
The pencil has a mean density of 0.5 oz/in.^{3}.
  c Find the mass of the pencil.
  d How many pencils would there be in a mass of 1 lb?

Areas and volumes of similar figures

1

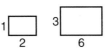

2

3

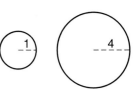

Consider all these pairs of similar figures.

1 Ratio of corresponding lengths in rectangles $= 3:1$
2 Ratio of corresponding lengths in triangles $= 6:3 = 2:1$
3 Ratio of corresponding lengths in circles $= 4:1$

Now consider areas:

1 Area of small rectangle $= 1 \times 2 = 2$ unit^2
   Area of large rectangle $= 3 \times 6 = 18$ unit^2

   Ratio of areas $= 18:2 = 9:1$

2 Area of small triangle $= \frac{1}{2} \times 5 \times 3 = 7.5$ unit^2

   Area of large triangle $= \frac{1}{2} \times 10 \times 6 = 30$ unit^2

   Ratio of areas $= 30:7.5 = 4:1$

3 Area of small circle $= \pi \times 1^2 = \pi \, \text{unit}^2$
Area of large circle $= \pi \times 4^2 = 16\pi \, \text{unit}^2$

Ratio of areas $= 16\pi : \pi = 16 : 1$

Hence:

Shape	Ratio of sides	Ratio of area
1 rectangle	3	9
2 triangle	2	4
3 circle	4	16

These results show a general rule for any similar figure:

ratio of areas = (ratio of corresponding sides)²

A similar result is also true for three-dimensional shapes:

ratio of volumes = (ratio of corresponding sides)³

Worked Examples

1 The scale drawing of a shape has an area of 126 cm². If the drawing is on a scale of 1 : 50, find the area of the actual shape.

Ratio of corresponding lengths $= \dfrac{50}{1}$

Therefore ratio of areas $\left(\dfrac{50}{1}\right)^2 = \dfrac{2500}{1}$

Hence actual area $= 2500 \times 126$
$\qquad\qquad\qquad = 315\,000 \, \text{cm}^2$

2 A metal tray weighs $\frac{1}{2}$ lb. How heavy will a similar tray be, with dimensions twice that of the original?

Ratio of corresponding lengths $= \dfrac{2}{1}$

Therefore ratio of volumes $= \dfrac{2^3}{1} = \dfrac{8}{1}$

Hence the weight of the larger tray $= 8 \times \frac{1}{2} = 4 \, \text{lb}$

3 A cylindrical container is 10 cm high and contains 400 ml of liquid. How much liquid will a similar container hold 15 cm high?

Ratio of corresponding lengths $= \dfrac{15}{10} = \dfrac{3}{2}$

Therefore ratio of volumes $\left(\dfrac{3}{2}\right)^3 = \dfrac{27}{8}$

Hence larger container will hold $\dfrac{27}{8} \times 400 = 1350 \, \text{ml}$

4 A rectangular slab 20 cm long weighs 48 kg. How much would a similar slab weigh if it was 15 cm long but was the same thickness?

Ratio of corresponding lengths $= \dfrac{15}{20} = \dfrac{3}{4}$

Since the thickness of both slabs is the same the ratio of weights is the same as the ratio of the areas.

The ratio of areas $\left(\dfrac{3}{4}\right)^2 = \dfrac{9}{16}$

Therefore the weight of the second slab $= \dfrac{9}{16} \times 48 = 27$ kg

---

PRACTICE 11.4.2   Try these questions with a calculator

1 On a photograph Demelza's height is 9.6 cm and her arm measures 4 cm. Demelza is actually 144 cm tall. How long is her arm?

2 An exact model is made of the same material as a statue. The model is 1 m high and weighs 2.5 kg. The statue is 10 m high. What is its weight?

3 A small jug, 10 cm high, holds 0.3 litre. How much would a similar jug hold if it was 17 cm high?

4 A bar of chocolate costs 95 p. How much would a similar bar cost with dimensions $\frac{3}{4}$ of the original?

5 On a map the scale is 1:10 000. A lake has an area of 2.5 cm^2 on the map. What is the real area of the lake?

6 A cone is 8 in. high and is made of thin metal weighing 10 oz. A similar cone **of the same thickness** weighs 27.44 oz. What is the height of this cone?

7 The area of the base of the smaller cone in question **6** is 4.4 in.^{2}. What is the area of the base of the larger cone?

8 Ruth blows up a balloon until it is spherical with a radius of 12 cm. She continues to blow until it has a radius of 48 cm. What fraction of the original thickness of the rubber is the new thickness?

9 The traffic police notice that it takes a motorist 3 seconds to completely fill a breathalyser bag. How long would it take the same motorist, blowing at the same rate, to fill a similar bag twice as big?

All the formulae for perimeters, areas and volumes have **dimensions**.
The dimension of a formula is the *power* to which the unit of length is raised.

1 All perimeters are of the *first dimension*, i.e. the power is 1.

For example, the perimeter of an equilateral triangle of side x units is $3x$ units, i.e. 3 times x to the *power 1*.

For a rectangle of length x units and width y units, it is $2x + 2y$ units, *both* terms are raised to the *power 1*.

Thus *all formulae for lengths must be of the first dimension.*

2 All areas are of the *second dimension*, i.e. the power is 2.

For example, $A = x^2$, for a square of side x units (x to the *power 2*)

$A = \pi r^2$, for a circle (r to the *power 2*)

A = lb, for a rectangle (lb means $l \times b$ which is (a length) $\times$ (a length) so has a *total power 2*)

Thus *all formulae for areas must be of the second dimension.*

3 All volumes are of the *third dimension*, i.e. the power is 3.

For example, $V = x^3$, for a cube of side x units (x to the *power 3*)

$V = \frac{4}{3}\pi r^3$, for a sphere (r to the *power 3*)

$V = \pi r^2 h$, for a cylinder (r^2h means $r^2 \times h$ which is (a length)$^2 \times$ (a length) so has a *total power 3*)

$V = lbh$, for a cuboid (i.e. (a length) $\times$ (a length) $\times$ (a length) so has a *total power 3*)

Thus *all formulae for volumes must be of the third dimension.*

The constants in the formulae, like 2, $\frac{4}{3}$, etc. have no dimensions. They are said to be *dimensionless*.

Worked Examples

a, b and c are different lengths.
State whether the following formulae could represent lengths, areas or volumes.

1 $3ab$ **2** $4a + 3b + 2c$ **3** $5a + 4a^2$ **4** $6a^2b$

1 This is of dimension 2. The formula could represent an area.
2 This is of dimension 1. The formula could represent a length.
3 The first term is dimension 1, the second is dimension 2. This formula has mixed dimensions so could not represent any physical quantity.
4 a^2b is of dimension 3. The formula could represent a volume.

PRACTICE 11.5.1

a, b and c are different lengths.
State whether each of the following formulae could represent a length, an area, a volume, or none of these.

1   $2ab$ 6 $b^2 + c^3$ 11 $8c(2a^2 + bc)$

2   $3a + 2b + 4c$ 7 $2a(b + c)$ 12 $\frac{1}{3}\pi a^2 c$

3   $4a + b^2$ 8 $3a + 4$ 13 $\frac{4}{3}\pi b^3$

4   abc 9 $a - b$ 14 $2(ab + bc + ca)$

5   $5a^2 c$ 10 $\frac{1}{2}b^2 c + \frac{1}{4}a^3$ 15 $2(a + b)$

16   The last four questions above represent well known formulae. State what each of them could be.

17   Sian thinks that $\frac{4}{3}\pi r^2$ is the volume of a sphere. Explain why she could not possibly be right.

Another formula for the area of a triangle

We have already seen that the area of a triangle is given by the formula

$A = \frac{1}{2} \times$ base $\times$ perpendicular height

i.e. $\frac{1}{2}bh$ in the diagram shown.

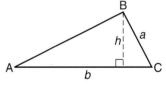

Sometimes we do not know h, but we *do* know the sides and angles of the triangle. By SOHCAHTOA in the triangle shown, we see that $\sin C = \dfrac{h}{a}$

i.e. $h = a \sin C$

Therefore the area is $A = \frac{1}{2}bh$

$\qquad\qquad\qquad\qquad = \frac{1}{2}b \times a \sin C$

i.e. $\qquad\qquad A = \frac{1}{2}ab \sin C.$

NOTE

C is the angle between the sides a and b.
If we know any two sides and the angle between them, we can find the area. Hence we get
$A = \frac{1}{2}ab \sin C$ or $\frac{1}{2}bc \sin A$ or $\frac{1}{2}ac \sin B.$

Worked Example

Find the area of the triangle shown:

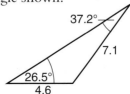

The angle between the two known sides is $180° - (26.5° + 37.2°) = 116.3°$
Hence $A = \frac{1}{2} \times 4.6 \times 7.1 \times \sin 116.3° = 14.64 \, \text{unit}^2$ (2 dp).

Length of an arc

The diagram shows a sector of a circle,
radius r and angle $\theta°$.
The part of the circumference AB is
called an *arc*.
The arc length, s, is the same fraction of
the circumference that $\theta°$ is of $360°$.

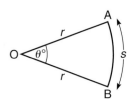

Hence $\dfrac{s}{2\pi r} = \dfrac{\theta°}{360°}$

i.e. $s = \dfrac{2\pi r \times \theta°}{360°} = \dfrac{\pi r\theta°}{180°}$

Worked Example

Find s. (Take $\pi = 3.14$)

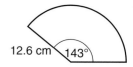

$$s = \frac{\pi r\theta°}{180°} = \frac{3.14 \times 12.6 \times 143°}{180°} = 31.4\,\text{cm (3 sf)}$$

Areas of sectors and segments

1 *Sector*

The diagram shows a sector of a circle, radius r
and angle $\theta°$.

Using the same principle as we did for the arc
length above:

area of the sector, A, is the same fraction of the
circumference that $\theta°$ is of $360°$.

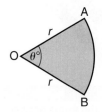

Hence $\dfrac{A}{\pi r^2} = \dfrac{\theta°}{360°}$

i.e. $A = \dfrac{\pi r^2 \times \theta°}{360°} = \dfrac{\pi r^2\theta°}{360°}$

Worked Example

Find the area of the sector shaded. (Take $\pi = 3.14$)

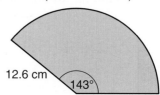

$$A = \frac{\pi r^2\theta°}{360°} = \frac{3.14 \times 12.6 \times 12.6 \times 143°}{360°} = 198\,\text{cm}^2\text{ (3 sf)}$$

2 *Segment*

The diagram shows a sector of a circle, radius r and angle $\theta°$.

A segment is formed as shown.

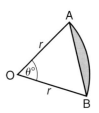

The area of the sector is $\dfrac{\pi r^2 \theta°}{360°}$

The area of the triangle OAB is $\frac{1}{2} \times r \times r \times \sin \theta° = \frac{1}{2} r^2 \sin \theta°$

Hence the area of the segment is $\dfrac{\pi r^2 \theta°}{360°} - \frac{1}{2} r^2 \sin \theta°$

Worked Example

Find the area of the segment in the above worked example.

The area of the segment in the example above is given by

$198 - \frac{1}{2} \times 12.6^2 \times \sin 143°$

$= 198 - \frac{1}{2} \times 158.76 \times 0.6018$

$= 198 - 47.8 = 150 \text{ cm}^3 \text{ (3 sf)}$

Surface area of a cylinder

If the curved surface of a cone is *cut* and opened up, we get a rectangle. One side of the rectangle is the same as the height, h, of the cylinder. The other side is the circumference of the circular base, $2\pi r$. Hence

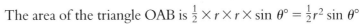

area of the curved surface = area of rectangle
                          = $2\pi rh$

When calculating the *total* surface area of a cylinder, we have to include a circular base if the cylinder is open, or two circular ends if it is closed. Hence the total surface area $= 2\pi rh + \pi r^2$ (if one end open) or $2\pi rh + 2\pi r^2$.

Worked Example

A cylindrical water butt, open at the top, is 1.5 m high and has a base of radius 30 cm. Calculate the area of wood used to make it.

$A = 2\pi rh + \pi r^2$

   $= 2 \times 3.14 \times 30 \times 150 + 3.14 \times 30 \times 30$

   $= 28\,260 + 2826$

   $= 31\,086 \text{ cm}^2$

Surface area of a cone

There is a formula for the curved
surface area of a cone.

If l is the slant height of the
cone, the formula is

curved surface area $= \pi r l$

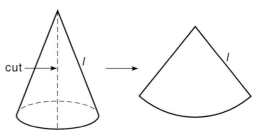

Therefore the curved surface area of the cone is $\pi r l$ and the total surface
area of the cone is $\pi r l + \pi r^2$ (or $\pi r(r + l)$).

Don't forget that l, r and h
are connected by Pythagoras'
theorem.

If we know any two of these
we can easily find the other
one.

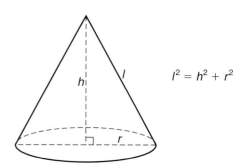

$l^2 = h^2 + r^2$

Worked Examples

a A cone has a base radius 3 cm and a height 5 cm. Find its volume.
(Take $\pi = 3.14$)

b A square based pyramid of side 2.4 cm has the same volume as the cone.
What is its height?

c Find the total surface area of the cone.

    a Volume $= \frac{1}{3} \times 3.14 \times 3 \times 3 \times 5$
           $= 47.1 \,\text{cm}^3$

    b Volume of pyramid $= \frac{1}{3} \times 2.4 \times 2.4 \times h$
                   $= 1.92h$
    If both volumes are the same, then $1.92h = 47.1$
                         i.e $h = 24.5$ cm (3 sf).

    c In the cone, $r = 3$ cm and $h = 5$ cm.

    Thus, by Pythagoras, $5^2 + 3^2 = l^2$
    i.e. $l^2 = 25 + 9 = 34$ and so $l = 5.831$ (4 sf).

    Hence curved surface area $= \pi \times 3 \times 5.831$ $= 54.93$
              area of base $= \pi \times 3^2$ $= 28.26$

    Thus total surface area $= 54.93 + 28.26$ $= 83.2 \,\text{cm}^2$ (3 sf).

Further Worked Examples

1   The earth can be considered as a sphere of radius 3960 miles. Calculate its volume. (Take $\pi = 3.14$ or use the π button on your calculator.)

$$V = \tfrac{4}{3} \times 3.14 \times 3960 \times 3960 \times 3960$$
$$= 2.6 \times 10^{11} \text{ miles}^3 \text{ (2 sf)}$$

2   A silver cube of side 10 m is melted down and recast into a sphere. Find the radius of the sphere.

Volume of cube $= 10 \times 10 \times 10 = 1000 \text{ m}^3$

Hence $\tfrac{4}{3} \times 3.14 \times r^3 = 1000$

i.e. $r^3 = \dfrac{1000}{\tfrac{4}{3} \times 3.14}$

                             $= 238.85$

Hence $r = 6.20 \text{ m (3 sf)}$.

PRACTICE 11.4.1   Try these questions with a calculator

(Take $\pi = 3.14$ or use the π button on your calculator.)

1   Find the areas of the following triangles.

a

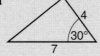

c

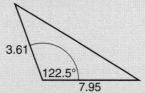

e

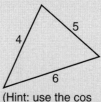

(Hint: use the cos rule first)

b

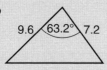

d

2   Find the lengths of arc *s*, and the areas of the following sectors.

a

b

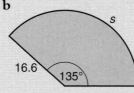

c

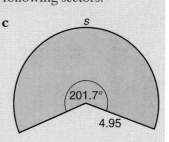

3 Find the areas of the shaded segments.

a

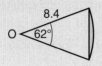

b

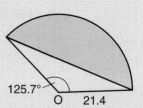

4 Find the curved surface areas of the following cylinders.

a

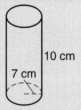

b

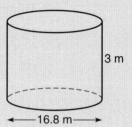

5 Find the total surface areas of the following cylinders.

a

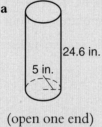

(open one end)

b

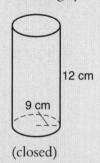

(closed)

6 Find the volumes of the following shapes.

a

c

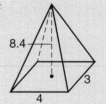

e

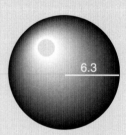

b

d

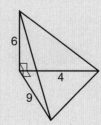

7 A circular pipe has an external radius of 24 cm and the metal is 4 cm thick. Find the volume of metal in a pipe 1 m long.

8 A cylindrical container has a base radius of 8 in. It is filled by the contents of a cone of base radius 6 in. and height 12 in. How high is the container?

9 10 000 lead shot, radius 0.6 cm, are melted down and cast into one big cannon-ball. What is the radius of the cannon-ball?

10 The diagram shows a frustum of a cone used for an elephant's stool at a circus.

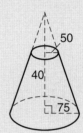

The radii of the top and bottom of the frustum are 50 cm and 75 cm and the height is 40 cm.

Calculate:
a the height of the *complete* cone,
b the volume of the *large* cone,
c the volume of the cone *removed*,
d the volume of the frustum.

11 The diagram shows a hopper for holding and distributing barley at the Glenaller Whisky distillery. It is a frustum of a square based pyramid, 2 ft at the top and 3 in. at the bottom. The vertical height of the hopper is 3 ft.

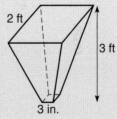

Using the methods of the previous question find the volume of the hopper.

12 A tunnel is in the shape of a major segment of a circle of radius 5 ft.

The height of the tunnel is 8 ft.

Calculate:
a the width of the floor, AB,
b the area of the minor segment shaded,
c the area of the major segment.

Hence find the volume of air in the tunnel if it is 100 ft long.

13 The diagram shows the view looking down on the top of a hexagonal prism of side 10 cm inserted into a circular hole in a block of polystyrene.

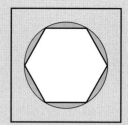

Calculate:
a the area between the hexagonal face and the circle (shaded),
b the volume of air if the package and its hole are 20 cm high.

14 A manufacturer wants to can 503 cm³ of soup. She can do so in cylindrical cans either 4 cm or 8 cm in radius. Calculate the height of the cans.

The manufacturer decides to use the can that requires least metal to make. Which one does she choose?

15 The heart shape shown consits of two semicircles with diameters AB and BC each 4 cm together with two circular arcs AD and CD. AD has centre C and CD has centre A.

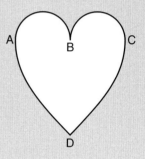

Calculate:
a the total perimeter of the heart shape,
b the area of the heart shape.

Perimeter

The *perimeter* is the distance around the edge of a shape.
The perimeter of a circle is called the circumference.

Area

An *area* measures the amount of space inside a plane shape.
An area is measured in square units.
1 square cm is written 1 cm².
There are other units of area: mm², m², in.², ft², yd², etc.
In metric measure 1 hectare (1 ha) = 10 000 m².
In imperial measure 1 acre = 4840 yd².
When calculating or measuring areas, we must use the appropriate unit.

Estimating areas

If a figure has curved sides, divide it up into small squares of known area and count them.

Where there is less than a half a full square at the edge of the shape, do not count it. Where there is more than half a full square, count it as one full square.

The rectangle

The area, A, of a rectangle is given by the formula, $A = lb$.

A square is a special case where all sides are of length l. Hence $A = l^2$.

The triangle

Area of a triangle $= \frac{1}{2}bh$, where b is the length of the base and h the perpendicular height down on to this base.

The base need not necessarily be the *bottom* of the triangle.

If the triangle is obtuse angled the height is measured as a perpendicular to the base produced.

The parallelogram

Area of a parallelogram $=$ base $\times$ perpendicular height $= bh$.

The rhombus

Area of a rhombus $= ah$, where $a =$ the length of a side and $h =$ the perpendicular height.

The circle

Area of a circle $= \pi r^2$, where r is the radius.

When doing a calculation, square r first, then multiply by π.

The trapezium

Area of a trapezium $= \frac{1}{2}(a + b)h$

or (sum of parallel sides) $\times$ (perpendicular height divided by 2).

Volume

Volume measures the total space contained in a three-dimensional figure.
There are several basic units of volume:
the cubic centimetre or cm^3,
the cubic inch or $in.^3$,
the cubic metre or m^3,
the cubic foot or ft^3.

Volumes of figures

Many three-dimensional figures can be put into one of three types:

1   *The sphere*

Volume of a sphere, $V = \frac{4}{3}\pi r^3$, where r is the radius.
A *hemisphere* is half a sphere.

2   *Shapes with constant cross section*

The general name for any shape with a constant cross section is *prism*.
Some prisms have special names:

The square or rectangular cross section produces a *cube* (all sides equal) or
cuboid.
The volume of a cuboid is $V = lbh$ (l is the length, b the breadth, h the height).
$V = l^3$ for a cube of side l.
The circular cross section produces a *cylinder*.
The volume of a cylinder is $V = \pi r^2 h$.
There is an easy way to work out the volume of a prism , whatever the shape
of the cross section:

  a   work out the area of the cross section,
  b   multiply by the height,
  c   volume of prism = area of cross section × length.

3   *Shapes which come to a point*

The general name for any shape which comes to a point is *pyramid*.
The point is called the *apex*.
There is a general formula for the volume:

$$\text{volume of a pyramid} = \tfrac{1}{3} \times \text{base area} \times \text{perpendicular height}$$
$$= \tfrac{1}{3} Ah$$

Some pyramids have special names:

The circular based pyramid is called a *cone,*
hence, volume of a cone, $V = \frac{1}{3}\pi r^2 h$

The triangular based pyramid is called a *tetrahedron.*
Other shapes are just called *pyramids* e.g. square, or rectangular, based
pyramid.

There is an easy way to work out the volume:

a work out the area of the base,
b multiply by the height,
c divide by 3.

Volume of pyramid = base area × perpendicular height ÷ 3.
Perpendicular height is the distance from the apex vertically down on to the base.
Slant height is the slanting distance up the side of a pyramid.
In the cone, slant height (*l*), perpendicular height (*h*) and base radius (*r*) are all connected by Pythagoras' theorem.
If the apex is vertically above the centre of the base the shape is said to be *right*, i.e. we would have a *right circular cone*, or a *right square pyramid*, etc.

Density

The *density* of a body is the mass contained in 1 unit volume.
Density is quoted in grams per cubic centimetre (g/cm^3) or kg per cubic metre (kg/m^3) or pounds per cubic inch (lb/in.^{3}), etc.
If M is the mass, V is the volume and d is the density, then

$$M = V \times d \quad \text{or} \quad V = \frac{M}{d} \quad \text{or} \quad d = \frac{M}{V}$$

Areas and volumes of similar figures

Ratio of areas = (ratio of corresponding sides)^2.
Ratio of volumes = (ratio of corresponding sides)^3.

Dimensions

All the formulae for perimeters, areas and volumes have *dimensions*.
The dimension of a formula is the power to which the unit of length is raised.
All formulae for lengths are of the first dimension i.e. the power is 1.
All formulae for areas are of the second dimension i.e. the power is 2.
All formulae for volumes are of the third dimension i.e. the power is 3.

Another formula for the area of a triangle (extension)

$A = \frac{1}{2}ab \sin C$
where C is the angle between the sides *a* and *b*.
If we know any two sides and the angle between them, we can find the area.
Hence we get $A = \frac{1}{2}ab \sin C$ or $\frac{1}{2}bc \sin A$ or $\frac{1}{2}ac \sin B$.

Length of an arc (extension)

$$s = \frac{2\pi r\theta^\circ}{360^\circ} = \frac{\pi r\theta^\circ}{180^\circ}$$

Areas of sectors and segments (extension)

$$\text{Area of sector} = \frac{\pi r^2\theta^\circ}{360^\circ}$$

$$\text{Area of segment} = \frac{\pi r^2\theta^\circ}{360^\circ} - \tfrac{1}{2}r^2\sin\theta$$

Surface area of a cylinder (extension)

Area of the curved surface $= 2\pi rh$.
When calculating the *total* surface area of a cylinder, we have to include a circular base if the cylinder is open, or two circular ends if it is closed.
Total surface area of a cylinder $= 2\pi rh + \pi r^2$ (if one end open) or $2\pi rh + 2\pi r^2$.

Surface area of a cone (extension)

Curved surface area $= \pi rl$
where l is the slant height and r is the radius.
Total surface area $= \pi rl + \pi r^2$ (or $\pi r(r+l)$)

Sample non-calculator papers

The following section contains a range of questions of the style that you will need to take for your non-calculator papers. Questions are provided for both the Intermediate and Higher Tiers for all three Modules. A range of question types has been given to give you some idea of the areas you may need to tackle.

Try and practise these questions and others as much as you can. This will enable you to develop experience and skill in answering different types of questions without a calculator. Practise also those that do require a calculator as much as possible.

Where you get stuck, remember that you can go to the relevant part of this book and revise or brush up on the key topics accordingly.

Good luck!

INTERMEDIATE TIER

Module 1 – Money management and number

1 Sue wishes to travel by train from Exeter (Central) to Salisbury.

Exeter St. Davids .... dp	1330	–	*1450*	1545	1620	1700	1741	1822	2029
Exeter Central .... dp	1334	–	1459	1549	1624	1704	1745	1826	2033
Pinhoe........................	1339	–	–	–	1629	1709	1750	–	2038
Whimple	1346	–	1508	–	1636	1716	1757	1835	2045
Feniton	1351	–	1514	–	1641	1721	1802	1841	2050
Honiton .... ar	1358	–	1521	1605	1648	1729	1809	1847	2057
Honiton .... dp	1358	–	1521	1605	1648	1729	1809	1851	2057
Axminster	1409	–	1532	1616	1659	1740	1820	1902	2108
Crewkeme....................	1422	–	1545	1629	1713	1753	1842	1923	2133
Yeovil Junction .... ar	1431	–	1554	1638	1722	1802	1851	1932	2142
Yeovil Junction .... dp	1432	–	1556	1639	1723	1803	1903	1938	2143
Sherborne....................	1439	–	1603	1646	1730	1810	1910	1944	2150
Templecombe	1446	–	1610	1653	1737	1817	1917	1952	2157
Gillingham............. ar	1454	1553	1617	1701	1745	1824	1924	1959	2205
Gillingham............. dp	1454	1553	1624	1701	1745	1829	1931	1959	2205
Tisbury	1504	1603	1634	–	1755	1839	1941	2010	2215
Salisbury .... ar	1519	1625	1649	1723	1809	1853	1955	2036	2235
Southampton Central........ ar	*1559*	*1659*	*1736*	*1759*	*1907*	*2004*	*2104*	*2202*	*2322v*
Portsmouth & S'sea .... ar	*1643*	*1743*	–	*1843*	*1948*	*2048*	*2147*	*2243*	*0004v*
Salisbury .... dp	1523	1636	–	1725	1815	1915	–	2045	2240
Grateley......................	–	1648	–	–	1827	1927	–	2057	2252
Andover	1541	1655	–	1743	1834	1934	–	2104	2259
Whitechurch (Hants).............	–	1703	–	–	1842	1942	–	2112	2307
Overton......................	–	1709	–	–	1848	1948	–	2118	2313
Basingstoke................ ar	1557	1717	–	1801	1856	1956	–	2126	2321
Reading.................. ar	*1628*	*1747*	–	*1846*	*1928*	*2028*	–	*2203*	*0003*
Woking .... ✈ ar	1617	1741	–	1820	1916	2017	–	2146	*0007*
Clapham Junction .... ar	1642	1802	–	1844	1936	2037	–	2211	*0046*
London Waterloo........... ⊖ ar	1650	1810	–	1852	1944	2051	–	2219	*0055*

She arrives at Exeter (Central) station at 1530 and catches the first train going to Salisbury.

How long does the train journey take in hours and minutes? *(4 marks)*

2 Steven receives his gas bill. The charge for the gas is £60 plus VAT at 5%.
  a Calculate the VAT charged. *(3 marks)*
  b Hence find the total amount Steven has to pay. *(1 mark)*

3 A hotel in Italy charges 165 000 lira for bed and breakfast. Mr Thomas is billed for 4 nights bed and breakfast The exchange rate was 3000 lira to the pound sterling (£). How much was Mr Thomas' bill in pounds sterling. *(3 marks)*

4 Mr and Mrs Loveridge and their three children are planning a week's holiday. The cost of staying at the hotel for one week is £150 for each adult and £100 for each child. The return rail fare is £35 for each adult and half price for children.
  a Calculate the total hotel costs. *(1 mark)*
  b Calculate the total rail fare. *(2 marks)*

5 Paint is sold in two sizes, large and regular. The large size costs £11.50 and contains $2\frac{1}{2}$ litres. The regular size costs £4.99 and contains 1 litre. Which size is better value for money? You **must** show all your working. *(3 marks)*

6 Meat should be cooked for 70 minutes per kilogram plus 35 minutes.
A joint of pork weighs 2 kg.
It is placed in the oven at 10.15a.m.
At what time will it be cooked? *(3 marks)*

7 Vinod invests £6000 at an annual rate of 4%.
After 5 months he withdraws all his money.
How much will he receive? *(3 marks)*

8 **a** Find the value of 4×2^3. *(1 mark)*

  b Find an approximate value of $\dfrac{4.96}{26.2 + 23.9}$. *(2 marks)*

  c Evaluate 7^{-2}. Give your answer as a fraction. *(1 mark)*

9 The formula for converting temperature from degrees Fahrenheit (F) to degrees Celsius (C) is

$$C = \frac{5}{9}(F - 32)$$

Calculate the Celsius equivalent of -22 degrees Fahrenheit? *(3 marks)*

10 $a = 3 \times 10^4$ $b = 4 \times 10^7$

  a Evaluate ab.
    Give your answers in standard form. *(2 marks)*

  b Evaluate $\dfrac{a}{b}$.

    Give your answers in standard form. *(3 marks)*

(Total: 35 marks)

Module 2 – Statistics and probability

1 Mr Hill collects information on the number of parents visiting his school each year as follows:

Year	1993	1994	1995	1996	1997	1998
No. of parents	400	540	not collected	570	480	570

He uses this information to plot a line graph. His graph is shown below.

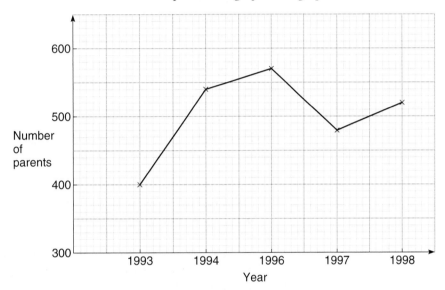

Give **three** criticisms of Mr Hill's graph.   *(3 marks)*

2 State whether the following are **discrete** or **continuous** variables.
   a The number of eggs laid by a chicken in one week.   *(1 mark)*
   b The time taken for a chicken to lay an egg.   *(1 mark)*

3 a The number of goals scored at six home matches was:

$$5, \quad 8, \quad 5, \quad 5, \quad 6, \quad 7$$

   What is the mean number of goals scored?   *(2 marks)*
   b The number of goals scored at six away matches was:

$$4, \quad 2, \quad 2, \quad 9, \quad 3, \quad 2$$

   i What is the modal number of goals scored?   *(1 mark)*
   ii What is the range of the goals scored?   *(2 marks)*

4 A dice is biased so that the probability of getting a six is $\frac{1}{4}$.
   The dice is rolled 100 times.
   a How many sixes would you expect to get?   *(2 marks)*
   b The number three appears 13 times.
      Give an estimate of the probability of getting a three when
      this dice is rolled.   *(1 mark)*

5 a List two types of question which should be avoided when designing a questionnaire. *(2 marks)*

  b It is intended to send the questionnaire to a random sample of 100 adults who all live in the same town.

   i State how you would obtain such a random sample. *(1 marks)*

   ii Criticize the following methods of obtaining the sample.
   Using the telephone directory. *(1 mark)*
   Asking adults outside a supermarket. *(1 mark)*

6 Jack and Jill are counting the number of people in each car that passes them.
Jack counts 15 cars and calculates the mean to be 2.2 people per car.
Jill counts 45 cars and calculates the mean to be 2.1 people per car.

Which of the two means would you expect to give the more reliable estimate of the mean number of people per car? Give a reason for your answer. *(2 marks)*

7 Fifty students at a college each ran 100 metres. The recorded times, to the nearest second, are shown below.

Time (nearest second)	12	13	14	15	16	17	18	19	20
Number of students	2	4	6	8	7	9	8	5	1

On graph paper, draw a frequency polygon to represent this information. *(3 marks)*

8 The weight of tea in a sample of 100 tea-bags is shown in the table.

Weight of tea in tea-bag, w (grams)	Frequency	Cumulative frequency
$2.9 \leqslant w < 3.0$	2	
$3.0 \leqslant w < 3.1$	6	
$3.1 \leqslant w < 3.2$	32	
$3.2 \leqslant w < 3.3$	41	
$3.3 \leqslant w < 3.4$	14	
$3.4 \leqslant w < 3.5$	4	
$3.5 \leqslant w < 3.6$	1	

  a Complete the cumulative frequency column of the table. *(1 mark)*
  b Draw a cumulative frequency curve for these data on graph paper. *(2 marks)*
  c Use your graph to estimate the number of tea-bags with a weight greater than 3.35 grams. *(1 mark)*

9 A seaside resort recorded the rainfall in millimetres and the number of deck chair tickets sold.
The scatter diagram illustrates some of these recordings.

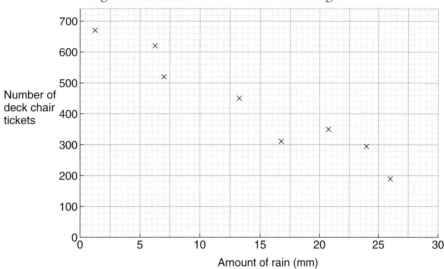

  a What does the scatter diagram tell you about the connection between the rainfall and the number of deck chair tickets sold?   *(1 mark)*
  b Draw a line of best fit on the scatter diagram.   *(1 mark)*
  c Use your line of best fit to work out the likely number of deck chair tickets sold when the rainfall is recorded as 10 mm.   *(2 marks)*

10 The probability that I am late for work on a Monday is 0.3.
The probability that I am late for work on a Friday is 0.1.
  a What is the probability that I am *not* late for work on a Monday?   *(1 mark)*
  b What is the probability that I am late for work on Monday *and* Friday?   *(2 marks)*

(Total: 35 marks)

Module 3 – Terminal module

1 The quadrilateral *ABCD* has angle *A* = 50°, angle *B* = 120° and angle *C* = 80°. The line *CD* is produced to *E*.

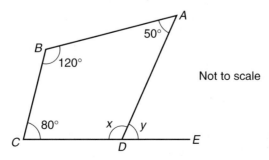

Not to scale

Calculate the size of
  a angle *x*,   *(2 marks)*
  b angle *y*.   *(2 marks)*

2 The grid shows the numbers from 1 to 50.

1	2	3	4	5	6	7	8	9	10
11	11	13	14	15	16	17	18	19	20
21	22	23	24	25	26	27	28	29	30
31	32	33	34	35	36	37	38	39	40
41	42	43	44	45	46	47	48	49	50

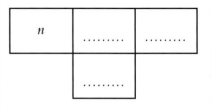

A **T** shape has been drawn on the grid. It is called T_{13} because the first number is 13. The sum of the numbers in T_{13} is $13 + 14 + 15 + 24 = 66$.

a The diagram shows T_n with three numbers missing. Complete the **T** shape in terms of n.   *(2 marks)*

b Find the sum of the numbers in T_n in terms of n. Give your answers in its simplest form.   *(2 marks)*

3 a Complete this table of values and use it to draw the graph of $y = 8 - 2x$.   *(4 marks)*

x	y
-1	
0	
1	
2	
3	

The graph of $y = 3x - 4$ has been drawn for you.

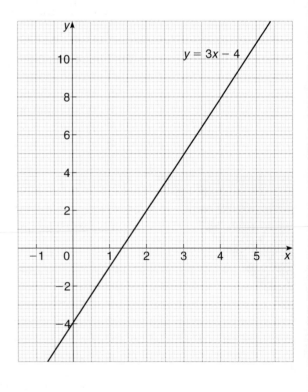

b Write down the coordinates of the point of intersection of $y = 8 - 2x$ and $y = 3x - 4$.   *(1 mark)*

4 Rachael receives two boxes.

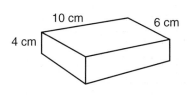 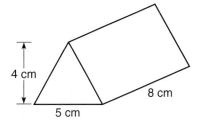

Calculate the difference between the volumes of the two boxes.
State your units. *(5 marks)*

5 A sequence of numbers begins

$$2, \quad 5, \quad 8, \quad 11, \quad \ldots$$

  a Write down the next number in this sequence. *(1 mark)*
  b Work out the 10th number in this sequence. *(1 mark)*
  c Find the nth term of this sequence. *(2 marks)*

6 A stopwatch records times to the nearest 0.1 second.

The time taken for Duncan to swim 100 metres is recorded as
88.5 seconds.
What are the maximum and minimum times that Duncan could
have taken? *(2 marks)*

7 The diagram shows three triangles P, Q and R.

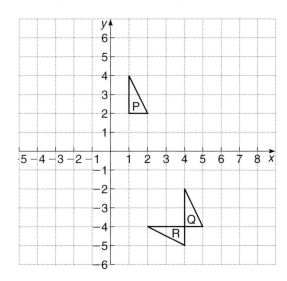

  a Describe fully the single transformation which maps triangle
     P onto triangle Q. *(2 marks)*
  b Describe fully the single transformation which maps triangle
     Q onto triangle R. *(2 marks)*

8 Solve these equations.

   a $\frac{1}{3}x + 2 = 9$ *(2 marks)*

   b $3(x - 3) = 2(x - 3)$ *(3 marks)*

   c $x^2 - 2x = 8$ *(3 marks)*

9 Tony is writing down some formulae for some shapes.
   The letters a, b and c represent lengths.

   $$a + b + c, \quad \tfrac{1}{3}\pi a^2 b, \quad \pi a(b + c), \quad \sqrt{b^2 + c^2}, \quad 2\pi ab, \quad \pi(2a + b^2), \quad \pi c\sqrt{a^2 + b^2}$$

   Which of these formulae could represent area?   *(2 marks)*

10 In the diagram AB
   is parallel to CD.

   $AB = OC = 12$ cm.
   $OB = 10$ cm.

   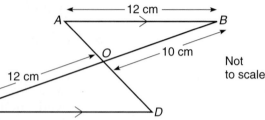

   Calculate the length of CD.   *(3 marks)*

11 Solve the simultaneous equations
   $$3x + y = 10$$
   $$x - y = 6$$ *(3 marks)*

                                                                  (Total: 44 marks)

Module 1 – Money management and number

1 Meat should be cooked for 70 minutes per kilogram plus 35 minutes.
   A joint of pork weighs 2 kg.
   It is placed in the oven at 10.15a.m.
   At what time will it be cooked?   *(3 marks)*

2 Find an approximate value of

   a $\dfrac{4.96}{26.2 + 23.9}$ *(2 marks)*   **b** $\dfrac{4.96}{26.2 + 23.9} \times 0.3^2$ *(2 marks)*

3 $a = 3 \times 10^4 \qquad b = 4 \times 10^7$

   a Evaluate ab.
        Give your answers in standard form.   *(2 marks)*

   b Evaluate $\dfrac{a}{b}$.

        Give your answers in standard form.   *(3 marks)*

4 Jenny's weekly National Insurance contributions are calculated as
   2% of £62
   plus 8.4% of her weekly earnings over £62.

   In one week Jenny's National Insurance contribution was £18.04.
   Calculate the gross weekly pay which Jenny received.   *(4 marks)*

5 The price of a percentage holiday is given as £450, to the nearest £10.

   a What is the minimum cost of this package holiday?   *(1 mark)*

   b What is the maximum cost for four adults of this package holiday?

                                                     (2 marks)

6 The shares in a company increased in value by 40% in 1998.
In 1999, the shares lost 30% of their value.
What was the percentage increase or decrease in the value of the shares in the two year period?   *(4 marks)*

7 **a** State which of these numbers are irrational.

$$3 \quad \pi \quad \sqrt{2\tfrac{1}{4}} \quad \sqrt[3]{8} \quad \sqrt{\tfrac{1}{4}} \quad \pi+1 \quad \sqrt{3} \quad (\sqrt{2})^3 \qquad \textit{(2 marks)}$$

   b Give a number, which when multiplied by π, gives a product which is a rational number.   *(1 mark)*

8 Write $0.03\dot{5}\dot{5}$ as a fraction in its simplest form.   *(4 marks)*

9 Simplify the following expressions, leaving your answer in surd form where appropriate.

   a $\sqrt{500}-\sqrt{5}$ *(2 marks)*

   b $\sqrt{18}\times\sqrt{32}$ *(3 marks)*

(Total: 35 marks)

Module 2 – Statistics and probability

1 Fifty students at a college each ran 100 metres. The recorded times, to the nearest second, are shown below.

Time (nearest second)	Number of students
12	2
13	4
14	6
15	8
16	7
17	9
18	8
19	5
20	1

On a graph paper, draw a frequency polygon to represent this information.   *(3 marks)*

2 A dice is biased so that the probability of getting a six is $\tfrac{1}{4}$.

The dice is rolled 100 times.

   a How many sixes would you expect to get?   *(2 marks)*

   b The number three appeared 13 times.
      Given an estimate of the probability of getting a three when this dice is rolled.   *(1 mark)*

3 A seaside resort recorded the rainfall in millimetres and the number of deck chair tickets sold.
The scatter diagram illustrates some of these recordings.

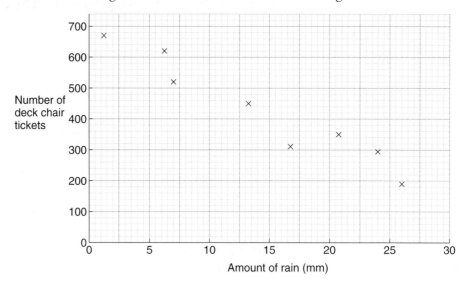

a What does the scatter diagram tell you about the connection between the rainfall and the number of deck chair tickets sold? *(1 mark)*
b Draw a line of best fit on the scatter diagram. *(1 mark)*
c Use your line of best fit to work out the likely number of deck chair tickets sold when the rainfall is recorded as 10 mm. *(2 marks)*

4 The weight of tea in a sample of 100 tea-bags is shown in the table.

Weight of tea in tea-bag, w (grams)	Frequency	Cumulative frequency
$2.9 \leqslant w < 3.0$	2	
$3.0 \leqslant w < 3.1$	6	
$3.1 \leqslant w < 3.2$	32	
$3.2 \leqslant w < 3.3$	41	
$3.3 \leqslant w < 3.4$	14	
$3.4 \leqslant w < 3.5$	4	
$3.5 \leqslant w < 3.6$	1	

a Complete the cumulative frequency column of the table. *(1 mark)*
b Draw a cumulative frequency curve for these data on graph paper. *(2 marks)*
c Use your graph to estimate the number of tea-bags with a weight greater than 3.35 grams. *(1 mark)*

5 The probability that I am late for work on a Monday is 0.3.
The probability that I am late for work on a Friday is 0.1.
a What is the probability that I am *not* late for work on a Monday? *(1 mark)*
b What is the probability that I am late for work on Monday *and* Friday? *(2 marks)*

6 The heights of 100 rose bushes are given in the following table.
The measurements are to the nearest centimetre.

Length (cm)	Frequency	Class width	Frequency density
60–74	5		
75–79	8		
80–84	14		
85–89	15		
90–94	18		
95–99	17		
100–109	14		
109–119	9		

  a Copy the table and complete the Class width and Frequency density
columns. *(3 marks)*

  b On graph paper, draw a histogram of Length (cm) against Frequency
density. *(3 marks)*

7 A box contains coloured counters. Each counter is coloured red or white
or blue and each counter is numbered 1 or 2 or 3 or 4.
When a counter is taken from the box at random the table shows the
probabilities of colour and number.

Colour of Counter

		red	white	blue
Number	1	0.1	0	0
on	2	0.1	0.1	0.1
Counter	3	0	0.2	0.1
	4	0.2	0.1	0

A counter is taken from the box at random.
  a What is the probability that it is white? *(1 mark)*
  b What is the probability that it is red **and** numbered 2? *(1 mark)*
  c What is the probability that it is white **or** numbered 1 (or both)? *(1 mark)*
  d What is the probability that it is white **or** numbered 3 (or both)? *(2 marks)*

8 The flow of water between input **X**
and outlet **Y** is regulated by three
valves, **A**, **B** and **C**.
If a valve fails the flow of water is
stopped at that point.

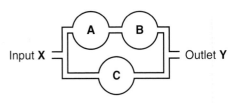

The probability of gate **A** failing is $\frac{1}{4}$.

The probability of gate **B** failing is $\frac{1}{8}$.

The probability of gate **C** failing is $\frac{2}{5}$.

Find the probability that at any instant there is no flow of water to the
outlet **Y**. *(4 marks)*

(Total: 32 marks)

Module 3 – Terminal module

1 Tony is writing down some formulae for some shapes.
The letters a, b and c represent lengths.

$$a + b + c, \quad \tfrac{1}{3}\pi a^2 b, \quad \pi a(b + c), \sqrt{b^2 + c^2}, \quad 2\pi ab, \quad \pi(2a + b^2), \quad \pi c \sqrt{a^2 + b^2}$$

Which of these formulae could represent area?   *(2 marks)*

2 A stopwatch records times to the nearest 0.1 second.

The time taken for Duncan to swim 100 metres is recorded as
88.5 seconds.
What are the maximum and minimum times that Duncan could
have taken?   *(2 marks)*

3 Solve these equations.
  a $3(x - 3) = 2(x - 3)$ *(3 marks)*
  b $x^2 - 2x = 8$ *(3 marks)*

4 In the diagram AB is parallel to CD.

$AB = OC = 12$ cm. $OB = 10$ cm.

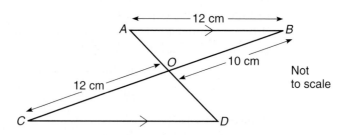

Calculate the length of CD.   *(3 marks)*

5 By factorising $x^2 + 2x$, find the exact value of $1998^2 + 2 \times 1998$.   *(3 marks)*

6 The diagram shows the graph of $y = \sin x$ for $-180 \leqslant x < 360°$.

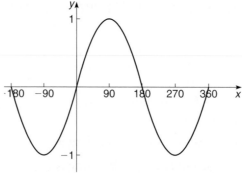

  a Find a value of x, other than $60°$, for which
       $\sin x = \sin 60°$.   *(1 mark)*
  b Find two values of x for which
       $\sin x = -\sin 30°$.   *(3 marks)*

7   The graph of $y = x^2 - 2x - 4$ is shown below.

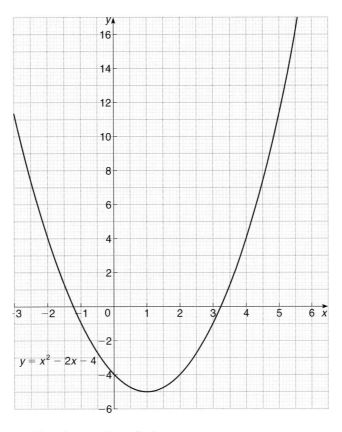

a   Use the graph to find
   i   the value of y when $x = 1.5$,   *(1 mark)*
   ii   the minimum value of y,   *(1 mark)*
   iii   the solutions to the equation $x^2 - 3x - 2 = 0$.   *(1 mark)*
b   Use the graph to find the solutions of the equation
   $x^2 - x - 8 = 0$.   *(3 marks)*

8   The sketches show the graphs of three functions.

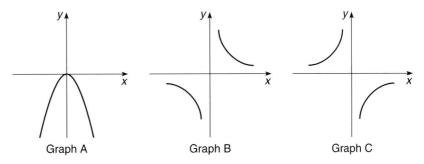

State the equation for graph A, graph B and graph C.
Choose the equations for the graphs from this list:

$y = 2x^3$, $y = -2x^2$, $y = \frac{2}{x}$, $y = x^2 - 2$, $y + \frac{2}{x} = 0$, $y = 2x^2$ *(3 marks)*

9 SPT is the tangent to the circle with centre O.
PQ is a diameter of the circle.
$<RST = 28°$.

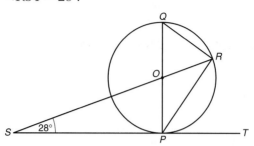

Calculate the size of angle RPT. *(6 marks)*

10 $OABC$ is a parallelogram. M is the midpont of BC.
$\overrightarrow{OA} = \mathbf{a}$ and $\overrightarrow{OC} = \mathbf{b}$.

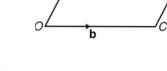

a Find, in terms of $\mathbf{a}$ and $\mathbf{b}$, expressions
for the following vectors

   i $\overrightarrow{OB}$ *(1 mark)*

   ii $\overrightarrow{CM}$ *(1 mark)*

  iii $\overrightarrow{AM}$ *(1 mark)*

P is a point on AM such that AP is $\frac{2}{3} AM$.

b Find, in terms of $\mathbf{a}$ and $\mathbf{b}$, expressions for

   i $\overrightarrow{AP}$ *(1 mark)*

  ii $\overrightarrow{OP}$ *(1 mark)*

c Write down two statements about the relationship between the line
segments OP and OB justifying your answers in each case. *(2 marks)*

11 Solve the equation $\dfrac{8}{x + 3} - \dfrac{1}{x} = 1$. *(5 marks)*

12 The variables x and y are related by a
formula of the form

$$y = ab^x$$

where a and b are constants.
The diagram shows the graph of y
against x.

Find the values of a and b. *(4 marks)*

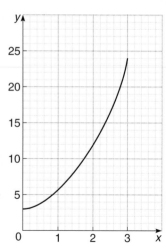

(Total: 51 marks)

These formulae may be useful in answering questions from Intermediate (★ only) and Higher Tiers

Area of trapezium $= \frac{1}{2}(a+b)h$

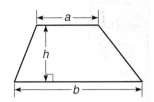

Volume of prism = area of cross section × length

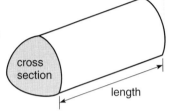

Volume of sphere $= \frac{4}{3}\pi r^3$

Surface area of sphere $= 4\pi r^2$

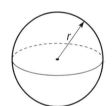

Volume of cone $= \frac{1}{3}\pi r^2 h$

Curved surface area of cone $= \pi r l$

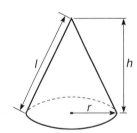

Area of triangle $= \frac{1}{2}ab\sin C$

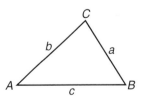

In any triangle ABC

sine rule $\quad \dfrac{a}{\sin A} = \dfrac{b}{\sin B} = \dfrac{c}{\sin C}$

cosine rule $\quad a^2 = b^2 + c^2 - 2bc\cos A$

The Quadratic Equation

The solutions of $ax^2 + bx + c = 0$ where $a \neq 0$, are given by

$$x = \frac{-b \pm \sqrt{(b^2 - 2ac)}}{2a}$$

ANSWERS

Chapter 1

Practice 1.1.1 – p. 4
1 49, 64, 81, 100, 121, 144
2 169, 10 000
3 a 7, 8.8, 9.48633…, 30, 35.12   **b** all exact except $\sqrt{90}$

Practice 1.1.2 – p. 5
1 a 5 to the power 2 or 5 squared
  b 9 to the power 2 or 9 squared
  c 15 to the power 2 or 15 squared
  d 4 to the power 3 or 4 cubed
  e 11 to the power 3 or 11 cubed
  f 6 to the power 4
  g 3 to the power 7
  h 2 to the power 10

2 a 25   **d** 64   **g** 2187
  b 81   **e** 1331   **h** 1024
  c 225   **f** 1296

3 a 5^4 **c** 8^3 **e** 3^6
  b 4^7 **d** 16^{10}

4 $A = 625$
5 $C = 343$
6 a $9 + 125 = 134$ **b** $25 + 64 = 89$
7 a $3^2 = 9$, $2^3 = 8$, so 3^2 is greater
  b $5^2 = 25$, $2^5 = 32$, so 2^5 is greater

Practice 1.1.3 – p. 7
1 a $23 - 2 + 5 = 26$ $23 - (2 + 5) = 16$
  b $17 - 2 \times 3 = 11$ $(17 - 2) \times 3 = 45$
  c $8 \times 5 - 1 = 39$ $8 \times (5 - 1) = 32$
  d $12 - 6 \div 3 = 10$ $(12 - 6) \div 3 = 2$

2 a 6   **c** 9   **e** 18
  b -4 **d** 9   **f** 13

3 a $4 \times (3 - 1) = 8$ **c** $(9 + 6) \div 3 = 5$
  b $(4 + 5) \times 2 = 18$ **d** $10 \div (5 \times 2) = 1$

Practice 1.2.1 – p. 8
1 a 1, 3, 5, 15
  b 1, 2, 3, 4, 6, 8, 12, 24
  c 1, 37
  d 1, 7, 49
  e 1, 2, 3, 4, 5, 6, 10, 12, 15, 20, 30, 60

2 a 1, 2   **c** 1, 2, 4   **e** 1, 3
  b 1, 2, 3, 6   **d** 1, 3, 5, 15

3 a 4   **d** 8   **g** 4
  b 5   **e** 24   **h** 15
  c 6   **f** 7

Practice 1.2.2 – p. 8
1 a 3, 6, 9, 12, 15, 18   **d** 12, 24, 36, 48, 60, 72
  b 5, 10, 15, 20, 25, 30   **e** 13, 26, 39, 52, 65, 78
  c 8, 16, 24, 32, 40, 48

2 9, 18, 27, 36, 45, 54
3 60, 72, 84, 96
4 14, 28, 42, 56, 70, … (any five)
5 15, 30, 45, 60, 75, … (any three)
6 28, 56, 84, 112, 140, … (any three)
7 a 10   **c** 20   **e** 28
  b 18   **d** 36   **f** 60

Practice 1.2.3 – p. 9
1 23, 29, 31, 37, 41
2 53
3 71, 73, 79, 83, 89

Practice 1.2.4 – p. 10
1 a 3, 5   **c** 3, 5, 7   **e** 41
  b 2, 3   **d** 3, 13
(remember that 1 is not a prime number so it cannot be a prime factor)

2 a $3 \times 3 \times 7$ or $3^2 \times 7$
  b $2 \times 2 \times 2 \times 3 \times 5$ or $2^4 \times 3 \times 5$
  c $2 \times 2 \times 2 \times 2 \times 3 \times 5 \times 5$ or $2^4 \times 3 \times 5^2$
  d $2 \times 5 \times 13 \times 13$ or $2 \times 5 \times 13^2$
  e $3 \times 3 \times 5 \times 7 \times 11 \times 11$ or $3^2 \times 5 \times 7 \times 11^2$

Practice 1.3.1 – p. 11
1 a $\frac{2}{4} = \frac{3}{6} = \frac{4}{8} = \ldots$ (any three)
  b $\frac{2}{5} = \frac{4}{10} = \frac{6}{15} = \frac{8}{20} = \frac{10}{25} = \frac{12}{30} = \ldots$ (any three)
  c $\frac{1}{3} = \frac{2}{6} = \frac{4}{12} = \frac{5}{16} = \frac{6}{18} = \ldots$ (any three)
  d $\frac{26}{200} = \frac{39}{300} = \frac{52}{400} = \ldots$ (any three)

2 a $\frac{4}{7}$ and $\frac{12}{21}$ **c** $\frac{6}{7}$ and $\frac{12}{14}$
  b $\frac{4}{9}$ and $\frac{24}{54}$ **d** $\frac{4}{100}$ and $\frac{12}{300}$

3 a $\frac{1}{2}$ **d** $\frac{2}{5}$ **g** $\frac{4}{7}$ (already in its lowest terms)
  b $\frac{3}{4}$ **e** $\frac{4}{5}$ **h** $\frac{4}{9}$
  c $\frac{4}{5}$ **f** $\frac{1}{4}$

Practice 1.3.2 – p. 12
1 $\frac{30}{50} = \frac{3}{5}$
2 $\frac{25}{60} = \frac{5}{12}$
3 $\frac{12}{15} = \frac{4}{5}$
4 $\frac{40}{200} = \frac{1}{5}$ (remember to convert to same units)
5 $\frac{3}{8}$ (there are 8 pints in a gallon)
6 $\frac{3}{5}$ (there are 100 cm in a metre)
7 $\frac{3}{10}$ (there are 1000 m in a kilometre)
8 $\frac{1}{200}$ (there are 1000 ml in a litre)
9 $\frac{1}{5000}$ (there are 1000 mg in a gram and 1000 g in a kilogram)

Practice 1.3.3 – p. 14
1 a $\frac{2}{3}$ **g** $\frac{31}{44}$ **l** $\frac{11}{56}$
  b $\frac{5}{7}$ **h** $\frac{1}{5}$ **m** $-\frac{1}{5}$
  c $\frac{7}{11}$ **i** $\frac{1}{7}$ **n** $-\frac{3}{9} = -\frac{1}{3}$
  d $\frac{6}{9} = \frac{2}{3}$ **j** $\frac{9}{40}$ **o** $-\frac{1}{10}$
  e $\frac{3}{6} = \frac{1}{2}$ **k** $\frac{9}{36} = \frac{3}{12} = \frac{1}{4}$ **p** $-\frac{1}{21}$
  f $\frac{24}{35}$

Practice 1.3.4 – p. 15
1 a $1\frac{5}{7}$ **e** $7\frac{11}{12}$ **i** $1\frac{1}{8}$
  b $12\frac{7}{12}$ **f** $6\frac{11}{20}$ **j** $1\frac{2}{5}$
  c $2\frac{1}{4}$ **g** $1\frac{4}{8} = 1\frac{1}{2}$ **k** $5\frac{8}{15}$
  d $3\frac{5}{10} = 3\frac{1}{2}$ **h** $1\frac{3}{8}$ **l** $1\frac{1}{36}$

Practice 1.3.5 – p. 16
1 a $7\frac{3}{7}$ **e** $15\frac{47}{40} = 16\frac{7}{40}$ **i** $1\frac{3}{5}$
  b $10\frac{9}{20}$ **f** $18\frac{59}{42} = 19\frac{17}{42}$ **j** $3\frac{5}{8}$
  c $3\frac{37}{40}$ **g** $1\frac{1}{5}$ **k** $5\frac{21}{40}$
  d $9\frac{9}{7} = 10\frac{2}{7}$ **h** $4\frac{3}{8}$ **l** $4\frac{17}{35}$

Practice 1.3.6 – p. 16

1 a $\frac{2}{15}$ **e** $\frac{6}{15} = \frac{2}{5}$ **i** $\frac{6}{4} = \frac{3}{2} = 1\frac{1}{2}$

b $\frac{6}{35}$ **f** $\frac{3}{9} = \frac{1}{3}$ **j** $\frac{1}{1} = 1$

c $\frac{8}{27}$ **g** $\frac{7}{5} = 1\frac{2}{5}$ **k** $\frac{51}{5} = 10\frac{1}{5}$

d $\frac{12}{20} = \frac{3}{5}$ **h** $\frac{7}{5} = 1\frac{2}{5}$ **l** $\frac{18}{1} = 18$

m $\frac{4}{5}$

n $\frac{16}{25}$ (remember that $(\frac{4}{5})^2 = \frac{4}{5} \times \frac{4}{5}$)

o $\frac{25}{16} = 1\frac{9}{16}$ (remember that $(1\frac{1}{4})^2 = 1\frac{1}{4} \times 1\frac{1}{4}$)

p $\frac{1000}{27} = 37\frac{1}{27}$ (remember that $(3\frac{1}{3})^3 = 3\frac{1}{3} \times 3\frac{1}{3} \times 3\frac{1}{3}$)

Practice 1.3.7 – p. 17

1 a 30 **c** 8 **3** 30 millimetres

b 6 **d** $\frac{32}{7} = 4\frac{4}{7}$ **4 a** 8 **b** 15

2 9 metres **5** 450

Practice 1.3.8 – p. 18

1 a $\frac{5}{6}$ **e** $\frac{1}{3}$ **i** $\frac{5}{3} = 1\frac{2}{3}$

b $\frac{11}{7} = 1\frac{4}{7}$ **f** 2 **j** 3

c $\frac{1}{2}$ **g** $\frac{5}{3} = 1\frac{2}{3}$ **k** 2

d $\frac{2}{7}$ **h** $\frac{2}{3}$ **l** $\frac{1}{2}$

2 6 bottles ($\frac{2}{3}$ litre remaining) **6** 40 minutes

3 $\frac{4}{15}$ **7** 40

4 1600 m or 1.6 km **8** £28

5 105 seconds

Practice 1.4.1 – p. 19

1 a 6 **c** 6000 **e** $\frac{6}{100\,000}$

b 600 **d** $\frac{6}{10}$

2 a 30 **b** 200 **c** $\frac{7}{10}$ **d** $\frac{8}{100}$

Practice 1.4.2 – p. 20

1 a $\frac{2}{5}$ **c** $\frac{14}{25}$ **e** $\frac{11}{40}$ **g** $\frac{111}{500}$

b $\frac{11}{20}$ **d** $\frac{23}{50}$ **f** $\frac{17}{40}$ **h** $\frac{469}{2000}$

2 a $4\frac{1}{2}$ **c** $10\frac{3}{25}$ **e** $70\frac{18}{25}$ **g** $2\frac{1}{8}$

b $7\frac{7}{20}$ **d** $20\frac{19}{25}$ **f** $12\frac{3}{25}$ **h** $17\frac{31}{200}$

Practice 1.4.3 – p. 21

1 a 0.6 **f** 1.3 **k** $0.\dot{3}$

b 0.7 **g** 15.2 **l** $0.\dot{5}$

c 0.04 **h** 22.12 **m** $0.5\dot{4}$

d 0.35 **i** 1.45

e 0.325 **j** 6.06

Practice 1.4.4 – p. 22

1 a 0.5 **e** 1.95 **i** 105.01

b 1.01 **f** 0.603 **j** 0.49

c 1.64 **g** 3.7 **k** 30.2

d 0.988 **h** 9.3

2 a 0.5 **d** 0.837 **g** 7.6

b 0.25 **e** 3.99 **h** 4.8

c 0.36 **f** 0.09 **i** 14.999

Practice 1.4.5 – p. 23

1 a 0.18 **d** 0.56 **g** 4.8

b 14.4 **e** 0.000 225 **h** 0.000 015

c 12 **f** 36

Practice 1.4.6 – p. 24

1 a 0.53 **d** 120 000 **g** 50

b 0.12 **e** 130 **h** 4000

c 4400 **f** 0.02

Practice 1.5.1 – p. 25

1 a 50% **d** 37.5% **g** 17%

b 25% **e** 70% **h** 16.666… or 16.7% (3sf)

c 40% **f** 15%

2 a $\frac{3}{5}$ **d** $\frac{9}{10}$

b $\frac{9}{20}$ **e** $\frac{5}{8}$

c $\frac{13}{20}$ **f** $\frac{33}{100}$ (note that 33% is not equal to $\frac{1}{3}$)

Practice 1.5.2 – p. 25

1 a 50% **c** 60% **e** 37.5%

b 20% **d** 35% **f** 41.25%

2 a 0.25 **d** 0.225 **g** 0.002

b 0.45 **e** 0.05 **h** 0.0001

c 0.9 **f** 0.025

Practice 1.5.3 – p. 26

1 $\frac{1}{2} = 50\%$, $\frac{26}{50} = 52\%$, $\frac{48}{100} = 48\%$, $\frac{505}{1000} = 50.5\%$, $0.46 = 46\%$, $0.488 = 48.8\%$, so the order is 0.46, 47.9%, $\frac{48}{100}$, 0.488, $\frac{1}{2}$, $\frac{505}{1000}$, 51.0%, $\frac{26}{50}$

2 a $0.76 = \frac{19}{25}$ **c** 57% = 0.57

b $\frac{3}{8} = 0.375$

Practice 1.5.4 – p. 27

1 50% **5** 4%

2 20% **6** 5%

3 10% **7** 20% (3 feet = 1 yard)

4 14.285… = 14.3% (3sf) **8** 18.75% (8 pints = 1 gallon)

Practice 1.5.5a – p. 29

1 a £4 **c** 18 apples

b 270 metres **d** 700 g

2 £210

3 19 cars (rounded to nearest whole number)

Practice 1.5.5b – p. 29

1 a £93.60 **c** 218.4 litres

b 174 m **d** 46 inches or 3 feet 10 inches

2 £368

3 £11.25

Practice 1.5.6a – p. 31

1 £625 **4 a** £5500 **b** £6050

2 £390 **5** 2%

3 £51

Practice 1.5.6b – p. 31

1 £259.60 **4 a** £3852 **b** £4121.64

2 £30.75 **5 a** £5590 **b** £4807.40

3 £32 **6** between 4th and 5th year

Practice 1.5.7a – p. 32

1 200 m **3** £600

2 75 acres **4** £800

Practice 1.5.7b – p. 32

1 70 m **3** 350

2 £12 800 **4** 50 square metres

Practice 1.5.8a – p. 33

1 18 225 **3 a** 30 360 **b** 34 914

2 400 **4** £9000

Practice 1.5.8b – p. 33

1 £26 000 **3** 44%

2 £4800 **4** £25 000

Practice 1.5.9a – p. 34

1 10%   2 6.25%   3 20%

Practice 1.5.9b – p. 34

1 6.67% (3sf)   3 18.2% (3sf)
2 2.37% (3sf)   4 $\frac{12}{168}$ = 7.14% (3sf) (in minutes)

Practice 1.5.10a – p. 36

1 44%   2 £460   3 £3416

Practice 1.5.10b – p. 36

1 7.89% (3sf)   2 11.8% (3sf)   3 44.1% (3sf)

Practice 1.6.1 – p. 37

1 a 3:4   g 10:1
  b 1:5   h 8:1
  c 1:3   i 3:10
  d 3:7 (already in its simplest form)   j 1:8
  e 1:4   k 8:5
  f 1:3   l 3:2
2 2:3
3 4:10 = 2:5
4 8:3 (1 m = 100 cm)
5 1:4 (16 ounces = 1 pound)
6 a 350:560 = 5:8   b 560:350 = 8:5

Practice 1.6.2 – p. 38

1 £800 and £1000
2 £500, £750 and £1750
3 £450 and £150 (ratio = 3:1)
4 £11 000, £7000 and £4000   £10 560, £7040 and £4400 (a year later)
5 Amy £5250, Brian £9000 and Catrina £3750

Practice 1.7.1 – p. 39

1 12°   2 5°   3 24°

4 a $^{+}14$ d $^{+}14$ g $^{+}1$ j $^{+}6$
  b $^{-}5$ e 0   h $^{-}9$ k $^{+}2$
  c $^{+}21$ f $^{-}10$ i $^{-}18$ l $^{-}5$

Practice 1.7.2 – p. 40

1 a $^{-}21$ f $^{-}6$ k $^{+}121$
  b $^{-}21$ g $^{+}1$ l $^{-}27$
  c $^{+}45$ h $^{+}6$ m $^{+}72$
  d $^{+}56$ i $^{+}2\frac{1}{2}$
  e $^{-}15$ j $^{+}25$

Practice 1.8.1 – p. 41

1 a rational   h rational ($=\frac{31}{20}$)   n irrational
  b rational ($=\frac{9}{4}$)   i rational ($=\frac{3571}{10\,000}$)   o irrational
  c irrational   j rational ($=\frac{1}{3}$)   p irrational
  d rational ($=\frac{3}{1}$)   k rational ($=\frac{7}{3}$)   q rational ($=\frac{3}{1}$)
  e irrational   l rational ($=\frac{1}{3}$)   r rational ($=\frac{2}{1}$)
  f rational = ($\frac{25}{1}$)   m irrational   s rational ($=\frac{3}{1}$)
  g rational ($=\frac{251}{10}$)

2 a 3.1, $3\frac{1}{2}$, $\sqrt{16}$, ...   b π, $\sqrt{10}$, $\sqrt{11}$, $\sqrt{12}$, ...

Practice 1.8.2 – p. 42

1 a 3   c 6   e $\sqrt{15}$
  b 7   d 10   f $\sqrt{88} = 2\sqrt{22}$
2 a 5   c $\sqrt{11}$ e $\sqrt{2}$
  b 5   d $\sqrt{2}$ f $\sqrt{3}$
3 a 10   d $4\sqrt{2}$ g $7\sqrt{6}$
  b $\frac{3}{2}$ or $1\frac{1}{2}$ or 1.5   e $6\sqrt{3}$ h $2\sqrt{3}$
  c $3\sqrt{2}$ f $4\sqrt{5}$ i $\sqrt{11}$

Practice 1.8.3 – p. 43

1 a $\frac{1}{3}$ e $\frac{234}{999} = \frac{26}{111}$ i $3\frac{8}{9}$
  b $\frac{5}{9}$ f $\frac{201}{999} = \frac{67}{333}$ j $12\frac{201}{999} = 12\frac{67}{333}$
  c $\frac{46}{99}$ g $\frac{303}{999} = \frac{101}{333}$ k $16\frac{35}{99}$
  d $\frac{26}{99}$ h $\frac{4024}{9999}$ l $201\frac{23}{99}$

2 $0.5\dot{7} = 0.5 + 0.0\dot{7} = \frac{1}{2} + \frac{7}{90} = \frac{52}{90}$
3 $0.\dot{5}\dot{0} = \frac{50}{99}$ so $0.\dot{5}\dot{0}$ is rational

---

Chapter 2

Practice 2.2.1 – p. 48

1 a 4^8 c 11^8 e 5^6
  b 3^7 d 7^6 f 6^9
2 a 3^{14} c 9^9 e 6^{25} g 16^9
  b 4^9 d 8^{14} f 7^{14}

Practice 2.2.2 – p. 49

1 a 5^5 c 8^6 e 21^3
  b 6^4 d 14^4 f 3^1 or 3
2 a 10^2 c 17^5 e 9^7
  b 8^4 d 16^1 or 16 f 4^5

Practice 2.2.3 – p. 49

1 a 5^6 c 6^7 e 6^3 g 16^2
  b 4^{18} d 18^{13} f 25^1 or 25 h 2^3
2 a 3^5 b 2^{11}
3 a 36   c 64   e 17   g 9
  b 64   d 64   f 18   h 22

Practice 2.2.4 – p. 51

1 a $\frac{1}{4^5}$ d $\frac{1}{12^4}$ g $\frac{1}{4^5}$
  b $\frac{1}{6^5}$ e $\frac{1}{7^{19}}$ h $\frac{1}{11^3}$
  c $\frac{1}{2^2}$ f $\frac{1}{6^3}$
2 a $\frac{1}{5}$ e $\frac{1}{12}$ i 1
  b $\frac{1}{9}$ f $\frac{1}{4}$ j 100
  c 1   g 1
  d 1   h 1

4 a 3^6 h 3^{14} o $10^0 = 1$
  b 4^{18} i 4^{15} p $7^0 = 1$
  c 6^{13} j 4^3 q $6^0 = 1$
  d 11^{11} k 9^1 or 9   r 4^{-1}
  e 6^6 l 5^5 s 5^{-3}
  f 4^{14} m 16^4 t 4^{-9}
  g 6^{10} n 6^4

Practice 2.3.1 – p. 52

1 a 1.4×10^4 d 1.58×10^{11} g 2.006×10^8
  b 9×10^6 e 4.5×10^9 h 2.1005×10^{13}
  c 1.3×10^8 f 3.75×10^{11}

2 a 1 300 000 **d** 1040 **g** 399 580
 b 1 430 000 000 **e** 889 800 000 **h** 399
 c 175 000 000 **f** 98 650 000 **i** 496.31
3 a 43 000 000 **c** 28 880 000 **e** 55 870 000
 b 197 000 000 **d** 17 483 000 000 **f** 2 980 200 000
4 c, a, e, b, f, d
5 a 14 000 000 **c** 82 360 000 **e** 165 242 000
 b 2 500 000 **d** 1 544 000
6 e, c, a, b, d
7 a 9.78×10^2, 4.2835×10^3, 1.26×10^4
 b 9.89×10^4, 99 000, 1×10^5
8 a 2.21×10^4 **b** 3.25×10^7 **c** 1.1×10^8
9 a $n = 5$ **c** $n = 7$ **e** $n = 1$
 b $n = 4$ **d** $n = 2$ **f** $n = 5$

Practice 2.3.2 – p. 53
1 a 3×10^{-3} **d** 1×10^{-1} **g** 6.55×10^{-6}
 b 7.5×10^{-5} **e** 6.25×10^{-7} **h** 9.225×10^{-7}
 c 7×10^{-4} **f** 8×10^{-12}
2 a 0.000 000 001 **d** 0.000 004 22
 b 0.000 000 000 08 **e** 0.000 040 05
 c 0.000 65 **f** 0.000 039 958
3 a 2.46×10^{-2}, 1.3×10^{-2}, 8.79×10^{-5}
 b 4.3×10^{-2}, 4.29×10^{-3}, 0.004 28
4 a 1.25×10^{-6} **b** 1.46×10^{-5} **c** 0.000 99

Practice 2.3.3 – p. 55
1 7×10^3 **10** 1.51×10^{10}
2 8.6×10^5 **11** 1×10^4
3 8.6×10^8 **12** 1.068×10^{-4}
4 1.157×10^4 **13** 9.5×10^{-17}
5 1.1081×10^8 **14** $6.535 36 \times 10^8$
6 9.85×10^{-3} **15** 6.76×10^7
7 1.372×10^{-6} **16** $1.150 16 \times 10^3$
8 1.1×10^2 **17** 1.866×10^{-2}
9 1.6×10^7 **18** 2.835×10^3

Practice 2.3.4a – p. 56
1 6×10^9 **6** 1.44×10^{-8}
2 4×10^{11} **7** 2×10^1 or 20
3 9×10^{16} **8** 3.5×10^2
4 2.4×10^8 **9** 7.5×10^3
5 7×10^{-1} or $\frac{1}{7}$ **10** 1.25×10^{-8}

Practice 2.3.4b – p. 56
1 7.119×10^7 **7** 7.7112×10^5
2 $8.411 85 \times 10^9$ **8** 8.5×10^3
3 1.9975×10^8 **9** 7.6×10^9
4 $1.770 18 \times 10^{20}$ **10** 2.21×10^{-2}
5 1.7664×10^{32} **11** 134 kilowatt hours
6 7.744×10^1 **12** 4.25×10^{-2} g

Practice 2.4.1 – p. 58
see answers to Practice 1.3.3, 1.3.4, 1.3.5, 1.3.6 and 1.3.8

Practice 2.4.2 – p. 59
1 81 **9** 0.25
2 64 **10** 0.0256
3 5 **11** 0.03
4 1 **12** 7
5 1 **13** 3
6 0.25 **14** 2
7 0.01 **15** 0.0625
8 0.0025 or 2.5×10^{-3}

Practice 2.4.3 – p. 60
see answers to Practice 2.3.3 and 2.3.4

Practice 2.4.4 – p. 61
1 288.7218 **5** 1.563 615 1
2 3.861 139 9 **6** 0.305 518 4
3 5.751 284 8 **7** 0.956 036 2
4 108.9951 **8** 9.651 282 8

Practice 2.5.1 – p. 61
1 2150 **4** 12 545
2 4884 **5** 17 608
3 13 694 **6** 37 715

Practice 2.5.2 – p. 62
1 32 **6** 59
2 45 **7** 68
3 89 **8** 78
4 46 **9** 77
5 28 **10** 93

Practice 2.6.1 – p. 63
1 $\dfrac{5 \times 100}{4 \times 0.5} = 250$

2 $\dfrac{10^2 - 4^2}{2 \times 10} = 4.2$

3 $6 + \dfrac{2}{5 + 5} = 6.2$

4 $25 \times 4 + \dfrac{5(100 - 30 \times 2)}{11 + 9} = 110$

5 $\dfrac{5 + 5}{\sqrt{4} + 2^2} = \dfrac{10}{6} = \dfrac{5}{3}$

6 $\dfrac{30 + \sqrt{1}}{(16 - 6)^2} = \dfrac{31}{100}$

7 $\dfrac{4^2 - 1^2}{\sqrt{25} + 7} = \dfrac{15}{12}$

8 $10 + \dfrac{\sqrt{1}}{3^2 + 12 \times 1} = 10\frac{1}{21}$

Practice 2.7.1 – p. 64
	4dp	3dp	2dp	1dp
1	4.2716	4.272	4.27	4.3
2	2.1606	2.161	2.16	2.2
3	11.7524	11.752	11.75	11.8
4	9.2295	9.229	9.23	9.2
5	13.8980	13.898	13.90	13.9

Practice 2.7.2 – p. 65
	4sf	3sf	2sf	1sf
1	437.8	438	440	400
2	2195	2190	2200	2000
3	0.8966	0.897	0.90	0.9
4	18.69	18.7	19	20
5	505.1	505	510	500

Practice 2.8.1 – p. 66
1 4.1^2 = 16.81
 4.2^2 = 17.64
 4.15^2 = 17.2225
 4.125^2 = 17.015 625
 4.1225^2 = 16.995 006
 4.1235^2 = 17.003 252
 4.1230^2 = 16.999 129
 $\sqrt{17} = 4.123$ (3dp) as answer lies between 4.1230 and 4.1235
2 $2.6 \times 2.6 \times 2.6$ = 17.576
 $2.7 \times 2.7 \times 2.7$ = 19.683
 $2.65 \times 2.65 \times 2.65$ = 18.609 625
 $2.67 \times 2.67 \times 2.67$ = 19.034 163
 $2.66 \times 2.66 \times 2.66$ = 18.821 096
 $2.665 \times 2.665 \times 2.665$ = 18.927 43
 $\sqrt{19} = 2.67$ (2dp) as answer lies between 2.665 and 2.67

3　$2.5 \times 2.5 \times 2.5$　　　　$= 15.625$
　　$2.6 \times 2.6 \times 2.6$　　　　$= 17.576$
　　$2.55 \times 2.55 \times 2.55$　　$= 16.581\,375$
　　$2.58 \times 2.58 \times 2.58$　　$= 17.173\,512$
　　$2.57 \times 2.57 \times 2.57$　　$= 16.974\,593$
　　$2.575 \times 2.575 \times 2.575$　$= 17.073\,859$
　　$2.573 \times 2.573 \times 2.573$　$= 17.034\,107$
　　$\sqrt{17} = 2.57$ (2dp) as answer lies between 2.57 and 2.573

Practice 2.9.1 – p. 67
1 a　3　　　　**d**　27　　　　**g**　$\frac{1}{4}$　　　　**j**　$\frac{1}{32}$
　b　3　　　　**e**　25　　　　**h**　$\frac{1}{12}$
　c　9　　　　**f**　16　　　　**i**　$\frac{1}{2}$
2 a　4　　　　**d**　-1　　　　**g**　-3　　　　**j**　$-\frac{2}{5}$
　b　0　　　　**e**　-2　　　　**h**　$-\frac{1}{3}$
　c　1　　　　**f**　-3　　　　**i**　$-\frac{1}{5}$

Practice 2.9.2a – p. 69
1　$a = kb^2$ and $k = 7$　　**a**　$a = 7$　　　　**b**　$a = 63$
2　$y = kx^3$ and $k = 2$　　**a**　$y = 128$　　　**b**　$y = \frac{1}{4}$
3　$y = \dfrac{k}{\sqrt{x}}$ and $k = 6$; $y = 2$
4　$e = kT$ and $k = \frac{1}{4}$; $e = 3$ cm

Practice 2.9.2b – p. 70
1　$p = \frac{k}{q^3}$ and $k = 10$　　**a**　$p = 0.08$　　　　**b**　$p = 5$
2　$V = kr^3$ and $k = 4.1875$; $V = 523$ g (3sf)
3　$v = 12\,000/a$　　**a**　$v = £6000$　　**b**　$v = £1200$　　**c**　$a = 6$ years

Practice 2.9.3a – p. 71
1　upper bound $= 19\,212$ g; lower bound $= 19\,188$ g
2　greatest difference $= £1900$ (£8450–£6550);
　　least difference $= £1700$ (£8350–£6650)
3　lower bound $= 18$ years; upper bound $= 19$ years (always take
　　care with ages as the student is 18 until her 19th birthday)

Practice 2.9.3b – p. 71
1　minimum $= 181.25$ sq ft; maximum $= 209.25$ sq ft
2 a　perimeter $= 420$ m　　　　**b**　2000 m^2
3 a　upper bound $= 150\frac{1}{2}$; lower bound $= 149\frac{1}{2}$
　b　upper bound $= 15.8$ m (3sf) ($150.5 \div 9.5$);
　　　lower bound $= 14.2$ m (3sf) ($149.5 \div 10.5$)
4　upper bound $= 48.2$ mph; lower bound $= 34.1$ mph (3sf)
5　upper bound $= 72.9$ mph (3sf) ($255 \div 3.5$);
　　lower bound $= 54.4$ mph (3sf) ($245 \div 4.5$)
6　largest $= (2.45)^2/1.55 = 3.87$ watts (3sf);
　　smallest $= (2.35)^2/1.65 = 3.35$ watts (3sf)

Chapter 3

Practice 3.1.1a – p. 75
1 a　£70　　　　**b**　175 m　　　　**c**　0.77 kg
2　£143

Practice 3.1.1b – p. 75
1 a　£190.40　　　　　　**2**　£299
　b　£108.74 (nearest penny)　**3**　£33.60 (nearest penny)
　c　96.85 ml

Practice 3.1.2a – p. 76
1 a　£540　　　　**c**　£2070
　b　£720　　　　**d**　£352
2 a　£540　　　　**b**　£583.20

Practice 3.1.2b – p. 76
1 a　£394.40　　　　　　**c**　£2549.85
　b　£322.22 (nearest penny)　**d**　£1405.53 (nearest penny)
2 a　£4005　　　　**b**　£4277.34
3　£2328.48

Practice 3.1.3a – p. 77
1　£650　　　　**2**　£16 000　　　**3**　£1300

Practice 3.1.3b – p. 77
1　£2800　　**2**　£2500　　**3**　£2650　　**4**　£296 000

Practice 3.2.1 – p. 79
1 a　0300　　　　**d**　1245　　　　**g**　1015
　b　1520　　　　**e**　0530　　　　**h**　2359
　c　2005　　　　**f**　1955
2 a　10.00 am　　　**d**　3.05 pm　　　**g**　10.01 pm
　b　11.30 am　　　**e**　11.59 am　　　**h**　12.01 am
　c　12.50 pm　　　**f**　11.50 pm
3　85 mins

4　1 h 55 mins　　　　**7**　9 h 35 mins
5　1 h 50 mins　　　　**8 a**　5.25 pm　　**b**　105 mins
6　2025　　　　　　　**9**　0225 (next day)

Practice 3.3.1a – p. 81
1　11 880 ft　　　**4**　32 m　　　　　**7**　2.5 feet
2　100 fl oz　　　**5**　4.57 g　　　　**8**　£3
3　4750 mm　　　**6**　0.000 765 km

Practice 3.3.1b – p. 81
1　252 lb　　　　　　　　**6**　80 fl oz
2　0.004 65 t　　　　　　**7**　9 m
3　0.005 m　　　　　　　**8**　£1.92 (nearest penny)
4　18 inches　　　　　　**9**　£1.65 (nearest penny)
5　7.04 oz　　　　　　　**10**　80 km/h

Practice 3.4.1 – p. 82
1 a　2 h 25 min　　　　　　**c**　1 h 40 min
　b　1 h 15 min　　　　　　**d**　45 min
2 a　10 min　　　**c**　17 min　　　**e**　0059 or 12.59 am
　b　27 min　　　**d**　34 min　　　**f**　0255 or 2.55 am
3 a　0840　　　　**d**　1 h 8 min　　**g**　1755
　b　27 min　　　**e**　46 min
　c　1 h 13 min　**f**　0926 (catch the 0819 train)
4 a　£70　　　　　　**c**　£84
　b　£8　　　　　　**d**　£4
5 a　£798 (£399 each)
　b　£128 (£64 each)
　c　£1412 (£353 each)
　d　£1823 (reduction of £25 for 8 year old)
　e　£276
　f　£1290 (reduction of £50 for both children)
　g　£375 (4 nights)
6 a　£22　　　　**c**　£36　　　　**e**　£48
　b　£22　　　　**d**　£3　　　　**f**　£112
7 a　**i** £66　**ii** £48　　　　**d**　£62 (no concessions)
　b　£2.50　　　　　　　　　**e**　£84 (concession for 2 children)
　c　£57 (see concessions)

8 a **i** 1550 miles **ii** 210 miles **iii** 5940 miles
  b **i** 1540 miles **ii** 6030 miles
  c 4600 miles   **e** Rome
  d 180 miles   **f** London & Paris
9 a 77 miles   **e** Dover & Edinburgh
  b 240 miles   **f** 189 miles
  c 448 miles   **g** 347 miles
  d Portsmouth & Southampton

Practice 3.5.1a – p. 89
1 £9.80   **5** £264
2 £8.40   **6 a** £168   **b** £328
3 £267   **7 a** £162.60   **b** £175.88
4 a £7.04   **b** £10.76   **8** £318.50

Practice 3.5.1b – p. 90
1 £191.25
2 Mon £3.20, Tue £3.00, Wed £3.68, Thu £3.36, Fri £2.60
3 Mon £45.00, Tue £52.50, Wed £63.00, Thu £59.25, Fri £45.00
4 Mon £29.82, Tue £23.10, Thu £36.39, Fri £23.33 (nearest penny)
5 £249.60
6 £163.40
7 £166.43 (nearest penny)

Practice 3.5.2 – p. 93
1 £2115
2 £2476.72
3 £360
4 no tax paid
5 £30.13 per week (nearest penny)
6 taxable income £3105; tax £621 per year
7 taxable income £22 305; tax £5001.50 per year
8 tax £4351.88 (nearest penny)
9 tax £3549.90
10 £62.04 per month (nearest penny)

Practice 3.6.1a – p. 95
1 a £693.25   **d** £2191.38 (nearest penny)
  b £540.50   **e** £11 614.88 (nearest penny)
  c £276.13 (nearest penny)
2 £108.10

Practice 3.6.1b – p. 95
1 a £693.25   **d** £2191.38 (nearest penny)
  b £540.50   **e** £11 614.88 (nearest penny)
  c £276.13 (nearest penny)
2 £108.10

Practice 3.6.2a – p. 96
1 £48.96 (nearest penny)   **2** £61.85 (nearest penny)

Practice 3.6.2b – p. 97
Answers are given to the nearest penny where appropriate
1 a £57.81   **c** £108.36
  b £80.36   **d** £44.98
2 a £46.15   **c** £22.59
  b £42.88   **d** £24.53 (172 units used)
3 a £51.08   **c** £62.39
  b £51.58   **d** £105.48

Practice 3.6.3 – p. 98
Answers are given to the nearest penny where appropriate
1 £112.59
2 a £139.91   **c** £303.79
  b £230.04   **d** £291.99
3 a £156.16   **d** £272.32
  b £211.69   **e** £181.30 (covering 91 days)
  c £105.26

Practice 3.6.4 – p. 99
Answers are given to the nearest penny
1 £66.89
2 a £56.18   **c** £116.94
  b £137.87   **d** £55.24
3 £93.39

Practice 3.6.5a – p. 101
1 £11.08 per month
2 NCD = £81; insurance = £162
3 a £74 (£37 each)
  b £96 (£48 each)
  c £84
  d £70 (1 year old infant free)
  e £92.50
  f £234 (one senior citizen in 16–64 age-group)
  g £444 (double premium on winter sports)
  h £259 (double premium on winter sports)

Practice 3.6.5b – p. 101
1 a £68.16   **c** £91.44 (nearest penny)
  b £75.33   **d** £177.33
2 a £12.54   **b** £30.15   **c** £18.54

Practice 3.7.1a – p. 103
1 a £581.60   **b** £101.60
2 a £526   **b** £61
3 £160

Practice 3.7.1b – p. 104
1 a £336   **b** £3399.60   **c** £599.60
2 a £22   **b** £257.20   **c** £37.20
3 10 months

Practice 3.7.2 – p. 106
1 a £10.74   **c** £5.00   **e** £5.00
  b £20.22   **d** £30.66
2 £132.24
3 amount = £1106.64; interest = 10.7% (3sf)
4 a £587.40   **c** £2348.16
  b £1171.20   **d** £10.56 over 24 months
5 a £410   **b** £35
6 a £25.20   **b** £142.40   **c** £16.40

Practice 3.7.3a – p. 108
1 208 francs   **3** £1000
2 34 520 yen   **4** £125

Practice 3.7.3b – p. 108
1 £7.61 (nearest penny)   **4** 258 dollars (nearest dollar)
2 £54.95 (nearest penny)   **5** 265 guilders (nearest guilder)
3 152 900 lira

Practice 3.7.4a – p. 111
1 £392   **2 a** £500   **b** £1125   **3** 2 years

Practice 3.7.4b – p. 111

Answers are given to the nearest penny where appropriate

1   simplest interest   amount

   a £52.50   £302.50

   b £121.50   £571.50

   c £362.50   £1612.50

   d £59.38   £534.38

   e £18.40   £708.40 (use $T = \frac{2}{3}$ years)

   f £533.85   £3033.85 (use $T = \frac{41}{12}$ years)

2 $T = 3$ years

3 $R = 3.5\%$

4 $R = 4.5\%$

Practice 3.7.5 – p. 113

1 £562.43 (nearest penny)

2 amount = £2119.87 (nearest penny); interest = £369.87

3 **a** $A = £306.26; I = £56.26$ **c** $A = £1480.36; I = £230.36$

   b $A = £491.41; I = £41.41$

4 **a** £3024.00   **b** £3028.48

5 £5253.13 (nearest penny)   **6** £3552.76 (nearest penny)

Practice 3.7.6 – p. 114

1 **a** £112 500   **b** £45 625

2 £70 200   **3** £6825

4 **a** £3312   **b** £276   **c** £82 800

5 **a** £4500   **c** £184.80

   b £2217.60   **d** £44 352

Practice 3.8.1a – p. 117

1 43 mph   **5** 1350 miles

2 $7\frac{1}{3}$ km/h or 7.33 km/h (3sf)   **6** 2.75 h or $2\frac{3}{4}$ h or 2 h 45 min

3 79 mph   **7** $\frac{2}{3}$ g/cm³

4 8 km/h   **8** 450 000 g or 450 kg

Practice 3.8.1b – p. 117

1 135 mph   **5** 28 min

2 75 km/h   **6** 2.7 g/cm³

3 $18\frac{2}{3}$ km or 18.7 km (3sf)   **7** 9×10^{-4} kg/cm³ or 0.9 g/cm³

4 $2\frac{1}{2}$ h or 2.5 h   **8** 1.30 cm³ (3sf)

Practice 3.9.1 – p. 119

1 **a** £526   **d** 14.6% (3sf)

   b £61   **e** APR = 29.1% (using original

   c £419   value for $R = 14.558\,473\%$)

2 **a** £3399.60   **d** $R = \dfrac{100 \times £599.60}{(£2464 \times 3)} = 8.11\%$ (3sf)

   b £599.60

   c £2464   **e** APR = 16.2% (3sf)

3 **a** £62.00   **c** $R = 11.6\%$

   b £749.60   **d** APR = 23.2% (3sf)

Practice 3.9.2 – p. 121

1 £8391.60

2 **a** £31 434   **b** £7279.20

3 £15 885.60

4 £786.47 per month (nearest penny)

5 £40.28 per week (nearest penny)

Practice 3.9.3 – p. 123

1 **a** earnings = £186.20

          10% of (£186.20 £76) = 10% of £110.20 = £11.02

   b earnings = £186.20

          8.4% of £110.20 = £9.26 (nearest penny)

2 **a** earnings = £267

          10% of £191 = £19.10

   b earnings = £267

          8.4% of £191 = £16.04 (nearest penny)

3 he pays no NI on this amount

4 10% on earnings between £3952 and £18 560

       = 10% of £14 608 = £1460.80

5 8.4% of earnings between £3952 and £27 820

       = 8.4% of £28 868 = £2004.91 (nearest penny)

       (Note that £27 820 is the upper earnings limit)

6 Class 2 contributions = £2 × 52 = £104

       Class 4 contributions = 7% of (£23 500 − £4385)

                              = 7% of £19 115

                              = 1338.05

       Total NI contributions = £1338.05 + £104 = £1442.05

Practice 3.9.4 – p. 124

1 £1424.46

2 £633.10

3 £473.88

4 £138.50 per person (nearest penny)

5 £514.39 (nearest penny)

6 £74.19 per monh (nearest penny)

Chapter 4

Practice 4.1.1 – p. 131

1 **a** quantitative   **d** quantitative   **g** qualitative

   b qualitative   **e** quantitative   **h** quantitative

   c qualitative   **f** quantitative   **i** qualitative

2 **a** continuous   **d** continuous   **g** discrete

   b continuous   **e** discrete   **h** continuous

   c continuous   **f** discrete

Practice 4.2.1 – p. 134

1 **a** give each student a unique number and choose numbers randomly using random number tables or else a computer

   b ensure that the sample is representative of the population as a whole by considering such factors as gender, type of course, age of student, etc.

2 depending on the sample size you might choose every nth name from the electoral roll

3 **a** the sample is restricted to shoppers only or shoppers at that particular store (the question doesn't say which food store)

   b the sample is restricted to surnames beginning with M

   c the sample is restricted to telephone owners and would not include those without a telephone or those who are ex-directory

4 people using a bus to get to work would probably have left already, the sample size is very small and the sample is restricted to telephone owners and would not include those without a telephone or those who are ex-directory

5 **a** the sample is restricted to men. Cambridge may not be representative of the country as a whole and 500 is quite a small sample in view of the population size

   b include men and women over 18 in the sample, sample a variety of different locations and increase the sample size

6 a the sample is not truly representative of the populations since the population of Marchwoode will be over represented by the chosen sample

b Little Whitton 140; Marchwoode 40; Newtonabbey 120

Practice 4.3.1 – p. 136

1 questions should not be personal or offensive

2 to ascertain likely problems, highlight areas needing further clarification and improve questionnaire design

3 a the question would be very difficult to answer accurately

b the question is not relevant to the survey

c the question is badly composed and doesn't make sense

4 a the question is biased as it expresses a view; alternative question: 'What do you think about our fruit juice?'

b the question is too personal and might not be answered; alternative question:
Tick your annual income:
£0–£4999 ☐ £10 000–£19 999 ☐
£5000–£9999 ☐ £20 000+ ☐

c the question is badly composed and doesn't make sense; alternative question: 'Do you agree with a new by pass?'

d the question is biased as it expresses a view; alternative question: 'How many cigarettes do you smoke a day?'

e the question is badly composed and doesn't make sense; alternative question: 'Do you prefer a non-smoking area?'
Yes ☐   No ☐

f the question is too personal and would be difficult to ask in a non-personal way

5 no instructions are given, the period of time is not specified (per week, per month, …?) and not all of the amounts are covered (what about £10.50?)

6 any suitable questionnaire

Practice 4.4.1 – p. 139

1

	tally	freq
4	‖	2
5	‖‖	3
6	‖‖‖	4
7	卌 ‖	6
8	卌 ‖	6
9	卌 ‖	6
10	‖‖‖	3
		30

2

	tally	freq
cash	卌 卌 卌 ‖‖	18
cheque	卌 卌 ‖	12
mastercard	卌 ‖	7
storecard	卌	5
visa	卌 ‖‖	8
		50

3

	tally	freq
blue	卌 卌 ‖‖	13
green	卌 ‖	6
red	卌 卌	10
white	卌 ‖	7
yellow	‖‖‖	4
		40

4

	tally	freq
bus	卌 卌 ‖	11
train	卌 卌 卌	15
walk	卌 卌 卌 卌	20
cycle	卌 ‖‖	9
car	卌	5
		60

Practice 4.4.2 – p. 142

1

	tally	freq
0–4	‖‖	3
5–9	卌 ‖	7
10–14	卌 ‖	6
15–19	卌	5
20–24	‖‖‖	4
25–29	‖	2
		27

2

	tally	freq
3.00 up to but not including 3.05	‖	1
3.05 up to but not including 3.10	卌	5
3.10 up to but not including 3.15	卌 ‖‖	8
3.15 up to but not including 3.20	卌 ‖	6
3.20 up to but not including 3.25	‖	2
		22

The group frequencies may alter if 3.05, 3.10, 3.15, … etc. are included in the previous intervals

3

wages	tally	freq.
£25 000–29 999	卌 ‖	7
£30 000–34 999	卌 卌	10
£35 000–39 999	卌 卌 ‖‖	14
£40 000–44 999	卌 ‖‖	8
£45 000–49 999	卌 ‖	6
£50 000–54 999	‖‖‖	4
£55 000–59 999	‖	1
		50

4

time (mins)	tally	freq.
$10 \leqslant t < 15$	‖	2
$15 \leqslant t < 20$	‖‖	3
$20 \leqslant t < 25$	卌 卌	10
$25 \leqslant t < 30$	卌 ‖‖	8
$30 \leqslant t < 35$	‖‖‖	4
$35 \leqslant t < 40$	卌 ‖	7
$40 \leqslant t < 45$	‖‖‖	4
$45 \leqslant t < 50$	‖	2
		40

Practice 4.5.1 – p. 145

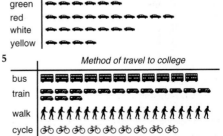

1 No. of people queuing at local post office

2 No. of people in local library at midday

3 Ice cream sales

4 Colour of cars in a car park

5 Method of travel to college

Practice 4.5.2 – p. 150

1

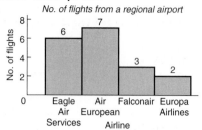

No. of flights from a regional airport

2

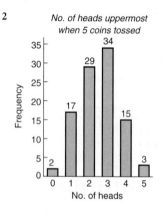

No. of heads uppermost when 5 coins tossed

3

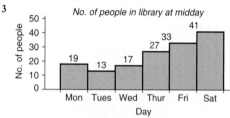

No. of people in library at midday

4

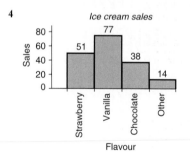

Ice cream sales

5

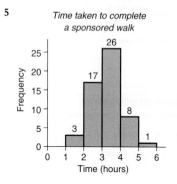

Time taken to complete a sponsored walk

6

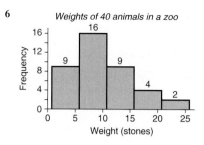

Weights of 40 animals in a zoo

7

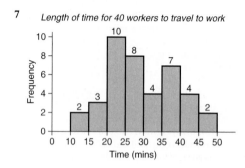

Length of time for 40 workers to travel to work

8

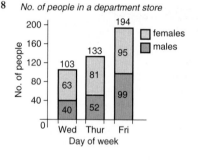

No. of people in a department store

9 a

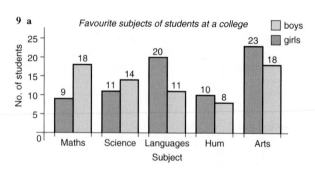

Favourite subjects of students at a college

b

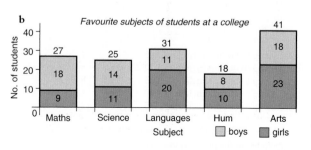

Favourite subjects of students at a college

10 a

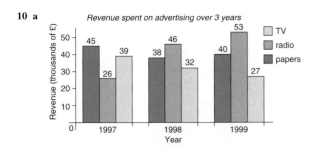

Revenue spent on advertising over 3 years

b

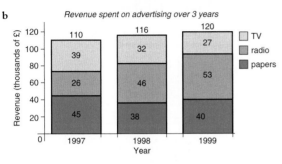

Revenue spent on advertising over 3 years

11 a day 1 = 83 vehicles, day 2 = 94 vehicles
  b 14 lorries   **c** 16 buses

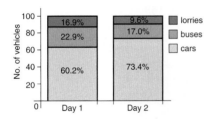

Practice 4.5.3 – p. 154

1

No. of microwave ovens sold at an electrical shop

2 Hours of sunshine at a holiday resort

3 Weight of a child recorded at birth and at the end of each month

4 Temperature in a lecture theatre at hourly intervals

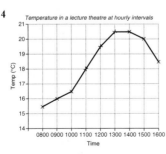

  a approx. 1230   **b** approx. 20.25 °C
(the answers are estimates as the line graph presumes that the temperature rises and falls uniformly between each hourly reading)

5 a 10   **b** 38   **c** 16
  d the answer is only an approximation as we are presuming that the graph continues uniformly between the hourly intervals
  e 38

Practice 4.5.4a – p. 158

1 Survey of favourite pets: Cat 100°, Dog 130°, Rabbit 60°, Bird 30°, Fish 40°.

2 Types of ticket sold on the Eurostar service to Paris: Business 184°, Pass holder 24°, Senior 48°, Child 34°, Leisure First 70°.

3 Ice cream sales: Strawberry 102°, Vanilla 154°, Choc 76°, Other 28°.

4 No. of flights from regional airport: Europa 40°, Falconair 60°, Air European 140°, Eagle Air 120°.

5 No. of heads uppermost when 5 coins are tossed: none 7°, one 61°, two 104°, three 122°, four 54°, five 11° .

Practice 4.5.4b – p. 159

1 Types of properties advertised in an estate agent's window: Semi-detached 76.5°, Flat 90°, Terraced 81°, Detached 63°, Bungalow 49.5°.

2 How 50 people paid for their goods: Visa 58°, Cash 130°, Cheque 86°, Mastercard 50°, Storecard 36°.

3 Number of people in local library at midday: Mon 46°, Tues 31°, Wed 41°, Thurs 65°, Fri 79°, Sat 98°.

4 a 12
  b 84°
  c Lost 84°, Won 144°, Drawn 132°

5 a car   **c** 30% of 200 = 60   **e** 180
  b 30%   **d** cycling   **f** 70

Practice 4.5.5 – p. 162

1

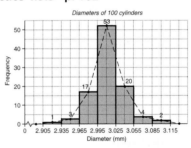

Diameters of 100 cylinders

2

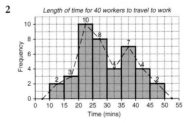

Length of time for 40 workers to travel to work

3

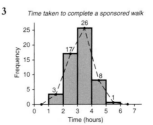

Time taken to complete a sponsored walk

4

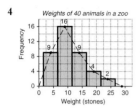

Weights of 40 animals in a zoo

Practice 4.5.6 – p. 164

1

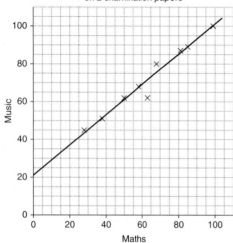

Marks awarded to 10 students on 2 examination papers

2

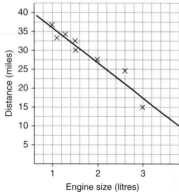

The height and weight of 8 students

3

Engine size and distance travelled on one gallon of petrol by 8 different cars

a 24 miles **b** $12\frac{1}{2}$ miles

the estimate in **b** is not so reliable as the estimate in **a** because we are making presumptions about the relationship between engine size and distance travelled outside the scope of the information given in the question

Practice 4.6.1a – p. 169

1

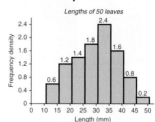

Lengths of 50 leaves

2

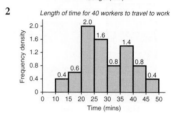

Length of time for 40 workers to travel to work

3

Distance (miles)	0–	2–	4–	6–	10–	15–20
No. of students	30	82	52	16	15	5

Practice 4.6.1b – p. 169

1

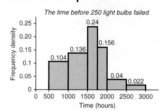

The time before 250 light bulbs failed

2

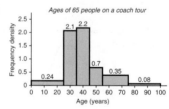

Ages of 65 people on a coach tour

Practice 4.6.2 – p. 170

1

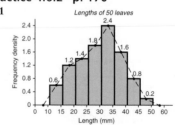

Lengths of 50 leaves

2

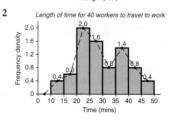

Length of time for 40 workers to travel to work

Chapter 5

Practice 5.2.1 – p. 178

1 a 6   **c** 33 and 35   **e** −1
  b 2   **d** 12.3 and 13.5
2 white
3 a 4 items   **b** 7   **c** 0 credit cards
4 21
5 7
6 2.5–3.5

Practice 5.2.2 – p. 181

1 a 6   **d** $101\frac{1}{2}$ **g** −2
  b 5   **e** 6
  c $5\frac{1}{2}$ **f** $6\left(\dfrac{5+7}{2}\right)$
2 $5\frac{1}{2}$
3 19

Practice 5.2.3 – p. 183

1 a 7   **d** $10\frac{1}{2}$ **g** 3.05
  b 6   **e** $20\frac{1}{2}$ **h** 305
  c 10   **f** $30\frac{1}{2}$ **i** −305

Practice 5.2.4 – p. 184

1 $\Sigma fx = 102$; $\Sigma f = 24$; mean = 4.25
2 mean = 240 ÷ 15 = 16 p
3 $\Sigma fx = 1414$; $\Sigma f = 80$; mean = 17.7 (3sf)
4 $\Sigma fx = 530$; $\Sigma f = 30$; mean = 17.7 (3sf)

Practice 5.2.5 – p. 187

1 $\Sigma fx = 730$; $\Sigma f = 32$; mean = 22.8 mm (3sf)
2 $\Sigma fx = 2235$; $\Sigma f = 75$; mean = £29.80
3 $\Sigma fx = 703.5$; $\Sigma f = 337$; mean = 2.09 mins (3sf)
4 $\Sigma fx = 4680$; mean = 62 kg (to an appropriate degree of accuracy)
5 $\Sigma fx = 2217$; $\Sigma f = 58$; mean = 38.2 mins

Practice 5.2.6 – p. 189

	mode	median	mean
1 a	4	3	3
b	6	$5\frac{1}{2}$	5
c	7	4	4.5
d	2	$3\frac{1}{2}$	4
e	no mode	$5\frac{1}{2}$	$5\frac{1}{2}$
f	no mode	$15\frac{1}{2}$	$15\frac{1}{2}$
g	−1	$-\frac{1}{2}$	−0.125

2 a 16   **c** 11   **e** 1
  b 12   **d** 46

f using

brothers	0	1	2	3	4	5
freq.	15	12	11	6	3	1

mean = $\frac{69}{46} = \frac{3}{2}$ = 1.5 (3sf)

3 a **i** 25.9 **ii** 27.5 **iii** 28
  b **i** the mean increases to 26.2
     ii the median is not affected
     iii the modal mark is not affected

4 the median gives the best measure as the mean will be affected by extreme values (£119 500) and the mode is inappropriate for such small numbers

Practice 5.3.1 – p. 191

1 a 16   **e** 16
  b 16   **f** 8.9
  c 11 cm   **g** $\frac{62}{80} = \frac{31}{40}$
  d 6.9 km

Practice 5.3.2 – p. 196

1

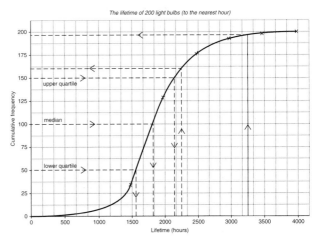

a 161
b 34
c 5
d median = 1800 hours
e interquartile range = 2133 − 1550 = 583 hours

2

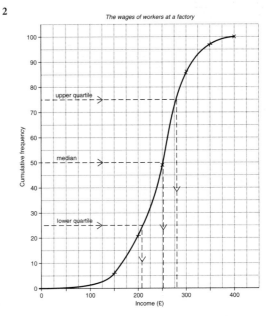

a £253
b £280 − £208 = £72

3

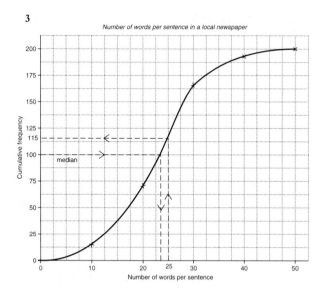

Number of words per sentence in a local newspaper

a   23.5   **b** $\dfrac{200-115}{200} \times 100\% = 42.5\%$

4

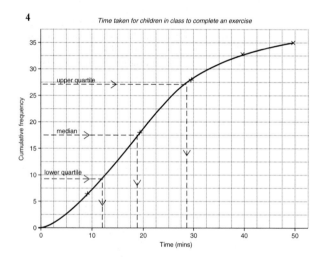

Time taken for children in class to complete an exercise

a   median = 19 mins; interquartile range = 29 − 12 = 17 mins
b   as the interquartile range for this class is bigger than in **a**, then
the spread of the time taken to complete the exercise is bigger

5

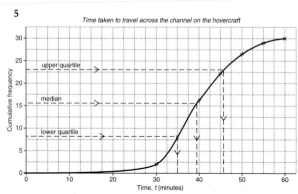

Time taken to travel across the channel on the hovercraft

median = 39.5 mins; interquartile range = 46 − 35 = 11 mins

Practice 5.4.1 – p. 199

1 a   no correlation
  b   moderate negative correlation
  c   moderate positive correlation
  d   no correlation/moderate negative correlation
  e   moderate positive correlation

2 a

moderate positive
correlation

c

moderate positive
correlation

b

no correlation

d

moderate negative
correlation

Practice 5.4.2 – p. 201

1

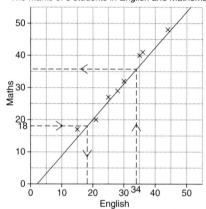

The marks of 8 students in English and Mathematics

a   there is a moderate positive correlation between English and
Mathematics
b   **i** 36   **ii** 18

2

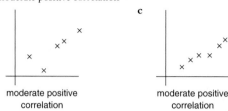

The petrol consumption of a car and the distance travelled

a there is a moderate positive correlation between the petrol consumption of a car and the distance travelled

b **i** 1.175 gallons **ii** 32.5 miles

3

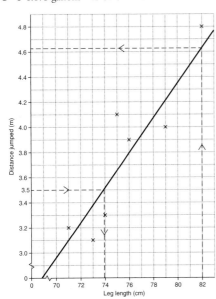

a **i** 73.6 cm **ii** 4.64 m

b the estimate in **a i** is more reliable because it is more within the scope of the data collected.

Practice 5.5.1 – p. 203

1 a mean = 6; mean deviation = 2

b mean = 6; mean deviation = 2.4

c mean = 3; mean deviation = 1

d mean = $3\frac{1}{3}$; mean deviation = $1\frac{1}{3}$

Practice 5.5.2 – p. 210

1 a mean = 4; s.d. = 2

b mean = 4; s.d. = 2.45 (3sf)

c mean = 1; s.d. = 3.16 (3sf)

d mean = 5; s.d. = 1.71 (3sf)

2 mean = 35 min; s.d. = 8.12 (3sf)

3 $\Sigma \bar{x} = 960\,000$; $\Sigma(x - \bar{x})^2 = 744\,000$; $\bar{x} = 96\,000$; s.d. = 8.63 (3sf)

4 $\Sigma x^2 = 92\,904\,000\,000$; s.d. = 8.63 (3sf)

(note that it may be better to work with the figures in thousands, i.e. 84, 94, 96, 90, …, etc.)

Practice 5.5.3 – p. 210

1 mean 1; s.d. = 4

a mean = 2; s.d. = 4   add 1 to each original number

b mean = 6; s.d. = 4   add 5 to each original number

c mean = 0; s.d. = 4   subtract 1 from each original number

d mean = 2; s.d. = 2 × 4 = 8   multiply each original number by 2

e mean = $\frac{1}{2}$; s.d. = $\frac{1}{2}$ × 4 = 2   divide each original number by 2

f mean = 3; s.d. = $\frac{1}{2}$ × 4 = 2   divide each original number by 2 and add $2\frac{1}{2}$

g mn = $\frac{1}{100}$; s.d. = $\frac{1}{100}$ × 4 = $\frac{1}{25}$ divide each original number by 100

Chapter 6

Practice 6.1.1 – p. 214

1 a $\frac{2}{5}$ **c** $\frac{4}{13}$ **e** $\frac{13}{24}$

b $\frac{8}{11}$ **d** $\frac{3}{10}$ **f** $\frac{13}{52} = \frac{1}{4}$

Practice 6.1.2 – p. 214

1 a $\frac{2}{36} = \frac{1}{18}$ **c** $\frac{4}{78} = \frac{2}{39}$ **e** $\frac{42}{105} = \frac{2}{5}$

b $\frac{3}{30} = \frac{1}{10}$ **d** $\frac{12}{84} = \frac{1}{7}$ **f** $\frac{9}{676}$

Practice 6.1.3 – p. 215

1 a 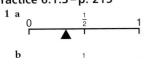   **c**

b   **d**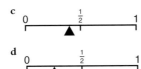

Practice 6.2.1 – p. 216

1 a $\frac{1}{2}$ **c** $\frac{13}{52} = \frac{1}{4}$

b $\frac{3}{6} = \frac{1}{2}$ **d** $\frac{1}{52}$

2 a $\frac{1}{11}$ **c** $\frac{2}{11}$

b $\frac{4}{11}$ **d** $\frac{0}{11}$ or 0

3 a $\frac{13}{26} = \frac{1}{2}$ **b** $\frac{6}{26} = \frac{3}{13}$ **c** $\frac{9}{26}$

4 $\frac{465}{500} = \frac{93}{100}$

5 a $\frac{10}{20} = \frac{1}{2}$ **c** $\frac{8}{20} = \frac{2}{5}$ **e** $\frac{8}{20} = \frac{2}{5}$

b $\frac{6}{20} = \frac{3}{10}$ **d** $\frac{7}{20}$ **f** $\frac{6}{20} = \frac{3}{10}$

6 a 4   **c** 12

b 16   **d** 8

7 a 17   **b** 3

8 a $\frac{10}{25} = \frac{2}{5}$ **c** $\frac{18}{25}$ **e** $\frac{25}{25} = 1$

b $\frac{8}{25}$ **d** $\frac{0}{25} = 0$

Practice 6.2.2 – p. 218

1 $\frac{2}{3}$ **4** 65%

2 0.996   **5** 0.4

3 0.998

Practice 6.2.3a – p. 220

1 30

2 5

3 4

4 a $\frac{30}{200} = \frac{3}{20}$ **c** $\frac{1}{2}$

b $\frac{36}{200} = \frac{9}{50}$ **d** 5

5 a experimental probability   **c** experimental probability

b equally likely outcomes

Practice 6.2.3b – p. 220

1 24

2 9 times

3 187

4 a $\frac{350}{1000} = \frac{7}{20}$ or 0.35   **b** 20 300 000

Practice 6.3.1 – p. 222

1 a mutually exclusive
b not mutually exclusive
c mutually exclusive
d mutually exclusive
e not mutually exclusive
f not mutually exclusive
g mutually exclusive

2 $\frac{5}{52}$

3 0.74

4 a $\frac{1}{12}$ **c** $\frac{5}{12}$
b $\frac{6}{12} = \frac{1}{2}$ **d** $\frac{2}{12} = \frac{1}{6}$

5 a $\frac{1}{3} + \frac{2}{5} = \frac{11}{15}$ **c** $\frac{1}{3} + \frac{2}{5} + \frac{1}{10} = \frac{25}{30} = \frac{5}{6}$
b $\frac{2}{5} + \frac{1}{10} = \frac{5}{10} = \frac{1}{2}$

6 the two events are not mutually exclusive as someone can be left-handed and wear glasses

Practice 6.4.1 – p. 223

1

	1	2	3	4	5	6
H	H1	H2	H3	H4	H5	H6
T	T1	T2	T3	T4	T5	T6

a $\frac{1}{12}$ **b** $\frac{3}{12} = \frac{1}{4}$

2

	1	2	3	4	5	6
R	R1	R2	R3	R4	R5	R6
R	R1	R2	R3	R4	R5	R6
R	R1	R2	R3	R4	R5	R6
R	R1	R2	R3	R4	R5	R6
G	G1	G2	G3	G4	G5	G6
G	G1	G2	G3	G4	G5	G6
G	G1	G2	G3	G4	G5	G6

a $\frac{4}{42} = \frac{2}{21}$ **b** $\frac{3}{42} = \frac{1}{14}$ **c** $\frac{12}{42} = \frac{2}{7}$

3 drawing a table to show the total score …

	1	2	3	4
1	2	3	4	5
2	3	4	5	6
3	4	5	6	7
4	5	6	7	8
5	6	7	8	9
6	7	8	9	10

a $\frac{2}{24} = \frac{1}{12}$ **b** $\frac{4}{24} = \frac{1}{6}$ **c** $\frac{1}{24}$

4 drawing a table to show the total score …

	1	2	3	4	5
1	2	3	4	5	6
2	3	4	5	6	7
3	4	5	6	7	8
4	5	6	7	8	9
5	6	7	8	9	10

a $\frac{1}{25}$ **b** $\frac{5}{25} = \frac{1}{5}$ **c** $\frac{2}{25}$

5

	1	2	3	4	5	6
HH	2	4	6	8	10	12
HT	1	2	3	4	5	6
TH	1	2	3	4	5	6
TT	0	0	0	0	0	0

a $\frac{3}{24} = \frac{1}{8}$ **b** $\frac{8}{24} = \frac{1}{3}$

6 a i $\frac{1}{10}$
ii $\frac{1}{5} + \frac{1}{20} + \frac{1}{10} + \frac{1}{20} = \frac{8}{20} = \frac{2}{5}$
iii $\frac{1}{5} + \frac{1}{20} + \frac{1}{10} = \frac{7}{20}$
iv $\frac{1}{10} + 0 + \frac{1}{20} + \frac{1}{10} + 0 + \frac{1}{20} = \frac{6}{20} = \frac{3}{10}$
(remember not to count blue and 4 twice)

b i 40 counters
ii 10 blue counters

Practice 6.4.2 – p. 226

1

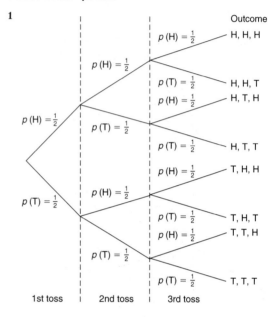

2

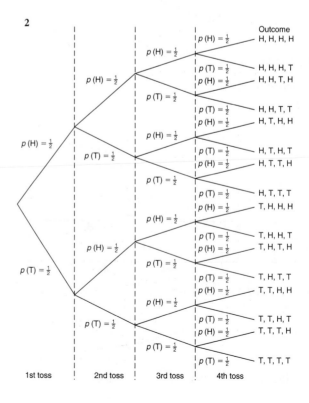

3

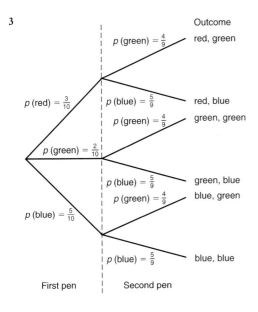

4

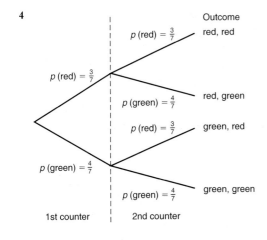

5

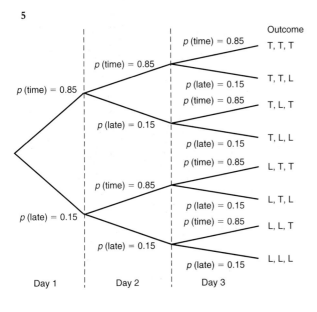

Practice 6.5.1a – p. 229

1 a $\frac{1}{2} \times \frac{1}{4} = \frac{1}{8}$ **c** $\frac{1}{2} \times \frac{1}{52} = \frac{1}{104}$

  b $\frac{1}{2} \times \frac{4}{52} = \frac{1}{26}$ **d** $\frac{1}{2} \times \frac{1}{52} = \frac{1}{104}$

2 a $\frac{3}{7} \times \frac{3}{7} = \frac{9}{49}$

  b $\frac{4}{7} \times \frac{4}{7} = \frac{16}{49}$

  c $\frac{3}{7} \times \frac{4}{7} = \frac{12}{49}$

  d p (one red and one green) $= p$ (first red and second green **or** first green and second red) $= \frac{3}{7} \times \frac{4}{7} + \frac{4}{7} \times \frac{3}{7} = \frac{24}{29}$

3

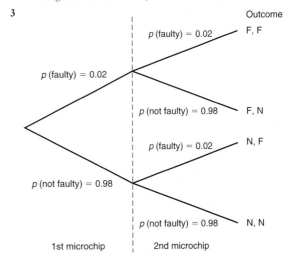

  a $0.02 \times 0.02 = 0.0004$

  b $0.0196 + 0.0196 = 0.0392$

4 a 0.4

  b $0.6 \times 0.6 = 0.36$

  c $0.24 + 0.24 = 0.48$

5 $\frac{1}{2^5} = \frac{1}{32}$

Practice 6.5.1b – p. 229

1 0.925 (the probability here is not affected by previous performance)

2 a $\frac{5}{8} \times \frac{5}{8} = \frac{25}{64}$ **b** $\frac{5}{8} \times \frac{5}{8} \times \frac{5}{8} = \frac{125}{512}$ **c** $\frac{485}{512}$

3 $\frac{1}{2^6} = \frac{1}{64}$

4 a $0.2 + 0.4 = 0.6$

  b $0.4 \times 0.4 = 0.16$

  c $0.24 + 0.24 = 0.48$

Practice 6.6.1a – p. 231

1

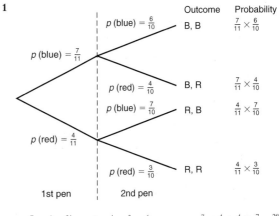

  a $\frac{7}{11} \times \frac{6}{10} = \frac{21}{55}$ **b** $\frac{4}{11} \times \frac{3}{10} = \frac{6}{55}$ **c** $\frac{7}{11} \times \frac{4}{10} + \frac{4}{11} \times \frac{7}{10} = \frac{28}{55}$

2

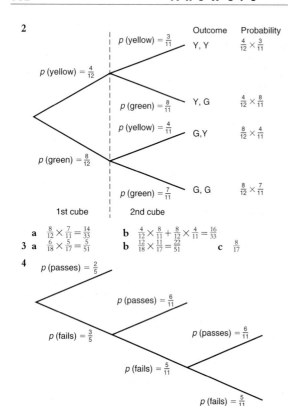

Outcome	Probability
Y, Y	$\frac{4}{12} \times \frac{3}{11}$
Y, G	$\frac{4}{12} \times \frac{8}{11}$
G, Y	$\frac{8}{12} \times \frac{4}{11}$
G, G	$\frac{8}{12} \times \frac{7}{11}$

a $\frac{8}{12} \times \frac{7}{11} = \frac{14}{33}$ **b** $\frac{4}{12} \times \frac{8}{11} + \frac{8}{12} \times \frac{4}{11} = \frac{16}{33}$

3 a $\frac{6}{18} \times \frac{5}{17} = \frac{5}{51}$ **b** $\frac{6}{18} \times \frac{11}{17} = \frac{22}{51}$ **c** $\frac{8}{17}$

4

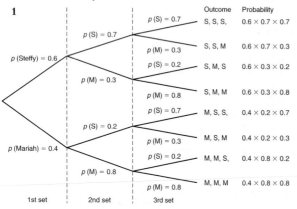

probability of passing on third time $= \frac{3}{5} \times \frac{5}{11} \times \frac{6}{11} = \frac{18}{121}$

Practice 6.6.1b – p. 232

1

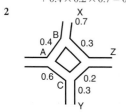

Outcome	Probability
S, S, S,	$0.6 \times 0.7 \times 0.7$
S, S, M	$0.6 \times 0.7 \times 0.3$
S, M, S	$0.6 \times 0.3 \times 0.2$
S, M, M	$0.6 \times 0.3 \times 0.8$
M, S, S	$0.4 \times 0.2 \times 0.7$
M, S, M	$0.4 \times 0.2 \times 0.3$
M, M, S,	$0.4 \times 0.8 \times 0.2$
M, M, M	$0.4 \times 0.8 \times 0.8$

a p(Mariah wins all three sets) $= p$(MMM)
$= 0.4 \times 0.8 \times 0.8 = 0.256$

b p(Steffy will win at least two sets)
$= p$(SSS or SSM or SMS or MSS)
$= 0.6 \times 0.7 \times 0.7 + 0.6 \times 0.7 \times 0.3 + 0.6 \times 0.3 \times 0.2$
$+ 0.4 \times 0.2 \times 0.7 = 0.512$

2

(diagram with X, B, A, Z, C, Y and values 0.7, 0.4, 0.3, 0.6, 0.2, 0.3)

a $0.4 \times 0.7 = 0.28$
b $0.6 \times 0.8 = 0.48$
c $0.4 \times 0.3 + 0.6 \times 0.2 = 0.24$

Practice 6.6.2 – p. 232

1

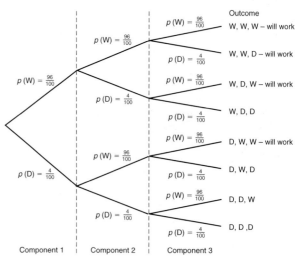

Outcome	
W, W, W – will work	
W, W, D – will work	
W, D, W – will work	
W, D, D	
D, W, W – will work	
D, W, D	
D, D, W	
D, D ,D	

a p(exactly two components work)
$= p$(WWD or WDW or DWW)
$= \frac{96}{100} \times \frac{96}{100} \times \frac{4}{100} + \frac{96}{100} \times \frac{4}{100} \times \frac{96}{100} + \frac{4}{100} \times \frac{96}{100} \times \frac{96}{100}$
$= 0.110\,592$

b p(machine will work) $= p$(at least two components are working)
$= p$(WWW or WWD or WDW or DWW)
$= \frac{96}{100} \times \frac{96}{100} \times \frac{96}{100} + \frac{96}{100} \times \frac{96}{100} \times \frac{4}{100}$
$+ \frac{96}{100} \times \frac{4}{100} \times \frac{96}{100} + \frac{4}{100} \times \frac{96}{100} \times \frac{96}{100}$
$= 0.995\,328$

(more simply you could add p(WWW) to your answer in part **a**)

2

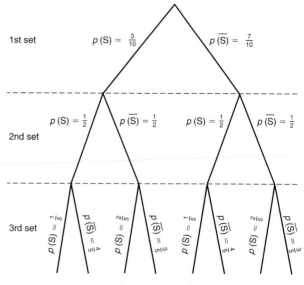

a $\frac{3}{10} \times \frac{1}{2} = \frac{3}{20}$ **c** $\frac{7}{10} \times \frac{1}{2} \times \frac{3}{5} = \frac{21}{100}$

b $\frac{3}{10} \times \frac{1}{2} + \frac{7}{10} \times \frac{1}{2} = \frac{1}{2}$ **d** $\frac{3}{10} \times \frac{1}{2} \times \frac{3}{5} + \frac{7}{10} \times \frac{1}{2} \times \frac{4}{5} + \frac{7}{10} \times \frac{1}{2} \times \frac{2}{5} = \frac{51}{100}$

3 a $0.7 \times 0.4 \times 0.1 + 0.3 \times 0.4 \times 0.9 + 0.7 \times 0.4 \times 0.9 = 0.388$

b $0.3 \times 0.6 \times 0.9 + 0.7 \times 0.4 \times 0.9 + 0.3 \times 0.6 \times 0.1$
$+ 0.7 \times 0.4 \times 0.1 = 0.46$

it is helpful on these questions to write out all the possible outcomes first

Chapter 7

Practice 7.2.1 – p. 239

1 a $6xy$
  b $-15cd$
  c e^8
  d f^6
  e $81m^4$
  f $-125n^3$
  g $81p^4$
  h $30qr$
  i $8st$
  j $\frac{1}{4}uv$
  k $120wxy$
  l $-120wxy$
  m $64xyz$
  n $-90abc$
  o $24def^2$
  p $g^{10}h^9i^4$
  q $56j^{12}k^7$
  r $180m^{10}n^{10}$
  s $3p^4$
  t $\frac{1}{3}q$
  u $5r^2s^2$
  v $-12t^6u^3v$
  w $5w^5x^5$

2 a $n = 3$
  b $m = 4$
  c $t = 1$
  d $b = 1$

Practice 7.3.1 – p. 240

1 a $5x + 4y$
  b $3c - 2$
  c $\frac{2p}{q^2}$
  d $4a + 2b$
  e $x^3 + \frac{x}{4}$

2 a $4y$
  b $y + 6$
  c $4y - 7$
  d $\frac{3y}{2}$
  e $2y$

Practice 7.3.2 – p. 241

1 a $20a$
  b $2b$
  c $-2c$
  d $12d + 15e$
  e $3f + 3g$
  f $-3h - 12k - 5l$
  g $7x + 3y - 7m - 1$
  h $p - 13q + 3$
  i $1\frac{1}{2}r + 2\frac{3}{4}s$
  j $7t - t^2 + 3u$

k no simpler form (NSF)
  l $2w^2 - w - 8$
  m $6x^2$
  n $\frac{8}{y}$
  o $\frac{4}{z^2} - \frac{1}{z}$
  p $11x^3 + x - 3$
  q $\frac{3b}{c}$
  r NSF
  s $12x^3y + 7x^2y^2 - 5xy^3$
  t $13z^3 + 4z^2$

Practice 7.3.3 – p. 243

1 a $2a + 6$
  b $6a - 2$
  c $6b - 21$
  d $8b + 12c$
  e $30f - 15g$
  f $-12x - 8y$
  g $-12y + 9z$
  h $21a - 14b$
  i $24c + 18d$
  j $6e - 10f$
  k $3wx + 6uy - 9wz$
  l $-12w^2 + 15wx - 9w$
  m $15x^2 + 10x + 35$
  n $28y^3 - 4y^2 + 12y$

2 a $5z + 15$
  b $-z - 15$
  c $-z + 15$
  d $6a + 2$
  e $4b - 18$
  f 13
  g $d - 6e + 9f$
  h $-11d - 7f$
  i $5x^2 + x - 23$
  j $8y^2 - 9y + 30$
  k $2x^3 + 18x^2 - 20x + 6$
  l $xy - 6x$
  m $3mn - 15m - 8n$
  n $23p^2 + 9pq$
  o $-7p^2 + 15pq$
  p $35yz + 21$
  q $-8t + 16$
  r $14x + 18y + 26z$

Practice 7.3.4 – p. 246

1 a $a^2 + 12a + 27$
  b $b^2 + 5b - 14$
  c $c^2 - 3c - 10$
  d $x^2 + x - 12$
  e $x^2 - 3x - 40$
  f $y^2 - 3y + 2$
  g $2x^2 + 17x + 21$
  h $6z^2 + 16z - 32$
  i $6x^2 - 21x - 12$
  j $10y^2 - 19y + 6$
  k $x^2 + 10x + 25$
  l $y^2 - 14y + 49$
  m $4z^2 + 4z + 1$
  n $9x^2 - 24x + 16$

2 a $x^2 + 10x + 21$
  b $2y^2 + 11y + 15$
  c $8z^2 + 10z + 3$

3 a **i** x^2 **ii** $2x$ **iii** $3x$ **iv** 6
  b $x^2 - 5x + 6$
  c HIFG = ACEG − ACDH − BCEF + BCDI (since BCDI has been subtracted **twice**)

Practice 7.3.5 – p. 247

1 a $2(a + 5)$
  b $4(4 - b)$
  c $2(5c - 6)$
  d $e(f - 3)$
  e $3h(g + 5k)$
  f $x(8x + 7)$
  g $2k(2k + 3)$
  h $y(9y - 31)$
  i $7z(y + 3z)$
  j $4xy(1 + 3x)$
  k $3st(5t + s)$
  l $5(2u + 3v - 4x)$
  m $3x(2x - y + 3)$
  n $\frac{yz}{5}\left(1 - \frac{y}{3} + \frac{3z}{5}\right)$
  o $\frac{2a^2}{b^2}(1 + 2a)$

Practice 7.3.6 – p. 248

1 a $(a + 2)(b + c)$
  b $(c - 1)(d + 2e)$
  c $(fg + 3)(fg - h)$
  d $(x + 2)(x + 3)$
  e $(y - 4)(y - 7)$
  f $(2z + 3)(z - 2)$

Practice 7.3.7 – p. 251

1 a $(a + 4)(a + 1)$
  b $(b + 5)(b + 10)$
  c $(c - 2)(c - 5)$
  d $(d - 10)(d - 1)$
  e $(e + 8)(e - 2)$
  f $(f + 15)(f - 5)$
  g $(g - 7)(g + 5)$
  h $(h + 3)(h - 8)$
  i $(j + 8)(j + 11)$
  j $(k + 4)(k + 5)$
  k $(m - 3)(m - 7)$
  l $(n - 5)(n - 5)$
  m $(p + 7)(p - 2)$
  n $(q - 3)(q + 11)$
  o $(r - 10)(r + 5)$
  p $(s - 6)(s + 5)$
  q $t(t + 3)$
  r $u(u - 4)$
  s $(v - 3)(v + 3)$
  t $(w - 5)(w + 5)$

Practice 7.3.8 – p. 253

1 a 17
  b -3
  c 9
  d -2
  e -2
  f -72
  g -2
  h 9

2 a 19
  b 0
  c -64
  d 2
  e -5

3 a 8
  b 16
  c -6
  d 12
  e 0
  f 13
  g 5
  h -25
  i 29
  j $4\frac{1}{2}$

4 a 25
  b 144
  c 6
  d ± 5
  e ± 8
  f ± 6
  g 6
  h 5

Practice 7.3.9a – p. 255

1 a 11
  b 24.6
  c 2
  d -4
  e $a = 5$

2 a 45
  b 600
  c 40
  d 112.5

3 a 20
  b -15
  c 100
  d 77
  e $F = 32$

4 a 20.16
  b 8

5 a 47
  b 4
  c $C = 4$

6 a i 40 **ii** 34
  b 3
  c 8

7 a $0.7\,\text{AU}$
  b $5.2\,\text{AU}$
  c $x = 96$

Practice 7.3.9b – p. 256

1 a 110 (3 sf)
  b 5.97 (3 sf)

2 a i 61 **ii** 62.6
  b i 2 **ii** 1.89 (3sf)
  c i 4.5 **ii** 6.425

3 a $36\,\text{km}$
  b $44.1\,\text{km}$
  c $123\,\text{m}$
  d $7.2\,\text{km}$
  e $d = 33.2$, yes she can
  f $100\,\text{km}$

4 a 19.6
  b 29.0
  c $1.86\,\text{m}$
  d $60.5\,\text{kg}$

Practice 7.3.10a – p. 258

1 a i -2 **ii** 1 **iii** 19
  b $\frac{2}{3}$
  c 4
  d $3x - 2$

2 a i 0 **ii** 5 **iii** 12
  b 5
  c $x(x + 4)$

3 a i −4 **ii** 12 **iii** 36
  b 5
  c outputs are −4, 12, 20, 28, 36, etc., i.e. all multiples of 4
  d $4(2x − 3)$

Practice 7.3.10b – p. 259
1 a 18.6 s
  b 15.5 s
  c 3.844 s
  d they are the same i.e. time of swing = length of pendulum

Practice 7.4.1 – p. 261
1 8
2 10
3 12
4 $\triangle = 6,\ \bigcirc = 8$
5 $\square = 5,\ \bigcirc = 3$
6 $\bigcirc = 5,\ \triangle = 7\frac{1}{2}$

Practice 7.4.2 – p. 263
1 a 3.5   **c** 2   **e** 12   **g** −2
  b 16   **d** $3\frac{2}{3}$ **f** 1   **h** −2

Practice 7.4.3 – p. 265
1 a $x = 3$ **e** $z = 20$ **i** $y = 21$
  b $x = −4$ **f** $x = −16$ **j** $y = −15$
  c $y = 21$ **g** $x = −4$ **k** $z = 3$
  d $y = 9$ **h** $x = \frac{2}{5}$ **l** $x = 48$

Practice 7.4.4 – p. 266
1 a $x = 6$ **e** $x = 4$ **i** $x = 7$
  b $x = 2$ **f** $x = 12$ **j** $x = 12$
  c $x = 10$ **g** $x = −4$
  d $x = 2$ **h** $x = 1$

Practice 7.4.5 – p. 267
1 $x + x + 1 = 21$; 10 and 11
2 $w + w + 4 + w + w + 4 = 36$; 7 and 11
3 $p + p + 15 = 18$; $p = 1.5$ lb
4 $a + a + 30 + a + 80 = 710$; 200
5 $m + m + 3 + 2m + 1 = 28$; 6 miles
6 $g + g + 19 + g + 33 = 223$; 57 kg, 76 kg, 90 kg
7 $2.5g = g + 12$; 8, 20
8 $1.5c + 1(20 − c) = 22$; 4
9 $\dfrac{3 + x}{5 + x} = \dfrac{5}{6}$; 7
10 $\frac{1}{2}x + \frac{3}{4}$ of $\frac{1}{2}x + \frac{3}{4}$ of $\frac{1}{2}x − 1000 = x$; $x = 4000$
11 $\dfrac{x}{80} + \dfrac{100 − x}{20} = 2$; 80.
12 $x + 3x + x + 50 = 600$; £110, £330, £160
13 a $x + 3$ **d** $x = 6$
  b $4x + 6$ **e i** 6 cm **ii** 9 cm **iii** 40 cm
  c $4x + 6 = 30$

Practice 7.4.6 – p. 271
1 a $a = 4, b = 3$ **c** $e = 1, f = −1$ **e** $j = 5, k = 5$
  b $c = 8, d = 3$ **d** $g = −1, h = 3$ **f** $m = 0, n = 3$

Practice 7.4.7 – p. 274
1 a $a = 6, b = 1$ **c** $e = 1, f = −2$ **e** $j = −3, k = 0$
  b $c = −3, d = 2$ **d** $g = −3, h = −5$ **f** $m = 3.5, n = 1.5$

Practice 7.4.8 – p. 275
1 26, 18
2 £8.50, £6.50

3 £11.50, £8
4 £9, £6.50
5 8 p, 5 p
6 £150, £200
7 60 g
8 25, 11
9 12, 28
10 6, 4
11 65, 40
12 3, −2
13 8 years, 12 years
14 147

Practice 7.5.1 – p. 278
1 a $x = 0$ or 5   **e** $x = 2$ or 6   **i** $x = 11$ or −3
  b $x = 0$ or −4   **f** $x = 3$ or 7   **j** $x = −9$ or 6
  c $x = 3$ or −3   **g** $x = −2$ or −1   **k** $x = −4$ (twice)
  d $x = 5$ or −5   **h** $x = 6$ (twice)
2 a $a = 3$ or −3   **f** $x = 0$ or 2.5   **k** $x = −4$ or −9
  b $b = 12$ or −12   **g** $x = 2$ or 6   **l** $x = 6$ or −5
  c $c = 0$ or −5   **h** $x = 4$ or 5   **m** $y = 9$ or −11
  d $d = 0$ or −1.8   **i** $x = −10$ or −3   **n** $z = 7$ or −10
  e $e = 0$ or 11   **j** $x = −9$ or −11
3 a $(x − 2)$ and $(x − 4)$ **b** $(x − 2)(x − 4) = 0$ $x^2 − 6x + 8 = 0$
4 a $(y + 5)$ and $(y + 3)$ **b** $(y + 5)(y + 3) = 0$ $y^2 + 8y + 15 = 0$
5 a $(z − 2)$ and $(z + 1)$ **b** $(z − 2)(z + 1) = 0$ $z^2 − z − 2 = 0$

Practice 7.5.2 – p. 280
1 −3 or 5
2 7 and 8 or −7 and −8
3 −8 and −15 or 8 and 15
4 −11 or 10,
  i.e. no. is 10 since −11 is not valid
5 $40 = n(n − 3)$; $n = −5$ or 8, i.e. no. of sides is 8 since −5 is not valid
6 −8 or 6, $d = 6$ since −8 is not valid
7 12
8 3 seconds
9 4 cm long since −9 is not valid

Practice 7.6.1 – p. 283
1 a $R = \dfrac{v}{I}$ **b** $I = \dfrac{v}{R}$

2 a $R = \dfrac{E}{I^2}$ **b** $I = \sqrt{\left(\dfrac{E}{R}\right)}$

3 a $u = v − at$ **b** $t = \dfrac{(v − u)}{a}$

4 a $u = \sqrt{(v^2 − 2as)}$ **b** $s = \dfrac{(v^2 − u^2)}{2a}$

5 a $v = \dfrac{2s}{t} − u$ or $v = \dfrac{(2s − ut)}{t}$ **b** $t = \dfrac{2s}{u + v}$

6 a $a = \dfrac{2(s − ut)}{t^2}$ **b** $u = \dfrac{(s − \frac{1}{2}at^2)}{t}$
                       or $u = \dfrac{s}{t} − \frac{1}{2}at$

7 a $x = \dfrac{aT}{k}$ **b** $a = \dfrac{kx}{T}$

8 a $x = \dfrac{\sqrt{(2aE)}}{k}$ **b** $a = \dfrac{kx^2}{2E}$

9 a $R = \dfrac{100I}{PT}$ **b** $T = \dfrac{100I}{PR}$

10 a $P = \dfrac{R}{Q + 3}$ **b** $Q = \dfrac{R}{P} − 3$ or $\dfrac{R − 3P}{P}$

11 a $v = \dfrac{M}{m} + u$ or $v = \dfrac{M + mu}{m}$ **b** $u = v - \dfrac{M}{m}$ or $u = \dfrac{mv - M}{m}$

12 a $a = \dfrac{c^2 b}{25}$ **b** $b = \dfrac{25a}{c^2}$

Practice 7.6.2 – p. 284

Answers to 3sf unless otherwise stated

1 a $r = \dfrac{c}{2\pi}$ **b** 7.96 cm

2 a $r = \sqrt{\left(\dfrac{A}{\pi}\right)}$ **b** 3.99 cm

3 a $h = \dfrac{3v}{\pi r^2}$ **b** 11.0 cm

4 a $v = \sqrt{\left(\dfrac{2E}{M}\right)}$ **b** 8.00 m/s

5 a $L = \dfrac{10T^2}{4\pi^2}$ **b** 2.28 m

6 a $x = \sqrt{\left(\dfrac{10A}{4 + \sqrt{3}}\right)}$ **b** 12.6 cm

7 a $r = 100\left(\sqrt{\left(\dfrac{A}{P}\right)} - 1\right)$ **b** 7.00%

Practice 7.7.1 – p. 286

1 a   **e**   **i**
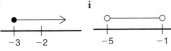

b   **f**   **j**
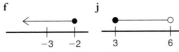

c   **g**   **k**
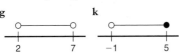

d   **h**   **l**
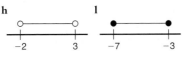

2 a   **g**
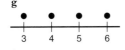

b   **h**
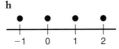

c   **i**

d   **j**

e   **k**
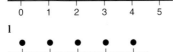

f   **l**

Practice 7.7.2 – p. 289

1 a   **e**

b   **f**

c   **g**

d   **h**

2 a 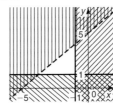   **c**

b   **d**

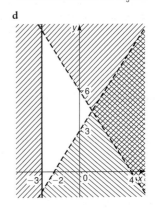

Practice 7.7.3 – p. 290

1 a $a > 6$ **e** $e > -1$ **i** $i > -3$

b $b \le 2$ **f** $f \le 1$ **j** $j \le -1$

c $c \ge -1.5$ **g** $g > -\dfrac{1}{2}$ **k** $k < 2$

d $d < \dfrac{-2}{3}$ **h** $h \ge -3\tfrac{1}{2}$ **l** $l \le 4$

Practice 7.7.4 – p. 291

1 $35g \le 420$, $g \le 12$

2 $6 \ge \dfrac{x}{90}$, $x \le 540$

3 $1000 + 1150p < 12\,500$, $p < 10$
4 $n \leq 99$, $n \geq 90$, i.e. $n = 90, 91, 92, 93, 94, 95, 96, 97, 98, 99$
5 $r > 30$, $r \leq 36$ (r is odd), hence $r = 31, 33, 35$
6 $r \geq 5$, $2r + 3 \leq 20$, hence $r = 5, 6, 7, 8$

Practice 7.8.1 – p. 293

Answers to 2dp
1 a 5.57   **c** 12.53   **e** 32.65
   b 9.70   **d** 24.45
2 a 5.19   **b** 1.28   **c** 3.10   **d** 2.10
3 4.18 c   **4** 6.73 cm   **5** 6.21 m   **6** 0.78 miles

Practice 7.9.1a – p. 295

1 a i 128   **ii** 243   **iii** 625   **iv** 216
   b i $\frac{1}{512}$ **ii** $\frac{1}{10}$ **iii** $\frac{1}{216}$ **iv** $\frac{1}{64}$
   c i 1   **ii** 1   **iii** 1   **iv** 1
   d i 5   **ii** 3   **iii** -3 **iv** 2
   e i 64   **ii** 81   **iii** 27   **iv** 32
2 a $p^0 = 1$ **c** $m^{1/6}$ **e** $2s^2$
   b $z^{9/20}$ **d** $n^{1/10}$
3 a $16x^6$ **e** y^{12} **i** $4^5 = 1024$
   b $\frac{1}{5}w$ **f** $16k$ **j** $\frac{1}{100f^2}$
   c $125p^3q^3$ **g** $4a^3$
   d $3t^3$ **h** $1^5 = 1$
4 a 5^4 **c** 6^{-2}
   b i 2^8 **ii** 4^4 **iii** 16^2 **d i** $2^{-2}, 4^{-1}$ **ii** $2^{-4}, 4^{-2}$
                      iii $2^3, 4^{1.5}$ **iv** $2^{-5}, 4^{-2.5}$

Practice 7.9.1b – p. 295

1 a 1.732   **c** 279.5   **e** 0.4472
   b 76.37   **d** 2.759 (all to 4 sf)

Practice 7.9.2 – p. 296

1 $(x - y)(x + y)$ **9** $\left(\dfrac{j}{6} - \dfrac{k}{9}\right)\left(\dfrac{j}{6} + \dfrac{k}{9}\right)$
2 $(z - 3)(z + 3)$ **10** $\left(5p - \dfrac{3q}{4}\right)\left(5p + \dfrac{3q}{4}\right)$
3 $(a - 4)(a + 4)$ **11** $r(r - 1)(r + 1)$
4 $(b - 1)(b + 1)$ **12** $s(s + t)(s - t)$
5 $(c + \frac{1}{4})(c - \frac{1}{4})$ **13** $2(7u - 8v)(7u + 8v)$
6 $(3d + 4e)(3d - 4e)$ **14** $(256 - 244)(256 + 244)$
                             $= 12 \times 500 = 6000$
7 $(7f + 11g)(7f - 11g)$ **15** $(4.91 - 4.9)(4.91 + 4.9)$
                             $= 0.01 \times 9.81 = 0.0981$
8 $\left(h - \dfrac{i}{5}\right)\left(h + \dfrac{i}{5}\right)$

Practice 7.9.3 – p. 298

1 5.233
2 a -7.043
   b 0.710; they are the two roots of the quadratic equation
3 3.72, 0.036
4 a $x_n(2 - 9x_n)$ gives $\frac{1}{9} = 0.1111$
   b $x_n(2 - 25x_n)$ gives $\frac{1}{25} = 0.0400$
   c $x_n(2 - \sqrt{2}x_n)$ gives $\frac{1}{\sqrt{2}} = 0.7071$

Practice 7.9.4 – p. 301

Answers are given to 2dp
1 $x = -0.47$ or -8.53 **8** $x = -1.83$ or 3.83
2 $x = -4.79$ or -0.21 **9** $x = -0.5$ or -3
3 $x = 3.41$ or 0.59 **10** $x = -1.43$ or -0.23
4 $x = 0.86$ or 8.14 **11** $x = 1.52$ or -0.92
5 $x = 0.22$ or -9.22 **12** $x = -1.57$ or 0.32
6 $x = -7.41$ or 0.41 **13** $x = 0.2$ or -3
7 $x = 9.52$ or -0.52 **14** $x = 0$ or -5

Practice 7.9.5 – p. 302

1 $\dfrac{a}{2}$ **9** $\dfrac{3p}{2}$ **17** $\dfrac{e + 2f}{5ef}$
2 $\dfrac{1}{3b^2}$ **10** NSF   **18** $\dfrac{5g}{g + h}$
3 $\dfrac{2}{5}$ **11** $\dfrac{-12u}{v}$ **19** $\dfrac{3(i + 2j)}{2i - j}$
4 $-\dfrac{2d}{3}$ **12** $\dfrac{-2u^2}{w}$ **20** $\dfrac{(m - 3)(m - 5)}{(m - 3)(m + 2)} = \dfrac{m - 5}{m + 2}$
5 $-\dfrac{7}{10g^2}$ **13** $\dfrac{5xz^2}{8y}$ **21** $\dfrac{m - 1}{m + 7}$
6 $\dfrac{8hi}{5}$ **14** $\dfrac{2 + 4a^2}{a}$ **22** $\dfrac{3p - 7}{4}$
7 $\dfrac{11k^2}{7j}$ **15** $\dfrac{4 + 5b}{3}$
8 $\dfrac{3m}{2}$ **16** $\dfrac{c - d}{2(c + d)}$

Practice 7.9.6 – p. 303

1 $\dfrac{4}{15}$ **5** $\dfrac{9i^2j^5}{4}$ **9** $\dfrac{2}{3}$
2 $\dfrac{1}{cd}$ **6** 2   **10** $\dfrac{3mn}{2(m + n)}$
3 $\dfrac{8e}{5fz}$ **7** $\dfrac{8k^2l^2}{9}$
4 $\dfrac{5h^3}{6g}$ **8** $\dfrac{m}{3}$

Practice 7.9.7 – p. 304

1 $\dfrac{5a}{6}$ **6** $\dfrac{7h + 2g}{2gh}$ **11** $\dfrac{3u^2 - 2u}{(u - 3)(u + 4)}$
2 $\dfrac{-7}{10b}$ **7** $\dfrac{20i - 9h}{15hi}$ **12** $\dfrac{w^2 - 11w}{(w + 4)(w - 1)}$
3 $\dfrac{25d}{12e}$ **8** $\dfrac{13p + 10q}{12}$ **13** $\dfrac{4z - 7}{z - 1}$
4 $\dfrac{3d^2 + 3e^2}{4de}$ **9** $\dfrac{2s + 8}{(s - 1)(s + 1)}$ **14** $\dfrac{3(a + 2)}{a - 3}$
5 $\dfrac{7}{6f}$ **10** $\dfrac{8t + 5}{t(t + 1)}$

Practice 7.9.8 – p. 305

1 a $x \geq 5$, $y \geq 4$, $2x + 3y \leq 28$
   b

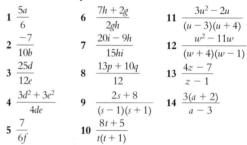
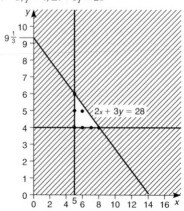

   c (s = sponge, g = gateaux) 5s and 4g, 6s and 4g, 7s and 4g, 8s and 4g, 5s and 5g, 5s and 6g, 6s and 5g
   d maximum 8 sponges, maximum 6 gateaux (**not** at the same time)

Chapter 8

Practice 8.1.1 – p. 313

1 a 9, 11   **e** June, July
   b 22, 27   **f** 0, −2
   c n, q   **g** 3, −3
   d 512, 2048   **h** 14, 14 (2, 5, 8, 11, 14, …; 6, 8, 10, 12, 14, …)

Practice 8.2.1 – p. 315

1 (add 2) 11, 13   **7** (multiply by −2) −40, 80
2 (add 2.5) 15.5, 18   **8** (multiply by 2 and add 1) 63, 127
3 (multiply by 2) 32, 64   **9** (multiply by 4 and subtract $\frac{1}{2}$)
4 (subtract 4) 0, −4   213.5, 853.5
5 (divide by 3) 1, $\frac{1}{3}$ **10** (multiply by −1) −2, 2
6 (subtract 3) −10, −13

Practice 8.2.2 – p. 317

1 a 17, 29, 74, $3n − 1$
   b 26, 46, 121, $5n − 4$
   c 96, 1536, 503 316 48, 1.5×2^n
   d 5, −7, −52, $23 − 3n$
   e 2, 0.125, 3.814×10^{-6}, $128 \times \frac{1}{2}^n$
2 $4n − 3$, 22 terms
3 $2 \times 5^{n-1}$, 6 terms
4 $-\frac{1}{2} \times (-2)^n$ or $(-2)^{n-1}$, 10 terms
5 $11 − 3n$, 40 terms
6 a 9   **b** 39   **c** 99
7 a 23   **b** 98   **c** 248
8 a 81   **b** 3^{19} **c** 3^{49}
9 a 16   **b** 524 288   **c** 2^{49}
10 a 13   **b** 89   **c** 987

Practice 8.2.3 – p. 319

1 a   6   11   18   27   38
       5   7   9   11
         2   2   2
     The final difference shows the form is $x^2 + bx + c$
     Thus: $1^2 + 5$, $2^2 + 7$, $3^2 + 9$, etc. difference goes up in 2s,
     hence $2x$ i.e. $6 = 1^2 + 2 \times 1 + 3$, $11 = 2^2 + 2 \times 2 + 3$,
     $18 = 3^2 + 2 \times 3 + 3$, …
     hence the required formula must be $x^2 + 2x + 3$
   b $x^2 + 5x − 4$ **d** $2x^2 + x − 1$ **f** $3x^2 − 4x + 5$
   c $2x^2 + 3x + 1$ **e** $3x^2 + 5x + 7$

Practice 8.2.4 – p. 321

1 a i 82   **ii** 154   **iii** 302
   c i $4x + 10 = 22, x = 3$ **iii** $4x + 10 = 282, x = 68$
     ii $4x + 10 = 102, x = 23$ **iv** $4x + 10 + 374, x = 91$
   d no – it does not fit on the grid
2 a i −3   **ii** 35   **iii** 62
   c i $x − 20 = −4, x = 16$ **iii** $x − 20 = 77, x = 97$
     ii $x − 20 = 33, x = 53$
   d no – it does not fit on the grid
3 a i 31   **ii** 1969   **iii** 5101
   c i $x^2 − 21x + 99 = −9, x = 9$ or 12, but $x = 9$ does not fit on
     the grid, thus $x = 12$
     ii $x^2 − 21x + 99 = 451, x = −11$ or 32, but $x = −11$ does not
     fit on the grid, thus $x = 32$
     iii $x^2 − 21x + 99 = 1179, x = −24$ or 45, but $x = −24$ does
     not fit on the grid, thus $x = 45$
4 a i 20   **ii** 20   **iii** 20

Practice 8.3.1 – p. 325

1 $y = 2 − 3(−1) = 5$, **no**
2 $y = 2 \times 2 − 7 = −3$, **yes**
3 $y = 2x - 6$
4 a $y = −3, y = 3, y = 17$

Practice 8.3.2a – p. 328

1 a   **h**

   b 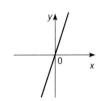   **i**

   c   **j**

   d   **k**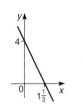

   e   **l**

   f   **m**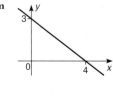

   g   **n**

o

p

2 a

5	15	25
75	225	375
95	245	395

c i 140 min   **ii** 290 min   **iii** 365 min

d 14 lb

Practice 8.3.2b – p. 329

1 a

10 000	25 000	55 000
180	390	810
160	400	880

b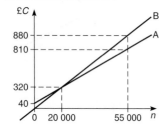

c (from graph) $n = 20\,000$, £320

d tariff B is cheaper, a saving of £12

e tariff A is cheaper, a saving of £60

Practice 8.3.3 – p. 330

1 a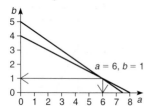

$a = 6, b = 1$

b 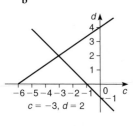 **c**

$c = -3, d = 2$ $e = 1, f = -2$

d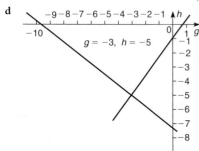

$g = -3, h = -5$

e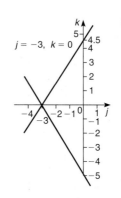

$j = -3, \ k = 0$

f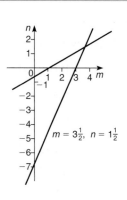

$m = 3\frac{1}{2}, \ n = 1\frac{1}{2}$

Practice 8.3.4 – p. 333

1 a 7   **c** 1   **e** 7

b -2 **d** $-4\frac{1}{2}$ **f** $2\frac{1}{3}$

2 a 5   **c** 1   **e** $1\frac{1}{2}$

b 7   **d** -2 **f** $1\frac{1}{3}$

3 a $1\frac{2}{3}$ **d** $-\frac{1}{5}$ **g** 1

b $\frac{1}{3}$ **e** $-1\frac{1}{5}$ **h** 0

c $-2\frac{1}{2}$ **f** $\frac{5}{9}$ **i** ∞ (infinity)

4 a 1   **c** -3

b 4   **d** $-1\frac{1}{2}$

5 a C   **c** A   **e** D

b E   **d** B

6 a 2

b $y = 2x + c$

c -2

d $y = 2x - 2$

7 $y = -3x$

8 $y = 4x - 2$

9 $5y = 12x + 11$

Practice 8.4.1 – p. 336

1 a 32°F   **b** 100°C   **c** 37°C   **d** 185°F

2 a i 310 m   **ii** 520 m   **iii** 580 m   **iv** 310 m

b 600 m

c i 3 min, 37 min   **ii** $9\frac{1}{2}$, $11\frac{1}{2}$, $27\frac{1}{2}$ and 30 min

d 20 min from home

e 18 min

f i at 10 min   **ii** 8 min   **iii** 300 m

g 1800 m

3 a $45 + 9 = 54$ miles   **b** 45 mph   **c** 1045 to 1142

4 a 2500   **b** 400   **c** 1500 to 3450

Practice 8.4.2 – p. 340

1 b $m \approx \dfrac{60}{17.6} \approx 3.4$ $c \approx 7$

c $y \approx 3.4x + 7$ **i** $y \approx 3.4 \times 4 + 7 \approx 20.6$

  ii $y \approx 3.4 \times 10 + 7 \approx 41$

2 b $m \approx \dfrac{-46}{14} \approx -3.3$ $c \approx 46$

c $y \approx -3.3x + 46$ **i** $y \approx -3.3 \times 2.54 + 46 \approx 38$

  ii $y \approx -3.3 \times 11.7 + 46 \approx 7.4$

  iii $y \approx -3.3 \times 14 + 46 \approx 0$

3 b $m \approx \dfrac{15.6}{2} \approx 7.8$; the resistance R

c i 2.6 A   **ii** 11.6 V

4 a and **c**

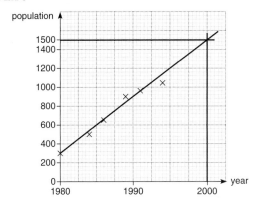

b 1989

d i ≈ 800   **ii** ≈ 1500

5 a and **b**

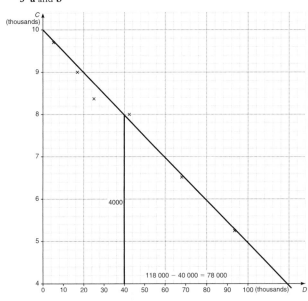

c i £10 000   **ii** $m \approx \dfrac{-4000}{78\,000} \approx -0.05$

d $C = 10\,000 - 0.05D$

e i £9500 approx.   **ii** £5000 approx.

f 50 000 miles approx.

Practice 8.5.1 – p. 343

1 a

c

b
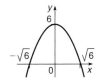
d

e

f

Practice 8.5.2 – p. 344

Answers to 1dp read from graphs

1 a i $(0,0)$ **ii** $x = 0$ **iii** $x = 0$
  b i $(0,6)$ **ii** $x = 0$ **iii** $x = 2.5, -2.5$
  c i $(1.5, -2.25)$ **ii** $x = 1.5$ **iii** $x = 0.3$
  d i $(2.5, -2.25)$ **ii** $x = 2.5$ **iii** $x = 1, 4$
  e i $(-1.2, -10)$ **ii** $x = -1.2$ **iii** $x = 0.7, -3$
  f i $(-1.3, 11.3)$ **ii** $x = -1.3$ **iii** $x = 0.6, -3.3$

2 a

v	d
0	0
10	5.3
20	14.7
30	28
40	45.3
50	66.7
60	92
70	121.3
80	154.7

b
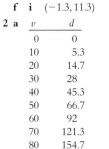

c i 9.5 m   **ii** 55.5 m   **iii** 137.5 m

d 42.4 mph

3 a $A = x(20 - x) = 20x - x^2$

b

x	A
0	0
4	64
8	96
12	96
16	64
20	0

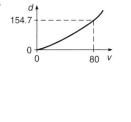

c i 59 cm²   **iii** 100 cm²   **v** 10 cm by 10 cm
  ii 11.4 cm by 8.6 cm   **iv** $x = 10$

4 a

x	h
0	0
10	9.72
20	18.9
30	27.5
40	35.6
50	43.1
60	50

b

c 45.8 m approx.

Practice 8.6.1 – p. 348

Answers to 1dp read from graphs

1 a
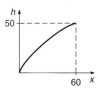
c
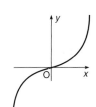

b
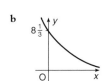
d
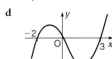

e

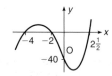

2 a i 3.6
　　ii 4.6
　b i 3.6 or 6.8
　　ii 10.6
　c (5, 3)

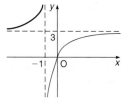

3 a i 1.4
　　ii 6.5
　b $y = 3$

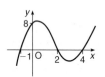

4 a 8.2
　b −4.1
　c i 5.6
　　ii −4

Practice 8.7.1a – p. 351

Answers to 1dp read from graphs
1 a $(y = 0)$
　　　$x = -2$ or 3
　b $(y = 1)$
　　　$x = -2.2$ or 3.2
　c $(y = 3)$
　　　$x = -2.5$ or 3.5
　d $(y = -2)$
　　　$x = -1.6$ or 2.6
　e $(y = -3)$
　　　$x = -1.3$ or 2.3
　f (intersection with $y = x$) $x = -1.7$ or 3.7
　g (intersection with $y = 2x$) $x = -1.4$ or 4.4
　h (intersection with $y = -x$) $x = -2.4$ or 2.4
　i (intersection with $y = x + 1$) $x = -1.8$ or 3.8
2 a $(y = 0)$
　　　$x = -2.5$ or 2
　b $(y = 2)$
　　　$x = -2.7$ or 2.2
　c $(y = 4)$
　　　$x = -2.9$ or 2.4
　d $(y = -1)$
　　　$x = -2.4$ or 1.9
　e $(y = -3)$
　　　$x = -2.1$ or 1.6
　f (intersection with $y = 2x$) $x = -2$ or 2.5
　g (intersection with $y = 2x - 2$) $x = -1.8$ or 2.3
　h (intersection with $y = 5 - 2x$) $x = -3.6$ or 2.1
3 at points A and B: $x^2 = 2x + 5$.
　　i.e. $x^2 - 2x - 5 = 0$; solutions
　　are $x = -1.5$ or 3.5
　　at points C and D: $x^2 = 6 - 3x$.
　　i.e. $x^2 + 3x - 6 = 0$; solutions
　　are $x = -4.4$ or 1.4

Practice 8.7.1b – p. 352

1 By either method the approximate solution is $x = -3.5$ or -2.5 or 1
2 a i, ii $(y = 0)$ $x = -2$
　　iii $(y = 2)$
　　　　$x = -2.35$
　　iv $(y = -3)$
　　　　$x = -1.5$
　　v $(y = 1)$
　　　　$x = -2.2$

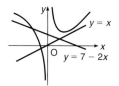

　b (intersection with $y = x$) $x^2 + \dfrac{8}{x} = x$, i.e. $x^3 - x^2 + 8 = 0$;
　　solution is $x = -1.7$

　　(intersection with $y = 7 - 2x$) $x^2 + \dfrac{8}{x} = 7 - 2x$,
　　i.e. $x^3 + 2x^2 - 7x + 8 = 0$; $x = -4.2$

Practice 8.7.2 – p. 354

Answers to 1dp read from graphs
1 a gradient = −4 and 2　　　**c** gradient = −8 and 4

　　　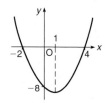

　b gradient = 3 and 27　　　**d** gradient = 3 and −3

2 a gradient = 3
　b $x = 1.5$

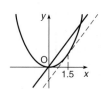

Practice 8.7.3 – p. 355

1 a 8 m/s
　b 14 m/s

2 a

　b i 30 m/s　　　　　　　　**iv** 47 m, 3 s
　　ii 10 m/s　　　　　　　　**v** 6.1 s
　　iii −20 m/s, i.e. 20 m/s downwards

3 a

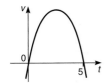

b i 6.25 m/s, 2.5 s   **iii** -3 m/s², i.e. it is decelerating
  ii 1 m/s²   **iv** after 5 s

c it is moving back towards its starting position

4

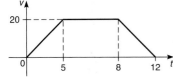

5

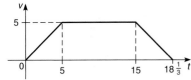

at $15 + \dfrac{5}{1.5} = 18\frac{1}{3}$ seconds from the start

Practice 8.7.4 – p. 357

1 a 200
  b 151.5
  c 412.5
  d 560

2 70.83

3 $6v = 30$, $v = 5$; it does not matter. The area of the triangle is the same whenever the maximum speed of 5 is obtained.

4 a 3.75 s   **b** 333.75 m   **c** 5 m/s²

5 16 m/s

6 24 m/s

7 $h = 16$ m/s and $T = 3$ s

Practice 8.7.5 – p. 361

Answers to 3sf where appropriate

1 mid-ordinate rule
  a $(3^3 + 5^3 + 7^3) \times 2 = 990$
  b $(2.5^3 + 3.5^3 + 4.5^3 + 5.5^3 + 6.5^3 + 7.5^3) \times 1 = 1012.5$
  trapezium rule
  a $(2^3 + 4^3 + 4^3 + 6^3 + 6^3 + 8^3) \times \frac{2}{2} = 1080$
  b $(2^3 + 3^3 + 3^3 + 4^3 + 4^3 + 5^3 + 5^3 + 6^3 + 6^3 + 7^3 + 7^3 + 8^3)$
    $\times \frac{1}{2} = 1035$

2 mid-ordinate rule
  a $4(18 - 5 - 9) = 16$
  b $2((12 - 5 - 4) + (24 - 5 - 16)) = 12$
  trapezium rule
  a $\frac{2}{2}((6 - 5 - 1) + (18 - 5 - 9) + (18 - 5 - 9) + (30 - 5 - 25)) = 8$
  b $\frac{1}{2}((6 - 5 - 1) + (12 - 5 - 4) + (12 - 5 - 4) + (18 - 5 - 9)$
    $+ (18 - 5 - 9) + (24 - 5 - 16) + (24 - 5 - 16)$
    $+ (30 - 5 - 25)) = 10$

3 a $4(\frac{24}{2} + \frac{24}{6} + \frac{24}{10}) = 73.6$
  b $3(\frac{24}{1.5} + \frac{24}{7.5} + \frac{24}{10.5}) = 80.5$

we cannot use the trapezium rule because the height when $x = 0$ is infinite

4 a $\frac{1}{4} \times \pi \times 2^2 = \pi$
  b $\frac{1}{4}(2 + 2 \times \sqrt{3.75} + 2 \times \sqrt{3} + 2 \times \sqrt{1.75} + 0) = 3.00$

5 $A = 9(2.5 + 9 + 12 + 15 + 16 + 17.5 + 17 + 14 + 10 + 3)$
  $= 1040$ m² approx.
  $V = 1040 \times 10 \times 10^6 = 1.04 \times 10^{10}$ litres

6 (using 4 strips) area is approximately 64 litres (2sf); it represents the amount of sewage discharged in 20 min

Practice 8.7.6 – p. 365

1 translation of 4 units in positive y-direction (to $x^3 + 4$); translation of 2 units in negative y-direction (to $x^3 - 2$)

2 translation of 2 units in negative x-direction (to $(x + 2)^3$); translation of 1 unit in positive x-direction (to $(x - 1)^3$)

3 $x^2 - 4x + 4 = (x - 2)^2$: a translation of 2 units in the positive x-direction

4 $2x^2 - 4x + 5 = 2(x - 1)^2 + 3$: a translation of 1 unit in the positive x-direction, followed by a translation of 3 units in positive y-direction, and multiplied by scale factor 2

5 $x^2 - 10x + 32 = (x - 5)^2 + 7$: a translation of 5 units in the positive x-direction, followed by a translation of 7 units in positive y-direction

6 $x^2 - 4x - 5 = (x - 2)^2 - 9$: a translation of 2 units in the positive x-direction, followed by a translation of 9 units in negative y-direction

7 a translation of 1 unit in the negative x-direction, followed by a translation of 3 units in positive y-direction; the new equation is $y = (x + 1)^2 + 3 = x^2 + 2x + 4$

8 a translation of 4 units in the negative x-direction, followed by a translation of 7 units in negative y-direction; the new equation is $y = (x + 4)^2 - 7 = x^2 + 8x + 9$

9 $2x^2 - 20x + 59 = 2(x - 5)^2 + 9$: a translation of 5 units in the positive x-direction, followed by a translation of 9 units in positive y-direction, and multiplied by scale factor 2

Chapter 9

Practice 9.1.1 – p. 375

1 a 120°   **d** 108°   **g** 54°
  b 144°   **e** 756°   **h** 49.5°
  c 540°   **f** 60°

2 270°

3 a 60°   **f** 70°
  b 129°   **g** $h° = m° = j° = 35°$, $g° = l° = i° = k° = 145°$
  c 11°   **h** 100°
  d 157°   **i** $p° = 62°$, $q = 46°$
  e 231°   **j** $r° = 87°$, $s° = 139°$

4 34°

5 124°

Practice 9.2.1 – p. 380

1 a 83°   **e** 61°   **i** 70°
  b 36°   **f** 112°   **j** 54°
  c 74°   **g** 36°   **k** 62°
  d 48°   **h** 24°   **l** 65°

2 $53\frac{1}{3}$

3 70°

4 9 cm and 19 cm

5 $(170 - 7x)°$

Practice 9.2.2 – p. 384

1 a 900°　　　　　　**5** 3
　b 1620°　　　　　　**6** 9
　c 3600°　　　　　　**7** 10
2 5 sides, 9 sides　　**8** 10 sides, 30 sides,
3 120°　　　　　　　　exterior angles 36° and 12° and
4 110°　　　　　　　　interior angles 144° and 168°

Practice 9.2.3 – p. 386

1 a 112°　　　　　　　**f** $m° = 128°, n° = 101°$
　b $b° = 50°, c° = 40°$　　**g** 128°
　c $d° = 69°, e = 41°, f° = 33°$　**h** $q° = 60°, r° = 150°$
　d $g° = 47°, h° = 90°,$　　**i** $s° = 88°, t° = 92°$
　　　$i° = 43°, j° = 47°$　　**j** $u° = 135°, v° = 45°$
　e $e° = 50°, k° = 110°$

Practice 9.2.4 – p. 389

Answers to 3sf
1 a 65.9 m　　　　**c** 58.1 in.　　　**e** 75.0 ft
　b 55.9 cm　　　**d** 196 in.
2 a 78.5 cm²　　　**b** 35.7 cm
3 40.2 cm²
4 a 5.37 m²　　　**c** 85.8 m²　　　**d** 45.5 cm²
　b 16.5 cm²
5 12.8 cm
6 a 37.7 in.　　　**b** 1260 in.　　　**c** 20.9 in/s
7 47.8

Practice 9.2.5 – p. 392

1 a cube　　　**b** BD, KH, AE, LI, FN, GM
2 A and D only
3 a cuboid　**b** square-based pyramid　**c** triangular prism
4 a

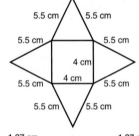

b

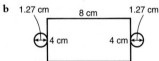

c

d

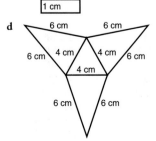

Practice 9.2.6 – p. 393

1 a

　c

b

　d

Practice 9.3.1 – p. 396

1 a

　f

b

　g
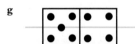

c

　h
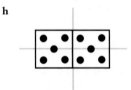

d
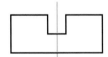
　i no axes of symmetry

e
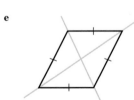

2 a H, I, X (depending on how it is written)
　b X (depending on how it is written)
　c O
　d H, I, N, S
　e X (depending on how it is written)
　f O
　g N, S

3 a **c** **e**

b **d**

4 a **c** **e**

b **d**

5 a 1 axis   **c** 4 axes and rotational symmetry of order 4
  b 1 axis   **d** 6 axes and rotational symmetry of order 3
6 a an infinite number
  c

Practice 9.4.1 – p. 400

1 $a = 9$ cm, $b = 4$ cm   **4** $g = 28.8$ cm, $h = 31.2$ cm
2 $c = 3.2$ cm, $d = 6.5$ cm   **5** $m = 2.25$ cm, $n = 6$ cm
3 $d = 7$ cm, $e = 10$ cm, $f = 3\frac{3}{7}$ cm

Practice 9.4.2 – p. 401

1 a yes – sides in ratio 1 : 3   **c** yes – sides and angles match
  b no – angles do not match   **d** yes – all circles are similar
2 3.75 in.
3 a no   **e** yes   **i** no
  b yes   **f** no   **j** yes
  c yes   **g** yes
  d no   **h** yes
4 10 times

Practice 9.5.1a – p. 405

Answers to 3sf
1 a 17 cm   **b** 25 cm   **c** 48 cm
2 64 m
3 4.8 m
4 a yes ($6^2 + 8^2 = 10^2$)   **d** no ($12^2 + 18^2 \neq 22^2$)
  b no ($10^2 + 15^2 \neq 18^2$)   **e** no ($12^2 + 21^2 \neq 24^2$)
  c yes ($7^2 + 24^2 = 25^2$)
5 8 m

Practice 9.5.1b – p. 405

1 a 10.2 cm   **b** 6.72 cm   **c** 8.39 cm
2 4.77 m
3 5.39 km   **5** 11 300 ft
4 8.06 yd   **6** 10.0 m
                        7 2.14 in.
8 AM = 9.03 cm, AB = 18.1 cm
9 a 2000 yd   **b** 2010 yd

10 a 4.47 cm   **c** 10.6 cm
  b 5.66 cm   **d** 8.94 cm
11 AB = 13.3 cm, BM = 6.64 cm, MC = 13.2 cm
12 22.8 m

Practice 9.6.1a – p. 412

1 6.76 m

Practice 9.6.1b – p. 412

Answers to 4sf or 3sf where appropriate
1 a 0.4384   **c** 0.9004   **e** 0.9943
  b 0.8387   **d** 0.9466   **f** 36.03
2 a 30°   **c** 72.3°   **e** 0°
  b 30°   **d** 90°   **f** 71.6°
3 a $a = 3$ cm, $b = 5.20$ cm   **c** $g = 34.0$ cm, $h = 43.0$ cm
  b $c = 32.5$ cm, $d = 37.1$ cm   **d** $i = 59.6$ cm, $j = 138$ cm
4 a $\theta° = 23.6°$ **b** $\theta° = 41.7°$ **c** $\theta° = 34.1°$
5 AB = 11.8 cm, ON = 4.13 cm

Practice 9.6.2 – p. 415

Answers to 3sf, angles to nearest 0.1°
1 1030 m, 247 m
2 29.6°
3 11.2 km, 047.6°
4 40.8°
5 95.8 ft
6 QR = 739 yd, PR = 946 yd, course = 2885 yd
7 20.6°
8 8.63°
9 65 ft
10 160 cm
11 23.0 ft
12 a $CB^2 = 65$, $AB^2 = 52$, $CA^2 = 13$, $65 = 52 + 13$
  b 29.7°
13 BC = 23.5 miles,
   OC = 12.5 miles
14 12.3°
15 a $h/\tan 59°$ **c** $h = 49.9$ m
  b $h/\tan 51.3°$

Practice 9.7.1 – p. 420

Answers to 3sf
1 a 16.6, 13.0, 18.6 cm
  b BH = 19.9 cm
  c **i** 25° **ii** 32.5° **iii** 20.6° **iv** 32.5° **v** 25° **vi** 64.9°
2 a 20.6 m   **b** 36.9°   **c** 8.37°
3 a 25 m   **b** 14.0° and 12.6°
4 a 63.2°   **b** 70.3°
5 104 ft due S, 191 ft due W, 217 ft
6 a 45°   **b** 35.4 m   **c** 49.1°
7 41.1°
8 11.3°

Practice 9.7.2 – p. 425

Answers to nearest 0.1°
1 50°   **10** 14°   **19** 164.3°
2 38.8°   **11** 68.7°   **20** 256.4°
3 68.9°   **12** 5°   **21** 303.7°
4 51°   **13** 33.9°   **22** 97.1°
5 12.3°   **14** 18.8°   **23** 262.9°
6 0.1°   **15** 63.7°   **24** 222.2°
7 88.7°   **16** 13.9°   **25** 317.8°
8 85.7°   **17** 83°   **26** 153.4°
9 62°   **18** 80.1°   **27** 333.4°

Practice 9.7.3 – p. 427

1 $\angle C = 69°$, $c = 42.3\,\text{m}$, $a = 30.3\,\text{m}$
2 $\angle A = 61°$, $b = 4.7\,\text{ft}$, $c = 4.56\,\text{ft}$
3 $\angle A = 62.5°$, $\angle C = 37.5°$, $c = 11.9\,\text{in.}$
4 $\angle A = 19.6°$, $\angle B = 54.4°$, $a = 4.99\,\text{yd}$

Practice 9.7.4 – p. 428

1 **a** 4.44 cm　　　**b** 7.92 cm　　　**c** 21.8 cm
2 **a** $\angle B = 38.6°$　　**b** $\angle A = 38.4°$
3 **a** 25.4 cm　　**b** 138.7°
4 **a** 9.13 cm, 54.5°, 77.5°　　**c** 20.8°, 28.3°, 130.9°
　b 51.6°, 65.2°, 18.6 cm　　**d** 36.9°, 53.1°, 90°
5 (BC = 8.27 cm), $\angle D = 48.9°$
6 7.77 km, 203.1°
7 37.2 yd
8 7.63 miles, 135.4°
9 21°

Practice 9.7.5 – p. 434

1 $\angle A = 72.5°$, $\angle C = 17.5°$　　7 $\angle K = 24°$
2 $\angle E = 50°$, $\angle F = 50°$　　　8 $\angle E = 137°$
3 $\angle K = 48°$, $\angle I = 42°$　　　9 $\angle J = 62°$
4 $\angle O = 70°$, $\angle N = 35°$, $\angle P = 55°$　　10 $\angle K = 61°$
5 $\angle S = 80°$　　　　　　11 $\angle P = 90°$, $\angle S = 49°$
6 $\angle Z = 41°$, $\angle Y = 38°$

Practice 9.7.6 – p. 438

1 **a**　congruent (SAS)
　b　congruent (ASA)
　c　congruent (RHS)
　d　congruent (SSS)
　e　not congruent (not corresponding sides)
　f　not necessarily congruent (AAA not a test for congruency)
　g　congruent (SAS)
　h　not possible to say
　i　not possible to say
　j　congruent (AAS)
2 Two vertically opposite angles and sides match (SAS)
3 Two pairs of matching sides and common diagonal (SSS)
4
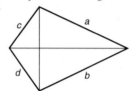
　　$a = b$, $c = d$, the longer diagonal
　　is common to both triangles,
　　thus congruent (SSS)
　　there are no pairs of matching
　　sides if the shorter diagonal is
　　taken, thus not congruent

5
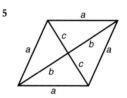
　　each triangle has sides marked
　　a, b and c, therefore there are
　　4 congruent triangles (SSS)

Chapter 10

Practice 10.3.1 – p. 453

1 (4, 8) (1, 6) (−3, −8) (−10, −4)
2 (0, −3), (3, −2), (1, 2)
3 (7, −1), (2, −1), (7, −6), (2, −6)
4 **a** $\begin{pmatrix} 4 \\ -2 \end{pmatrix}$　　**b** $\begin{pmatrix} -3 \\ 6 \end{pmatrix}$　　**c** $\begin{pmatrix} 8 \\ 14 \end{pmatrix}$　　**d** $\begin{pmatrix} 4 \\ 0 \end{pmatrix}$
5 **a** it is parallel to the x-axis　　**b** it is parallel to the y-axis

6 **a, b**
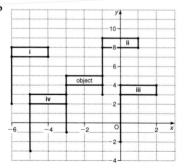

7 $A = \begin{pmatrix} 9 \\ -6 \end{pmatrix}$, $B = \begin{pmatrix} 8 \\ -7 \end{pmatrix}$, $C = \begin{pmatrix} -12 \\ -5 \end{pmatrix}$　　　8 (7, −2)

Practice 10.4.1 – p. 456

1
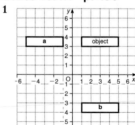

2
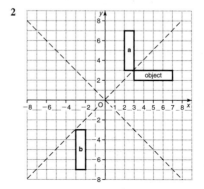

3

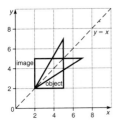

4

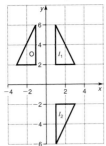

I_2 it is facing the same way as the object but is twice as far from line B as the object is from line A

5

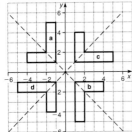

6

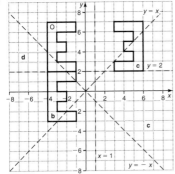

7

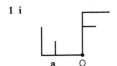

Practice 10.5.1 – p. 461

1 i

ii

iii

iv

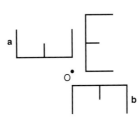

v

vi   **vii**   **viii**

2

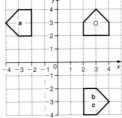

3

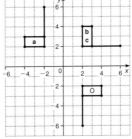

4 a, b

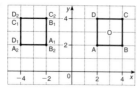

c no, $A_1B_1C_1D_1$ are the vertices after **a**
and $A_2B_2C_2D_2$ are the vertices after **b**,
hence the two transformations **a** and **b** are not the same

5 a 90° rotation clockwise about (0, 0)
b 180° rotation about (0, 0) (clockwise or anticlockwise)

6

Practice 10.6.1 – p. 464

1 a

c

b

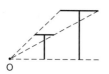

d

2 a sf 5   **b** sf 2.5   **c** sf 2

3 a

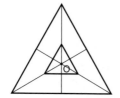

b

c

4

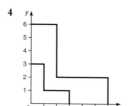

5 a

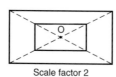

Scale factor 2

b

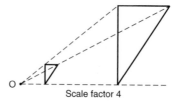

Scale factor 4

c

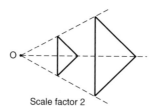

Scale factor 2

d

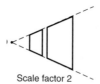

Scale factor 2

Practice 10.6.2a – p. 467

1 a 16.8 miles   **b** 8.8 miles
2 a 4 cm   **b** 35.2 cm
3 78 miles

Practice 10.6.2b – p. 467

1 3.28 cm
2 a $1 : \frac{1}{4} \times 1760 \times 3 \times 12 = 1 : 15\,840$, i.e. $1 : 16\,000$ (2sf)
b 550 yd
c 3.41 in.
3 a 1204 m   **b** 17.9 cm

Practice 10.7.1 – p. 469

1

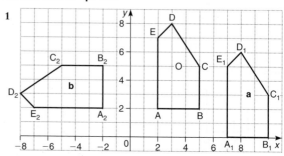

2

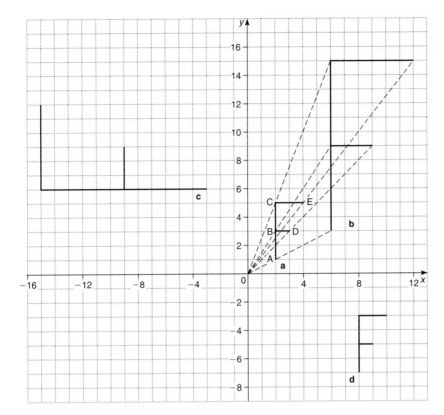

3

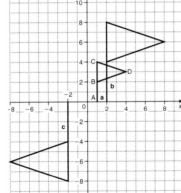

6 a

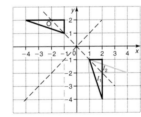

b rotation 180° about (0, 0)

7 a

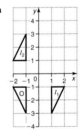

b reflection in the x-axis

8 a

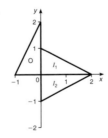

b reflection in the line $y = x$

Practice 10.7.2 – p. 471

1 the equilateral triangle; the square; the hexagon

2 yes

3 yes

4 a

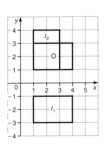

5 a

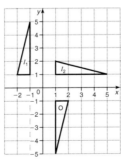

b reflection in the line $y = x$ **b** rotation $+90°$ about (0, 0)

Practice 10.8.1 – p. 473

1 left as an exercise for the reader

2

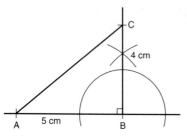

AC = 6.4 cm

3

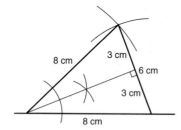

the base is bisected perpendicularly

4 left as an exercise for the reader
5 left as an exercise for the reader
6 left as an exercise for the reader

Practice 10.8.2 – p. 476

1

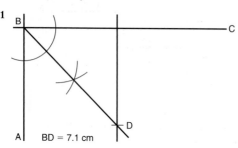

BD = 7.1 cm

2

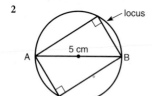

3

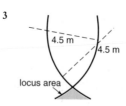

4

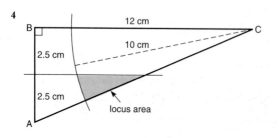

5 a, b

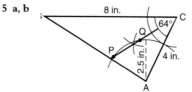

P and Q are common to both loci

6

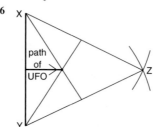

a 5.8 miles
b i 2088 mph **ii** 30 seconds

7 a
b

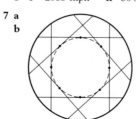

c locus is another circle of radius 3 in.

Practice 10.9.1a – p. 479

1 a 5 **b** 13 **c** 25
2 10

Practice 10.9.1b – p. 479

1 a 6.32 **b** 5.39

2 $\begin{pmatrix}4\\5\end{pmatrix} \to \sqrt{41}$, $\begin{pmatrix}-5\\3\end{pmatrix} \to \sqrt{34}$, $\begin{pmatrix}-1\\-4\end{pmatrix} \to \sqrt{17}$, $\begin{pmatrix}7\\-1\end{pmatrix} \to \sqrt{50}$;

$\begin{pmatrix}7\\-1\end{pmatrix}$ has the largest modulus

Practice 10.9.2 – p. 480

1 a $AB = \begin{pmatrix}3\\2\end{pmatrix}$, $CD = \begin{pmatrix}1\\-1\end{pmatrix}$, $EF = \begin{pmatrix}0\\-5\end{pmatrix}$, $OP = \begin{pmatrix}3\\4\end{pmatrix}$,

$QR = \begin{pmatrix}3\\-4\end{pmatrix}$, $ST = \begin{pmatrix}5\\0\end{pmatrix}$, $WX = \begin{pmatrix}-8\\6\end{pmatrix}$, $YZ = \begin{pmatrix}-3\\-6\end{pmatrix}$

b $QR = 5$, $YZ = \sqrt{45} = 6.71$

Practice 10.9.3 – p. 483

1

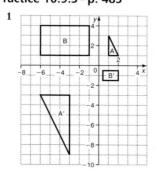

2 $p = b$, $q = 4a$, $r = 2a + 2b$, $s = a + 4b$, $t = -3b$, $u = -a + b$,
$v = -a - 4b$, $w = -2a + 4b$, $x = 8a - 7b$, $y = -8a - b$,
$z = 8a + 8b$

3 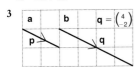 $q = \begin{pmatrix} 4 \\ 2 \end{pmatrix}$

c $|p| = \sqrt{5} = 2.236$
$|q| = \sqrt{20} = 4.472$
q is twice the length of p

4 a i $\begin{pmatrix} 4 \\ 10 \end{pmatrix}$ ii $\begin{pmatrix} 7 \\ 17 \end{pmatrix}$ iii $\begin{pmatrix} -8 \\ 19 \end{pmatrix}$ iv $\begin{pmatrix} -3 \\ 0 \end{pmatrix}$ v $\begin{pmatrix} 3 \\ 44 \end{pmatrix}$

b $\begin{pmatrix} 5 \\ -1 \end{pmatrix}$, $\begin{pmatrix} -5 \\ 1 \end{pmatrix}$; they have the same modulus (i.e. are the same length) but are in opposite directions

c $p + q = \begin{pmatrix} 3 \\ -5 \end{pmatrix}$, $|p + q| = \sqrt{34} = 5.83$, $|p| + |q| = \sqrt{5} + \sqrt{25} = 7.24$, clearly $|p + q| \neq |p| + |q|$

5 $m + n - 4m = -3m + n$

6 a $\frac{2}{3}x$ d $\frac{2}{3}x - y$
  b $\frac{1}{4}y$ e $-x + \frac{1}{4}y$
  c $-\frac{2}{3}x + \frac{1}{4}y$

7 $\overrightarrow{MN} = \frac{1}{2}d$, $\overrightarrow{NP} = -\frac{1}{2}c$, $\overrightarrow{PM} = \frac{1}{2}c - \frac{1}{2}d$

8 $\overrightarrow{PQ} = \frac{1}{2}s - \frac{1}{2}t$

9 $\overrightarrow{AB} = \overrightarrow{DC} = -f - g$, $\overrightarrow{AD} = \overrightarrow{BC} = -f + g$

10a 2a   d $a + b$
  b 4b   e $-a - 4b$
  c $2a + b$ f $-2a - 4b$

Practice 10.9.4 – p. 487

1 a

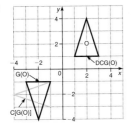

b the single transformation is equivalent to a return to the original object i.e. object and image are the **same**.

2 a A, B, C, D and G are all self-inverses
  b not always, AB is the same as BA, for example, but AE and EA are different

3 a b

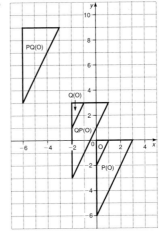

c clearly PQ and QP are not the same

4

c clearly PQ and QP are not the same (diagram)

5 a reflection in the y-axis
  b reflection in the x-axis or a rotation of 180° about $(1, 0)$
  c reflection in the line $y = 1$
  d enlargement of the triangle formed by the vertices $(0, 3)$, $(0.5, 1.5)$ and $(-0.5, 1.5)$ by scale factor 2, centre $(0, 3)$
  e reflection in the line $x = 2$ or rotation of 180° about $(2, 2.5)$

Chapter 11

Practice 11.1.1 – p. 497

Answers to 2sf

1 3 miles	3 5 pints	5 290 yd
2 11 kg	4 150 cm	6 790 g

Practice 11.2.1a – p. 499

1 a 18.2 m   b 56 ft   c 32 m
2 9.8 cm   3 13 in.   4 40 cm

Practice 11.2.1b – p. 499

1 a 11.3 in.   b 17.5 yd   c 32 cm
2 15.7 cm

Practice 11.3.1 – p. 500

1 13 or 14 cm²
2 45 miles² (nearest 5 square miles)

Practice 11.3.2 – p. 507

1 32 cm²	8 168 cm²	15 25.7 cm²
2 64 cm²	9 87.7 cm²	16 5.37 cm²
3 48 cm²	10 93.5 cm²	17 0.5 m²
4 78 cm²	11 104 cm²	18 32.1 in.²
5 18.3 cm²	12 108 cm²	19 10.1 in.²
6 93.8 cm²	13 24.5 cm²	20 121 cm²
7 11.3 cm²	14 21.2 cm²	

Practice 11.4.1 – p. 513

Answers to 3 sf where appropriate

1 96
2 10 800
3 140
4 216
5 343
6 302
7 27.7
8 76.7
9 800
10 a 182 cm^3
   b 109 g
11 a 10.7 cm^3
   b 409.3 cm^3
   c 39 slices altogether
12 8.42 cm
13 0.21 cm

14 a 6 in.
   b 205 in.^{3}
15 8
16 a 471 cm^3
   b 3.70 kg
17 a 2.60×10^{11} miles^3
   b 3.657×10^{26} lb
   c 1.97×10^8 miles^2
   d 39 400 days, i.e. 107.9 years approx.
18 a i 0.0585 in.^{2}
     ii 0.3507 in.^{3}
     iii 0.0301 in.^{3}
     iv 0.321 in.^{3}
   b 8.58%
   c 0.175 oz
   d 91

Practice 11.4.2 – p. 517

1 60 cm
2 2500 kg
3 1.47 litres
4 $(0.75)^3 \times 95 = 40$ p
5 25 000 m^2
6 $2.744 = \left(\dfrac{h}{8}\right)^2$, $h = 13.3$ in.
7 $2.744 \times 4.4 = 12.1$ in.^{2}
8 $\left(\frac{12}{48}\right)^3 = \frac{1}{64}$
9 $2^3 \times 3 = 24$ s

Practice 11.5.1 – p. 519

1 area
2 length
3 none
4 volume
5 volume
6 none
7 area
8 none
9 length
10 volume
11 volume
12 volume
13 volume
14 area
15 length

16 volume of a cone; volume of a sphere; surface area of a cuboid; perimeter of a rectangle, parallelogram, rhombus or kite

17 r^2 represents an area, $\frac{4}{3}\pi$ is a constant, thus the whole formula can only be an area

Practice 11.6.1 – p. 523

1 a 7
   b 30.8
   c 12.1
   d 29.3
   e 9.92
2 a 10.5, 52.3
   b 39.1, 324
   c 17.4, 43.1
3 a 7.02
   b 316
4 a 440 cm^2
   b 158 m^2
5 a 851 cm^2
   b 1190 cm^2
6 a 106
   b 314
   c 33.6
   d 36
   e 1050
7 55 300 cm^3
8 2.25 in.
9 12.9 cm
10 a 120 cm
   b 707 000 cm^3
   c 209 000 cm^3
   d 498 000 cm^3
11 Total height = 41.14 in., total volume = 7900 in.^{3}, small volume = 15.43 in.^{3}, hopper volume = 7885 in.^{3} (4sf)
12 a 8 ft
   b 11.2 ft^2
   c 67.3 ft^2; 6730 ft^3
13 a 54.4 cm^2
   b 1090 cm^3
14 $h_1 = 10$ cm, $h_2 = 2.5$ cm, $A_1 = 352$ cm^3, $A_2 = 528$ cm^3, 4 cm can
15 a $2 \times (2\pi + \pi \times 8 \times \frac{60}{180}) = 29.3$ cm
   b $\pi \times 2^2 + 2(\pi \times 8^2 \times \frac{60}{360} - \frac{1}{2}8^2 \times \sin 60°) + \frac{1}{2}8^2 \times \sin 60°$
     $= 51.9$ cm^2

Answers to sample non-calculator questions

Intermediate tier

Module 1 – Money managemant and number

		Mark	Alternative Answer/Comments
1	Train arrives at 1723	B1	
	Time is $1723 - 1549$	M1	
	= 1 hour 34 minutes	A1 A1	
	Total	**4**	
2 a	VAT = 5% of £60		
	$= \frac{5}{100} \times £60$	M1	
	$= 3$	A1	
	$= £3$	B1	£ sign
b	Total paid is £63	A1	
	Total	**4**	
3	Bill is $165\,000 \times 4 = 660\,000$	B1	
	Hotel bill is $660\,000 \div 3000$	M1	
	$= £220$	A1	
	Total	**3**	
4 a	£600	B1	
b	$2 \times 35 + 3 \times \frac{1}{2} \times 35$	M1	
	£122.50	A1	
	Total	**3**	

		Mark	Alternative Answer/Comments
5	Large: cost £4.60/litre	M1 A1	($\div$ same for both)
	Regular: cost £4.99/litre	M1	
	$\therefore$ large is best value	B1 dep	
	Total	**3**	
6	Cooking time $= 2 \times 70 + 35$ min		
	$= 175$ min		
	Time = 1310 hr or 1.10 pm		
	Total	**3**	
7	Interest $= 6000 \times \frac{4}{100} \times \frac{5}{12}$	M1	
	$= £100$	A1	
	Vinod withdraws £6100	B1	
	Total	**3**	
8 a	$4 \times 2^3 = 32$	B1	
b	$\dfrac{4.96}{262 + 23.9} \approx \dfrac{5}{50}$	B1	
	$= 0.1$	B1	
c	$7^{-2} = \dfrac{1}{7^2} = \dfrac{1}{49}$	B1	
	Total	**4**	
9	$C = \frac{5}{9}(F - 32)$		
	$= \frac{5}{9}(-22 - 32)$	M1	
	$= \frac{5}{9}(-54)$	A1	
	$= -30$	A1	
	Total	**3**	

		Mark	Alternative Answer/Comments			Mark	Alternative Answer/Comments
10 a	$ab = 3 \times 10^4 \times 4 \times 10^7$			b	$\dfrac{a}{b} = \dfrac{3 \times 10^4}{4 \times 10^7}$		
	$= 12 \times 10^{11}$	B1			$= 0.75 \times 10^{-3}$	B1 B1	0.75 only implies B1
	$= 1.2 \times 10^{12}$	B1			$= 7.5 \times 10^{-4}$	B1	
					Total	**5**	
					Total for paper	**35**	

Module 2 – Statistics and probability

		Mark	Alternative Answer/Comments
1	Intermediate values have no meaning and should not be joined	B1	
	Irregular horizontal scale	B1	
	Vertical axis does not start at 0	B1	
	Total	**3**	
2 a	Discrete	B1	
b	Continuous	B1	
	Total	**2**	
3 a	Mean $= \dfrac{5+8+5+5+6+7}{6}$	M1	$= 6 A$
b i	Mode $= 2$	B1	
ii	Range $= 9 - 2$	M1	
	$= 7$	A1	
	Total	**5**	
4 a	No. of sixes $= 100 \times \frac{1}{4}$	M1	
	$= 25$	A1	
b	Probability $= \frac{13}{100}$	B1	
	Total	**3**	
5 a	Any two valid questions (award 1 mark each)	B1 B1	
b i	Any valid method	B2	B1 for part correct
ii	*Telephone directory* Would only question those with a telephone who are not ex-directory	B1	
	Supermarket Would only question those who shop at this particular supermarket	B1	
	Total	**6**	

		Mark	Alternative Answer/Comments
6	Jill's mean	B1	
	Because her sample size is bigger.	B1	
	Total	**2**	
7	Appropriate scale + axes labelled	B1	
	Plots at correct heights within correct classes	B1	
	Plots at midpoints joined to form a polygon	B1	
	Total	**3**	
8 a	2, 8, 40, 81, 95, 99, 100	B1	
b	7 points at their (increasing) CFs	B1	$\pm \frac{1}{2}$ small square
	plots at upper class boundaries and joined by curves or lines	B1	For an increasing curve
c	$600 - ?? = ???$	M1	From an increasing CF graph $100 -$ reading at 3.35 grams
	Total	**4**	
9 a	As rainfall increases the number of deck chair tickets sold decreases	B1	
b	Line of best fit shown	B1	
c	About 520	M1	reading from graph
		A1	
	Total	**4**	
10 a	Not late $= 0.7$	B1	
b	Probability $= 0.3 \times 0.1$	M1	
	$= 0.03$	A1	
	Total	**3**	
	Total for paper	**35**	

Module 3 – Terminal module

		Mark	Alternative Answer/Comments
1	$x = 360 - (120 + 80 + 50)$	M1	
	$x = 110°$	A1	
	$y = 180° - 110°$	M1 ft	
	$y = 70$	A1 cao	
	Total	**4**	
2 a	$n + 1, n + 2, n + 11$	B2	2 correct B1
b	$n + n + 1 + n + 2 + n + 11$	M1	must be in terms of n
	$4n + 14$ **or** $n4 + 14$ **or** $2(2n + 7)$	A1 ft	$3n + 14 \Rightarrow$ SC1
	Penalise further incorrect algebra, e.g. $4n + 14 = 18n \Rightarrow$ M1 A0		
	Total	**4**	

		Mark	Alternative Answer/Comments
3 a	10, 8, 6, 4, 2	B2	3 correct B1
	correct plots, correct line	M1 A1	
b	(2.4, 3.2)	B1 ft	each value ± 0.1
	Total	**5**	
4	$6 \times 10 \times 4 = 240$	M1	
	$\frac{1}{2} \times 5 \times 4 \times 8 = 80$	M1	
	('their' 240) $-$ ('their' 80)	M1	
	160	A1	
	cm^3	B1	
	Total	**5**	

		Mark	Alternative Answer/Comments
5 **a**	14	B1	
b	29	B1	
c	nth term $= 2 + 3(n-1)$	M1	
	$= 3n - 1$	A1	
	Total	**4**	
6	Maximum $= 88.55$ seconds	B1	
	Minimum $= 88.45$ seconds	B1	
	Total	**2**	
7 **a**	Translation	M1	
	$\begin{pmatrix} 3 \\ -6 \end{pmatrix}$	A1	
b	Reflection	M1	
	$y = -x$	A1	
	Total	**4**	
8 **a**	$\frac{1}{3}x = 7$	M1	
	$x = 21$	A1	
b	$3x - 9 = 2x - 6$	M1	Expand bracket
	$x - 9 = -6$	M1	oe
	$x = 3$	A1	
c	$x^2 - 2x - 8 = 0$	M1	

		Mark	Alternative Answer/Comments
c	$x^2 - 2x - 8 = 0$	M1	
	$(x-4)(x+2) = 0$	M1	
	$x = 4$ or -2	A1	
	Total	**8**	
9	$\pi a(b+c),\ 2\pi ab,\ \pi c\sqrt{a^2+b^2}$, all three	B2	3 correct B2 −1 each error or omission
	Total	**2**	
10	For similar Δ ratio of lengths $= 12:10:6:5$	B1	
	$CD = \frac{12}{10} \times 12$	M1	
	$= 14.4\,\text{cm}$	A1	
	Total	**3**	
11	$3x + y = 10$		
	$\underline{x - y = 6}$		
	$4x = 16$	M1	
	$x = 4$	A1	
	$y = -2$	A1	
	Total	**3**	
	Total for paper	**44**	

Higher tier

Module 1 – Money managemant and number

		Mark	Alternative Answer/Comments
1	Cooking time $= 2 \times 70 + 35$ min	M1	
	$= 175$ min	A1	
	Time $= 1310$ hr or 1.10 pm	B1	
	Total	**3**	
2 **a**	$\frac{4.96}{26.2 + 23.9} \approx \frac{5}{50}$	B1	
	$= 0.1$	B1	
b	$\frac{4.96}{26.2 + 23.9} \times 0.3^2$	B1	
	$\approx 0.1 \times 0.1$	B1	$0.3^2 \approx 0.1$
	≈ 0.01	B1	
	Total	**4**	
3 **a**	$ab = 3 \times 10^4 \times 4 \times 10^7$		
	$= 12 \times 10^{11}$	B1	
	$= 1.2 \times 10^{12}$	B1	
b	$\frac{a}{b} = \frac{3 \times 10^4}{4 \times 10^7}$		
	$= 0.75 \times 10^{-3}$	B1 B1	0.75 only implies B1
	$= 7.5 \times 10^{-4}$	B1	
	Total	**5**	
4	Amount at 2% is £1.24	B1	
	Amount at 8.4% is £16.80	M1	
	Earnings above £62 is	M1	
	$\frac{16.80}{8.4} \times 100 = £200$		
	$\therefore$ Weekly pay is $= £262$	A1	
	Total	**4**	

		Mark	Alternative Answer/Comments
5 **a**	£445	B1	
b	Maximum $= 4 \times £454.99$	M1	
	$= £1819.96$	A1	£1820 gets B1
	Total	**3**	
6	Original value 100%		
	At end of 1998 value 140%	B1	for 140
	During 1999 lost $\frac{30}{100} \times 140\%$	M1	
	$= 42\%$		
	$\therefore$ New value $140 - 142$		
	$= 98\%$	A1	
	$\therefore$ Shares lost 2% of their value (or their value decreased by 2%)	A1	
	Total	**4**	
7 **a**	$\pi,\ \pi + 1,\ \sqrt{3},\ (\sqrt{2})^3$	B2	
b	e.g. $\frac{1}{\pi}, \frac{2}{\pi}, \frac{3}{\pi}, \ldots$	B1	
	Total	**3**	
8	$x = 0.03\dot{5}$		
	$100x = 3.53\dot{5}$	M1	
	$99x = 3.5$	M1	
	$x = \frac{3.5}{99}$	A1	
	$= \frac{7}{198}$	A1	
	Total	**4**	
9 **a**	$\sqrt{500} = 10\sqrt{5}$	B1	
	$10\sqrt{5} - \sqrt{5} = 9\sqrt{5}$	B1	
b	$\sqrt{18} \times \sqrt{32} = 3\sqrt{2} \times 4\sqrt{2}$	B1	either
	$= 12\sqrt{4}$	M1	
	$= 24$	A1	
	Total	**5**	
	Total for paper	**35**	

Module 2 – Statistics and probability

		Mark	Alternative Answer/Comments
1	Appropriate scale + axes labelled	B1	
	Plots at correct heights within correct classes	B1	
	Plots at midpoints joined to form a polygon	B1	
	Total	**3**	
2 a	No. of sixes $= 100 \times \frac{1}{4}$	M1	
	$= 25$	A1	
b	Probability $= \frac{13}{100}$	B1	
	Total	**3**	
3 a	As rainfall increases the number of deck chair tickets sold decreases	B1	
b	Line of best fit shown	B1	
c	About 520	M1	reading from graph
		A1	
	Total	**4**	
4 a	2, 8, 40, 81, 95, 99, 100	B1	
b	7 points at their (increasing) CFs	B1	$\pm\frac{1}{2}$ small square
	plots at upper class boundaries and joined by curves or lines	B1	For an increasing curve
c	$600 - ?? = ???$	M1	From an increasing CF graph $100 -$ reading at 3.35 grams
	Total	**4**	

		Mark	Alternative Answer/Comments
5 a	Not late $= 0.7$	B1	
b	Probability $= 0.3 \times 0.1$	M1	
	$= 0.03$	A1	
	Total	**3**	
6	5, 5, 5, 5, 5, 5, 10, 10		
	Class widths completed correctly	B1	
	1, 1.6, 2.8, 3, 3.6, 3.4, 1.4, 0.9		
	Frequency densities completed correctly	B2 B1	maximum of B1 for 2 errors
	Correct histogram	B3	
	Total	**6**	
7 a	P (white) $= 0.4$	B1	
b	P (red and 2) $= 0.1$	B1	
c	P (white and 1) $= 0.5$	B1	
d	P (white and 3) $= 0.5$	B2	
	Total	**5**	
8	Probability		
	$= A\bar{B}\bar{C} + \bar{A}B\bar{C} + \bar{A}\bar{B}C$	M1	or B1 for $1 - \ldots$
	$= \frac{3}{4} \times \frac{1}{8} \times \frac{2}{5} + \frac{1}{4} \times \frac{7}{8} \times \frac{2}{5} + \frac{1}{4} \times \frac{1}{8} \times \frac{2}{5}$	A1	
	$= \frac{6}{100} + \frac{14}{100} + \frac{2}{100}$	A1	
	$= \frac{22}{160} = \frac{11}{80}$	A1	
	Total	**4**	
	Total for paper	**32**	

Module 3 – Terminal module

		Mark	Alternative Answer/Comments
1	$\pi a(b + c)$, $2\pi ab$, $\pi c\sqrt{a^2 + b^2}$, all three	B2	3 correct B2 -1 each error or omission
	Total	**2**	
2	Maximum $= 88.55$ seconds	B1	
	Minimum $= 88.45$ seconds	B1	
	Total	**2**	
3 a	$3x - 9 = 2x - 6$	M1	Expand bracket
	$x - 9 = -6$	M1	oe
	$x = 3$	A1	
b	$x^2 - 2x - 8 = 0$	M1	
	$(x - 4)(x + 2) = 0$	M1	
	$x = 4$ or -2	A1	
	Total	**6**	
4	For similar Δ ratio of lengths $= 12 : 10 : 6 : 5$	B1	
	$CD = \frac{12}{10} \times 12$	M1	
	$= 14.4$ cm	A1	
	Total	**3**	
5	Attempt to factorise	M1	
	$1998 (1998 + 2)$	M1	
	$3\,996\,000$	A1	
	Total	**3**	

		Mark	Alternative Answer/Comments
6 a	$120°$	B1	
b	$-180° + 30°$, $180° + 30°$, $360° - 30°$	M1	For method
	$-150°, 210°, 330°$ (only two)	A1 A1	
	Total	**4**	
7 a i	-4.75	B1	
ii	-5	B1	
iii	-0.5 to -0.6 and 3.5 to 3.6	B1	
b	-2.3 to -2.4 and 3.3 to 3.4	M1	
		A1 A1	
	Total	**6**	
8	Graph A is $y = -2x^2$.	B1	
	Graph B is $y = \frac{2}{x}$.	B1	
	Graph C is $y + \frac{2}{x} = 0$.	B1	
	Total	**3**	
9	$<SPO = 90°$ $<SOP = 62°$	B1	
	$<ROP = 180° - 62°$ (angles on straight line)	M1	
	$<ROP = 118°$	A1	
	$<PQR = \frac{1}{2} \times 118°$ (angle at centre)	M1	
	$<PQR = 59°$	A1	
	$<PRT = 59°$ (alternate segment)	B1	
	Total	**6**	

		Mark	Alternative Answer/Comments
10 a	**i** $\mathbf{a}+\mathbf{b}$	B1	
	ii $\frac{1}{2}\mathbf{a}$	B1	
	iii $\mathbf{b}-\frac{1}{2}\mathbf{a}$	B1	
b	**i** $\frac{2}{3}(\mathbf{b}-\frac{1}{2}\mathbf{a})$	B1	or $\frac{2}{3}\mathbf{b}-\frac{1}{3}\mathbf{a}$
	ii $\frac{2}{3}(\mathbf{a}+\mathbf{b})$	B1	
c	OP lies on the line OB	B1	
	$OP=\frac{2}{3}\times OB$	B1	
	Total	**7**	

	11	Mark	Alternative Answer/Comments
	$8x-(x+3)=x(x+3)$	M1	Multiply by $x(x+3)$
	$8x-x-3=x^2+3x$	M1	
	$x^2-4x+3=0$	M1	
	$(x-1)(x-3)=0$	M1	
	$x=1,3$	A1	
	Total	**5**	

	12	Mark	Alternative Answer/Comments
	$3=ab^0$	M1	
	$a=3$	A1	
	$24=3\times q^3$ or similar $12=3\times b^2$	M1	
	$b=2$	A1 ft	
	Total	**4**	
	Total for paper	**51**	

INDEX